CONTOUR
MAP
1:24,000

W9-ACX-017

Front end paper shows part of

CUMBERLAND QUADRANGLE
Maryland–Pennsylvania–West Virginia

(a 7½′ quadrangle)

and

AIR PHOTO
of same area at same scale

U.S. GEOLOGICAL SURVEY
Department of the Interior
WASHINGTON 25, D.C.

FRACTIONAL SCALE: 1:24,000
(representative fraction)

LINEAR SCALE:

0 ⊏═══⊐ ⊏═══⊐ ⊏═══⊐ ½ mile

CONTOUR INTERVAL: 20 feet

BOUNDING PARALLELS
of whole quadrangle:
39° 37′ 30″ N *and* 39° 45′ N

of this portion:
39° 38′ 35″ N *and* 39° 41′ 38″ N

BOUNDING MERIDIANS
of whole quadrangle:
78° 45′ W *and* 78° 52′ 30″ W

of this portion:
78° 45′ 34″ W *and* 78° 48′ 45″ W

Henry M. Kendall *Miami University, Oxford, Ohio*

Robert M. Glendinning *University of California, Los Angeles*

Clifford H. MacFadden *University of California, Los Angeles*

INTRODUCTION TO GEOGRAPHY

THIRD EDITION

Harcourt, Brace & World, Inc.

 NEW YORK · BURLINGAME

FRONTISPIECE: *Air photo of the Cordillera Blanca, in the Peruvian Andes, by Cornell Capa from Magnum.*

THE "Geologic Time Scale" in Appendix A was adapted from that of J. Lawrence Kulp in *Science*, April 14, 1961. Used by permission of *Science* and the author.

COPYRIGHT, 1951, © 1958, 1962 BY HARCOURT, BRACE & WORLD, INC.

Library of Congress Catalog Card Number: 62–13975

PRINTED IN THE UNITED STATES OF AMERICA

Preface to the Third Edition

GEOGRAPHY *is concerned fundamentally with the nature of man's habitat, with the similarities and differences which occur from place to place
throughout that habitat, and with the significance to man of the variety and
change within it. One may attain the objectives of geography in a number
of ways. Of these, two are pre-eminent: that which makes use of the systematic, or topical, approach and that which makes use of the regional
approach. Both approaches employ analysis and synthesis. In the preface to
the first edition of* Introduction to Geography, *the authors expressed their
preference, and the reasons behind it, for the choice of the systematic approach for beginning students in college or university. Continued re-examina-
tion of this preference has convinced them that no reversal or major alteration in approach is necessary or desirable. In the reworking of the text for this
edition, changes have been made in the order of presentation, in the concepts
expressed when necessitated by new knowledge, and in the statistical matter,
which has been brought up to date. The framework is essentially unchanged;
the details have been altered to fit the passage of time.*

*Perhaps of greater importance from the point of view of the student are
two other changes. World distributions of population, natural resources, commodities, and the like are now displayed on a different version of the interrupted sinusoidal projection and color has been used on most of the maps and
diagrams. The first change has been made because it seems unrealistic to
separate into two parts the most extensive geographical unit on the earth, the
Africa-Europe-Asia land mass, though the distortion of the European and
northeastern Asiatic areas is somewhat greater than on the projection previously used. In the second change, an attempt has been made to use color only
to emphasize the particular features to which attention is called in the text
and to clarify the subject of each map and diagram for the student. It is hoped
that these two changes will enhance the book's effectiveness for teaching.*

*As previously, Part I outlines the content and objectives of geography and
provides some examination of the tools which geography uses. Part II is concerned with the physical elements of the human habitat. Here, a notable
change in order of topics has been made. Because the greater part of the
earth's surface is water, it appears logical to begin with that element. This is
followed by the study of landforms, for it is on the portions of the earth's crust
which rise above the great water areas that man has his permanent home.*

Climate is approached next since it forms the envelope over water and land alike. Soil and life forms complete the individual presentation of the physical elements. Part II concludes with a brief suggestion of the synthesis of all of the elements into physical geographic regions. Minerals, though actually a physical part of the habitat, are of particular significance when man uses them. Hence, their treatment has been left in a position close to the chapter on industrialization in Part III. In Part III, all chapters have been re-examined in the light of the rapid changes which have occurred in the recent past and which continue to occur even as the book is on press. The chapter on industrialization has been completely rewritten. Here it should be noted that dates had to be selected as the final limit for changes in the political pattern of the world and for the availability of statistical evidence. For the former, this date was the end of 1961; for the latter, in most part, 1959—the latest available from the United Nations.

Like the previous editions, this one has been designed for an introductory course of two semesters, terms, or quarters. A shorter course providing a workable summary of fundamentals may be devised, however, by eliminating Chapters 5, 6, 8, and 9 in Part II and Chapters 17 through 23 in Part III.

For this edition, a workbook has been prepared by Drs. John L. Thompson and Bertha Boya Thompson. It has taken account of both laboratory and nonlaboratory versions of the course and provides a substantial adjunct to the present volume.

The color plates at the front of the book have been revised and new ones have been added. The maps on Plates II to IX have been newly drawn by Mr. Jean Paul Tremblay. The new maps in the text have been drawn by Messrs. Lothar Roth, Jean Paul Tremblay, and Douglas Waugh.

We are deeply appreciative of the many suggestions made by our colleagues and fellow geographers, who have been so generous to us in this attempt to provide a better and a more serviceable book.

H. M. K.   *Oxford, Ohio*
R. M. G.   *Los Angeles, California*
C. H. M.   *Pacific Palisades, California*

JANUARY 21, 1962

Contents

III ELEMENTS OF THE CULTURAL SETTING

IV THE VARIED AND CHANGING SCENE

APPENDICES

List of Maps

xiv | *List of Maps*

PLATE I

THE SOLAR SYSTEM

Pluto

Neptune

Uranus

Saturn

Halley's Comet

Mars

Venus

Sun

Earth

Mercury

Moon

Jupiter

The Asteroids

HARRY LAZARUS

Mercury Venus Earth Moon Mars

Jupiter

Saturn

Uranus

Neptune

Pluto

RELATIVE DIAMETERS OF THE PLANETS

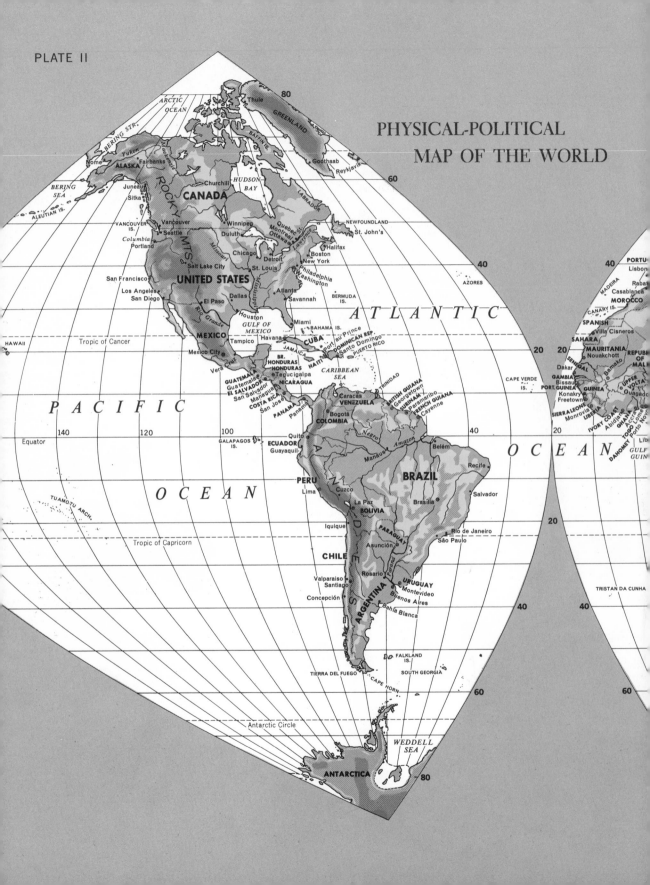

PLATE II

PHYSICAL-POLITICAL
MAP OF THE WORLD

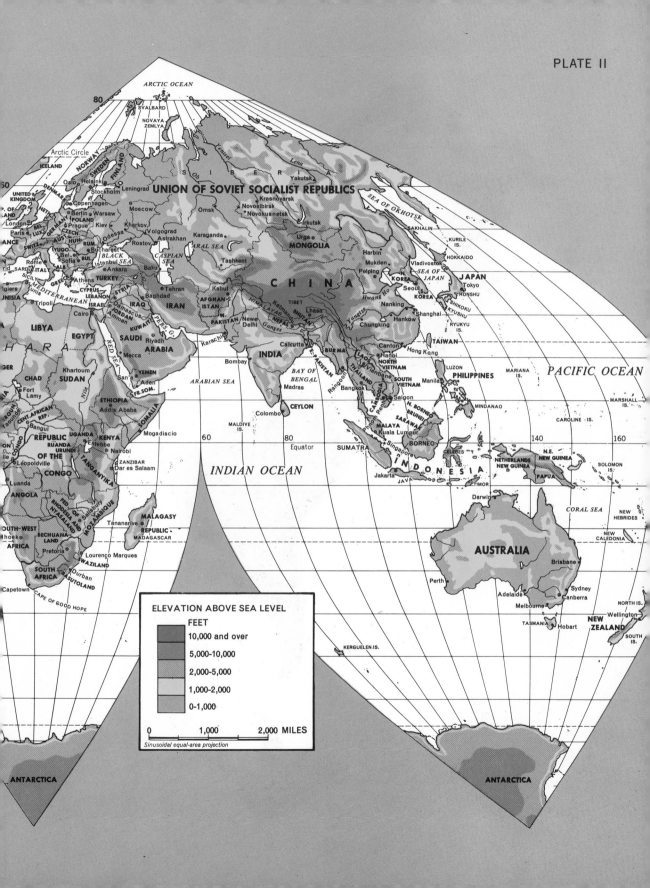

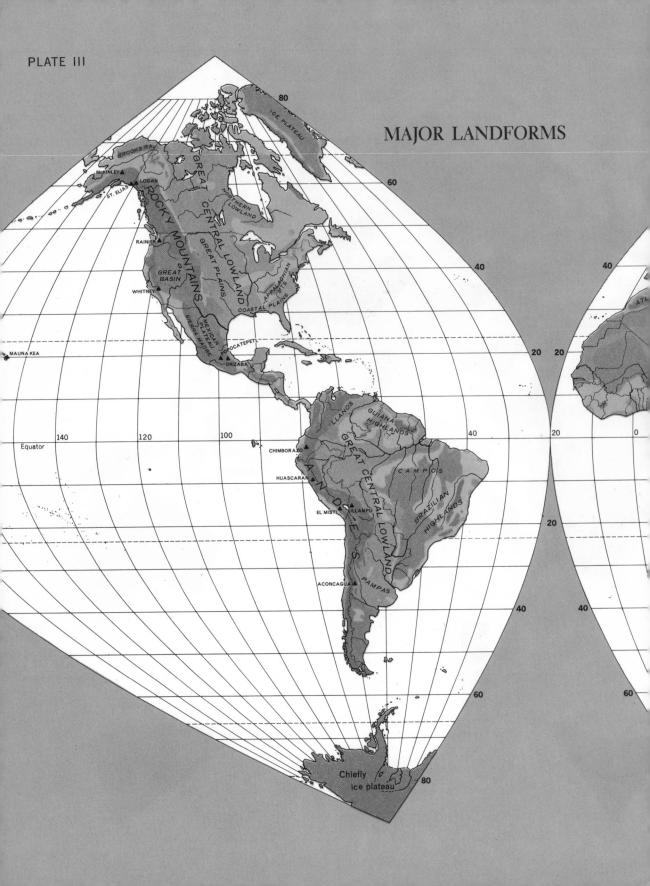

PLATE III

MAJOR LANDFORMS

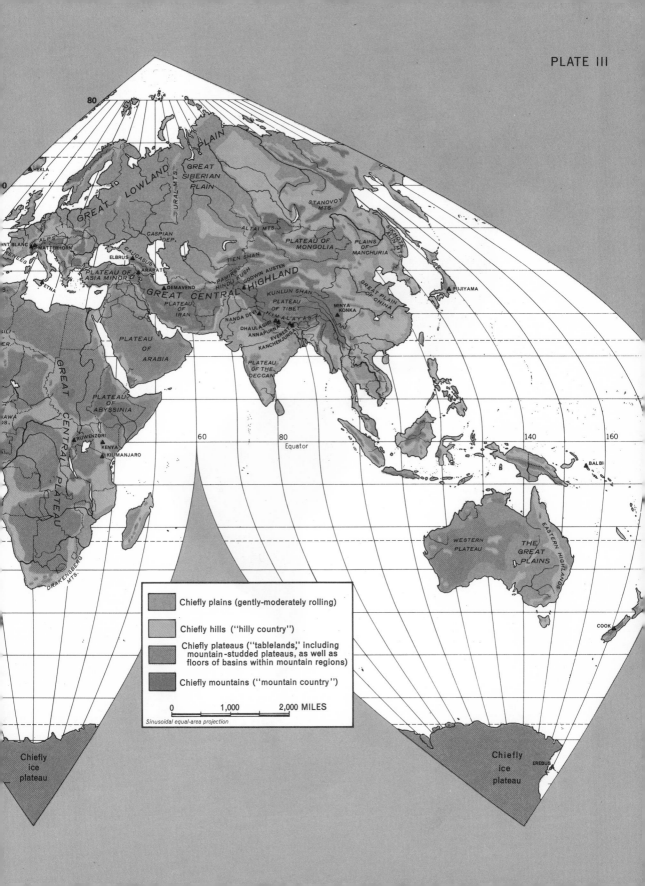

PLATE III

80

HEKLA

NT BLANC MATTERHORN ALPS
PYRENEES

ETNA

GREAT LOWLAND PLAIN

GREAT
SIBERIAN
PLAIN

URAL MTS.

CASPIAN
DEP.

CAUCASUS
ELBRUS ARARAT
PLATEAU OF
ASIA MINOR

DEMAVEND

ALTAI MTS.

STANOVOY
MTS.

TIEN SHAN
PAMIRS
HINDU KUSH GODWIN AUSTEN

GREAT CENTRAL HIGHLAND
PLATEAU
OF IRAN

KUNLUN SHAN

PLATEAU OF
MONGOLIA

PLAINS
OF
MANCHURIA

SIKHOTE ALIN MTS.

GREAT PLAIN
OF CHINA

FUJIYAMA

PLATEAU
OF TIBET

NANDA DEVI HIMALAYAS
DHAULAGIRI
ANNAPURNA
EVEREST
KANCHENJUNGA

MINYA
KONKA

PLATEAU
OF
ARABIA

PLATEAU
OF THE
DECCAN

SILI
ER
AWA
S

GREAT CENTRAL PLATEAU

PLATEAU
OF
ABYSSINIA

RUWENZORI
KENYA
KILIMANJARO

DRAKENSBERG
MTS.

60   80   140   160
                   Equator

BALBI

WESTERN
PLATEAU

EASTERN HIGHLANDS

THE
GREAT
PLAINS

COOK

Chiefly plains (gently-moderately rolling)

Chiefly hills ("hilly country")

Chiefly plateaus ("tablelands," including
    mountain-studded plateaus, as well as
    floors of basins within mountain regions)

Chiefly mountains ("mountain country")

0   1,000   2,000 MILES

Sinusoidal equal-area projection

Chiefly
ice
plateau

Chiefly
ice
plateau

EREBUS

PLATE IV

CLIMATIC TYPES

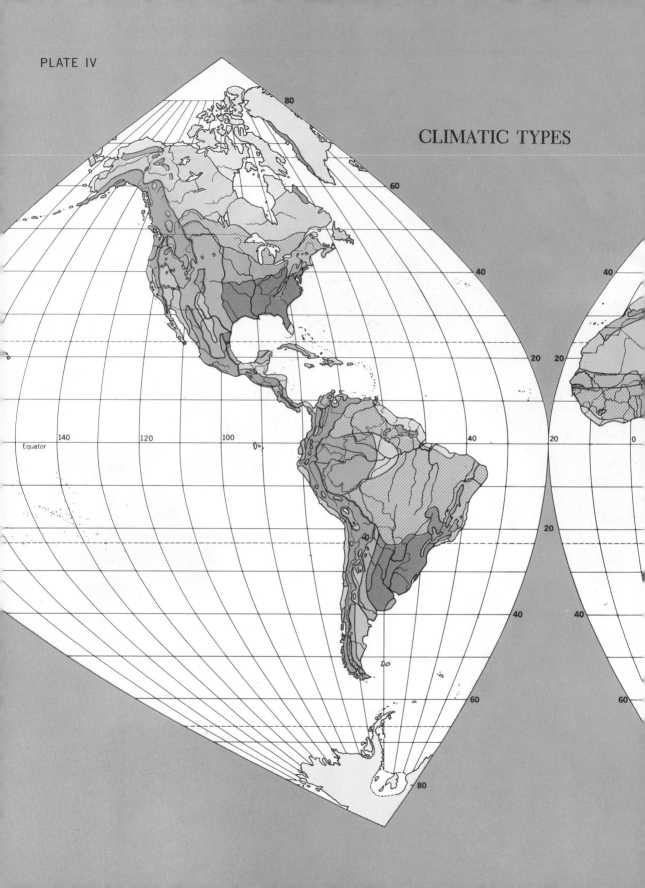

PLATE IV

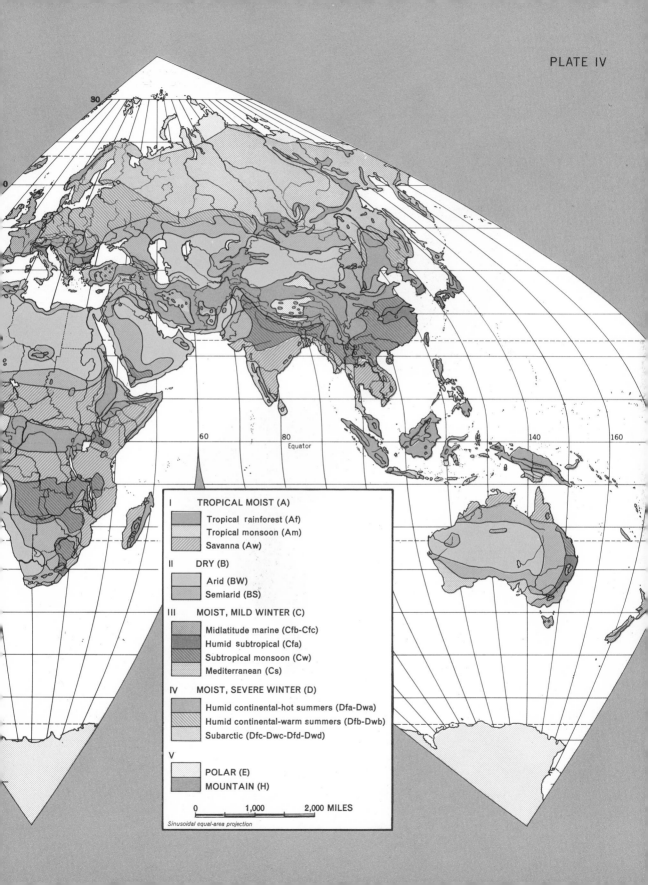

80

0

60   80   140   160
      Equator

I   TROPICAL MOIST (A)

    Tropical rainforest (Af)

    Tropical monsoon (Am)

    Savanna (Aw)

II   DRY (B)

    Arid (BW)

    Semiarid (BS)

III   MOIST, MILD WINTER (C)

    Midlatitude marine (Cfb-Cfc)

    Humid subtropical (Cfa)

    Subtropical monsoon (Cw)

    Mediterranean (Cs)

IV   MOIST, SEVERE WINTER (D)

    Humid continental-hot summers (Dfa-Dwa)

    Humid continental-warm summers (Dfb-Dwb)

    Subarctic (Dfc-Dwc-Dfd-Dwd)

V

    POLAR (E)

    MOUNTAIN (H)

0   1,000   2,000 MILES

Sinusoidal equal-area projection

PLATE V

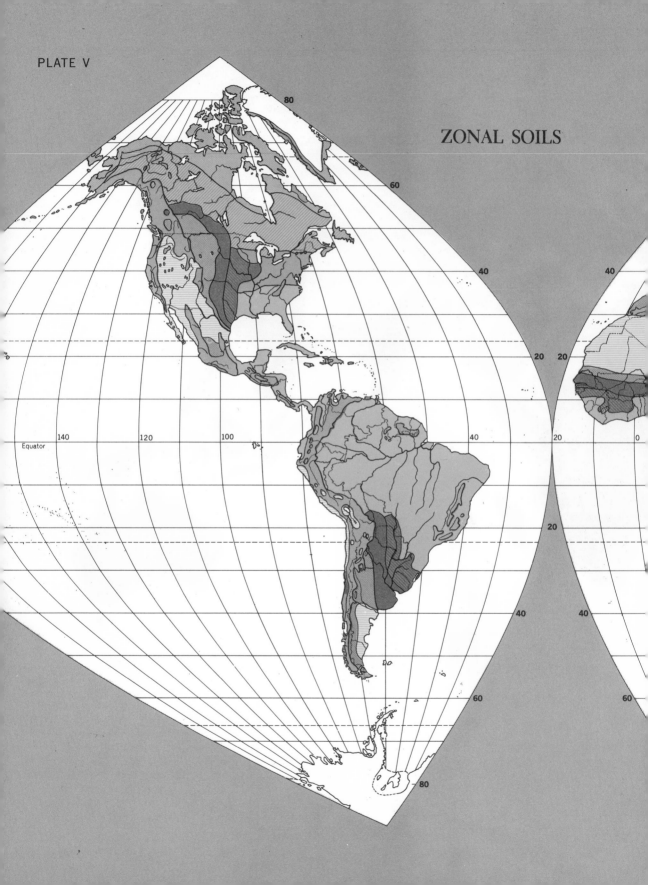

ZONAL SOILS

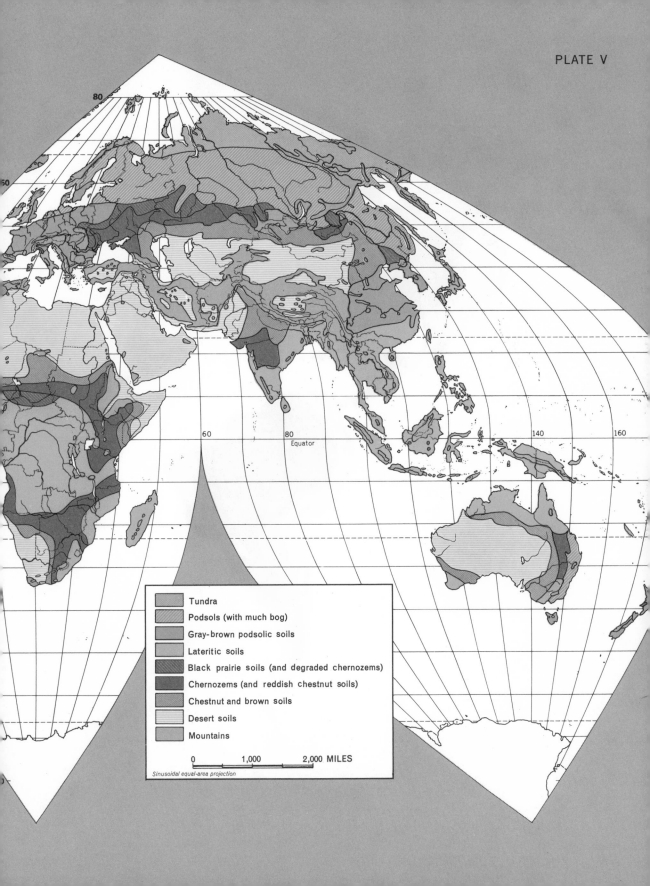

PLATE V

Tundra
Podsols (with much bog)
Gray-brown podsolic soils
Lateritic soils
Black prairie soils (and degraded chernozems)
Chernozems (and reddish chestnut soils)
Chestnut and brown soils
Desert soils
Mountains

0   1,000   2,000 MILES

Sinusoidal equal-area projection

PLATE VI

NATURAL VEGETATION

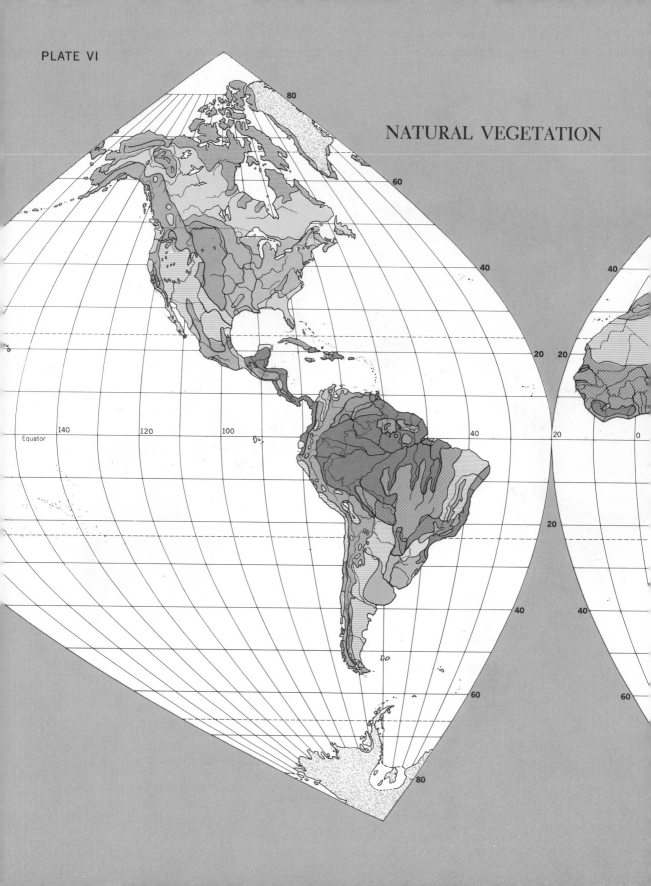

Equator

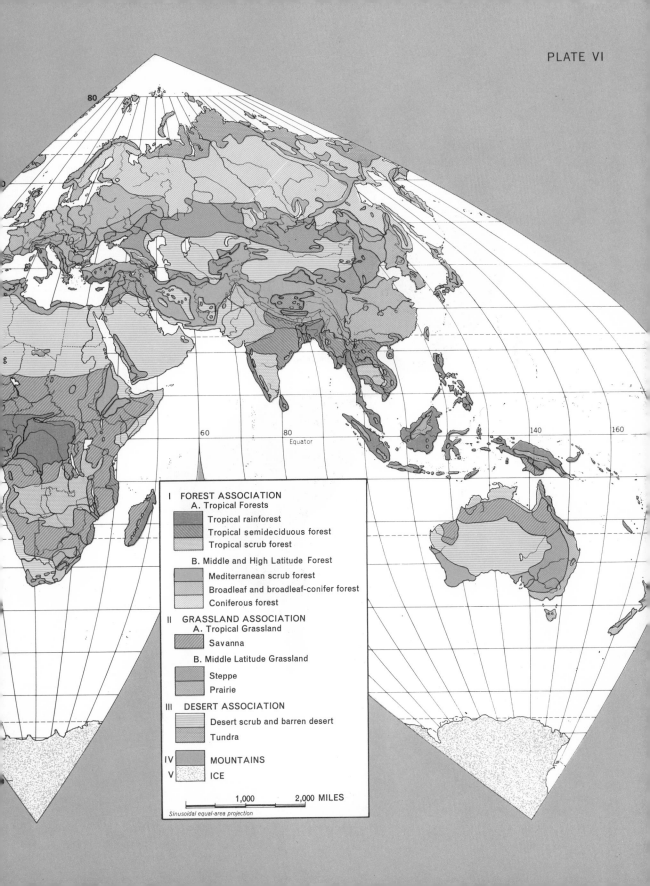

PLATE VI

80

60

80
Equator

140

160

I FOREST ASSOCIATION
A. Tropical Forests

Tropical rainforest

Tropical semideciduous forest

Tropical scrub forest

B. Middle and High Latitude Forest

Mediterranean scrub forest

Broadleaf and broadleaf-conifer forest

Coniferous forest

II GRASSLAND ASSOCIATION
A. Tropical Grassland

Savanna

B. Middle Latitude Grassland

Steppe

Prairie

III DESERT ASSOCIATION

Desert scrub and barren desert

Tundra

IV MOUNTAINS

V ICE

1,000   2,000 MILES

Sinusoidal equal-area projection

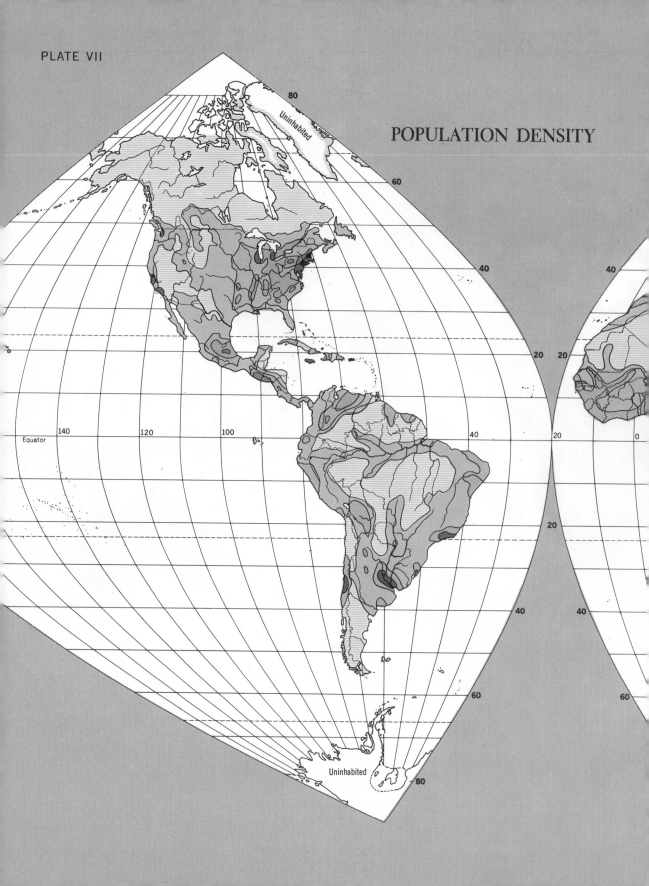

PLATE VII

POPULATION DENSITY

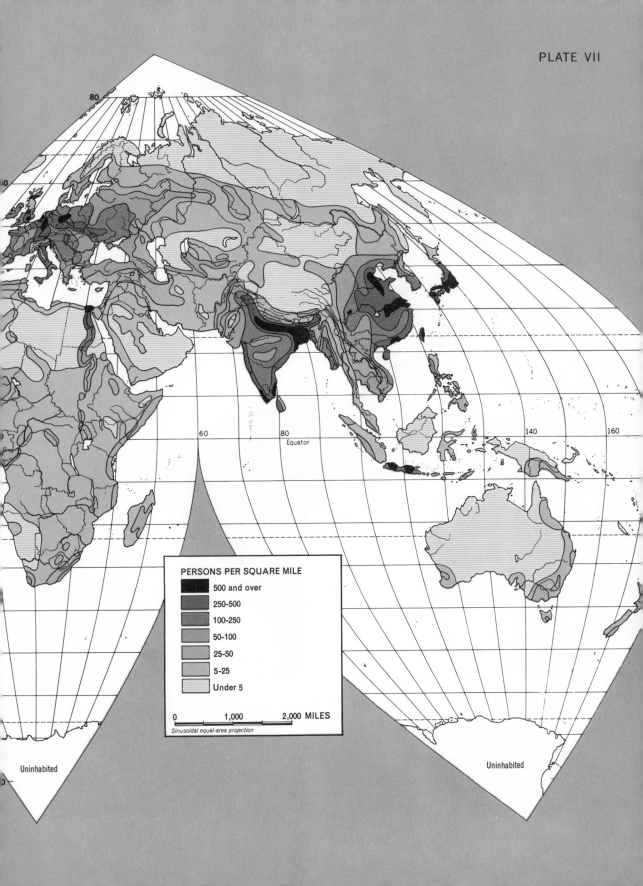

PLATE VII

PERSONS PER SQUARE MILE

- 500 and over
- 250-500
- 100-250
- 50-100
- 25-50
- 5-25
- Under 5

0   1,000   2,000 MILES

Sinusoidal equal-area projection

Equator

80

60

80

140

160

Uninhabited

Uninhabited

PLATE VIII

PREDOMINANT
ECONOMIES

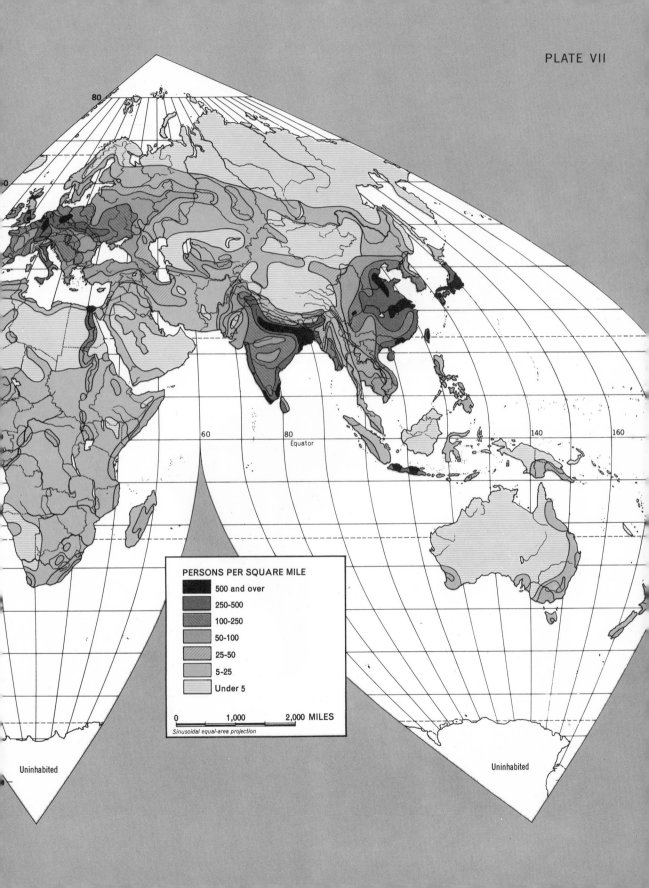

PLATE VII

PERSONS PER SQUARE MILE

500 and over

250-500

100-250

50-100

25-50

5-25

Under 5

0   1,000   2,000 MILES

Sinusoidal equal-area projection

80

60

80
Equator

60

140

160

Uninhabited

Uninhabited

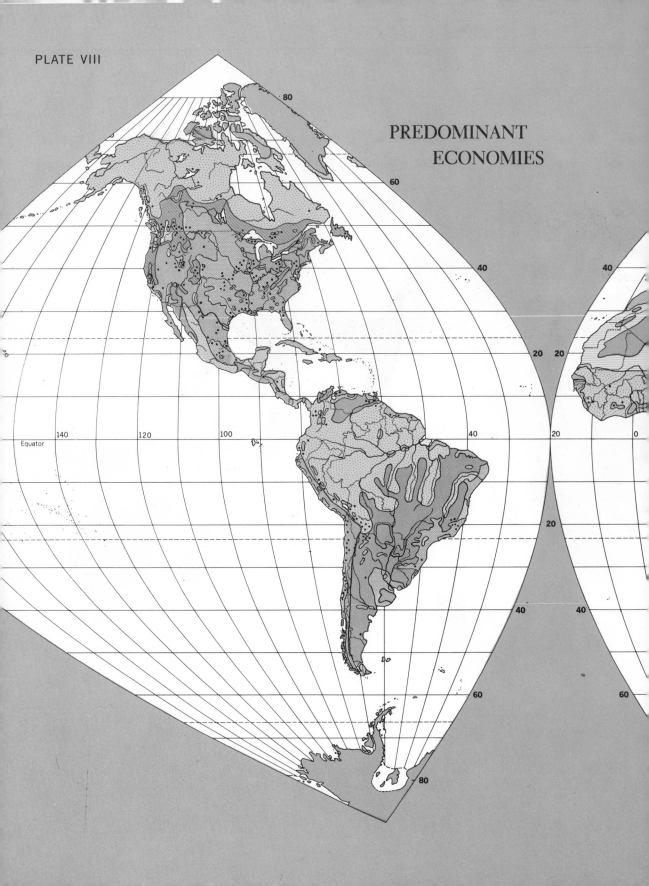

PLATE VIII

PREDOMINANT
ECONOMIES

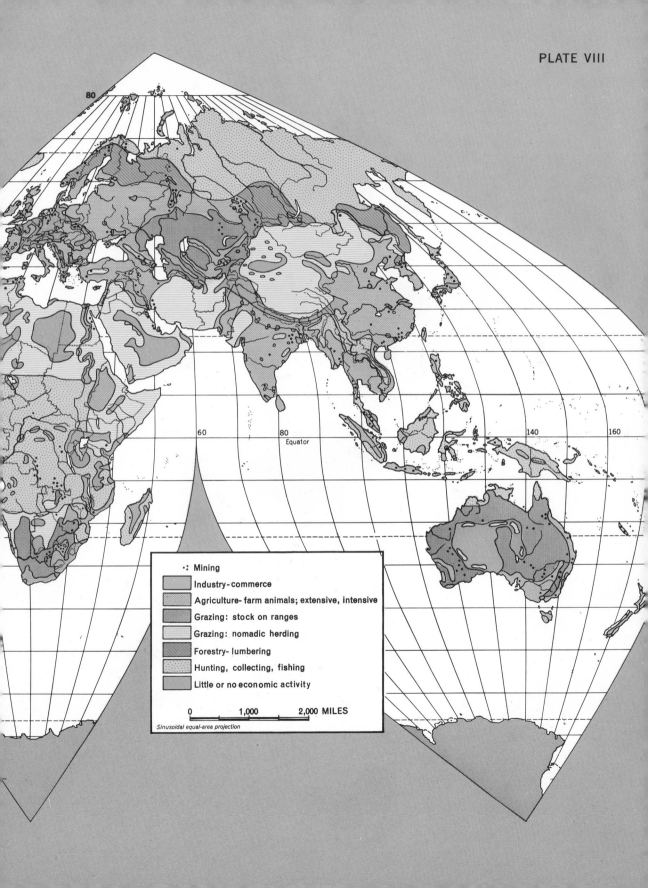

PLATE VIII

80

60   80
Equator

140   160

•∴ Mining
Industry-commerce
Agriculture- farm animals; extensive, intensive
Grazing: stock on ranges
Grazing: nomadic herding
Forestry- lumbering
Hunting, collecting, fishing
Little or no economic activity

0   1,000   2,000 MILES
Sinusoidal equal-area projection

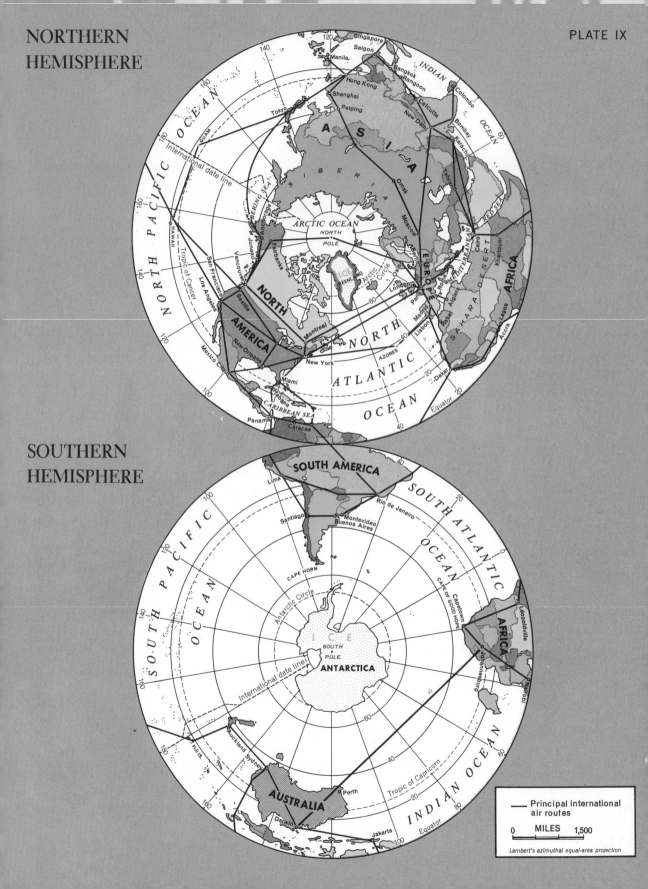

I

INTRODUCTORY SURVEY

I Some Objectives of Geographic Study

STANDARD OIL CO. (N.J.)

❡ ON THIS *planet, man lives in a kind of shell, relatively thinner than the shell of an egg. He has his permanent home on those fragments of land which stand above the great oceans and seas, but below the great thickness of atmosphere which envelops the planet. He has dug or bored into the solid crust of the earth, primarily to obtain minerals for his own use. He has ascended above the earth and now uses the atmosphere actively, to travel from one part of the solid crust to another. Yet the deepest mine extends only a scant two miles below the surface, while the greatest height to which man commonly ascends is slightly over twenty-four miles. Only within this shell, twenty-six miles in thickness, are physical conditions which make life possible known to exist. This is the space which man knows from direct contact and close observation; this is the space which he uses and alters to his own ends;*

and this is the space which places broad restrictions on his activities. Continued probing into the crust of the earth and exploration of outer space are slowly expanding man's living space vertically as the gradual movement over the earth's surface expanded it horizontally in the past. Still, a very thin shell and all that lies within it—animate and inanimate, including even man himself—constitute the human habitat. One of the main objectives of geography is to picture man's habitat and to show his relationship to it.

MAN'S HABITAT

Physical or Natural Elements

ANALYSIS of the human habitat shows that its nature results from the coexistence and interrelation of a host of different elements. Some of these are *physical* or *natural elements*. They include the features of water, land, atmosphere, soils, plant and animal life, and minerals—all of those elements which exist within the habitat except man and his works (TABLE 1).

The physical elements form the base upon which man depends for his livelihood. He has learned to control or modify some of them. He has tamed animals to serve him and plants to provide him with food. He has discovered how to divert water for the irrigation of his crops. He has learned to warm himself by burning a black mineral which he calls coal. Yet man has still to accept certain other physical elements as limitations upon his activities. For example, he uses the atmosphere for the passage of his airplanes, but because he has not yet been able to control atmospheric conditions, his airplanes are often grounded.

Man may alter the physical elements to varying degrees; he may struggle to alter them and

fail; or in some instances he may merely accept them as they are. But he cannot ignore them; they are the basic, fundamental stuff of his life on earth.

WATER • Man's life on earth is in a major sense an island life, for even the continents are in reality large islands surrounded by still larger oceans. But man's water world does not end there: the soils contain water, the earth materials under the soil contain water, even the very air holds much water in vapor form and drops some of it to make life possible on the land. Later discussions will emphasize the earth's waters, under such topics as *water bodies*, *streams*, and *underground water*.

LANDFORMS • Standing above the great oceans and seas is the exposed portion of the earth's crust. It expresses itself to the eyes of man in large forms such as continents and islands; in medium-sized forms such as mountains, tablelands, hills, and plains; and in smaller forms such as valleys, ridges, deltas, and sand bars. These many shapes of the top of the earth's crust, regardless of size, are *landforms*. Both local and world-wide expressions of this sort will be examined, not only in and of themselves, but also in terms of their significance to man and his ways of life.

WEATHER AND CLIMATE • Most completely all-pervasive in affecting life on the earth are the conditions and behavior of the atmosphere, especially the conditions of the lower portions of the atmosphere in which

1–1

[OPPOSITE, TOP] THE *earth is the habitat of man; geography provides the framework for observing variety and change in that habitat. Some of the elements of geography are here pictured, as they are combined in a small area in southeastern France.*

TABLE *1*

Generalized Check List of Elements of the Human Habitat

PHYSICAL OR NATURAL ELEMENTS	CULTURAL OR HUMAN ELEMENTS
A. HYDROSPHERE (WATER)	A. MAN
1. Oceans and seas	1. Population
2. Waters of the land	a. Numbers
a. Surface water	b. Distribution over the earth
b. Ground water	c. Density
3. Glaciers and icecaps	2. Cultural groups
B. LITHOSPHERE (EARTH)	a. Major groups
1. Earth materials	b. Other groups
a. Bedrock	3. Cultural institutions
b. Regolith, especially soils	a. Languages
c. Minerals	b. Religions
2. Surface configuration	c. Political units
a. Continents and islands	B. WORKS OF MAN
b. Major landforms	1. Settlements
c. Minor landforms	a. Rural
C. ATMOSPHERE (AIR)	b. Urban
1. Weather	2. Forms resulting from economies or ways of life
2. Climate	a. Hunting, fishing, and gathering
D. BIOSPHERE (LIFE)	b. Pastoralism
1. Native plants	c. Agriculture
2. Native animals	d. Exploitation of earth resources, i.e., lumbering and mining
	e. Manufacturing
	3. Routes of transportation and communication

man and other forms of life exist. The sum total of such conditions at any one moment of time and in any one place comprises *weather*; over a long period of time, it comprises *climate*. Ensuing chapters will emphasize the nature, consequences, and distribution of the conditions and behavior of the atmosphere.

SOILS • When solid rock is sufficiently broken up and when the residue has evolved to the point where it is capable of supporting plant life, it is known as *soil*. There are many types and varieties of soil, some highly productive and some virtually worthless, but, regardless of worth, they contribute still another part to the physical scene. Where productive, they

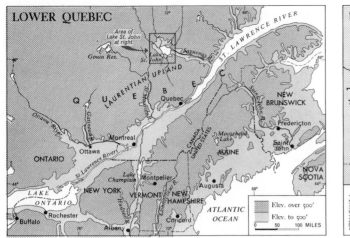
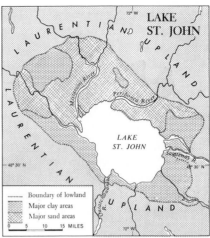

1–2   LAKE ST. JOHN, *in Lower Quebec, is located in an area known as the Lake St. John Lowland which is surrounded by the vast Laurentian Upland.*

provide one of the most fundamental of natural resources.

NATIVE VEGETATION AND ANIMAL LIFE • Many kinds of natural plants grow wherever soils are present. Seldom do they grow alone, but rather in groups or combinations. As a whole they comprise *native vegetation*; in specific combinations, they are *vegetation associations*, such as particular types of forests and grasslands. Living in among the natural plants are many varieties of animals ranging from flies and mosquitoes to deer and elephants. These, as opposed to man's domesticated animals, comprise *native animal life*. Because of the intimate relationships between plants and animals they are discussed together, rather than separately, in this book.

MINERAL RESOURCES • Bedrock and loose earth materials present man with many products which he can use directly or can process and transform into useful goods. Some examples are iron ore, petroleum, building stone, salt, tin, and gold. All such are termed *mineral resources*.

In their manifold combinations these physical elements of geography, from water to mineral resources, make up the physical setting. To speak more accurately, they comprise the many *kinds* of physical settings which occur over the earth. The elements noted need to be understood of and by themselves; just as important, they need to be understood and appreciated as they occur in natural combinations. To give emphasis to them as elements and, at the same time, to stress their significance in combination, the following thumbnail sketch is presented. This sketch is presented only as an example of what is meant by "physical setting" and by "relationships between and among the natural elements." It is brief, and, because of the present stage of our inquiry, it avoids all use of technical language.

Physical Setting

EXAMPLE: THE LAKE ST. JOHN LOWLAND • Some 100 miles north-northwest of the city of Quebec in Canada is an area known as the Lake St. John Lowland (FIG. 1–2). The center of the area is a relatively large body of fresh water which covers more than 300 square miles. Entirely surrounding this lake is a nearly level plain rising slowly to the steep edge of a more elevated country, which is gently rolling. Within the plain are deep soils. On the encompassing higher land, soils are thin and stony or are interrupted by nearly barren hills and ridges of solid rock as well as numerous ponds and lakes. Although all of the soils of the plain are deep, they vary markedly. To the south and east of the lake, the plains soils are chiefly fine, relatively compact clays; to the north and west, they are mainly coarse sands. Flowing from the higher land and tumbling by means of numerous falls and rapids into the plain are many large and small streams. One of the larger is the Peribonca river, which is about one mile in width at its mouth. Nearly all of the streams have cut deep channels into the plain so that its surface is appreciably interrupted. In several portions, most notably just north of the lake, are large swamps.

Originally the plain and the surrounding highland were covered with forests. Where the clay soils occur there were forests comprised largely of such trees as birch and maple with a sprinkling of conifers, such as spruce and cedar. The latter occurred chiefly where soils were swampy. Where the sandy soils occur there were forests of tall pines. On the rocky upland there were, and still are in most sections, forests of spruce, cedar, poplar, and birch. By clearing the clay-soil areas for farming purposes, man has almost entirely removed the original forest to the south and east of the lake (FIG. 1–3). Because of fires, the trees of most of the sandy lands have been replaced by a poor scrubby growth largely comprising jack pine, mosses, blueberry bushes, and fernlike plants known as bracken. The sandy areas were not generally used for farming purposes because of the low productivity of the soil and also because many sections of the sandy soils were swampy. Such swampy sections are marked by dense growths of spruce and cedar.

Overlying lake and plain alike, and extending far across the encircling higher lands, is a climate which is characterized by long, cold, snowy winters and short, warm, rainy summers. It is a climate of great seasonal change. Those who live there often say, by way of exaggera-

ROYAL CANADIAN AIR FORCE

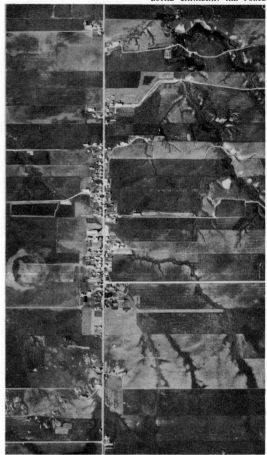

1–3

AIR photo of the farms in the clay-soil area of the Lake St. John Lowland.

tion: "There are two seasons here. There is winter, and there is a time when it is difficult to travel with sleighs." Actually, the summers are warm, and hot spells are not uncommon. However, there is no gainsaying the severe cold of the long winters. This strong seasonal behavior of the atmosphere is reflected in many other physical conditions as well as in the activities of the inhabitants. The surface of the lake is frozen with thick ice for about five months out of the year. The same is true of the rivers, except where the water at certain falls and rapids is moving too fast to freeze.

Swamps and small streams are frozen completely, and the soils are frozen to depths of two or three feet and are covered with a snowy mantle about three feet thick. Broadleaf trees such as birches and poplars become dormant during the cold period and stand completely barren of foliage. The conifers, appearing even darker against the white snow cover, retain their needles but, of course, cannot grow in the cold weather.

With the coming of spring the entire appearance of the countryside changes. The ice on the lake becomes wet and gray, and melts away. The river ice breaks up and moves downstream with a great deal of noise as the cakes of ice bump and grind against one another and against the banks. The mantle of snow disappears and the swamps and soils thaw out. New, green leaves appear on the broadleaf trees and the needleleaf trees become a brighter and fresher green. Songbirds and ducks, which had gone south to escape the cold, reappear. The deer, and an occasional moose, come out of their winter quarters in the spruce and cedar swamps. And swarms of mosquitoes, persisting through most of the summer, plague man and beast alike. The farmers, in the clay areas, do their spring plowing, plant their crops, and turn the domestic animals out to pasture.

Thus, in this sample area, one may see a certain type of physical setting, with its own particular conditions and patterns of arrangement of the natural elements, and with a marked seasonal rhythm incident to the behavior of the atmosphere. Moreover, there appear many relationships between and among the physical elements such as the association between the nearly level plain and deep soils, between the cold season and the migration of birds, between waterlogged soils and cedar swamps, between warm weather and open water and cold weather and snow and ice, and so on through many others. No mention was made of mineral resources. In this area they are insignificant except for some quarry-ing of building stone and the use of sand and gravel surfacing on roads. Also, man and his activities were mentioned only in passing because the discussion centered on the physical setting.

Concept of Physical Complexes

Ensuing chapters will discuss in some detail the nature of the physical elements, one by one, and in terms of world distributions and patterns. As these chapters are studied it will be necessary to remember that none of the natural conditions occurs alone and unrelated to the others. One may point out that vegetation *is* related to climate, that soils *are* related to both vegetation and climate, that the shapes of valleys *are* related to the work of streams and to the climatic behavior which determines how much water is supplied to the streams; these are only partial and somewhat random examples, but they do make clear that physical conditions are interrelated and that knowledge of individual conditions produces no geographic completeness until it is enlarged to become a knowledge of *physical complexes*.

Cultural or Human Elements

In addition to the physical elements which make up the human habitat, there is man himself and the features which result from his presence. These are the *cultural* or *human elements*. Man's numbers, his distribution over the earth, and the density of population; man's cultures with such institutions as language, religion, and political units; his ways of using the physical equipment; marks of his settlements and fields; and lines of transportation and communication which he stretches over the earth's surface—these are some of the items of the cultural scene (TABLE 1).

Both physical and cultural elements are combined and closely interrelated throughout the habitat. Yet the combinations are in no wise constant. The proportion of the whole contributed by each element varies from place to place. In addition, the elements themselves change through time.

Various combinations of the physical elements present different possibilities of use to man. Because man is present in differing numbers, because ways of doing things vary from one human group to another and from one time to another, or because one group of human beings discovers possibilities which another overlooks, cultural settings vary as much as do physical settings. Thus, to the physical complexes which are presented to man, there are added many which man himself creates, either by addition, removal, or both.

POPULATION • From the geographical point of view, the basic questions about man concern numbers; distribution, or arrangement, including movement, throughout the physical habitat; and density or number per unit area. Some parts of the face of the earth are entirely devoid of human inhabitants; other parts are occupied by large numbers of people living in close proximity with one another. In the first instance, the physical setting is altered not at all. In the second instance, alteration may be so great as almost completely to change the character of the physical setting. Though two portions of the habitat may have been very nearly alike before man entered the scene, they may be quite unlike as a result of his activity.

CULTURAL GROUPS • The manner in which human beings live and make a living in an area is not the same for all peoples. Even given essentially the same physical setting, two different groups may create quite contrasted scenes. For example, the character of the rice-growing areas of southeastern China is a far cry from that of the rice-growing areas in the southeastern United States. Differences exist largely because the traditions, or the learned ways of behaving, of one group of human beings differ from those of another. So also do the material manifestations—the houses, the roads, the fields, the equipment, and the like—

of one group differ from those of another. The sum of the traditions for any one distinctive human group and of the material manifestations of those traditions is spoken of as that group's *culture*.

The character of any specific portion of the earth is conditioned in part, then, by the culture of the group which inhabits it. In addition much of the individuality of any area derives from the fact that it has been occupied through a period of time. Through time the culture of any one group evolves new forms and passes through several stages, or several groups with different cultures may occupy the land successively. Often this succession results in features of the cultural setting, like the location of settlements or the pattern of roads and fields, which may persist long after an economic stage has been passed or after one culture group has been replaced by another. To understand the present situation in any area, the *sequent occupance* must often be examined.

CULTURAL INSTITUTIONS • In the present-day world there are many cultural institutions which leave their impress definitely and concretely upon the landscape; there are others less easy to recognize which, nevertheless, have profound effects in creating differences and similarities between the several parts of the human habitat. Among the less tangible cultural institutions are language, religion, and political units. Man's way of making a living, of thinking, and of reacting to the varieties of cultural and economic scene must take account of his language by which he communicates, of his religion by which his code of moral conduct is directed, and of his political organization by which he is governed. Often these intangibles tend to unite areas of physical dissimilarity; frequently, they tend also to create differences where none might otherwise exist. Any full understanding of the whole human habitat must make allowance for, or allot full credit to, cultural institutions of this particular sort.

SETTLEMENT • Perhaps the most common indicator of man's presence and activity in an area is his dwelling and the other buildings which go along with it. Individually, the house gives a clue to the sort of living which man carries on and thus suggests other forms which he has created. For example, a farmhouse with its associated buildings usually looks different from a city residence; the former calls to mind cropped fields, fences, pastures, and wood lots whereas the latter does not. Collectively, houses provide conspicuous forms which are man-made and which contrast with the nature-made features of the physical setting. The characteristics of *settlement*, as the arrangement of human groups over the face of the earth may be called, include not only the people, but also the details of their relationship to the habitat.

ECONOMIES • Settlement is at least partly adapted to the physical setting, but it also reflects the main activities by which human groups make a living, their *economies*. The largest and most complex groupings evidence the economy which we call *manufacturing*, wherein most of the individuals are not directly concerned with securing a livelihood through use of the land itself, but rather through the transformation of all sorts of raw materials. Somewhat less complex is the economy which we call *agriculture*, wherein man uses land for direct production of plants and animals and materials produced by them. There is also the economy, commonly still less complex than agriculture, which depends solely upon animals, called *pastoralism*. And, finally, simplest of all is the *hunting-fishing-collecting* economy, wherein man hunts other animals, fishes in streams and lakes and oceans or gathers plant products, thus gaining a living directly from the physical resources of the local area which he occupies. These, then, are the four chief economies: manufacturing, agriculture, pastoralism, and hunting-fishing-collecting.

Two other ways of living must be added to those already listed. Mainly as a result of the increasing importance of manufacturing, there has been an extension of hunting-fishing-collecting from its original form as a simple way of existence for a single group to a way of accumulating surpluses of raw materials. Mining, forestry, and large-scale hunting and fishing have come to be vital to the modern world. The pursuit of these activities may be thought of as a fifth economy, *exploitation*.

Finally man has come to move more freely over the earth's surface. He has acquired knowledge of transportation which allows him to free himself from dependence upon one small segment of the human habitat. In consequence, all parts of the human habitat are being drawn closer and closer together in their effects upon one another. The function of world linkage has become so significant as to create one more economy, *commerce*.

ROUTES OF TRANSPORTATION AND COMMUNICATION • The net of transportation and communication ties the whole human habitat together. The extent of the net measures the amount of human activity in different parts of the earth, and as the strands become more numerous and closer together, the earth and all of its peoples are tied together more and more closely. Few parts of the habitat are now really difficult of access. Less and less can one human group remain isolated from the others.

Just as with the physical features and their combinations in physical complexes, the understanding of the cultural features and of the part they play in the whole habitat is furthered by consideration of a specific example. It should be noted that reference is first made to the character of the physical setting, for this is the matrix in which the cultural features are embedded. The geography of an area includes both; one alone is not the complete story. Only when the physical background is presented can the geographic significance of the cultural elements be fully appreciated. The following sketch suggests some aspects of the variety which is induced into the different parts of even a small segment of the habitat through man's activities.

The Vézère Valley: A Type Study

PHYSICAL SETTING • The Vézère river is one of several right-bank tributaries of the Dordogne in the southwest part of central France (FIG. 1–4). Like many of the other tributaries, this one has cut its way westward from the upland area known as the Massif Central to the extensive lowland of southwestern France. Its course leads across a low limestone plateau which fringes the western side of the Massif Central. A portion of the valley where the river crosses the limestone plateau, in the vicinity of the villages of Sergeac, St. Léon-

sur-Vézère, and Le Moustier, is here chosen to illustrate characteristics of the cultural setting and of the changes in those characteristics through time.

In this portion of its course, the Vézère is less than 100 feet wide, and it follows a winding course over the wide floor of an entrenched valley (FIG. 1–5). On the outsides of the bends, steep slopes rise directly from the river to the plateau level about 100 feet above. On the insides of the bends, there are relatively large, scroll-shaped valley flats extending gradually away from the stream to less abrupt valley sides. The course of the stream is blocked in places by shallow rapids because the present river has cut regularly below the level of the flats. There are few tributaries and, in consequence, the valley sides stretch unbroken, whether they are at the river's edge or as much as half a mile back from the river (FIG. 1–4).

Some of the detail is suggested by a cross section of the valley (FIG. 1–6). Starting on the general level of the plateau, on the outside of one of the bends in the river, the surface declines gently toward the brink of the valley. The gentle slope gives way to a cliff from 25 to 45 feet in height. At its base a more gradual slope is again produced by an unassorted accumulation of weathered rock materials, or *colluvial base*, and this leads directly down almost to the stream's edge. In some places the base of the cliff is eroded so as to form an overhang of as much as 25 feet; in other places the overhang is less and is masked by the accumulation of rock debris.

Across the stream there is a low steep bank from the top of which the surface extends nearly level away from the river. This is the valley flat; in places it is as much as half a mile wide, but in other places it is much narrower. At the outer edge of the flat, the valley side is reached, this time much more gently sloped and with no bedrock exposed.

This same profile is repeated wherever one crosses the valley except that the steep and the gentle sides alternate. Farther downstream the

H. M. KENDALL

1–4

A VIEW downstream along the Vézère river near St. Léon in southwest central France. Note in the background the even skyline of the plateau into which the valley has cut.

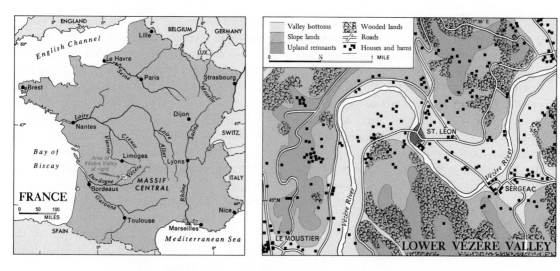

1–5 THE Vézère valley, located in southwest central France on the west side of the Massif Central, exhibits several surface division types, varied woodland cover, and scattered settlement.

valley is more deeply entrenched so that the cliffs are more prominent. Farther upstream the valley is shallower and the cliffs are not so high.

Soil covering is closely related to the different types of surface. On the upland to either side of the valley, it is thin and stony, with irregular fragments of partially decomposed limestone scattered through it. On the valley flats, alluvial material, fine grained in general, is deeply spread; only on the edges of the flats at the valley sides are there any considerable areas of gravel. On the valley sides, rock debris and the products of its consequent weathering are mixed with alluvium so that areas of easily worked materials are spottily distributed.

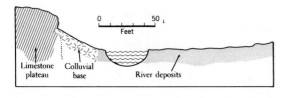

1–6

A CHARACTERISTIC cross section of the Vézère valley.

Much of the upland and much of the valley sides remain forested or have been reforested (FIG. 1–5), while the valley floor appears to have had an original cover chiefly of grass. The forest that remains is dominantly of chestnut and oak, though there are many poplars in the valley bottom and the stream is lined in places with willows. Some parts of the upland appear too dry for forest and the cover in these places consists of low bushes intermixed with grasses.

The dryness of the upland is made more noticeable by the absence of much surface water. This results primarily from the nature of the rock material of which the plateau is made. The whole area is open to the west and is close enough to a windward ocean to have a moist, mild winter climate so that the dryness is not climatic. Precipitation averages approximately thirty-five inches per year. Ground water is plentiful, especially in the valley, where springs abound along the cliffed sides. Rarely are the valley flats too dry to support plant growth, even during prolonged droughts. When melting snows of the Massif Central augment the waters of the Vézère, the valley flats are often inundated. Flooding provides an additional source of soil moisture.

There are no mineral resources in or near this section of the valley. Thus it is upon the land surface, climate, vegetation, and soil that the livelihood of the inhabitants must depend.

CULTURAL SETTING • Human beings have lived in this area for thousands of years. They have occupied it in different ways and their settlements have used different parts of it as the cultures have changed.

In the Vézère valley, the discovery of prehistoric artifacts has led to a knowledge of the way in which early man lived and of the kinds of places which he used for dwellings. It is therefore possible to reconstruct something of the cultural setting of this long-past period.

For his dwellings, prehistoric man chose two kinds of sites. He lived either in solution caves in the limestone of the plateau or in rock shelters. Both of these types of site are found on the steep valley sides, but not on the gentler slopes. The rock shelters were really places where the erosive processes had created a sufficient overhang at the base of the cliffs to offer some protection from the weather.

Though the overhang is now masked in many places by the accumulation of rock debris, it is probable that it was open at the time prehistoric man used it, for he is not known to have had any implement with which to excavate large amounts of earth. What was more important was the height of the rock shelter or cave opening above usual flood-water level. From either type of site the land drops steeply to the river's edge.

Relatively little is known about prehistoric man's way of living. What is known has been gleaned from such remnants of his culture as have withstood the ravages of time. Stone implements which have been found by excavating cave floors or earth fill adjacent to the rock shelters are those of the hunter or fisher. Cave roofs and walls are decorated with drawings of a wide variety of fish and animals. Among the animals are bison, horses, and deer. Mixed in with the implements are bone fragments showing teeth marks; meat was an important element in the diet. That man of this period knew fire is attested by the remnants of charred bone. But there is nothing to indicate whether or not agriculture was practiced. The lack of pictorial representation of plant life on the cave walls, in contrast to the plentiful representation of animal life, implies that agriculture was not important.

It is suggested, then, that prehistoric man lived by the hunting-fishing-collecting economy. He chose his dwelling site for protection, but also for nearness to the streams and to the upland forests. He had no interest in the relatively flat lands, the easily cultivated lands of the valley floor.

In contrast to the concentration on the steeper valley sides by prehistoric man, the present-day inhabitants seek out the valley floor and the remnants of the upland surface on either side of the valley (FIG. 1–5). The roads follow the outer edge of the valley flats or the edge of the upland surface, avoiding steep slopes wherever possible. Houses, hamlets, and villages are similarly restricted to the flatter lands. The gentler valley slopes are partly in cultivation, but the steep slopes are little used.

Both on the relatively sparsely populated upland and in the more densely peopled valley floor, there is a tendency toward clustered arrangement of dwellings. Upland hamlets occupy sites where the upland surface breaks to the gentler valley sides. Valley hamlets and villages are on portions of the flats which, because they are higher, are less subject to flood, or where, because of poor soil, cultivation is difficult or unprofitable. In the section of the valley under consideration, three kinds of sites are utilized (FIG. 1–5). Sergeac is near the downstream end of its flat where the flat gives way to a gently rising valley side. St. Léon is on the outer edge of its flat opposite a spur against which the river is flowing; this position gives control over the best fording place in this part of the course of the Vézère. Le

Moustier is on the lower part of a steep valley side and the adjacent flat where a tributary valley joins that of the Vézère.

Each of these villages consists of a stretch of the main road along the valley where houses are grouped closely together. Rows of two-story houses line each side of the road. In some of them, a room on the first floor is set aside as a store. Here and there, a narrow opening between houses gives access to the section back from the street. Behind each house there is a small garden. And beyond that, another irregular row of houses is to be found.

The older houses are made of limestone blocks partly covered with plaster. Roofs are made of thin, flat, overlapping slabs of limestone. Some of the houses are whitewashed, but most of them are the dun shade of the original plaster covering. Newer houses use frame construction with slate or tile roofs. The few isolated houses in the valley are built in the same way; each one has its barn of similar construction.

The people of this area are farmers first and foremost. The gardens adjacent to the houses supply kitchen needs, but in addition each family cultivates fields on the valley flats or on the lower valley sides. In fields much less than an acre in size, wheat and maize are the main grain crops. Together they equal in importance the crops of potatoes and other vegetables. Apple, pear, peach, and plum trees dot the farmland, but no land is specifically given over to orchard alone. Vineyards, which formerly covered nearly all of the south-facing valley slopes, are now unimportant, since the phylloxera, a kind of plant lice, have destroyed the vines. In some places, truffle-bearing oaks have replaced the vines, but most of the upper slopes are uncultivated. Wheat is the main grain crop of the uplands; most of the small remainder of cultivated land there is used for vegetables.

Plow cultivation is not common, the ordinary implements being the mattock, the spade, and the hoe. Largely because of this, crops are intermixed, with no clear-cut division into fields of one crop only (FIG. 1–7). Each field consists of a patchwork of a few rows of maize, a 15- to 20-foot strip of wheat, and several rows of vegetables of different kinds. Thus the cultivation is intensive rather than extensive.

The raising of hogs accompanies the garden agriculture in the valleys and sheep grazing accompanies it on the upland. There are some cattle, primarily for the supplying of dairy products. Each household has its small poultry flock in which geese predominate. The hogs and geese are essential to the production of the one commercial agricultural product of the area. Hogs are used to locate truffles, subterranean fungus growths on the roots of certain oak trees; geese are fattened on maize so that their livers become fatty and large. The livers and the truffles are combined to make the commercial delicacy *foie gras truffé*.

Except for this one item of commerce, production is directed toward the supplying of local demand. The area is one of plenty so far as food, shelter, and clothing are concerned, but "extras" or luxuries of life, common in the industrial or urban portions of the Western world, are lacking. Poor articulation with the transportation pattern of the rest of France emphasizes this isolation.

Thus an agricultural people live and create ways and means of living that contrast sharply with those produced by an earlier group. The flatter lands and their use principally to provide plant products are the objects of modern attention. Collectively, the cultural features of the habitat at the present time differ vastly from those in prehistoric times even though the facts of the physical setting have been little altered in the Vézère valley.

Variety and Change

Two qualities, variety and change, are ever present in the human habitat. The first of these can be easily observed by travel over the

1–7 THE patchwork of small fields in the Vézère valley, viewed from a point near the top of the steep valley side. The river flows too close to the base of the steep slope to be visible in this picture.

surface of the earth. Change becomes evident only with the passage of time and is therefore less easy to observe.

Different combinations of both physical and cultural elements produce *variety* within the total habitat. No two areas are exactly alike. Nearly three-fourths of the earth's surface is water. No permanent settlement of the oceans is possible, though their temporary use as routes and as sources of food and raw material is very significant to man. The atmosphere is unsuited to permanent habitation. In contrast, land areas do provide usable sites.

Yet there is great difference between any two areas of land. Some are thickly wooded like the hill lands of New England; others are carpeted with grasses like parts of the Great Plains; and still others are devoid of vegetation like parts of Death Valley. In some places, as in our own West, rugged mountains interrupt the smoothness of the surface and form barriers to human movement over the land.

These are a few of the easily observed differences, but there are many others, just as important to man, which are not always immediately evident. Some areas are underlain by coal or petroleum deposits. The soils of one area are fertile while those of another are infertile. Some places have climates which are moist, where ample rain falls regularly; in other regions, rain falls so infrequently and in such small amounts as to be a curiosity.

By no means are differences from place to place confined to the physical elements. Some parts of the earth are closely built up to form great cities like New York. Others are thinly peopled and empty of most signs of human activity. Intensively cultivated lands, where a tremendous amount of labor is used per unit of land, as in Japan, contrast vividly with the extensively cultivated American wheat lands where very little labor is used per unit of land.

Time produces change within any one section of the human habitat. Volcanic eruptions like those of Mont Pelée in 1902 on the West

1–8   MANY of the elements of geography are here pictured as they appear in a small area in Vermont. Compare with FIG. 1–1.

Indian island of Martinique cause sudden and terrible change. Reforestation after lumbering operations is a slower form of change. Still slower is the wearing away of mountain surfaces by streams. This is so slow as to be almost imperceptible to man. Yet, bit by bit through ages of time, the shape of the mountain surface is continuously changing.

Change is not confined to the physical elements of the habitat. Settlements increase or decrease in size and importance. A simple fishing village becomes an important port, as did Amsterdam in the Netherlands. Great ports of one age decline through the silting up of their harbors, as did Bruges and Ghent in Belgium. A net of paved highways spreads over an area previously served only by dirt roads or trails. The cutting of great water channels across land masses, like the cutting of the Panama and Suez canals and the construction of the Great Lakes–St. Lawrence Seaway, is change of magnificent and sudden proportions. It alters the actual surface of the earth even as it modifies the direction of man's activities. Whether it involves the physical or the cultural elements, and whether the rate is fast or slow, change is continuous and is everywhere present.

Man's Habitat | 15

SOME MAJOR GEOGRAPHICAL OBJECTIVES

IT IS to provide a framework for observation of variety and change in man's habitat and man's relationship to that habitat that geography bends a large part of its efforts. Geography attempts to picture man's habitat at a specific time through the study of arrangements of natural and human elements over the earth. The effect of the past in the creation of the present is recognized; the effect of the present on the future is implied. Part of the task of geography is to answer such questions as these: What kinds of physical and cultural features are encountered on this planet which man finds to be his home? Where throughout the habitat are they encountered? Why are they distributed the way they are? Of what significance in human affairs are these distributions? These are among the basic questions with which geography is concerned and for which it seeks the answers.

One geographical point of view is suggested by the growing realization, on the part of all of us, of world interdependence. In the early periods of human history, man made simple use of what he found within any small segment of the whole habitat. His world was limited to the area traversed in the constant search for the necessities of life. Many detailed features like rivers, swamps, gorges, and mountain slopes controlled his routes and offered him easily protected dwelling sites. Vegetation provided food either directly or indirectly through supporting an edible animal population; it also supplied materials for clothing and shelter. Streams offered water and supplementary food in the form of fish. Steady and long-continued rains, snow, and ice or periods of bright sunshine made necessary some variety of clothing and shelter. Life in small groups produced only limited human contacts. Such elements, combined within a relatively small area, were man's world and he was closely tied to it. Primitive means of transportation and simplicity of manner of living effectively isolated one fragment of the habitat from another.

Through the passage of centuries, man's manner of life has increased in complexity. Correspondingly, through increased range of movement, he has expanded his known world until the whole surface of the planet is finally known. Increased speed and ease of movement have bound together fragments of the habitat shell; indeed, in the time sense, the shell has actually begun to contract. Domestication of animals provided beasts of burden and thus increased the range of man's movements. Navigation, even so primitive as the use of rafts, opened new highways. The invention and application of the steam engine materially increased the speed with which man could travel over the surface of both land and water. Oceans, at one time serious barriers, became highways. Railroads cut to a fraction the time of overland movements. In our own century, the internal combustion engine, first a conqueror of surface space and then conqueror of the lower portion of the atmosphere, has carried the process farther, as has more recently the jet engine. No longer can any group remain wholly isolated.

The increased complexity of present-day life is typified by the development of huge urban populations. For the individual in an urban community, emphasis is no longer on the direct production of all the goods essential to his life but rather on such specialized functions as the manufacture or distribution of one particular product or the provision of manifold services. Primitive man was concerned only with satisfying his food needs and providing himself with shelter for protection and comfort. He lived or perished through his own efforts as a hunter. Human groups in those times were small and contacts between them were infrequent. Later, with the domestication of animals and plants and with the use of metals, living became less rigorous. More nearly complete use of the physical part of the habitat made possible larger groupings of men. Contacts between groups were more frequent. Surpluses of foods, clothing, shelter materials, and implements were accumulated. And commerce, the exchange of goods between human groups, came into being. Man no longer had to go after what he needed within a narrowly encompassed area; it was brought to him from ever-increasing distances. Some men could specialize in one activity like growing wheat, raising animals, weaving cloth, or making implements. Specialized workers could secure their own needs from others who carried their products to places ill-equipped for their production and returned with items which they in turn could not produce. In this way, large groups could live without the necessity of securing the absolute essentials of life from a mere fragment of the whole habitat.

So far has the process gone under Western civilization that no areas remain self-sufficient. Long tentacles of trade spread throughout the world and along them are sucked raw materials which make possible the continuance of the urban mode of life. What once were considered luxuries, desirable yet unessential, are now classed as basic necessities. Only with a decrease in the level of living can the dependence of one area upon another be overcome. Our world is no longer a fragment of the habitat shell; it is the whole shell.

SCOPE OF THIS BOOK

Specific Objectives

THE entire human habitat and man's place in that habitat are our concern; hence our attention must be focused upon features of world scale. We must consider broad categories of both physical and cultural facts. We are not concerned with a complete recital of earth knowledge. Hence, our analysis of features which combine to differentiate portions of the earth must be limited to major elements. Our objectives may be summarized positively under five main headings: (1) to present an orderly treatment of the major physical elements with which man contends and cooperates; (2) to outline the principal ways man makes use of the physical setting in which he lives; (3) to present the distribution over the earth of both the physical and cultural elements of the human habitat; (4) to interpret the variety which exists; and (5) to offer a standard against which change may be measured. Through these objectives, a basic outline for the understanding of the world in which we live is offered.

Outline of Approach

There are many lines of approach to the above objectives. We choose here to begin our study of the human habitat by examining certain phases of the earth as a planet (CHAPTER 2). From this emerges a broad appreciation of the shell habitat we are about to analyze. Here is the common ground for the general beginning of many studies, but particularly of three —astronomy, geology, and geography.

Because physically we as human beings are so much smaller than the object of our study, we resort to a special means of reducing facts about that object to workable size: we employ a code or set of symbols—the map. We must, therefore, give some attention to maps, their construction, and their uses. By means of them observations may be compiled, distributions ascertained, and interrelationships deduced. If the pertinent data concerning the habitat are not reduced to map representation, the element of distribution and the nature of the ties between distributions cannot fully be appreciated. At all times, however, the map must be thought of as a code or set of symbols. Otherwise, interpretation of it will be false. Map essentials are treated in CHAPTER 3.

Following the delimitation of the field of study and the acquisition of the major tool, we shall proceed to an orderly examination of the physical and cultural facts. As we have said, the greater part of the surface of the earth is covered by oceans and seas. On the land itself, lakes, rivers, and swamps are features of major prominence. Even within the crust of the earth, water is intimately fused with soil and with certain rock structures. Human, plant, and animal life are all narrowly limited by availability of water. Oceans provide both highways and sources of support. In addition, the function of water in inland transport and in the development of power is important. Thus we turn (CHAPTER 4) to a consideration of water features.

Man's permanent base on this planet is on the great land masses which rise above the oceans. On these land masses, the most conspicuous features are the major landforms (mountains, hills, plateaus, and plains). These, in turn, are shaped by many agents into detailed forms which influence, favorably or unfavorably, many human activities. The pattern of landforms, both major and minor, makes for variety throughout the habitat. These matters are treated specifically in CHAPTERS 5, 6, and 7.

The atmosphere, which makes all life possible, next claims our attention. The conditions within that gaseous envelope, weather and climate, affect the whole habitat profoundly. We proceed with the questions: What kinds of climate are there? Where is each type found? Why is the arrangement such as it is? And what is the significance of climate to man? These matters are treated in CHAPTERS 8, 9, 10, and 11.

A less obvious feature of the habitat, soil, is fully as essential to life forms as climate, landforms, and water. Growing out of the soil is the cover of natural vegetation. It provides a source of materials needed by man and also the life essentials for an animal population which man has, at least in part, bent to his uses. Following the study of climate, we direct our attention to those of soil (CHAPTER 12) and plant and animal life (CHAPTER 13).

Finally, the minerals, which are the basis of man's complex economy, provide the element at the very bottom of the shell habitat. To extract them from the earth, man has penetrated farthest below the actual surface and has thus pushed his habitat into the solid portion of the planet. Because the use of minerals and their significance to man form part of the cultural portion of the habitat, we have delayed treatment of them (CHAPTERS 20, 21, and 22) until we study man's most complex economy, manufacturing.

All of these forms collectively, combined in different quantities in separate areas, produce the conditions which provide the ultimate physical limits of man's activity.

From an understanding of the physical habitat, one passes to a consideration of man and his activities. The most prominent among the cultural elements is the distribution of population over the earth (CHAPTER 15). Yet this is almost overshadowed by a factor which is not directly visible or instantly comprehensible. This factor is culture, the sum of the "capabilities and habits acquired by man as a member of society." While the physical setting places certain broad restrictions on man's activities, culture may, and frequently does, offer more serious obstacles. Conversely, culture may provide means of overcoming physical restrictions. Availability of water in a desert is undoubtedly a measure of restriction for a human group. If such a group does not know the technique of well drilling or other methods of water acquisition, it finds the desert almost useless. Another group, having a means of tapping an underground water supply, discovers a setting in which it can live satisfactorily. If the culture includes knowledge of irrigation methods, barren desert may be made to support great densities of population, like those of the Nile valley in Egypt.

Throughout man's long history, numerous great culture groups have arisen and have produced distinctive economies, or ways of living. When progress has been maintained, the groups have increased in size and the culture they represent has spread to affect large portions of the world; other groups have barely maintained themselves and their areal influence has declined like that of the Mayas in Middle America or has disappeared altogether. In the present period, two great cultures dominate the world scene: that of Europe and the Americas (which is called Western, or Occidental) and that of southern and eastern Asia (which is called Eastern, or Oriental). Other smaller and less complex cultures still remain in considerable numbers and add materially to the mosaic pattern which man has imposed upon the physical habitat.

Among the patterns of cultural elements which are effective conditioners of man's activity, we have selected language, religion, and political association as illustrations (CHAPTER 16). These are only three of the many cultural forces which must be recognized if any true measure of variety and change within the whole human habitat is to be made.

From a realization of the significance and variety of cultures, one passes to the easily observable, concrete forms—such as fields, roads, buildings, and settlements (CHAPTERS 16 and 24)—in which they are expressed. Distinctive economies—from the most elemental hunting, fishing, and gathering to the most intricate urban life—create notable variety in the habitat. The practice of these varied economies by individual culture groups, particularly as expressed by forms of settlement and of land use, results in variety from place to place over the whole earth. What are the settlement and land-use forms? Where are they found? Why are they so distributed? What is the significance of their distribution? These are the questions toward which our attention is directed (CHAPTERS 17, 18, 19, and 23).

The world pattern of transportation routes is in reality the best summary of these studies (CHAPTER 24). The route ways of the land, the sea, and the air constitute a network which holds together the parts of the pattern of population distribution. The population pattern and the transportation pattern are, accordingly, among the principal sources of information about the world. Our final aim is to understand the blending of physical and cultural elements which constitute the human habitat.

· CHAPTER OUTLINE ·

Some Objectives of Geographic Study

MAN'S HABITAT
Physical or Natural Elements
    WATER
    LANDFORMS
    WEATHER AND CLIMATE
    SOILS
    NATIVE VEGETATION AND ANIMAL LIFE
    MINERAL RESOURCES
Physical Setting
    EXAMPLE: THE LAKE ST. JOHN LOWLAND

Concept of Physical Complexes
Cultural or Human Elements
    POPULATION
    CULTURAL GROUPS
    CULTURAL INSTITUTIONS
    SETTLEMENT
    ECONOMIES
    ROUTES OF TRANSPORTATION AND COMMUNICATION

• REVIEW QUESTIONS •

1. What constitutes the human habitat?

2. Are the limits of the human habitat fixed permanently, or might they be altered? If alteration is possible, suggest how it might be accomplished.

3. What is the purpose of discussing the physical and the cultural elements of the human habitat separately? On what basis is the division made?

4. Give examples based on your own experience to support the statement, "Physical elements change their expression from one part of the earth to another."

5. Distinguish between weather and climate.

6. What is the difference between "landforms" and "earth's surface"?

7. Natural vegetation is noted briefly in this chapter. What other kind of vegetation is there?

8. "Of all the physical conditions present in the Lake St. John Lowland and immediately surrounding territory, conditions of climate and conditions of landforms are most important." Would you agree with this statement? Justify your answer.

9. In your own words, what is a "physical complex" as that term is used geographically?

10. Suggest some of the more prominent cultural institutions of the people of the United States.

11. Illustrate the meaning of "sequent occupance," referring to the area you know best.

12. Give examples of each of the economies, drawn, if possible, from your own experience or general knowledge.

13. Discuss the physical setting and the human occupance of an area which you know well. Do this in the way suggested by the type study of the Vézère valley.

14. From your own experience, give some examples of the variety to be found within the human habitat.

15. Is the quality of change constant throughout the human habitat? Explain your answer by reference to what you have observed personally.

16. What are some of the major objectives of geography?

17. What are the four basically geographical questions which must be answered about each of the physical and cultural elements if one is to obtain an understanding of the human habitat?

18. Suggest ways in which an understanding of the human habitat can be applied to, and is of great significance to, everyday life.

2–1

[OPPOSITE, TOP] THIS southwestward view of the California–Arizona area of the United States was photographed from a Viking-12 rocket at a point about 116 miles above the earth. Note the curvature of the earth indicated by the sharp break between the whitish lower and black upper atmosphere.

2 Gross Features of the Earth

⟨ THE *attention of geography is focused on the earth, particularly on the surface of the earth. Nevertheless, since man is actively exploring the great spaces
beyond the earth in his continuing effort to understand his habitat, and
possibly even to expand it, it is important to realize the earth's place in that
broader scheme of things known as the solar system. Though the earth
seems so large to us, it is only a minor member of the system; in fact, the
system's center and its giant, the sun, is itself only one of the myriad of stars
and is far from being the greatest of those. Yet the sun is all-important to living things on earth. From it comes the energy which makes life possible.*

THE SOLAR SYSTEM

THE solar system of which the earth is a part consists of a central sun about which move nine planets with their satellites. In addition, the system includes a group of planetary fragments known as asteroids and a whole host of more chaotic wanderers known as comets and meteors (PLATE 1). There is continuous movement within the system and the system itself is moving as a unit through interstellar space.

The details of the structure and operation of all parts of the solar system are not particularly the concern of geography. Nevertheless, understanding of the nature of the human habitat can best be obtained if one realizes the basic relationships between the earth as a planet and the sun as the major member of this solar system.

The Sun

Compared with all the other parts of the solar system, the sun is truly huge. It is a spherical, gaseous body about 1,300,000 times the volume of the earth. The sun's diameter is 109 times that of the earth. If the sun were a hollow sphere and the earth were placed at its center, the surface of the sun would be 432,000 miles from the earth. Even the moon in its orbit would be only halfway from the earth to the sun's surface. The earth is literally a speck compared to such a huge body.

The sun is the only self-luminous body within the whole solar system. It is, in fact, the system's mammoth heating and lighting plant. Even on the sun's outer surface, the temperature is estimated to be about 5700° centigrade. The planets and their satellites are lighted and heated by the energy emitted from this huge, tremendously hot surface.

Since energy is radiated in all directions from the spherical surface of the sun, only a minute portion at best can be intercepted by any one planet. The particular amount intercepted depends in considerable part upon the size of the planet and upon its distance from the sun. The effectiveness of the energy actually received depends upon the detailed motions of the planet and upon the nature of the planet's atmosphere. Thus the earth's size and its distance from the sun, its movement in the solar system, and the nature of its atmosphere are significant from a geographical point of view.

The Planets

The nine planets travel around the sun in paths, or *orbits*, which are approximately circular. Each is held in its orbit by a nice balance of two opposing forces, *gravitational attraction* and *centrifugal force*.

GRAVITATIONAL ATTRACTION • The sun exerts an attractive force upon all members of the solar system. This force acts to keep the planets from "sailing out into space" as they whirl about in their orbits. The same force exerted by the earth acts to keep the moon revolving about the earth instead of flying away in an erratic path. That the oceans, loose rock fragments, soil, buildings, and even we ourselves do not fly off the earth's surface is a result of the operation of the same force. We know this force as gravitational attraction, or gravity. The general physical law of gravity is stated as follows: *any two particles of matter attract each other with a force proportional to the product of their masses and inversely proportional to the square of the distance between them.*

Since the sun has a mass so many times greater than that of any of the planets, it exercises strong attraction upon all of them. They are thus retained within the system of which the sun is the center.

CENTRIFUGAL FORCE • If gravitational attraction acted alone, the sun would draw the planets in upon itself, eventually to destroy them in its own fiery mass. That this does not

TABLE 2

Some Relative Features of Size Within the Solar System

(Earth equals 1.00)

MAJOR MEMBERS OF SOLAR SYSTEM	MEAN DISTANCE FROM SUN	MEAN DIAMETER	MEAN VOLUME
Sun		109.10	1,300,000.00
Mercury	.39	.39	.06
Venus	.72	.97	.92
Earth	1.00	1.00	1.00
Mars	1.52	.53	.15
Jupiter	5.20	10.95	1,312.00
Saturn	9.54	9.02	734.00
Uranus	19.19	4.00	64.00
Neptune	30.07	3.92	60.00
Pluto	39.46	.51(?)	.13(?)

SOURCE: Compiled from appendix material in Henry N. Russell, Raymond S. Dugan, and John Q. Stewart, *Astronomy, Volume I, The Solar System*, rev. ed., N. Y.: Ginn, 1945. Reproduced by permission of the publishers.

happen is the result of what we call centrifugal force. This force tends to cause matter to fly away from any center of rotation, like mud flying off the rim of a turning wheel.

Since the planets are revolving bodies, each one develops considerable centrifugal force. The balance between the gravitational effect of the sun and the centrifugal effect of each of the planets determines the detailed paths which they follow around the sun.

RELATIVE POSITION OF THE PLANETS • The planet nearest the sun is Mercury. Its orbit has a mean distance from the sun of nearly 37,000,000 miles. Next outward from the center is Venus, at a mean distance of 67,000,000 miles. And third from the sun is the earth, at a mean distance of nearly 93,-000,000 miles. Compared to that of the outer-

most of the planets, the earth's distance is relatively small. Pluto, farthest removed from the sun, lies at the tremendous mean distance of 3,670,000,000 miles, about 39 times as far away as the earth.

As they are stated, these figures of distance mean relatively little to the average person. It is somewhat more graphic to realize that a jet airliner cruising at the speed of 500 miles per hour would require over 21 years of steady flying to travel from the earth to the sun! Similarly, to fly from Pluto to the sun would require about 850 years of continuous flying! Even with its great speed (186,000 miles per second), light from the sun takes over 8 minutes to reach the earth; it takes nearly 5½ hours to reach Pluto.

Though Mercury is the smallest of all the

planets, it is so close to the sun that it receives a tremendous amount of heat. However, its motions are such that the same side of the planet is always exposed to the sun's rays. That side is always scorchingly hot while the other side is permanently very cold. On this basis alone, life is unlikely on that planet. On the other hand, though Jupiter is the largest of the planets, some 1300 times as large as the earth, it is so far away that the sun's energy received at its surface is not great enough to raise its "midsummer" temperature even as high as the lowest observed air temperature on the earth. The earth is just far enough from the source of energy, it has just the proper atmosphere, and its motions as a planet are such as to produce the very narrowly limited conditions under which life as we know it can exist.

Some of the relative features of size within the solar system are shown in TABLE 2.

THE PHYSICAL EARTH

Size and Shape

THE earth is essentially a sphere with a diameter of approximately 8000 miles and a maximum circumference just short of 25,000 miles. Actually, there is distortion from true sphericity, particularly in both polar regions: the polar diameter of the earth is 7,899.98 miles; midway between the poles, the diameter is 7,926.68 miles. The difference between the two is 26.70 miles. Though this difference may appear to be very considerable, it results in only minor departure from true sphericity. This can be illustrated by reference to a globe. It is doubtful whether a globe 18 inches in diameter is much nearer a true sphere than is the earth. The 26.70 miles difference between the earth's diameters is represented by $6/100$ of an inch when reduced to the scale of an 18-inch globe.

The great heights of rugged mountains reaching far above the earth's plains provide another measure of the earth's departure from the shape of a true sphere. In the Himalaya mountains north of India, Mount Everest reaches some 29,028 feet above sea level. This height of nearly $5\frac{1}{2}$ miles is the greatest known elevation on the earth's surface. The greatest known depth of ocean is in the Pacific off the eastern side of the Marianas. There the bottom lies 36,960 feet below the ocean's surface, a depth of 7 miles. The difference between the highest elevation of land and the greatest depth of ocean is approximately $12\frac{1}{2}$ miles. If Mount Everest were truly represented rising above the average surface of an 18-inch globe, it would "jut out" only $12/1000$ of an inch. If the ocean's greatest depth were shown to true scale, it would indent the surface of the globe only slightly more than $15/1000$ of an inch. Both of these amounts are less than the ordinary thickness of paper covering a globe's surface.

Movements

The earth performs two basic types of movement. It turns, or *rotates*, about an axis extending through the sphere from what is called the North Pole to what is called the South Pole. At the same time it moves, or *revolves*, in a very slightly elliptical path around the sun.

ROTATION • The earth rotates at a uniform rate about an axis which is its shortest diameter. It makes one complete turn, always toward the east, in approximately 24 hours, a period of time which we call a day. The speed of rotation for points along the earth's greatest circumference is approximately 1500 feet per second, or slightly over 1000 miles per hour. Yet, we have no conscious feeling of rapid movement at the earth's surface. This is primarily because the motion is essentially uniform.

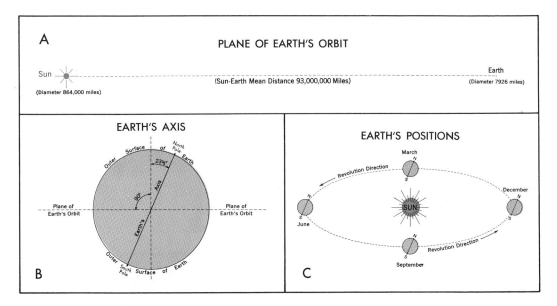

A. PLANE OF EARTH'S ORBIT

Sun
(Diameter 864,000 miles)

(Sun-Earth Mean Distance 93,000,000 Miles)

Earth
(Diameter 7926 miles)

B. EARTH'S AXIS

C. EARTH'S POSITIONS

2-2   SOME *important features of the earth's relationship to the sun. A. The plane of the earth's orbit passes through the sun. B. The earth's axis is inclined 23½° from the vertical with respect to the plane of its orbit. C. The inclination of the earth's axis remains constant everywhere along the earth's orbit about the sun, here sketched obliquely from above*

Rotation brings about the alternation of day and night and creates the phenomena of sunrise and sunset. It modifies movements within the atmosphere and the oceans. In later chapters of this book, some of the more significant effects of the earth's rotation will be treated in greater detail.

REVOLUTION • As it spins on its axis, the earth also moves in a definite orbit around the sun. The time required for one complete journey is approximately 365¼ days. The speed of the journey averages 18½ miles per second! As with rotational speed, uniformity obliterates the feeling of rapid movement.

The earth's orbit lies in a plane which passes through the sun, but the axis about which the earth rotates is neither in that plane nor perpendicular to it. The axis is inclined from the perpendicular by 23½ degrees (FIG. 2-2). No matter what the position of the earth in its orbit, the inclination of the axis remains constant. Upon this relationship depend seasonal changes so noticeable on the earth's surface.

The Face of the Earth

The face of the planet earth is far from uniform. The solid crust bulges outward in some places and sags inward in others. The sags or hollows contain the main water masses and the bulges rise above them as land masses. Together these features create a basic visible pattern for the earth as a whole. They are the features which sketch the broad outlines, the major lineaments, of the face of the earth.

MAJOR LAND MASSES • All land is surrounded by water. When the land area is large, the term *continent* is applied. When the land area is small, the term *island* is used. There is no precise definition for either term. Custom directs the usage, and usage itself is unfortunately not uniform.

Traditionally, we think of Europe, Asia, and Africa as three continents; actually, they are all part of one land mass, deeply indented by seas and broken by the man-made channel of the Suez Canal. This land mass is the largest

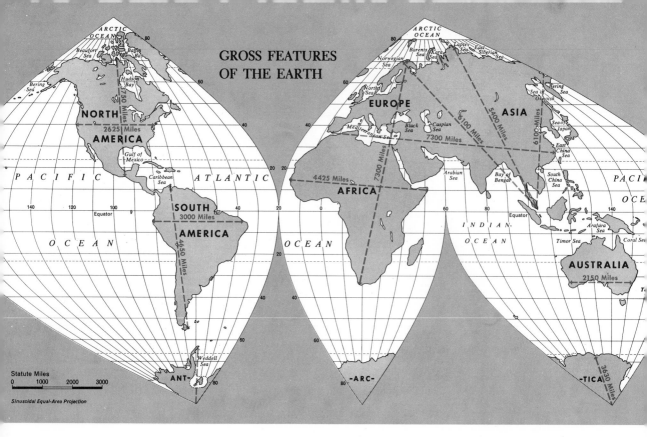

2–3   THE world's oceans, major seas, and the land masses and continents with some approximate distances shown. Note that the linear scale of the map is correct only along the equator and on the central meridian of each lobe.

in the world with a total area of approximately 32,700,000 square miles, some 9 times the size of the United States (FIG. 2–3).

The second largest of the land masses is that which includes both North and South America together with the narrow strip of land, Middle America, which connects them. Here, likewise, tradition impels us to think in terms of two continents. Actually, there is only one land mass (FIG. 2–3) although it is broken by a man-made channel, the Panama Canal. The Americas have an area of about 16,300,000 square miles, slightly less than half the size of the largest land mass.

Third in size is Antarctica, which is mostly ice-covered but has an area of approximately 5,100,000 square miles (FIG. 2–3). And last among the land masses large enough to war-

rant the name of continent is Australia, some 3,000,000 square miles in extent (FIG. 2–3).

The four land areas large enough to be called continental have a total area of roughly 57,000,000 square miles (TABLE 3). Over the whole surface of the globe, there is a total of about 350,000 square miles more of land, made up of scattered islands of assorted sizes. Yet, with all these bits of land included, only 29 per cent of the earth's surface is land; oceans cover almost three-quarters of the whole globe.

MAJOR WATER BODIES • There are commonly recognized only four bodies of water designated as oceans. These are the Pacific, Atlantic, Indian, and Arctic, in order of decreasing size. The Pacific, extending over an area of 64,000,000 square miles, fills the monstrous oval between the Americas and the east-

TABLE 3

Approximate Major Land and Water Areas

(In square miles)

Earth's surface	196,940,400
Total area in water	139,715,400
Total area in land	57,225,000

OCEAN AREAS

Pacific	63,985,000
Atlantic	31,529,000
Indian	28,357,000
Arctic	5,541,000
Ocean total	129,412,000

CONTINENTAL AREAS

Asia	17,035,000
Africa	11,635,000
North America	9,435,000
South America	6,860,000
Antarctica	5,100,000
Europe	3,850,000
Australia	2,975,000
Continental total	56,890,000

SOME REPRESENTATIVE SEAS

Mediterranean	1,145,000
Bering	878,000
Caribbean	750,000
Okhotsk	582,000
East China	480,000
Yellow	480,000
Japan	405,000
North	221,000
Red	178,000
Black	169,000
Baltic	158,000

SOURCE: From *Goode's World Atlas*, 11th edition, Rand McNally & Co., Chicago, 1960.

ern coasts of Asia and Australia (FIG. 2–3). All the land surface in the world could be placed within the Pacific and there would remain an area of water approximately twice the size of the United States.

The Atlantic fills the gap between the east coast of the Americas and the western coasts of Europe and Africa (FIG. 2–3). It is pinched to a width of 1800 miles between the "nose" of Brazil and the western "bulge" of Africa. Yet its area is nearly the same as that of the largest land mass in the world, 31,529,000 square miles. The Indian Ocean, lying between Africa, Asia, and Australia, is nearly as large (FIG. 2–3).

In the North Polar region, which has no continent similar to Antarctica, there is the Arctic Ocean separating the Euro-Asiatic and the American shores, and opening southward through narrow channels to both the Atlantic and the Pacific.

The similar water surfaces formed where oceans indent continental shores or where chains of islands nearly enclose parts of ocean are known as *seas*. Along the island-fringed margins of the northern and western Pacific lie the Bering, Okhotsk, Japan, East China, and South China Seas, to mention only the more prominent ones (FIG. 2–3). Between Australia and the islands which fringe its northern and eastern shores lie the Timor, Arafura, Coral, and Tasman Seas. In the western Atlantic, the Caribbean indents and nearly separates the Americas while on the eastern side of that same ocean are the North, Baltic, Mediterranean, and Black Seas. The Ross and Weddell Seas extend southward from the Pacific and Atlantic Oceans, respectively, indenting the Antarctic shores. From the Arctic, the Greenland, Norwegian, Barents, White, Kara, Laptev, East Siberian, and Beaufort Seas reach southward to bite into the land. Seldom are these seas clearly demarcated or sharply separated from one another, but they are all moderately closely encompassed by land.

Though man is confined for his permanent

The Physical Earth | 27

home to slightly more than a fourth of the earth's total surface, he cannot neglect the watery three-fourths. The oceans and seas are essential to all his activities; they determine the many atmospheric variations which make land areas habitable in some instances and uninhabitable in others. He has made them serve as routes from one land mass to another; he has learned to secure from them raw materials and many items of food. The arrangement, or pattern, of land and water is the pattern upon and from which variety is developed over the face of the earth. The distribution of land and water, or continents and oceans, if one prefers, is a basic geographic fact upon which rests the whole study of world variety.

• CHAPTER OUTLINE •

Gross Features of the Earth

THE SOLAR SYSTEM
  The Sun
  The Planets
    GRAVITATIONAL ATTRACTION
    CENTRIFUGAL FORCE
    RELATIVE POSITION OF THE PLANETS

THE PHYSICAL EARTH
  Size and Shape

Movements
  ROTATION
  REVOLUTION
The Face of the Earth
  MAJOR LAND MASSES
  MAJOR WATER BODIES

• REVIEW QUESTIONS •

1. What constitutes the solar system? Of what importance is it that the earth is part of the solar system?
2. What is the only source of energy in the solar system? How is this significant to man?
3. State the law of gravity. What is centrifugal force? Give some examples of the action of both forces from your own experience.
4. Where does the earth fit in the system of planets in terms of relative distance from the sun and relative size? Would it make any difference to man if the earth were its present size, but in the relative position of Venus? Of Saturn?

5. Describe the movements of the earth within the solar system. Of what significance are these movements?
6. Distinguish between continents and islands.
7. What is the difference between a continent and a land mass?
8. List the continents in order of decreasing size.
9. What is the difference between an ocean and a sea?
10. List the oceans in order of decreasing size.
11. Locate all the place names mentioned in this chapter on an outline map of the world.

3–1

[OPPOSITE, TOP] PHOTOGRAPH *of a portion of a relief model of the United States at the Babson Institute, Wellesley Hills, Mass. Lower right-hand corner: Cape Cod. Lower left: New York City. Upper left: Lake Erie.*

3 The Tools of Geography

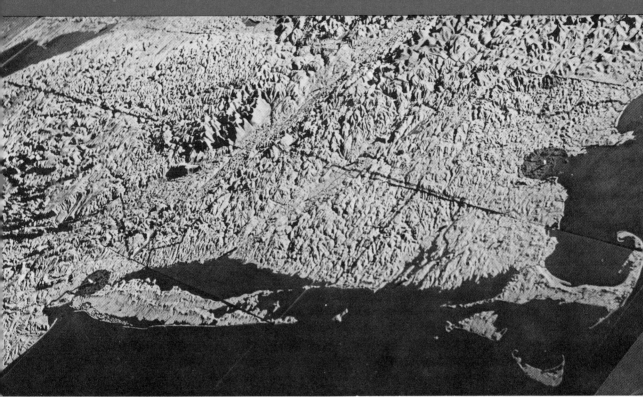

PHOTO BY BARRETT GALLAGHER, COURTESY BABSON INSTITUTE

❲ EACH *discipline or field of knowledge has certain tools and devices on which it depends to help further its objectives. Among those used by geography are ancient ones like globes and maps and modern ones like relief models and climatic charts. As is true so often, the proven tools of one field may be of great value in other fields as well. Maps, so essential to geographical inquiry, are used to major advantage in history, economics, geology, transportation, journalism, and many other fields. Relief models serve the purposes of military tactics, civil engineering, geology, and so on, as well as those of geography. The more commonly used tools of geography have wide application, so wide that knowledge of them is needed by each citizen in his everyday life.*

The Tools of Geography | 29

THE globe is man's closest approximation to the earth itself. It is a scale model of the entire earth of such a size, or scale, that one can see it, handle it, and comprehend it, all at one time. It is, almost literally, the "world brought indoors." If carefully constructed, it will show the true shape of the earth. It will portray the shapes of the oceans and continents correctly. And it will enable one to make accurate size comparisons, such as the size of Africa compared to that of North America or the size of Europe compared to that of Australia. The fact that globes are more common now than ever before is indicative of their utility. Many families consider a globe to be a necessary part of the equipment of the modern home.

Early and Modern Globes

The Greeks, more than 1600 years before Columbus, felt certain that the earth was approximately spherical. It was they who first reproduced the earth in the form of a globe. The earliest globe was probably made by Crates about the year 150 B.C. (FIG. 3–2). Since that time, hundreds of persons have constructed globes of various sizes and types, globes carrying varying degrees of detail concerning the earth as a whole. All the early globes, especially those made prior to the Age of Discovery (roughly 1400–1700 A.D.), portrayed much guesswork. For example, the globe of Crates showed the then known world which lay along the shores of the Mediterranean Sea and extended into southern Asia. It also showed three other continents the existence of which was mere speculation; they were drawn in simply to balance the globe and to provide it with a degree of symmetry. The amazing part of the speculation is that, in a sense, it predicted the existence of the Americas and Australia.

The oldest of existing globes is at the Germanic Museum in Nuremberg, Germany. Constructed by Martin Behaim, it was completed in the year 1492 (FIG. 3–2). It gave no hint of the Americas, but the globes which were made within the next few years showed at least the general outline of the Atlantic shores of North and South America and some sections of the Pacific shores. From then on, globes presented more and more of the earth as we know it today, although not before the mid-1700's did fancy and surmise give way entirely to the major facts of land and water distribution.

Modern globes are carefully constructed models of a world which is thoroughly known; in fact, man knows much more of the world than can be portrayed on the surface of a

3–2 THE earliest globe was probably made by Crates, a Greek philosopher, approximately 150 B.C. The oldest existing globe in the world today is the Behaim globe, now preserved in the Germanic Museum in Nuremberg.

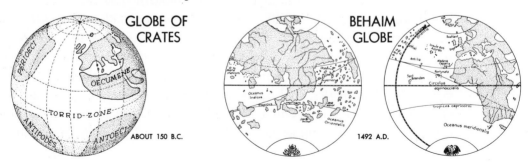

GLOBE OF CRATES

ABOUT 150 B.C.

BEHAIM GLOBE

1492 A.D.

GLOBE GORES

When bent and fitted these form the "covers" for the globes at right and left.

GLOBE TIPPED   GLOBE STRAIGHT

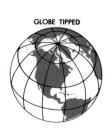
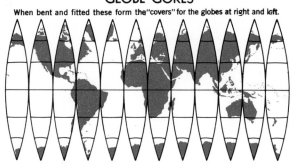

3–3   MODERN *globes are usually made by fitting carefully printed and cut strips, called gores, onto spherical forms.*

globe of any reasonable and readily useful size. They are made most commonly of cardboard or papier-mâché (inexpensive globes), or of glass or pressed steel (expensive globes). On spherical forms of these materials, carefully prepared strips, known as *gores* (FIG. 3–3), are laid. The amount of detail which a globe shows depends on its size. Obviously one with a diameter of 18 inches can tell more of the nature of the world than can one with a diameter of 6 inches. However, for most purposes a globe must be small enough to be examined readily and, if need be, to be picked up and moved about.

The Lines on the Globe

A glance at even the simplest globes reveals several lines. Some of them extend between two diametrically opposite points which represent the North and South Poles; others intersect these at right angles in parallel circles, the largest one representing the equator which divides the surface of the globe into two equal parts. More detailed globes may show additional lines, but it is the lines which normally appear on the most modern globes that concern us here.

MERIDIANS AND PARALLELS • The lines on the globe that run from pole to pole, and thus due north and south, are called *meridians*.

Each is half of a *great circle,* which is a line extending around the earth and having a center which coincides with the center of the earth. A great circle divides the earth into hemispheres. It will be noted that no matter how far apart any two meridians are at the equator, they meet at the poles.

The lines on the globe that cross the meridians at right angles, and thus run due east and west, are called *parallels.* Each is a true circle, though only the equator which lies halfway between the poles is a great circle. The parallels on a globe are spaced at regular intervals both north and south of the equator, diminishing in circumference as they approach the poles. Being truly parallel to each other, they never meet, as do the meridians.

Meridians are used to measure distance or plot a position east or west of a line of reference. By international agreement, this line is the meridian that passes through Greenwich, England (London, for all practical purposes). It is called the *Prime Meridian.* The east or west position or distance measured therefrom is known as *longitude* and is expressed in degrees or fractions thereof. West longitude extends halfway around the earth to the west of the Greenwich meridian and east longitude extends halfway around to the east. Since a circle comprises 360 degrees, west and east longitude each reach from 0 (Greenwich) to

LINES ON THE GLOBE

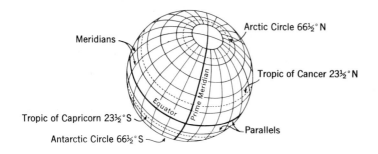

Meridians — Arctic Circle 66½° N
Tropic of Cancer 23½° N
Prime Meridian
Equator
Tropic of Capricorn 23½° S
Antarctic Circle 66½° S
Parallels

MERIDIANS

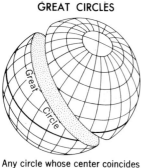

Any meridian is one half
of a Great Circle

PARALLELS

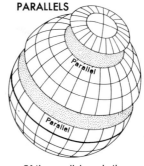

Of the parallels, only the
Equator is a Great Circle

GREAT CIRCLES

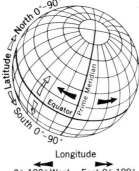

Any circle whose center coincides
with the center of the globe
is a Great Circle

REFERENCE LINES

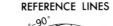

Longitude
0°–180° West   East 0°–180°

3–4

THE *most important lines on the globe are parallels and meridians, including such special ones as the Prime Meridian, the equator, the Tropics of Cancer and Capricorn, and the Arctic and Antarctic Circles. These are indicated singly and in combination above. Also shown, lower left, is a great circle. At lower right is shown the measurement of longitude east and west of the Prime Meridian and the measurement of latitude north and south of the equator.*

180 degrees (FIG. 3–4). If a plane reported its longitude as 30 degrees west (30° W), it would be west of the Prime Meridian and one-twelfth of the way around the world from that meridian (FIG. 3–5). If the longitude of another plane were stated as 90 degrees east (90° E), its location would be somewhere on the meridian which lies one-fourth of the way around the world, to the east, from the Greenwich line (FIG. 3–5). Each degree of distance is broken down into minutes and seconds. A minute (′) is 1/60 of a degree and a second (″) is 1/60 of a minute.

Parallels are used to measure distance or position north and south of the equator. This distance is known as *latitude* and, like longitude, is expressed in degrees and parts of degrees. From the equator to either pole, on the earth's surface, is one-quarter of a circle, or 90 degrees. Thus, north latitude and south latitude both extend from 0 to 90 degrees (FIG. 3–4). If a plane were halfway between the equator and the North Pole, it would be somewhere on the parallel of 45 degrees north (45th parallel, north) and its latitude would be stated as 45° N (FIG. 3–5). If a plane were one-third of the way from the equator to the South Pole, its latitude would be 30° S, and it would be somewhere on the 30th parallel, or circle, of south latitude (FIG. 3–5).

It has been noted that meridians and parallels intersect one another at right angles. The result is a grid which enables one to determine positions, or locations, east and west of the Prime Meridian and north and south of the equator. However, the grid does more than that; it enables one to locate exact positions, or fixed points. If a plane were at the point where the Prime Meridian crosses the equator, its position would be stated as 0 degrees longitude and 0 degrees latitude; in this instance it would be located over the Gulf of Guinea, off the west coast of Africa. If a plane were where the meridian of 105° E crosses the parallel of 32° N, it would be located over interior China, a bit south of the southern border of Mongolia. Its position (Plane A) on the globe is shown in the lower portion of FIG. 3–5. The same portion of FIG. 3–5 also shows the position on the globe of planes located at 21° S, 63° E, and at 42° N, 22° W.

To appreciate most fully the utility of the simple globe lines (meridians and parallels) which have just been discussed, place a pencil mark on the surface of a tennis ball. Then, attempt to describe the location of the pencil mark on the ball's spherical surface. It cannot be done—unless there is invented some system of lines which enables one to measure "left and right" and "up and down." Sooner or later, one would be forced to establish an axis and polar points where the axis intersected the

LONGITUDE AND LATITUDE

WEST LONGITUDE

Planes at 30° W. Long.

NORTH LATITUDE

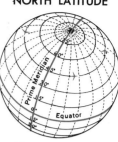

Planes at 45° N. Lat.

EAST LONGITUDE

Planes at 90° E. Long.

SOUTH LATITUDE

Planes at 30° S. Lat.

LONGITUDE AND LATITUDE

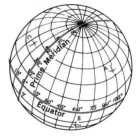

Plane A (nose) at 32°N, 105°E
Plane B (nose) at 21°S, 63°E
Plane C (nose) at 42°N, 22°W

3–5

POSITIONS *on the globe of airplanes at different latitudes and longitudes.*

surface of the ball, and to draw meridians and parallels. Then there would be a grid by means of which the location of the pencil mark could be described. The problem of location on the tennis ball is the same as the problem

INCLINATION OF EARTH'S AXIS

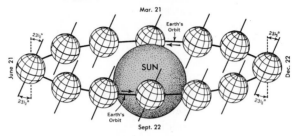

The axis is always tipped 23½° from the vertical
as the earth makes its journey around the sun.

THE POSITION OF THE EARTH ON JUNE 21 AND DECEMBER 22

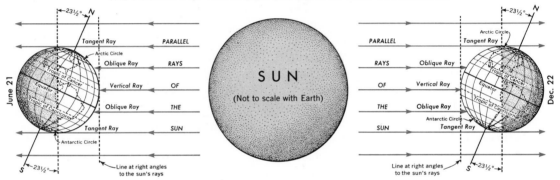

The Tropics of Cancer and Capricorn mark the northern and southern limits of the sun's vertical rays.
The Arctic and Antarctic Circles mark the "across-the-poles" limits of the sun's oblique and tangent rays.

3–6   *THIS figure should be read along with the text. Note, above, the positions of the earth as it travels around the sun. Note, below, the angle of strike of the sun's rays at different latitudes on June 21 (summer solstice of Northern Hemisphere) and on December 22 (summer solstice of Southern Hemisphere).*

of location on the spherical surface of the earth. And the solution of both problems is the same.

SPECIAL PARALLELS • A few of the parallels on the globe are shown by special symbols and, in addition, are named. These are the *Tropic of Cancer, Tropic of Capricorn, Arctic Circle,* and *Antarctic Circle.* They, among all the parallels, are given particular recognition because they mark certain conditions and results of relationships between earth and sun.

In December, the earth's axis is so inclined that more of the Southern than the Northern Hemisphere is exposed to the rays of the sun. In fact, the sun's rays, which are essentially parallel, reach beyond the South Pole but not quite to the North Pole. Thus, even though the earth turns on its axis, the South Polar regions have continuous sunlight through each rotation, while the North Polar regions have continuous darkness (FIG. 3–6).

In June, since the earth's axis is still parallel to its position in December, it is the Northern

Hemisphere that receives more sunlight, which now extends beyond the North Pole but not quite to the South Pole. As the earth rotates, it is the North Polar regions that have continuous sunlight and the South continuous darkness.

Between these extreme positions of late December and late June, the earth occupies two positions in which the sunlit half and the dark half stretch from pole to pole. Then, as the earth rotates, the 24-hour path of every point on earth lies half its length across the illuminated face of the earth and half its length across the dark face. Thus, in late March and late September, the length of light and dark periods is equal over the whole globe.

In this manner, the progression of the earth through its orbit causes variation in the length of day and night for different places upon its surface. The date when the South Pole is turned most directly toward the sun, December 21 or 22, is known in the Northern Hemisphere as the *winter solstice*. Then, days are longest throughout the Southern Hemisphere and nights are longest in the Northern Hemisphere. The date when the North Pole is turned most directly toward the sun, June 21 or 22, is known in the Northern Hemisphere as the *summer solstice*. Then, days are longest in the Northern Hemisphere and nights are longest in the Southern Hemisphere.

About March 21 and September 21, the earth is midway between the solstice positions. At both of these times, day and night lengths are equal over the whole globe. The former date is known as the *vernal equinox* and the latter as the *autumnal equinox*. For the Southern Hemisphere, all of these terms (winter and summer, vernal and autumnal) are reversed.

In part because of variations in the length of day and night, the heating of the earth's surface differs both from place to place and from time to time. This difference is the basic cause of the seasons. The part of the year during which heating is greatest we recognize as *summer*. That part during which heating is least is known as *winter*. The period between winter and summer is called *spring*, and that between summer and winter, *autumn*. In the Northern Hemisphere summer is the June-July-August part of the year, but in the Southern Hemisphere summer is the December-January-February season.

Throughout a considerable belt centering midway between the poles, there is little difference in heating during the whole year. There, seasons cannot be based on temperature differences. Within this belt, the sun at noon appears directly overhead on two days during the year. The months just before, during, and just after these days are called the *high sun periods*. The months between are known as the *low sun periods*.

Four parallels mark the positions of apparent sun migration from season to season. The earth's axis is always tipped approximately $23\frac{1}{2}°$ from the vertical, as shown in FIG. 3-6. Moreover, it is always tipped in the same direction in reference to outer space (FIG. 3-6). The energy given off from the sun reaches the earth as parallel bands of radiant energy (FIG. 3-6). Because the earth's surface is a curving one, only one "bundle" of sun's rays can strike vertically; all others, being parallel to one another, must strike obliquely (FIG. 3-6). When the earth, in its revolutions about the sun, is in such a position that the Northern Hemisphere is tipped most directly toward the sun (tipped $23\frac{1}{2}°$), the vertical rays will strike $23\frac{1}{2}°$ north of the equator (FIG. 3-6). This in itself would be of no particular consequence were it not for the fact that vertical rays provide more heat than oblique rays and the amount of heat energy which is received, latitude by latitude, is vitally significant to man and to all forms of life. To mark this farthest north reception of the sun's vertical rays, the parallel of $23\frac{1}{2}°$ N is given a special symbol and its own particular name, the *Tropic of Cancer* (FIG. 3-6). Six months later, when the Southern Hemisphere is tipped most directly toward the sun, the vertical rays are received 23½° south of the equator and the position of their strike is designated the *Tropic of Capricorn* (FIG. 3–6). During the remainder of the year the vertical rays strike somewhere between Cancer and Capricorn.

Like Cancer and Capricorn, the lines of the Arctic and Antarctic Circles are related to the angle of the sun in reference to the earth's surface at particular times of the year. At the time when the Northern Hemisphere is tipped most directly toward the sun and the vertical ray is striking at Cancer, the most oblique rays in the Northern Hemisphere are striking across the North Pole and 23½° beyond (FIG. 3–6). The line marking this farthest strike of the sun across the "top" of the world is the parallel known as the Arctic Circle (FIG. 3–6). Since it is 23½° from the North Pole, its latitude is 66½° N (23½° plus 66½° making the 90° of north latitude). Six months later, when the Southern Hemisphere is tipped more directly toward the sun, and the sun's rays are vertical at Capricorn, the most oblique rays south of the equator strike over the South Pole and 23½° beyond (FIG. 3–6). This farthest strike across the South Pole is indicated by the Antarctic Circle at 66½° S (FIG. 3–6). A study of FIG. 3–6 will show that the Circles also mark the positions of the most oblique rays when the given hemisphere is tipped most directly away from the sun on December 22. On that date, the most oblique rays reach *only to within* 23½° of the North Pole: they reach only *to* the Arctic Circle.

STANDARD TIME ZONES • At first thought, standard time may seem to have no connection with globes or with lines which appear on globes. Yet the invention of standard time came in response to man's need for keeping track of time on the rotating globe on which he lives. The time belts which he has established to determine the hours of the day are based on longitude and, hence, on the globe lines (meridians) which enable him to measure longitude.

A person who lives in one place and has no contact or business with any other parts of the world might well wonder wherein there is any problem of keeping track of the hours of the day. He looks at the sun; when it rises it is morning, when it is at the highest point in the sky it is noon, when it sets it is night. It is as simple as that—or is it?

The earth is a spheroid with only one major source of light—the sun. As the earth travels around the sun, it rotates on its axis. If it rotated in such a fashion as to present the same face, the same half, to the sun at all times as does the planet Mercury, then that half would always have day and the other would always be in darkness. However, the speed of rotation is such that the earth presents all its faces to the sun within the period which man has designated as the 24-hour day. This means, then, that there is a succession of mornings, noons, nights, and midnights. Yet, no one of them can occur all over the earth at the same time. For example, if it is noon at Chicago, it is midnight on the opposite side of the earth; when it is noon at Singapore, it is midnight at a place on the opposite side of the earth.

Because the earth rotates *toward the east*, each morning approaches from the east, as does each noon, or sunset, or midnight. Thus, noon at Chicago means that it is past noon at New York City and not yet noon at such a place as Denver. Actually there are as many noons, or noon positions of the sun, as there are longitudinal positions on the face of the earth. Even in Chicago itself, since it is a large metropolitan region, there are several noon positions of the sun. It is noon, by the sun, in the eastern part of Chicago before it is noon in the central section, and it is noon in the central section before it is noon in the western part of the city.

One can appreciate that watches set by the noon position of the sun would show slightly different times for eastern, central, and western Chicago; also, that a watch set by the noon sun for central Chicago will show a marked difference in time compared to one set by the noon sun in the central section of New York City. The difficulties of keeping track of the time, for purposes of business, travel, etc., are apparent whether within a comparatively small region or from place to place over the earth's surface.

There used to be as many times in the United States as there were communities from coast to coast. Each settlement had its own time, determined by the noon passage of the sun across the meridian which marked the longitudinal position of the community. As long as each community lived more or less unto itself, as long as travel was slow and there were no telegraphs, telephones, radios, or televisions, it did not matter much. However, by 1883, rapid travel by rail and the quick speeding of messages by wire were common. A person sending a telegram from Chicago at noon might need to know at what time the message would be received in New York or in San Francisco. If it was sent from Chicago at 8:00 A.M., would it be received in San Francisco before daylight, or before the opening of business offices? If a person living outside of Chicago wanted to catch a train in Chicago, he needed to know what time Chicago was using in comparison to the time of his own community. Something had to be done: time had to be standardized.

In 1883, the railroads agreed upon *standard time belts*. In the ensuing years, the entire United States followed suit, as did most of the remainder of the world. The United States was divided into four belts. Each belt extended from north to south and the four belts were arranged in longitudinal succession from the Atlantic to the Pacific (FIG. 3–7). A *central meridian* was chosen for each belt and the time within each belt was determined by the time of that central meridian (FIG. 3–7). The east-west width, or longitudinal extent, of each belt was determined by the rate of travel of the noon sun across the country. This rate of travel by the sun, resulting of course from the rate of rotation of the earth on its axis, is 15 degrees in one hour ($15° \times 24 = 360°$, or one complete rotation, as from noon to noon). Thus, each time belt was 15° of longitude in width, or, saying it in another fashion, each belt was one hour wide. All persons within each belt accepted the time of the center of the belt (central meridian), and the division lines between belts were well known so that persons crossing them would know where to change their timepieces. In this manner, time became standard and there were four basic times in the United States, instead of a very large number.

Under such an arrangement a person living, say, in San Francisco and wishing to hear a radio broadcast from New York City can make the proper calculations. If the program is to be on the air from New York City at 6:00 P.M. New York time, he must go to his radio at 3:00 P.M. San Francisco time. New York has Eastern Standard Time; San Francisco has Pacific Standard Time (FIG. 3–7). The difference in time is three hours—one hour for each belt west of the Eastern time belt. Because New York is east of San Francisco, it will have 6:00 P.M., or any other time, before San Francisco does, and it will have it three hours before. Thus, if it is 6:00 P.M. in New York City, it is only 3:00 P.M. in San Francisco.

Theoretically, the central meridians are spaced every 15° east and west, beginning at the Prime Meridian, along which the time is known as Greenwich Time. Theoretically, too, each time belt is bounded to the east and west by meridians, that is, each belt is set off by two meridians spaced 15° apart. Thus, the Greenwich Time belt would extend from $7\frac{1}{2}°$ W to $7\frac{1}{2}°$ E; the Eastern Standard Time belt of the United States, with a central meridian at 75° W, would extend from $67\frac{1}{2}°$ W to $82\frac{1}{2}°$ W. If such were actually the case, the limits of the time belts would be straight north-south lines evenly spaced around the world. Examination of FIG. 3–7 will show that

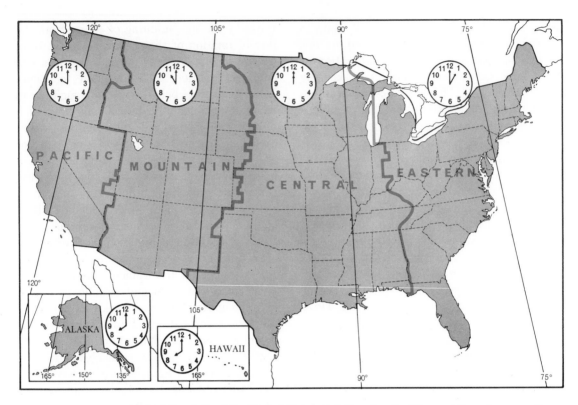

THE *standard time belts of the United States as of August 1961. The meridians shown are the so-called "central," or "standard," meridians for the time belts. Standard time for Alaska was set by Congress as that of the 150° W meridian; actually, four times are used as indicated in* FIG. 3–8.

the limits are not straight, but only approximately so; they merely correspond with the trend of the meridians. The reason for this is that the limits were so drawn as to avoid, as much as possible, the splitting of a given population and trade area. Thus the limits may deviate from true meridional trends for purposes of local convenience. FIGURE 3–8 shows the time belts of the world. It will be noted that they, like those within the United States, show deviations from true meridional positions of the time belt boundaries.

INTERNATIONAL DATE LINE • This is another line which appears on most globes. It follows, from pole to pole, the general course of the 180th meridian in the mid-Pacific, although in some places it deviates therefrom (FIG. 3–8). It is at this line that each new

calendar day is born. For example, July 1 is born at midnight at the international date line, travels west, around the earth, and dies 24 hours later back at the date line. Other dates (days) do the same. Thus there is a westward procession of days, as there is a westward procession of hours of the day. Just as it is not the same time all over the earth, as discussed above, it is not the same day all over the earth. If, on June 30, one proceeds *westward* across the date line, it becomes July 1 as soon as the line is crossed. If the date is July 1 and one crosses the line in an *eastward* direction the date automatically becomes June 30. One adds a day in crossing the line going west and subtracts a day in crossing the line going east.

The problem of keeping track of the days is quite similar to the one of determining the

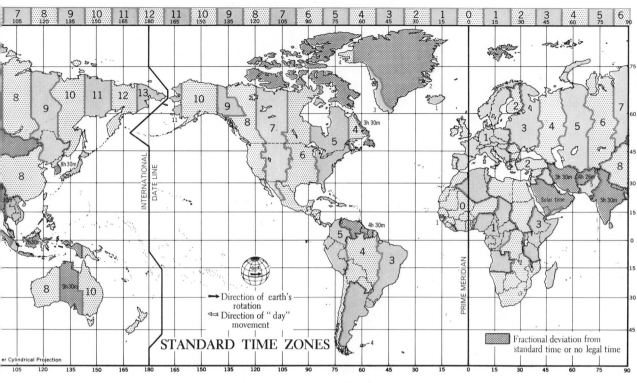

→ Direction of earth's rotation
⇐ Direction of "day" movement

Fractional deviation from standard time or no legal time

3–8 STANDARD *time belts of the world. The earth is divided into 24 time zones, each covering 15° of longitude. The time of the "0" zone is based on the 0° meridian (Greenwich) and is generally adopted as standard time for 7°30′ eastward and westward. Each of the zones beyond is designated by a number representing the hours to be added to or subtracted from that zone's standard time to get Greenwich Mean Time. Irregularities in the zonal pattern are due to adjustments for national and economic convenience.*

hours of the day. There has to be agreement as to where each begins and ends. The choice of a "birth line" for the days in mid-ocean is a wise one, for there are few lands and few inhabitants to be affected (FIG. 3–8). If the date line were placed so as to intersect one or more continents and, hence, areas in which there are many persons and much human activity, the situation would be very troublesome. Imagine the results if the date line were the meridian of Chicago. It might be daytime of December 25 in Chicago. December 25 would have been born there at midnight to begin its westward march. But to the east, as at New York City, it would not yet be December 25; December 25 would not have had time to

travel around the earth to New York City. The calendar date would still be December 24 at New York; it would be Christmas in Chicago, but the day before Christmas in New York! This is only one example, but it will serve to illustrate the wisdom of the days being born (and dying) at a more convenient meridional location.

The partial deviation of the date line from the 180th meridian is a further attempt to prevent complications for man. The line deviates so as to throw certain island groups (and the easternmost finger of Siberia) entirely to one side or the other. Otherwise, the dates would be different within the same island cluster, or even from one side of a particular

Globes | 39

island to the other (FIG. 3–8). As it is, it is actually possible for a South Sea Islander to leave his abode to go fishing on, say, Monday, to fish several hours on Sunday, and yet return home on Monday. In the instance just mentioned, the fisherman lived immediately west of the date line, he crossed the line to fish east of it, and recrossed the line as he returned home on a westward course.

All of the foregoing discussions concerning globes and lines of the globe are useful because they indicate man's nearest approach to true representation of the earth on which he lives, of relative locations on its surface, and of the significant facts about the earth's motions. As the discussion proceeds, it will be seen that many items noted already are basic to the understanding and use of maps as well.

MAPS

THE map is the most important geographical tool. Were it not for the high cost of surveying, final drawing, and printing, a great deal of the geography of any region or district might be portrayed by maps alone. Particularly would this be true if a sufficient number of maps were prepared, if the map explanations were full and complete, and if some of the maps were combinations of several others—so as to provide understanding of geographical relationships in addition to isolated factual data. As it is, geographical materials contain as many maps as is practical. Text analyses and descriptions are normally keyed closely to the maps themselves. The science of map making is known as *cartography*, a term which appears very often in geography.

Definition

Our modern term *map* is derived from the Latin word *mappa*. This word signifies napkin, or cover cloth, in the sense of tablecloth. Just as a cloth may cover, or give coverage, to a table, so does a map provide coverage for the earth or any of its parts. By studying a map, one may tell what covers, or is on, the earth's surface. By definition, a *map*, as used in reference to the world, is a representation of all, or a portion of, the earth, drawn to scale and usually on a plane, or flat, surface.

Utility

That maps have been made for more than four thousand years, and are made in greater numbers today than ever before, is sufficient proof of their usefulness. Within the past few years, collections of maps, called *atlases*, also have been published in numbers far in excess of any previous time. The new emphasis on maps and atlases reflects not only the needs of modern armies, navies, and air forces, but also the desire of nearly every literate person to know about the world. People have learned that maps can bring the world to them, either in whole or in part, and that many maps can provide much understanding of the earth and its inhabitants.

Small maps help to tell what the earth is like in general. Very large maps tell a detailed story of the nature of even very small sections of the earth. Maps of the latter sort may be put to many and very specific uses. One map may show the extent of a farmer's land and the detail of virtually everything which appears on the farm; another, the extent of the United States Corn Belt; still another, the location of the iron and steel mills of Europe. There is no apparent end to the uses of maps, whether for purposes of national defense, general knowledge, travel, business, or merely a hiking trip.

OLDEST KNOWN MAP (2500 B.C.)
Clay Tablet from Ga-Sur.

MAP OF ERATOSTHENES (200 B.C.)

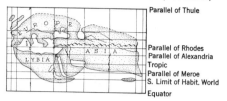

Parallel of Thule

Parallel of Rhodes
Parallel of Alexandria
Tropic
Parallel of Meroe
S. Limit of Habit. World
Equator

PTOLEMY'S MAP (2nd Cent. A.D.)

OLDEST KNOWN CHINESE MAP (1137 A.D.)

OLD CHINESE MAP

WALDSEEMULLER'S MAP (1507 A.D.)

RIBERO'S MAP (1529 A.D.)

3–9

SOME *types of old maps, representing changing map techniques and increasing knowledge of the world.*

Early Maps

The earliest maps were crude and inaccurate affairs. Perhaps the first map was nothing more than a rough sketch of game trails and water holes traced in the dust with the end of a sharp stick. The first map of definite record shows a portion of Mesopotamia, modern Iraq; it is in the form of a small tablet of baked clay (FIG. 3–9). This was made about 2500 years before Christ was born and is now preserved in the Semitic Museum, Harvard University.

The Phoenicians, those first real traders on the sea lanes, made use of simple charts for navigating the Mediterranean. A bit later, they charted their way into the open Atlantic, from the "tin coast" of Cornwall in England to the far shores of western Africa. Then, as the Greeks rose to power and started their trade and colonization of the Mediterranean world, other simple maps were made to keep track of places, of regions, and of routes from one spot to another. The earliest of the Greek maps was probably made by Anaximander (611–547 B.C.). His map showed the then known world, consisting of southern Europe, western Asia Minor, and the northern margin of Africa. A map made by Eratosthenes about 200 B.C. showed, in addition, the broader outlines of the British Isles, a larger section of Asia Minor, and a greatly distorted India. This map contained both meridians and parallels (FIG. 3–9). Ptolemy of Alexandria produced one of the most famous of early maps, some time during the second century A.D. (FIG. 3–9), as well as an atlas of twenty-eight maps. At about the same time, Roman cartographers were busy attempting to lay out, in map form, the world as they knew it or, in part, guessed it to be.

While all this was going on in the Mediterranean world, the Chinese were constructing their early maps (FIG. 3–9). They had prepared a few simple maps at least 200 years before the time of Christ. After their invention of paper, perhaps in the first century A.D., both general and detailed maps became numerous. Chinese cartography continued to make advances through the Middle Ages, the period when European cartography went into virtual eclipse. Likewise, the Arabs, with their early knowledge of astronomy and mathematics, developed their own cartography and maintained it on a high and advancing level while Europe retrogressed.

As Europe rose slowly from the Dark Ages, there was a marked and renewed interest in maps, particularly in improved maps of the countries of central and southern Europe. By 1500 there were world maps which showed, although in considerably distorted form, Europe, Africa, and most of Asia. The activities of explorers spurred the preparation of maps and globes, although for a few years after the voyage of Columbus the known parts of the Americas continued to appear as parts of Asia. However, by 1507 a map appeared which indicated the separate existence of the Americas and a fuller appreciation of the true size of the earth (FIG. 3–9). In 1529, another map

showed not only parts of the Americas and Asia, but made room in between them for the vast Pacific, which Magellan's voyage had disclosed to an amazed world.

Some of the more famous maps soon to follow were made by the Flemish cartographer Kremer, better known as Mercator. He constructed maps of Europe, including more accurate maps of the Mediterranean than were previously available, and, in 1568, the well-known Mercator chart of the world. From then on, what might be called modern cartography began to flourish; French map makers came to excel; English map makers, with shipping lanes and an empire to keep track of, came to rival the French; a few craftsmen emerged in Italy and Spain—the world was well on the way to knowing itself more fully and more accurately.

Map Projections

NATURE AND USE • A *map projection* is any orderly arrangement of parallels and meridians on a plane. The pattern formed by these lines is called the *grid*. Each projection has its own peculiar grid. Some grids appear very simple, others very complicated (FIG. 3–10).

Map projections are necessary because the earth is not flat and yet man wishes to show all or part of its spherical surface on a flat sheet of paper. The ideal way to show the earth, its parts, and its many conditions is by means of the globe. But globes beyond a certain size cannot be readily handled or carried about; nor can globes be bound in atlases or other books. So man depends largely on maps which are flat, and on the projections which make the construction of maps possible.

There is no such thing as a perfect map projection. Each projection may have one major advantage and also several disadvantages. Each projection should be used for its own particular purpose and the user should be aware of its limitations. Many map projections, or the maps made on them, have fallen into general

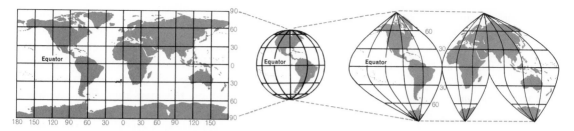

3–10   Left: *The relatively simple grid of one type of cylindrical projection.* Center: *The globe.* Right: *The relatively complicated grid of the sinusoidal projection. Why is a globe the most satisfactory device for showing the relation to the earth of its parts?*

disrepute because so often they have been used for purposes other than those for which they were designed. One example is the Mercator projection (FIG. 3–11). It has been severely criticized, chiefly because it does not show the sizes of all parts of the earth correctly. Of course it doesn't. It was not designed to show sizes correctly, any more than a hammer was made for sawing. The Mercator was designed primarily to aid in the navigation of ships at sea.

The lack of perfection in map projections is a direct reflection of the fact that one cannot take the spherical earth and flatten it out on a map sheet without distorting or tearing it. Nor can one lift the grid of the parallels and meridians from the globe and lay that grid out on a piece of paper without greatly spreading it, compressing it, or bending it all out of shape. One may imagine the grid of the globe as a wire framework, with some wires representing parallels and others meridians (FIG. 3–12). Next, he may imagine trying to flatten that wire framework so as to form it into a flat plane *without* changing the original relationships of one wire to another. It cannot be

A CONFORMAL PROJECTION

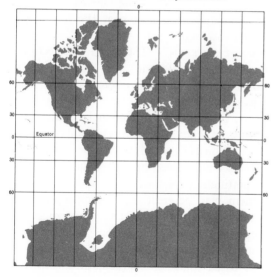

3–11

THE earth as it appears on the Mercator projection (one of several conformal projections). Note how Greenland and other high-latitude areas assume sizes out of proportion to actual sizes (compare with FIG. 3–13).

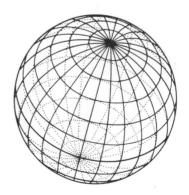

3–12

A GLOBE *as a wire frame of parallels and meridians.*

done. Neither can any map projection show the earth correctly in all regards. However, the parallels and meridians (grid) may be arranged in such a manner as to tell the truth in at least one regard. The grid may be arranged so as to portray *area* or *shape* or *directions* or *distances* correctly, but it is impossible to show all of these at one time—if one is chosen, some of the others must be sacrificed partly or completely.

Projections which show area correctly are called *equal-area projections*. One of several such projections is the Mollweide (FIG. 3-13). On it the parallels and meridians are plotted in such a manner that any parts of the earth, as Alaska and Africa, have the same proportions to each other on the map as they have to each other on the globe—but shapes are badly distorted. Projections which portray shapes correctly, or correctly within stated limits, are known as *conformal projections*. One example is the previously mentioned Mercator (FIG. 3-11). Its grid is so drawn that comparatively small parts of the earth have the same shapes as they do on the globe. There is no projection which can show the shapes of large areas correctly—only the globe itself can do that. Thus one may gain a true picture of the shape of Hawaii or of Chesapeake Bay from a conformal projection, but to see the true shape of Europe or North America, he must look on the globe.

AN EQUAL-AREA PROJECTION

3-13

THE earth as it appears on the Mollweide projection (one of several equal-area projections).

In general, the equal-area and conformal projections are encountered most commonly. However, the other two major groups of projections should at least be mentioned by name. Those which show direction correctly from a stated point on the map are called *azimuthal* or *zenithal projections*. Those portraying distances correctly from a stated point are known as *equidistant projections*.

Many detailed variations exist, but the four major groups, equal-area, conformal, azimuthal (zenithal), and equidistant, include the bulk of all ordinary map projections. There are a few which do not fall within any one of these major categories. In other words, there are some which distort area, shape, directions, and distance all at one and the same time, although the degree of distortion may be relatively so minor as still to provide a reasonable facsimile of the earth. In any event, they are all attempts to show the spherical earth on a flat map. Moreover, they represent "controlled attempts," for the person plotting the grid knows how he is arranging the parallels and meridians and he knows what the results are in each instance.

CONSTRUCTION • The word "projection" means throwing forward, or, in one sense, throwing onto, as onto a screen. Most map projections cannot be derived by actual projection, they must be arrived at by the careful plotting of lines and control points on the basis of mathematical formulae. However, some may be derived by true projection. It is not pertinent to discuss all of these, but one of them may be treated as an example. The consideration of it will aid in visualizing and comprehending map projections, whether they all are truly projected or not. Even many of those based solely on mathematical construction look as though they could be obtained from projections onto a screen.

The orthographic projection is one which can be derived by actual projection. The map from it looks like a photograph of the globe (FIG. 3-14). It can show only one hemisphere

ORTHOGRAPHIC PROJECTIONS

Equatorial Aspect   **Oblique Aspect**   **Polar Aspect**

3–14 THREE *different views ot the earth as it appears on the orthographic projection.*

at a time, just as one can photograph only half the globe at one time. In this instance, let us suppose that the view is directly toward the equator (FIG. 3–14, left), although it might be centered on the North Pole or at 45° N, as also shown in FIG. 3–14, or anywhere else. This is the equatorial aspect of the orthographic projection. One may "see" it projected by mentally visualizing the following: first, a wire model of half the globe, with the poles at the top and bottom of the wire framework, as shown in FIG. 3–15; next, a source of light located so far away that the light rays are parallel lines. Then, a flat plane, or screen, onto which the shadows of the wires, representing parallels and meridians, are thrown by the light. The result, indicated in part of FIG. 3–15, is a map projection in which the equator

ORTHOGRAPHIC PROJECTION
The parallel rays of light pass through the half-globe and are perpendicular to the turned screen.

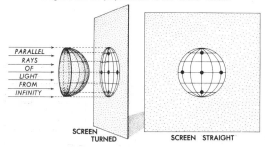

PARALLEL RAYS OF LIGHT FROM INFINITY

SCREEN TURNED   SCREEN STRAIGHT

3–15

A SIMPLE *example of how to obtain the equatorial aspect of the orthographic projection.*

and the parallels are straight lines, the central meridian extends straight from pole to pole, and the other meridians are curved lines. It will be noted that the central portion of the grid looks true, but that distortion becomes increasingly great as the margins are approached and the meridians begin to "come together."

In the instance just discussed, the projection was onto a flat plane; therefore, it might be termed one of the flat plane projections. Another instance of projection onto a plane is shown in FIG. 3–16. In addition to projections onto flat planes, there are those which are projected onto cones and cylinders. The general idea of conic and cylindrical projections is shown in FIGS. 3–17 and 3–18. Further treatment of specific conic and cylindrical projections, as well as other projections, is contained in any standard work on cartography.

The foregoing discussion, brief as it is, provides a basis for the understanding of what a map projection is, why map projections are necessary, the four major group names which include most projections, and some notion of how projections may be arrived at. A discussion of the projection which is used for most of the world and continental maps in this book follows.

THE INTERRUPTED SINUSOIDAL PROJECTION • The grid of this projection is shown in FIG. 3–19B. It appears here as a nearly three-lobed, irregularly shaped figure, joined at the equator in the Atlantic. The parallels are straight, evenly spaced lines and each half lobe

STEREOGRAPHIC PROJECTION

The diverging rays of light pass through the half-globe and are perpendicular to the turned screen only at its center.

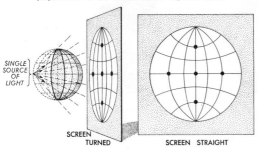

3–16

ANOTHER type of "projection onto a plane" (compare with previous figure). On the equatorial aspect of the stereographic projection shown here, there is only one straight parallel, and distances between meridians are increasingly distorted both east and west. Note, also, that the "parallels" are not parallel to one another, with resulting north-south distortion. Such east-west and north-south distortions of the grid result in distortions of land and water areas when they are plotted on the grid.

north and south of the equator has one central meridian which cuts through the continental land mass and crosses the parallels at right angles. The other meridians are curved in accordance with a specific mathematical formula. East-west distances and directions are true on all parallels, and north-south distances

A SIMPLE CONIC PROJECTION

Source of light is at center of globe.

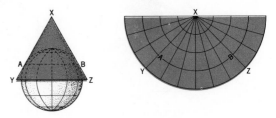

3–17

A simplified example of a conic projection (projection onto the surface of a cone). At the left, a cone fitted over the globe and touching (tangent) at parallel A–B. At the right, the cone cut down the side and flattened out to form a map grid.

and directions are true on the *central meridian of each half lobe*. The projection as a whole is of such a nature (*equal-area*) as to allow proper size comparisons from one area to another. On it, for example, one may see the true picture of the size of Europe as compared to the size of North America or of Australia or Asia.

The interrupted sinusoidal projection had its origin in an uninterrupted form in which the entire world was shown with an oval-like shape (FIG. 3–19A). It was known at first as the Sanson-Flamsteed projection and later as the

3–18   ILLUSTRATION of the derivation of one type of cylindrical projection. Here, what is on the globe is projected onto a cylinder placed over the globe and tangent at the equator. The result is the map shown at the right.

A CYLINDRICAL PROJECTION

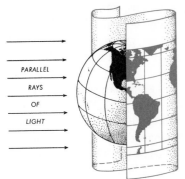

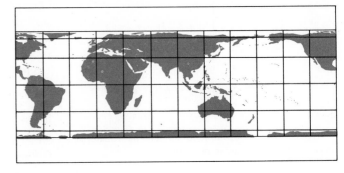

SINUSOIDAL PROJECTION
(Sanson-Flamsteed)

A

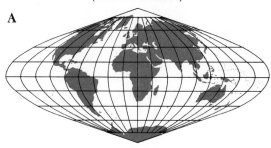

INTERRUPTED SINUSOIDAL PROJECTION

B

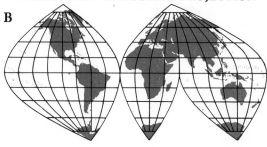

3–19

TWO *aspects of the sinusoidal projection.* A. *The uninterrupted.* B. *The interrupted as is used in this book.*

Mercator-Sanson-Flamsteed projection. On it the parallels are straight and evenly spaced; but there is only one central meridian for the whole grid. While it allows areas to be seen in their proper size relationships, it contains greater distortion of shapes than the more modern, interrupted form; hence, it is seldom used for world maps of today. The newer, interrupted form, with its several, rather than one, central meridians, preserves the usefulness of the original and at the same time eliminates most of the shape distortions (compare FIGS. 3–19A and 3–19B). Its use in this book derives primarily from the fact that it allows correct size comparisons to be made and it provides essentially true shapes for the land masses. In other words, it is equal-area and it closely approaches conformality.

The chief disadvantage of the interrupted sinusoidal projection is that it *is* interrupted.

However, it must be recalled that no projection can solve all the problems incident to showing the earth on a flat piece of paper. When attention is focused on the land, the grid of this projection can be so drawn that the interruptions occur in water areas (as in the maps on this projection that appear throughout this book); when the focus is on the oceans, the grid can be so constructed as to have the "splits" occur in the continents.

Map Essentials

A map, in order to fulfill its purpose most completely, must possess certain essentials. These are *title, legend, scale, latitude and longitude,* and *direction.* Latitude and longitude may be indicated in such a fashion, as noted later, as to obviate the need for any special method of showing direction. One or more of these essentials may be omitted at times, especially where maps appear in close relation to text discussion and are thus explained by a great deal of expository material which makes clear what the map is about and where it belongs in the world scene. Otherwise, if it is to stand by itself and be used separately from text material, a map should possess each one of the essentials mentioned.

TITLE • A map, like a book, is telling some kind of a story or explaining some problem or condition. One would not think of issuing a book without a title; no map should be prepared without its proper title. If it is a map showing the world distribution of natural vegetation, then a statement to that effect should appear somewhere on the map or the map margin. If it is a map of the average annual precipitation in the state of Ohio, then the map should say just that by means of a clearly visible title. It should not be necessary to examine a map at great length before finding out what the map is dealing with.

LEGEND • If a very large map were prepared for a comparatively small area, the name of every place or condition shown could be printed, or written out, on the map itself (FIG. 3–20). However, most maps are of such a size in proportion to the areas which they represent that map symbols are necessary. For example, a given map spread over two pages may be drawn to show the location of all the climates of the earth (see PLATE IV). On such a map, there is not enough room to print in the names of all the climates, especially in sections where a certain climate occurs in a relatively small area. Symbols, in the form of colors or lines, have to be used. In a much more extreme instance, that of a *topographic map*, which is attempting to show a multitude of features and conditions on the same sheet, there is the need for numerous symbols of many sorts (FIG. 3–21). All such symbols, whether few or many, have to be shown separately and explained somewhere on the map. Such explanation is called a *legend*. Because the symbols are often enclosed or boxed in by lines, the term *legend box* is used commonly in referring to the

legend. Also, because the legend helps to unlock an understanding of the map, the term *key* may be substituted for it. An examination of the maps in this book will show several types and positions of legends and how they serve to make the maps more useful.

SCALE • A map is useless to a major degree unless it has on it some device, or statement, which will enable one to measure distance and compute area. Any such device is known as the *map scale*. The need for indication of scale may be emphasized by two examples. A map of the highways of Texas presented without scale would not allow one to ascertain the distance between towns or the mileage of a trip from one section to another. A map of the United States Cotton Belt without scale would not help one to know the distance across or the size of that region.

There are several methods for indicating scale. One very simple way is to print on the map that "one inch equals one mile" or "one inch equals fifty miles" or whatever the actual scale of the map may be. This method is not completely satisfactory, for the map user has to guess at the length of an inch or he has to have a ruler handy when he studies a map. In addition, such a map may be enlarged or reduced in size after it is drawn; in either instance, the statement of scale would no longer be true.

Another manner of showing scale is by means of the *representative fraction*, or *fractional scale* (see bottom of FIG. 3–21). It is, as the name implies, a fraction. If the fractional scale of a given map is $\frac{1}{50}$, that signifies that one unit on the map is equal to 50 *of the same units* on the earth. If an inch is chosen as a convenient unit of measurement, then one inch on the map is equal to 50 inches in reality. A fractional scale of 1/63,360 means that one inch on the map equals 63,360 actual inches on the earth (this is the scale of the map shown in FIG. 3–21). There are 63,360 inches in one mile, therefore this scale is often referred to as the inch-to-a-mile scale. Again, as

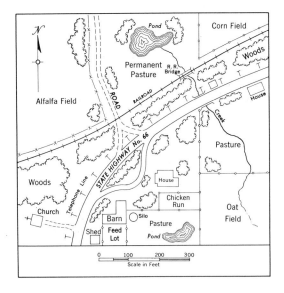

3–20

EXAMPLE *of a detailed map of a small area, drawn large enough (on large scale) so that all features can be named on the map itself without need for a separate legend (contrast with* FIG. 3–21).

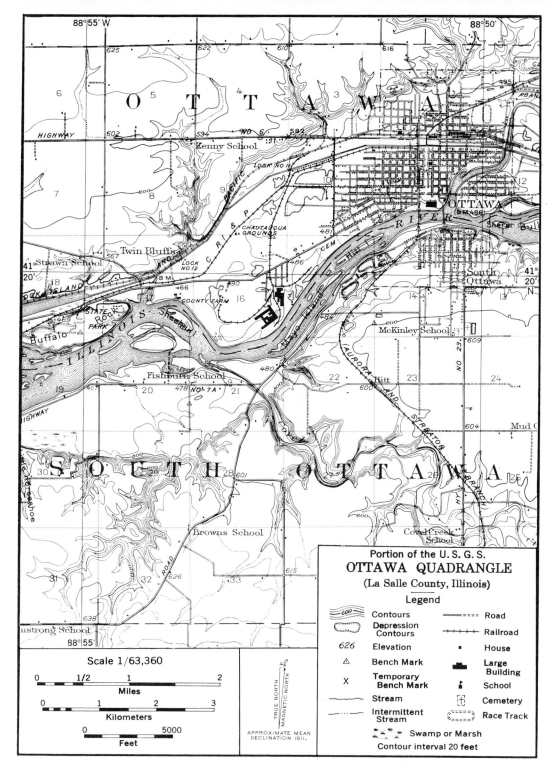

3-21 EXAMPLE *of a map of such scale and detail that many of the features shown must be indicated by special symbols that are explained in a separate legend box (lower right).*

in the instance of verbal scales, the fractional scale should not be placed on maps which are to be reproduced in either enlarged or reduced form. For example, if the original scale were $\frac{1}{50}$ and the map were enlarged twice on its linear dimensions then the representative fraction of the reproduction should be $\frac{1}{25}$ (on the original, one inch equaled 50 inches; on the copy twice enlarged, one inch equals 25 inches). Conversely, if the original were reduced by half on its linear dimensions, the new scale would be $\frac{1}{100}$, for now one unit on the map is equal to 100 of the same units in actuality.

The best and most nearly foolproof method of indicating scale is by means of a graduated line. This is called the line scale, or *linear scale*. It is merely a line with marks on it, as on a ruler. It may be of any convenient length. FIGURE 3–21 contains three expressions of linear scale. It will be noted that they are carefully and accurately constructed and that each one states the unit of measurement involved, as feet, miles, or kilometers. Such a scale enables one to measure distances with any type of straightedge, as the edge of a sheet of paper. If two houses appear on a map and one wishes to know how far apart they actually are, he can lay the straightedge next to them and mark their positions with a pencil. Then, by laying the marked part of the straightedge along the linear scale, he can read directly the distance which separates them. Unlike the verbal and fractional scales, the linear scale will stand enlargement or reduction and still read correctly in terms of the map. This is because the linear scale will change in the same proportion as any other line, or lines, on the map: it cannot go out of scale.

LATITUDE AND LONGITUDE • A map which shows latitude and longitude can "kill two birds with one stone." First of all, indications in degrees of latitude and longitude, either along the margin or on the parallels and meridians which cross the map, will tell the position on the earth of the area in the map. Secondly, a map with parallels and meridians distinguished clearly from each other will show direction, since parallels extend east and west and meridians north and south (FIG. 3–21).

DIRECTION • Some maps, whether they possess meridians and parallels or not, indicate direction by means of a *north arrow*. North arrows may be marked *true north* or *magnetic north*; or there may be two arrows which join at their bases, one of them marked true north and the other magnetic north (FIG. 3–21). An arrow marked true north is in complete alignment with a meridian and points to the North Pole. An arrow marked magnetic north is simply in alignment with the flows of magnetic force which course through the earth. The angle between true north and magnetic north is known as the *magnetic declination*. If the lines of magnetic force followed meridians, and if they did not fluctuate in position through time, true north would coincide with magnetic north. But the magnetic lines follow wavy paths and these paths shift with the years. Moreover, they do not flow from true pole to true pole, but between the *magnetic poles*. The north magnetic pole is located on Canada's Prince of Wales Island, at approximately 75° N and 101° W (FIG. 3–22). A magnetic compass used at some positions in higher latitudes than the magnetic pole actually points south instead of north! The south magnetic pole is located in Antarctica near the Adélie Coast, at approximately 67° S and 142° E. It, too, does not coincide with the true pole. Thus a magnetic compass, aligning itself with the wavy flows of the earth magnetism, does not point true north except when it is used in such a position on the earth that the north magnetic pole happens to line up with the true North Pole.

To allow corrections of magnetic north to true north, maps are prepared which show magnetic declination. Each line on such maps is an *isogonic line* (FIG. 3–22); all points located on a given isogonic line have the same declination. The line along which there is no

3–22

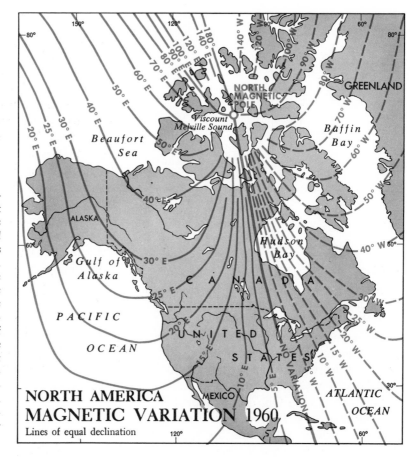

MAGNETIC declinations (variations of the compass) in part of the northern hemisphere as of 1960. The solid and dashed lines are isogonic lines (lines of equal magnetic declination). The heavy line is the agonic line (line of no magnetic declination). The dashed lines are in areas where the magnetic compass points west of true north; the solid lines are in areas where it points east of true north. The north magnetic pole is located approximately 75° N, 101° W. (Adapted from U.S. Hydrographic Chart No. 1706, for 1960).

magnetic declination is called the *agonic line* (FIG. 3–22). Maps of magnetic declination are carefully dated and new ones are prepared at intervals, usually every five years. This is necessary because of the variation, from one year to another, in the position of the magnetic flows. FIGURE 3–22 shows the positions of the isogonic lines in the United States in 1960. A surveyor using a magnetic compass in southern California in 1960 would have found that his compass pointed about 15° *east* of true north (the declination was about 15° east). In central Maine, in the same year, the declination was about 20° west; that is, the magnetic compass pointed approximately 20° *west* of true north. A person using a magnetic compass there would have had to correct to the extent of

20°. He could have done this readily by facing in the direction in which his compass pointed and then turning 20° to the right, or east; he would then have been facing true north (FIG. 3–23). Or, if his compass had a stationary dial, he could have rotated the compass until the north mark on the dial lay 20° to the right of the north end of the compass needle.

Relief Maps

Maps have only two dimensions. Relief features, such as hills or mountains, valleys or ridges, are not flat; they have three dimensions. The problem thus arises of how to show relief features on flat maps. Several solutions, or partial solutions, have been devised. No one of

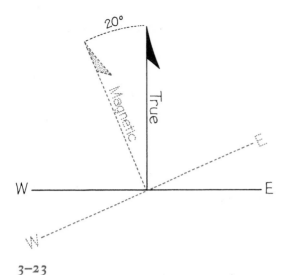

3-23

A DIAGRAM *to illustrate correction of magnetic north to true north at a point on the earth's surface where the magnetic declination is 20° west.*

them is perfect, yet each is a useful tool to aid in giving cartographic expression to the irregular features of the land.

HACHURE MAPS • One of the simplest types of relief maps is the *hachure map*. It uses lines (hachures) which are drawn up and down slopes. The proper arrangement of the lines gives the impression of the third dimension. If the lines are given different lengths and weights, they provide some indication of variations in the individual slopes which, in combination, comprise the major relief features.

SHADED MAPS • By means of "lighting effects" another type of relief map can be made. The light, in a sense, is thrown at strongly oblique angles, as though the rays were those of the early morning or the late afternoon sun. In this fashion, all slopes which receive the light are highlighted and those which face away from the light are in shadow. The result is a *shaded map*, or "light and shadow map." It makes the relief features appear much as they do when viewed from an airplane.

CONTOUR MAPS • Most useful and most exact of all relief maps is the *contour map*. In the United States, this type of map is used

for the standard topographic maps issued by the United States Geological Survey, Department of the Interior. A portion of such a map appears in FIG. 3–21; others are used in the end papers of this book. An examination of them will show many lines which bend and curve across their surfaces. Each one of these is a *contour line*, and a sufficient number of them enables one to see and read the third dimension from the flat map. To the trained eye such a map does not appear flat at all, it appears much as though it were actually a three-dimensional model of the surface of the land.

A contour line is one which connects or extends through points which are the same elevation above sea level. If a given contour is marked with the number "600," it means that any and all points on that line have the same altitude and that their altitude is 600 feet (meters, if the map uses the metric system) above sea level. The datum plane (the level from which the measurement begins) is not always sea level, but usually so; if it is not, there is a statement on the map to indicate what the datum plane actually is.

To grasp the idea of contour lines and contour levels, one may imagine a somewhat irregular, cone-shaped island in the sea. The shape of such an island is shown diagrammatically in the upper portion of FIG. 3–24, with the view straight at the island, as from a ship nearby. Sea level is the datum plane. The intersection of this plane with the surface of the island provides the 0-foot contour line; that is, the sea edge itself is the 0-foot contour. Now, if another plane, parallel to the datum plane and 10 feet above it, is passed through the island, the intersection of that plane with the island's surface provides the 10-foot contour line. The next plane, parallel to the first two and 10 feet above the second, intersects the island's surface to provide the 20-foot contour line. Additional and equally spaced horizontal planes provide the 30-foot, 40-foot, and 50-foot contours. The island is not quite high enough to be intersected by a horizontal plane 60 feet above sea level. Therefore, no 60-foot contour line can be traced on the surface of the island.

Next, if the conical island is tipped forward,

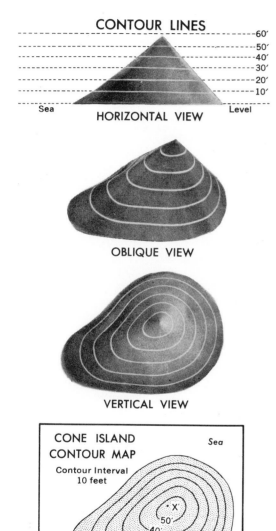

CONTOUR LINES

HORIZONTAL VIEW

OBLIQUE VIEW

VERTICAL VIEW

CONE ISLAND CONTOUR MAP
Contour Interval 10 feet

3–24

CONTOUR lines (lines of equal altitude) as they appear on three views of a roughly conical island and as they appear on a contour map of the same island.

as shown in the second portion of FIG. 3–24, we obtain an oblique view of the island and begin to see the contour lines at a different angle. We can now see more than their very edges and can discern a bit more of their behavior on the slightly irregular conical surface. Finally, if we look straight down on the island (third portion of FIG. 3–24), as from an airplane, we can see all parts of each individual contour line and how the several contour lines indicate the shape of the island. They indicate the shape in ground plan and, by their positions and numbering, the shape in a vertical sense. The fourth part of FIG. 3–24 is a somewhat dressed-up edition of portion three. It is a simple contour map of "Cone Island." If the island were a true, rather than irregular, cone, the contour lines would be perfect circles. Also, if the slope of the island were absolutely uniform from the sea's edge to the very top, the contour lines would be evenly spaced. The fact that the contour lines are not perfect circles and not quite uniform in spacing indicates the departure of the island's shape from that of a completely symmetrical cone.

In general summary, contour lines represent the intersection at the earth's surface of a number of horizontal contour planes—the exposed edge of each plane becomes a contour line. A sufficient number of contour lines makes possible the expression of surface form and enables one to read the third dimension from a flat map. Looking at the contour sketch map at the bottom of FIG. 3–24, one can see that the sea level outline of the island is rounded, that the island slopes upward rather uniformly to a single higher area, and that the vertical distance from the sea's edge to the top portion is between fifty and sixty feet. The discussion immediately following will elaborate further on contour lines and contour maps.

In using a contour map, one must know the *contour interval*. The contour interval is the *vertical* distance between contour lines, or the difference in elevation between two adjacent contours. In the instance of the map discussed

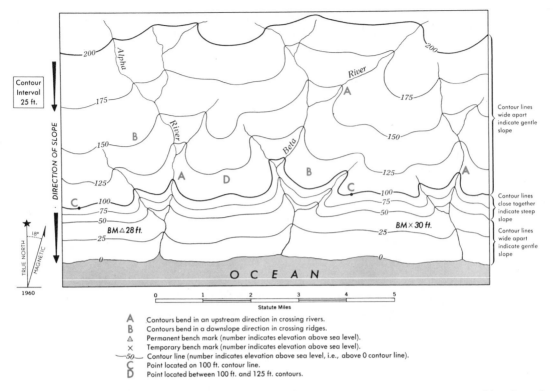

Contour
Interval
25 ft.

DIRECTION OF SLOPE

Contour lines
wide apart
indicate gentle
slope

Contour lines
close together
indicate steep
slope

Contour lines
wide apart
indicate gentle
slope

TRUE NORTH   MAGNETIC
18°
1960

O C E A N

Statute Miles
0   1   2   3   4   5

A   Contours bend in an upstream direction in crossing rivers.
B   Contours bend in a downslope direction in crossing ridges.
△   Permanent bench mark (number indicates elevation above sea level).
×   Temporary bench mark (number indicates elevation above sea level).
—50—   Contour line (number indicates elevation above sea level, i.e., above 0 contour line).
C   Point located on 100 ft. contour line.
D   Point located between 100 ft. and 125 ft. contours.

3–25   AN example of a simple contour map, illustrating the behavior of contours, types of bench marks, and determination of elevations.

above, the contour interval was 10 feet. An examination of the contour map which appears in the lower part of FIG. 3–24 will indicate that no matter how far one travels between successive contour lines on that map he has gone up or down exactly 10 feet. If he should start from one contour line, cross another, and stop at a third, he will have changed altitude exactly 20 feet—from the 10-foot to the 30-foot contour.

The behavior of the contour lines on the map tells the story of the relief. If the lines lie close together, the slope of the land is relatively steep; if they lie farther apart, the slope is comparatively gentle. FIGURE 3–25, a simple contour map, shows such behavior clearly. Where contour lines cross valleys they bend in an up-valley direction. This is because they, being contour lines, must follow the same level

throughout their courses. As they reach the tops of the valley sides, they must proceed upstream until they encounter parts of the valley bed which lie at the same altitude as the valley sides did farther downstream. In a similar way, contour lines bend in a downstream direction as they cross the noses of ridges. Again, a study of FIG. 3–25 will aid in understanding such behavior.

In addition to their value for showing relief features, contour maps are useful for determining the altitude of specific points. For points which lie on contour lines, the altitude can be read directly and accurately; a point located on the 100-foot line has an altitude of 100 feet above sea level (c in FIG. 3–25). Certain points in every area mapped by the U.S.G.S. carry *bench marks* and may lie between the contour lines of the area map. Bench marks indicate points whose elevations have been accurately measured. When the bench marks are permanent they are shown on the map as an open triangle, with the exact altitude of the point printed alongside (FIG. 3–25, southwest portion of map). The triangle indicates that there is an actual marker, usually a circular bronze plate set in a small concrete base. The marker may carry no more than a reference number, but often it contains an imprinted statement of such items as exact latitude and longitude, the altitude in feet, the direction of true north and magnetic north, the date on which the marker was placed, and the name of the agency which placed it there. Contour maps show bench marks which are not permanent by means of small crosses accompanied by altitude figures (see FIG. 3–25, southeast portion, between the 25-foot and 50-foot contours).

For points which lie between contour lines, and for which there is provided no statement of exact altitude by permanent or temporary bench marks, altitudes cannot be accurately determined. They can be determined *only within the contour interval of the map*. If a given point is located somewhere between the 100-foot and the 125-foot contours, and the contour interval is 25 feet, all one can say is that the altitude is greater than 100 feet but less than 125 feet (D in FIG. 3–25). The fact that a point lies about halfway between the 100-foot and the 125-foot contours does not necessarily mean that its altitude is 112½ feet. Such would be the case if the slope were absolutely uniform between the two contour levels, but there is no way of telling, from the map, if that is true. For example, the slope may make most of its rise immediately above the 100-foot level, and then rise quite gently all the rest of the way to the next contour line. In this instance, the altitude of 112½ feet would lie very close to the 100-foot line.

LAYER MAPS • Another method of showing the form of the land on maps is developed through the use of color. This device is used commonly for maps which show a great deal of territory on a relatively small map sheet— in other words, on small-scale maps. Each color, including black and white gradations as well as greens, yellows, browns, etc., shows the location of a given altitude zone, or layer, on the map and gives rise to the term *layer map*. A layer map is really another kind of contour map, because the top and bottom of each layer is a contour line. The color of each layer merely covers the parts of the land which lie between two given contour lines. Another, more technical, term for this type of map is *hypsometric map*. A hypsometric map of the United States usually displays several colors because there are several altitude zones from one part of the country to another. On a particular map, green may be used to show all parts of the United States which lie between sea level and 500 feet above sea level; a lighter green for sections which have altitudes ranging from 500–1000 feet; yellow for 1000–2000 feet; and so on. Red or purplish-red is often used to indicate elevations in excess of 10,000 feet. An example of a layer, or hypsometric, map appears in the front portion of this book (see PLATE II).

Other Relief Devices

MODELS • Ground relief may be indicated by devices other than maps. The relief model is one of these. It actually possesses the third dimension and does not have to simulate that dimension by means of hachures, colors, shadings, or contour lines. An example of a relief model cannot be reproduced here, on a flat page, but a photograph of one appears in FIG. 3–1. Note how readily one may see the form of the land on a device of this sort.

PHYSIOGRAPHIC DIAGRAMS • This device has been used and perfected in the past few years. By means of so-called physiographic symbols, it creates in a drawing the impression of a relief model; the symbols, in a sense, resemble the shapes of hills, valleys, escarpments, etc., and they provide a sort of oblique airplane

PHYSIOGRAPHIC DIAGRAM

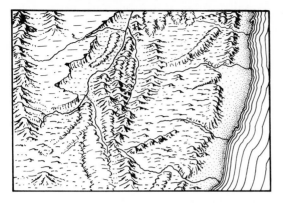

3–26

EXAMPLE *of a physiographic diagram (terrain diagram, landforms diagram). Note how physiographic symbols are used to show landform conditions—such as hills, escarpments, coastal plain, etc.*

BLOCK DIAGRAM

3–28

A BLOCK *"cut out" of the upper portion of the earth's crust. Note relationships between the geologic structure (front edge of block) and several of the shapes of the land surface itself.*

view of the earth's surface. Because they are created on flat surfaces, they are sometimes referred to as physiographic maps. However, they are not in correct scale in all portions and the symbols, at times, prevent expression of conditions in some of the lower lands, as in the instance of small valleys which lie behind high mountains—the symbol used for the mountains conceals the valleys which lie behind them. An example of a *physiographic diagram* or a *terrain diagram* is provided by FIG. 3–26.

PROFILES • At times, certain conditions of relief may be shown clearly by means of surface profiles. These represent the upward profile of the land in much the same manner that an artist may draw a profile of one's face. If the surface profile is drawn along a line which extends at right angles to the "grain" of the land, it can tell a considerable story of the relief. FIGURE 3–27 is a generalized profile drawn along a line which extends through portions of Tennessee. It includes parts of the Cumberland Plateau, the ridge and valley section, and the southern Appalachian Mountains. These features possess a marked northeast-southwest

3–27　A GENERALIZED *surface profile drawn approximately northwest-southeast across the eastern part of Tennessee and into North Carolina. The vertical scale is exaggerated, as compared with the horizontal scale, in order to give the impression of surface changes much as they appear to the eye of the observer in the field.*

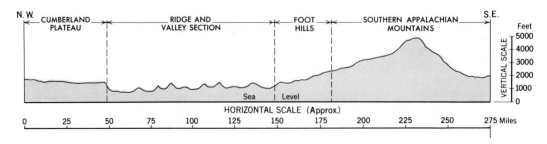

trend. By drawing the profile at right angles to this trend, that is from northwest to southeast, a meaningful result is obtained. When such a profile is titled, properly labeled, and provided with both horizontal and vertical scales, one who has never seen the area may receive a reasonably clear-cut impression of the variations and conditions of the relief. It is much as though he actually walked across the area, from one end of the profile line to the other. As a device, the profile will present him with a taste of reality and variety for one part of the earth's surface.

BLOCK DIAGRAMS • The *block diagram*, too, is a non-map device. It is one which, in a

sense, combines the features of a physiographic diagram and a surface profile. It is drawn in perspective as a block of the earth's crust (FIG. 3–28). The upper edges of the block provide surface profiles and the top of the block provides a panoramic view. In addition, if desired, the edges of the block may carry a partial picture of what lies below the surface and hence show some of the relationships which exist between relief features and the underlying rock structure. In FIG. 3–28 one may see readily some of the outstanding relationships between individual rock layers and specific surface features.

CHARTS

THERE is much geographical material which lends itself readily to expression on charts. Again, it is not the purpose here to discuss all of the kinds of charts which may be used. Instead, some samples will be taken to illustrate the nature and geographic utility of charts.

Climatic Charts

Perhaps the most commonly encountered charts in introductory geography are *climatic charts*. They may be very simple or relatively complex. In either case, it is their function to tell, in graphic form, the story of the long-time behavior of the atmosphere at a given place.

FIGURE 3–29 shows the type of climatic chart used in this book. Temperature is indicated in the upper part and precipitation in the lower. In the temperature portion of the chart, the Fahrenheit scale is indicated along the left-hand side and the centigrade equivalents along the right. For precipitation, the scale in inches is on the left and centimeter equivalents on the right. Vertical dashed lines

in both sections indicate the equinoxes and the solstices. A horizontal dashed line emphasizes freezing temperature. Across the bottom of each section are the initial letters of each month with J (January) at the left and D (December) at the right. The data used are given on the face of the chart.

On the completed chart appear a curving line and several vertical columns. The curving line is the *temperature curve*. It is arrived at by using the average monthly temperatures as indicated by the data and plotting them as points above the letters which indicate each of the months. For example, the data show that the average monthly temperature for January in Santa Monica is 53° F. By using the Fahrenheit scale at the left of the chart the position of this temperature can be ascertained and a point indicating that temperature placed above the "J" which represents January. The same is done for each month of the year. Then, by connecting the points with a smooth line, the temperature curve is obtained. In the lower part of the chart appear the *precipitation columns*. They are obtained by using the average precipitation for each month and plot-

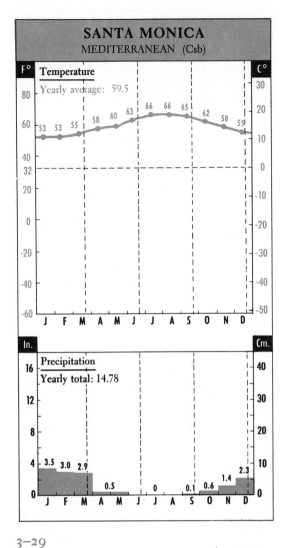

SANTA MONICA
MEDITERRANEAN (Csb)

Temperature
Yearly average: 59.5

53 53 55 58 60 63 66 66 65 62 58 55

J F M A M J J A S O N D

Precipitation
Yearly total: 14.78

3.5 3.0 2.9 0.5 0 0.1 0.6 1.4 2.3

J F M A M J J A S O N D

3-29

A TYPE of climatic chart, for Santa Monica, California.

ting that monthly average above the proper letter abbreviation. For example, the data show that the average monthly precipitation for January is 3.5 inches. By using the precipitation scale at the left of the chart the position of that number of inches may be determined and indicated as a crossline in the January column. Then the column may be filled in solidly up to the level of the crossline. It is as though the January column were a container which had collected the fall of moisture from the skies; in this instance, enough fell to fill the container to a height of 3.5 inches. Plotting the other columns in the same manner provides a precipitation column for each month of the year.

The completed chart expresses the degree of seasonal rhythm in both temperature and precipitation and does it more effectively than the cold figures of the unplotted climatic data. Moreover, a number of completed charts enables one to lay several graphic pictures alongside one another so that the outstanding features of the climate of many different places may be compared and contrasted, almost at a glance.

Transect Charts

Another type of chart which may be very useful for certain geographical purposes is the *transect chart* (FIG. 3–30). It might also be called the surface profile chart, or, because it can carry so much geographical information, the geographical chart. The major basis of the transect chart is a surface profile. The profile shows the general nature of the relief features of the area which is being transected, and on top of the profile is constructed a framework to contain several categories of geographic fact. By means of vertical as well as horizontal lines, space is provided for descriptive material for each of the surface divisions shown on the profile. Below the profile, geologic information may be provided, if desired. An examination of FIG. 3–30 will indicate the large degree to which the geographical picture of a given area may be portrayed in this fashion.

Other Charts

In addition to those noted already, there are many other types of charts which serve as geographical tools, as well as tools for other disciplines. Examples are horizontal and vertical bar charts and pie charts. Such charts need no discussion here. They appear in many

A GENERALIZED TRANSECT CHART OF THE LAKE ST. JOHN AREA, PROVINCE OF QUEBEC, CANADA

Category	HIGHLAND (left)	LOWLAND (Lake St. John area)	HIGHLAND (right)
SETTLEMENTS	FEW FARMS, VILLAGES, TOWNS	FARMS, VILLAGES, TOWNS	LUMBER CAMPS
COMMUNICATIONS	FEW ROADS, ONE R.R.	ROADS, R.R., ETC. — MANY 2nd AND 3rd CLASS ROADS. CANOE ROUTES. ONE R.R. TAPS AREA. TELEPHONES AND RADIOS — UNCERTAIN PASSENGER AND FREIGHT SERVICE DURING SUMMER SEASON	CANOE ROUTES
MANUFACTURING	HYDRO ELECTRIC POWER	POWER, PULP, ETC. — HYDRO ELECTRIC POWER AND PAPER PULP. CHEESE FACTORIES, BLUEBERRY CANNERIES	
HUNTING AND FISHING	FURS, SOME HUNTING AND FISHING FOR SPORT	SPORT — HUNTING AND FISHING FOR SPORT — SPORT FISHING	FURS, SOME HUNTING AND FISHING FOR SPORT
LUMBERING	PULPWOOD, TIES, SOME LUMBER	FIRE-WOOD, POSTS — FIREWOOD, POSTS, FENCE RAILS	MUCH PULPWOOD, SOME LUMBER
AGRICULTURE AND ANIMAL HUSBANDRY	HAY AND DAIRY TYPE	HAY AND DAIRY TYPE. CHIEF CROP IS HAY. OTHERS OATS, WHEAT, BARLEY. CHIEF DOMESTIC ANIMAL: THE DAIRY COW. OTHERS: HORSES, SHEEP	
MINING	SMALL GRANITE QUARRIES	SHALE, LIMESTONE QUARRIES — SAND AND GRAVEL PITS	
CLIMATE	AVERAGE ANNUAL TEMPERATURE 34°F. AV. TEMP. WARMEST MONTH (JULY) 65°F. AV. TEMP. COLDEST MONTH (JAN.) 0°F.	CLIMATIC TYPE Dfb (KÖPPEN), CHARACTERIZED BY LONG, SEVERE WINTERS AND SHORT, WARM SUMMERS. AVERAGE ANNUAL PRECIPITATION 30 INCHES. AV. PRECIP. WETTEST MONTH (JULY) 3.6 INCHES. AV. PRECIP. DRIEST MONTH (MAR.) 1.5 INCHES.	ABSOLUTE MIN. TEMP. −49°F. ABSOLUTE MAX. TEMP. 97°F. AV. 90 DAYS FROST FREE, 4 MONTHS SNOW FREE
NATIVE ANIMAL LIFE	PLENTIFUL: MOOSE, DEER, RED FOX, RABBIT, OTTER, PORCUPINE, MUSKRAT, ETC.; DUCK, BITTERN; FISH	RABBIT, FOX, ETC. — WILDFOWL VERY PLENTIFUL. FISH: ESP. OUANANICHE, PIKE, PERCH — RABBIT, FOX, SKUNK, MUSKRAT, WEASEL, ETC. WILDFOWL: ESP. DUCKS. FISH: ESP. TROUT, PIKE, PERCH	PLENTIFUL: MOOSE, DEER, RABBIT, WOLF, FOX, MINK, PORCUPINE, MUSKRAT, ETC. DUCK, BITTERN, FISH
DRAINAGE	YOUTHFUL DRAINAGE PATTERN, GLACIALLY DERANGED (FLOW)	YOUTHFUL DRAINAGE PATTERN (FLOW) — LAKE ST. JOHN DRAINED BY THE GRANDE DÉCHARGE, AND THE PETITE DÉCHARGE, TO THE EAST — YOUTHFUL DRAINAGE PATTERN (FLOW)	YOUTHFUL DRAINAGE PATTERN, GLACIALLY DERANGED (FLOW)
NATIVE VEGETATION	CONIFERS: CHIEFLY SPRUCE, BALSAM, SOME CEDAR, AND OTHER SWAMP VEGETATION	MIXED FOREST, ETC. — MIXED FOREST: CHIEFLY SPRUCE, BIRCH, ASPEN, JACK PINE. CONSIDERABLE AREAS OF CEDAR AND TAMARACK SWAMP. BLUEBERRY AND REINDEER MOSS UNDER-COVER — MIXED FOREST	CONIFERS: CHIEFLY SPRUCE, BALSAM. SOME CEDAR. AND OTHER SWAMP VEGETATION
SOIL	IMMATURE SOILS, PATCHY VENEER OF SAND, GRAVEL, BOULDERS, SOME SWAMP MUCK, ROCK OUTCROPS	MARINE CLAYS AND SANDS — IMMATURE SOILS. THICK MANTLE OF MARINE CLAYS AND SANDS. SOME SWAMP MUCK AND RECENT RIVER ALLUVIUM — MARINE CLAYS, ETC.	IMMATURE SOILS, PATCHY VENEER OF SAND, GRAVEL, BOULDERS. SOME SWAMP MUCK, ROCK OUTCROPS
GEOLOGY AND LAND SURFACE	GLACIATED SURFACE OF LAURENTIAN SHIELD. MOSTLY SCOUR, SOME DRIFT	MARINE TERRACES, YOUTHFULLY DISSECTED — MARINE TERRACES, YOUTHFULLY DISSECTED	GLACIATED SURFACE OF THE LAURENTIAN SHIELD. MOSTLY SCOUR, SOME DRIFT

Profile labels: HIGHLAND — MARINE TERRACES YOUTHFULLY DISSECTED — LAKE ST. JOHN 334' ABOVE SEA LEVEL — ISLE DE LA TRAVERSE — PERIBONCA R. — LOWLAND — GLACIALLY SCOURED BARE ROCK — HIGHLAND

Elevations: 1000', 800', 500', 334' ABOVE SEA LEVEL

Compass: N / S

Legend:
- QUATERNARY: Sands, Clays (Stratified)
- ORDOVICIAN: Utica Shales
- ORDOVICIAN: Trenton Limestone
- PRE-CAMBRIAN: Laurentian 334+ Gneiss, Granite
- 2 and 3 probably overlain by drift

Scale of Miles: 0 — 5 — 10

Vertical scale exaggerated

R. M. GLENDINNING

3-30 A TRANSECT chart is a kind of geographic shorthand. At the base is a geologic cross section of an area (in this case running north-south through the midportion of the Lake St. John area). Particulars of each of the geographic elements are noted directly above the portions of the cross section to which they apply.

places, in popular as well as professional publications.

The tools of geography are many. The foregoing discussions have not pretended to be all-inclusive, nor have they pretended to provide complete treatment of the particular tools which were discussed. However, the general basic knowledge which may be obtained from the preceding pages will furnish a working foundation for the understanding and use of such fundamental tools as globes, maps, map projections, special relief devices, and charts. With that foundation, the materials and ideas which follow can be more effectively studied and interpreted.

· CHAPTER OUTLINE ·

The Tools of Geography

GLOBES
Early and Modern Globes
The Lines on the Globe
  MERIDIANS AND PARALLELS
  SPECIAL PARALLELS
  STANDARD TIME ZONES
  INTERNATIONAL DATE LINE

MAPS
Definition
Utility
Early Maps
Map Projections
  NATURE AND USE
  CONSTRUCTION
  THE INTERRUPTED SINUSOIDAL PROJECTION
Map Essentials
  TITLE
  LEGEND

SCALE
LATITUDE AND LONGITUDE
DIRECTION
Relief Maps
  HACHURE MAPS
  SHADED MAPS
  CONTOUR MAPS
  LAYER MAPS
Other Relief Devices
  MODELS
  PHYSIOGRAPHIC DIAGRAMS
  PROFILES
  BLOCK DIAGRAMS

CHARTS
Climatic Charts
Transect Charts
Other Charts

· REVIEW QUESTIONS ·

1. What are the chief advantages and disadvantages of a globe as compared to a map of the world?
2. Name the lines which commonly appear on globes. Among these, name the lines which usually are indicated by a special symbol and are given special names.
3. Explain why the grid is necessary.
4. How far apart (expressed in degrees and fractions thereof) are the Tropic of Cancer and the Tropic of Capricorn? What is the distance (in degrees and fractions thereof) from the Antarctic Circle to the South Pole?
5. If you were halfway between the equator and the South Pole and one quarter of the way around the earth to the east of the prime meridian, what would your latitude and longitude be? Consult a globe or world map

to see where you would be in terms of land and water areas.

6. Draw simple diagrams to show where the noon rays of the sun would strike the earth's surface vertically on June 21, on December 22, on March 21, and on September 23.

7. Explain why the noon sun is never directly overhead at Chicago.

8. Why does a place located within the tropics receive vertical noon rays from the sun twice during each year? Suggest some ways in which this condition is important to man.

9. If it is 10:00 A.M. (Standard Time) in San Francisco, what time (Standard) is it in New York City? Is this fact of any importance to the citizens of either place? How?

10. You are at a given place on the earth's surface, the date is June 21, the sun is *directly* overhead, and Greenwich Time is 3:00 P.M.; what is the latitude and longitude of your position?

11. You are aboard a ship which is crossing the international date line in a westward direction. Just before you crossed the line, the date was April 15. What is the date as soon as the line is crossed?

12. What is meant by the term "map projection" and why are map projections necessary?

13. Explain the statement, "There is no such thing as a perfect map projection."

14. To show world distribution of forests, would you choose a map based on an equal-area, a conformal, an azimuthal, or an equidistant projection? Why?

15. What are the essentials of a true and complete map?

16. If a given map has a fractional scale of 1/24,000 and two points on that map are six inches apart, how far apart, in feet, are those two points actually?

17. What is the fractional scale of a map whose verbal scale is stated as "one-half inch equals one mile"?

18. Explain why a map that is to be enlarged or reduced should show only a linear scale.

19. What is the difference in meaning between "true north" and "magnetic north"?

20. The contour interval of a given map is 50 feet. Explain what is meant.

21. Distinguish between "relief model" and "relief map"; between "relief map" and "physiographic diagram"; between "physiographic diagram" and "block diagram."

22. What is the difference between a "transect chart" and a "surface profile"?

23. Justify the plotting of climatic data on climatic charts as opposed to leaving such data in ordinary numerical form.

24. What, if any, justification is there for saying that a transect chart might be called a geographical chart?

II

ELEMENTS OF THE PHYSICAL SETTING

4 The Earth's Waters

PHILIP GENDREAU

⟨ THE *fact that the surface of the earth is chiefly water is something which we, as dwellers on the land, are apt to ignore or completely forget. As noted earlier, the Pacific Ocean alone covers nearly one-third of the globe. The combined areas of all water bodies, including oceans, seas, and lakes, add up to nearly two and one-half times that of all the land of the earth. In other words, about 71 per cent of the earth's surface is water* (TABLE 3, *p.* 27). *In addition to the large expanses just mentioned, there are small ponds, waters which run as streams on the top of the land, and other waters which lie or move within the upper portion of the earth's crust. And there is water in vapor form and in condensed form in the atmosphere. Thus, water is an important and practically all-pervasive element in man's habitat.*

USES OF WATER

Domestic Use

WATER is fundamentally important for drinking purposes. Town and city dwellers, accustomed to obtaining drinking water by the mere turning of a faucet handle, are generally unaware of the amount they use and cannot fully appreciate this type of water use. However, countless millions of persons who live in the world's rural areas and have to spend much time in carrying water from a spring or stream, or pumping or lifting it from a well, know its significance fully. Most aware are those who live in steppes and deserts, where drinking water is most precious because it is most scarce. Other home, or domestic, uses of water are many: for cooking, washing, bathing, and for lawn and garden. On the farm, the daily consumption of water, per capita, ranges from 10 to 50 gallons. (This does not include many more gallons used by farm animals. A milk cow, for example, consumes about 15 gallons each day.) In the city, the quantity of water used is far greater. One can appreciate the problem of ordinary domestic water supply in a city of several million persons, particularly in those cities which have outgrown their local supplies and must send many miles away for the bulk of their water. Los Angeles, California, has two great aqueducts which reach out across hills, deserts, and mountains for about 300 miles (FIG. 4–2). So dependent is Los Angeles that major abandonment would quickly follow if the water supply were stopped. Other large urban centers, even those in more humid regions, are only slightly less dependent.

Industry

In town or city wherever manufacturing and processing are going on, there is demand for water far in excess of domestic requirements. Water is needed to wash materials, to add to materials and goods, to flush sewage, to make steam in boilers, to cool or air-condition equipment and buildings, and to serve many other purposes. Chicago alone is said to use from 1 billion to 1¾ billion gallons of water *each day*, the larger portion being used outside of the home. Just to supply Chicago with water is a gigantic business in itself.

Irrigation

Particularly in the dry regions, man needs water for other than drinking and household uses. He needs water for stock and still more where his economy depends on the production of irrigated crops. Irrigation water may come from shallow or deep wells, from springs, from rivers, or it may be imported over long distances by means of ditches and pipes. The amount of water available largely determines the size and importance of any region's development, whether it be a small coastal valley of southern California or an extensive portion of the lower Nile valley.

The following short discussion suggests some of the aspects of change wrought in the economy of a small segment of the landscape of southern California by the introduction of adequate water supply to an area of meager precipitation and scant and intermittent surface water.

THE SANTA MARIA VALLEY • Physically, the Santa Maria valley (FIG. 4–2) is one of southern California's many small, scattered plains that dot the Pacific coastline. The valley faces broadly to the Pacific Ocean and narrows gently upward into the seaward slopes of the Coast Range, there to divide into two upper valleys which carry rivers that are very

---

4–1

[OPPOSITE, TOP] THE waters of the earth surround this coral isle in the Pacific, near Papeete, Tahiti. Here is much water and comparatively little land, as is true of the earth's surface as a whole.

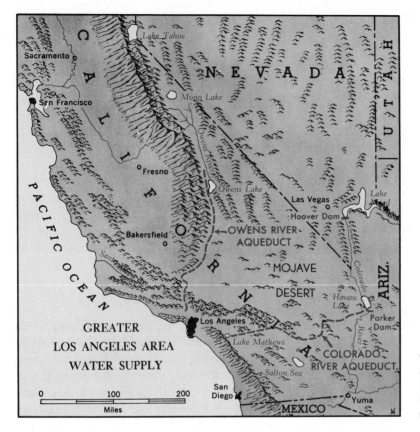

Within the map:

CALIFORNIA

NEVADA

UTAH

ARIZ.

Lake Tahoe

Sacramento

San Francisco

Mono Lake

Owens River

Fresno

Owens Lake

Las Vegas

Hoover Dam

Bakersfield

OWENS RIVER AQUEDUCT

MOJAVE

DESERT

Lake Mead

Colorado River

Havasu Lake

Parker Dam

GREATER
LOS ANGELES AREA
WATER SUPPLY

Los Angeles

Lake Mathews

COLORADO
RIVER AQUEDUCT

Salton Sea

San Diego

0   100   200
Miles

MEXICO

Yuma

Santa

Pacific Ocean

4-2

two great aqueducts (dashed lines) bring "outside water" to the Los Angeles metropolitan area.

stable hydrologically. Climatically, the valley is characterized by very low rainfall in winter, followed by severe and protracted summer drought. Except during rare flood years, natural surface waters in the valley are almost totally lacking, even in the main channel of the Santa Maria river itself.

Until fairly recent years, most of the Santa Maria valley appeared to all who saw it as merely another dry-land waste with little apparent economic use, even as seasonal grazing land. The earliest cattlemen who pushed northward with the Spanish-Mexican occupation of southern California, roughly a century and a half ago, carefully avoided such areas, except as something to be crossed as rapidly as possible. And later, when many large, free grants of land were made, under the Mexican Land Grants Act, with "ranchos" frequently including dozens of square miles, no one would

accept the Santa Maria valley, even as a gift. The valley was surrounded by Mexican ranchos, but never included in them.

It was not until nearly two decades after California became a state, and other neighboring areas had been largely settled, that individuals first came into the valley with any idea of taking up lands and establishing permanent settlements. By then, a meager water supply had been found in a few shallow, dug wells. With such small promise of water for man and animals, the initial settlers moved into the valley in 1867 and established the first small and feeble beginnings of the thriving economy of the valley today. By 1880, with more wells producing water for domestic and animal uses, the economic fortunes of the Santa Maria valley had improved considerably. But during the winter of 1897–98 the valley experienced a nearly total drought and all dry-farmed crops failed completely. Considered in retrospect, this catastrophe was a blessing in disguise, for out of it came the introduction of irrigation. Irrigation was first practiced in very simple form, using water from dug wells, but slowly increasing demands for irrigation water eventually brought about the necessary developments of deep, drilled wells and large power pumps.

Many kinds of irrigated crops, from grains to tree fruits, were experimented with through the early years of the present century. But commercial vegetable production, first introduced in the mid-twenties, expanded phenomenally until by 1930 it outranked all other crops combined. By this time, it utilized most of the valley's irrigated acreage and accounted for most of the commercial income. The expansive trend of commercial vegetable agriculture has continued unabated to the present time, keeping pace with the increasing availability of water supply, as more and more deep, drilled wells have tapped the invisible underground water.

Thus, with successive increases in water supply during the past few decades, the economic fortunes of the Santa Maria valley have been reassessed many times. Each stage has been more elaborate than its predecessor, and each stage has also been far more economically productive and financially profitable than the stage before. Land-use adjustments have been implemented almost continuously, until they have become practically a way of life and an economic creed. They have brought this once nearly barren land to an extremely high state of productivity, a productivity based upon an ever-expanding irrigation system and a commercial specialty foodstuff production with large surpluses for export to national markets.

It should be pointed out, too, that the use of water for irrigation is not restricted to regions deficient in precipitation. Near large cities in humid lands great amounts are used to encourage a rapid and certain growth of truck crops for urban markets. In the extensive and humid rice-lands of the Orient, the wet-land or *paddy* rice requires untold billions of gallons of slowly circulating irrigation water throughout the season of growth, even in those parts of the rainy tropics which receive very heavy precipitation.

In the United States, about 40 per cent of all water used is used for irrigation. Currently, this amounts to about 83 billion gallons per day! Figure out how many gallons this means each year.

Power

Water still is used to turn mill wheels in most of the world's inhabited regions. In areas of modern industrial development, it is used to spin turbines which are connected to generators. The generators transform the water power into electric energy which is sent to home and factory by transmission lines. Numerous drainage basins have largely been brought under control, from headwaters to mouth, for the particular purpose of generating great quantities of this type of electric energy.

Transportation

Since primitive man first made a raft or hollowed out a log canoe, water has served as a highway, a highway built and maintained by nature and so buoyant that carriers using it can support and move burdens far greater than can be supported in land or air vehicles. To this day, despite autotrucks, freight trains, and cargo planes, many of the world's water roads, whether the Rhine river or the North Atlantic, continue to be vital links in transportation.

Food and Raw Materials

Modern men are becoming increasingly aware of the resources contained in the many waters of the world. From the seas and oceans come foods in the form of fish, plants, and other marine life. Many persons believe that the world will become more and more dependent on food from the oceans as population increases and as much of the land is worn out by continued crop production. Seaweed, in addition to furnishing food, provides potash and iodine as well as stuffing for cushions and mattresses. Salt water furnishes salt and, recently, has furnished large quantities of magnesium. It is even a possible large-scale source of an additional fresh water supply, since salt-water conversion processes have been perfected. The sea contributes other materials also, from furs and hides to pearls and sponges.

Similarly, many fresh waters also provide fish, shells, and furs.

Recreation

Whether seashore, tree-lined brook or river, small pond, or large lake, water is useful to swim in, to go boating and fishing on, or just to look at. Many a small lake has proved to be a "gold mine" when developed for resort purposes, and many a piece of land has sold for a sum far above ordinary market price merely because it contained a bubbling spring or a small stream. Even the little lily ponds or artificial lagoons in a city park reflect the artistic and the recreational value of water.

WATER BODIES

Oceans and Seas

As previously noted, most of the earth is covered by interconnected bodies of water. Not only do these bodies vary greatly in size and depth, but also in the many patterns which they produce as they trace their edges against the land. To draw the outlines of the major water bodies is to delineate automatically the outlines of the land masses.

NAMES AND TERMS • In order of decreasing size, the oceans are the Pacific, Atlantic, Indian, and Arctic (TABLE 3, p. 27). The Arctic Ocean is sometimes referred to as a sea.

The term *sea* is indefinite. It is applied, in general, to bodies of water which are conspicuously smaller than the oceans and which are "tucked into" the land in such fashion as to leave only narrow oceanic connections or no connections at all. Thus, the term is applied to the Mediterranean and the Baltic, as well as to the Aral Sea and the Salton Sea. The term usually implies that waters are saline, but neither the Sea of Galilee nor the Great Lakes, which are often referred to as "inland seas,"

are salty. TABLE 3 lists some of the larger seas, and gives their approximate areas.

OCEAN BOTTOMS AND DEPTHS • Formerly, it was thought that the bottoms of the great water bodies were mainly comprised of smooth plains and monotonous plateaus. It was reasoned that sediments washed in from the land, materials dropped physically and precipitated chemically in waters far offshore, and the accumulation of skeletons of myriads of marine organisms would collect in low places until inequalities of sea bottom would cease to exist. It is now known that the floors of the seas and oceans possess landforms nearly as varied as those of the continents themselves. There are towering mountain ranges, broad plateaus, hilly regions, and plains of varying relief (FIG. 4–3).

In addition to the major landforms, there are countless smaller ones. Even the ancient notion of ocean basins has broken down partly. For example, we still speak of the Pacific Basin as though it were a washbowl whose sides slope uniformly downward to a central low spot. Actually, the Pacific contains many separate

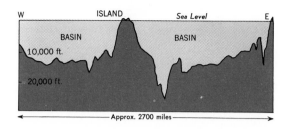

4-3

GENERALIZED *profile, with considerable vertical exaggeration, to illustrate landform conditions of a section of the bottom of the Atlantic Ocean.*

and distinct basins, both large and small, and their location, size, and shape have a great deal to do with varying conditions of water itself. The same is true of the Atlantic (FIG. 4-3) and other oceans.

The facts were brought to light largely through the invention and use of the *sonic depth finder.* This instrument sends an impulse downward through the water and receives the echo of that impulse back at the instrument a bit later. The speed of the impulse through the water is known and by recording the time necessary for it to travel to the bottom and back, and dividing by two, the depth of the water can be calculated. The depth finder has been so perfected that a vessel traveling at full speed can make a continuous record of depths along its course. With thousands of soundings thus quickly and cheaply obtained, it is a relatively simple matter to prepare contour maps of the ocean bottom. Hitherto, the slow and laborious method of using a weighted sounding line from a stationary vessel produced few and expensive data on the nature and shape of the bottom areas.

The average depth of the Pacific Ocean is about 14,000 feet, of the Atlantic about 13,000 feet, of the Indian about 13,000 feet, and of the Arctic about 4000 feet. Like so many averages, these have only limited usefulness. From man's standpoint, the depths which are of greatest meaning are those which are shallow. It is in shallow waters that man needs to know the actual depths in order to navigate his vessels safely; it is in the same waters that marine life which man seeks is especially abundant (FIG. 4-4).

As might be expected, most of the shallow waters are adjacent to the edges of the continents and large islands, although there are some which occur even in mid-ocean. The shallow waters next to the continents lie on the continental shelf (FIG. 4-5), a gently sloping extension of the continent itself and a reminder of the times when large shallow seas covered most of what are now the land masses, either in whole or in part at a given time. Depths on some continental shelves range from 0 to 60 fathoms, on others from 0 to 80 fathoms (1 fathom equals 6 feet), with the lesser depths inshore and the greater ones several miles at sea. Almost immediately beyond the 60–80 fathom line, the bottom drops away abruptly to much greater depths, often to 1000 fathoms in a few miles. For example, the continental shelf as measured southeast from the coast of New Jersey is about 90 miles in width (FIG. 4-5). This means that the 80-fathom depth lies about 90 miles from the coast; but 15 or 20 miles seaward from there are depths as great as 1000 fathoms or more, depending on exact position. It must be noted at this time, that major continental shelves differ greatly in width. Off the eastern United States, for example, is a relatively wide continental shelf, but off the western coast the average width of the continental shelf is only 18 miles.

The oceanic regions of greatest depth have their bottoms so far below the surface that they are known as *deeps.* Those huge synclinal (down-folded) depressions which lie out in front of great mountain arcs are known as *fore-deeps.* They owe their existence to the same crustal deformations which produced neighboring hills or mountains. One of them, the Mariana Trench, just east of the Mariana Islands and about 1400 miles east of the Philippines, has a record depth of 36,690 feet. If Mt. Everest were placed in this trough, even

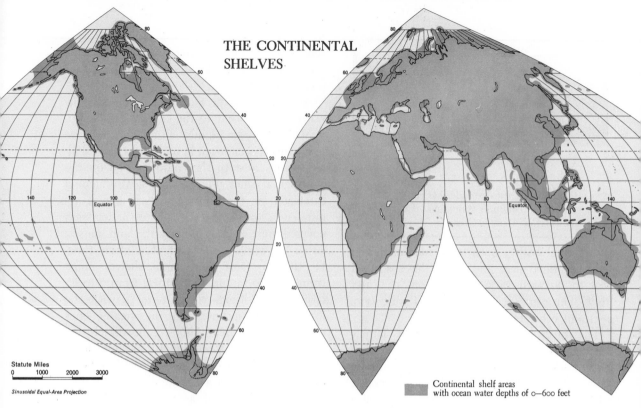

THE CONTINENTAL SHELVES

Statute Miles
0   1000   2000   3000

Sinusoidal Equal-Area Projection

Continental shelf areas
with ocean water depths of 0—600 feet

4-4   THE ocean's continental shelf areas with water depths of 0-600 feet (0-100 fathoms) are particularly significant to man, both as fishing grounds and for ship navigation. Note the varying widths of the continental shelves.

its summit would be well over one mile below the surface of the ocean. The deepest section of the Atlantic, the Milwaukee Depth just north of Puerto Rico, has a depth of some 30,000 feet.

WATER MOVEMENTS • While one may think of the seas and oceans in only two dimensions, as "so long and so wide," they are actually three-dimensional. Their restless waters move not only horizontally, but also vertically and obliquely. Some of these movements result in the transportation of significant amounts of water from one part of the ocean to another, like the flow of polar waters equatorward and of tropical waters toward the poles, or like the up-welling of water from a depth of several hundred feet and the slow descent of surface waters.

Other movements, such as storm, tidal, and

seismic waves, do not result in any significant transportation. In tidal movements, the waters merely bulge in obedience to the mass attraction of the moon and sun. Because the earth rotates, the bulges travel, but the water in them merely goes up and down and there is little, if any, transportation. Much the same sort of behavior occurs in seismic waves (*tsunamis*). These are set up as a result of sudden and violent disturbances of a section of sea bottom, by block-fault movement or by volcanic activity. Some seismic waves are 50 feet in height and travel at speeds as great as 500 miles per hour. If they strike low and inhabited coasts, property damage and loss of life are heavy. One such wave, originating from crustal movements in the Gulf of Alaska, struck the Hawaiian harbor of Hilo in the spring of 1946 with disastrous results to per-

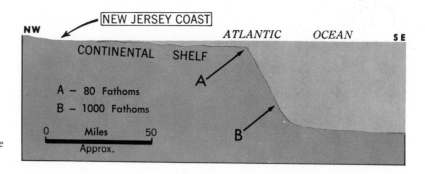

4–5

THE *continental shelf off the New Jersey coast.*

sons, buildings, ships, and harbor installations. Another such wave in May, 1960, killed over 200 persons in Hawaii, Japan, and Okinawa. Yet, despite all the commotion they cause, seismic waves, like storm and tidal waves, do not cause waters to move from one region to another.

The movements which do result in transportation of large quantities of ocean water are called *currents*. These are of many sorts, some are cold and others warm, some are highly saline and others only weakly saline, some operate at great or intermediate depths and others move at and near the surface. Of them all, it is those at or relatively near the surface which are most significant geographically. It is these surface currents which affect ship navigation, the presence and numbers of commercial fish, and water and air conditions in shore and near-shore areas. Their effects on air (climatic) conditions will be mentioned later in the discussion of climatic controls in CHAPTER 8.

Between the Tropics of Cancer and Capricorn most of the surface currents and, hence, the greatest volumes of water, are moving steadily toward the west. This is in accord with the strong frictional drag of the easterly winds (Trade Winds), which tends to pile up the surface waters against the eastern margins of the land masses in low latitudes. This westward movement of tropical water is a twofold one, being comprised of the North Equatorial Current and the South Equatorial Current (FIG. 4–6). Between them is a smaller,

reverse, compensating flow known as the Equatorial Countercurrent. In the part of the Indian Ocean from the equator to southern Asia there is a seasonal reversal of currents in accord with the behavior of the monsoon winds (see CHAPTER 9).

The warm surface waters which move toward and tend to pile up against the eastern parts of islands and continental shores of much of the tropics are forced to turn poleward. This is a result primarily of their bumping into the land and secondarily of deflection incident to their movement on the surface of a rotating earth. The waters of the North Equatorial Current turn northward and those of the South Equatorial Current turn southward. As they travel, deflection to the right of course in the Northern Hemisphere and to the left in the Southern Hemisphere causes them to pull slowly away from the eastern shores of the continents as they move poleward. By the time the middle latitudes are reached, rotational deflection and the force of the Prevailing Westerly winds, under whose influence they now come, cause them to take courses toward the east. This direction is just the reverse of their movements in tropical waters. The eastward journey carries them once more across the oceans where they split near the western margins of the land masses. Part of this split is the result of bumping into land and part is the result of deviation incident to earth rotation.

The splitting of the ocean currents in middle latitudes is well illustrated by the North At-

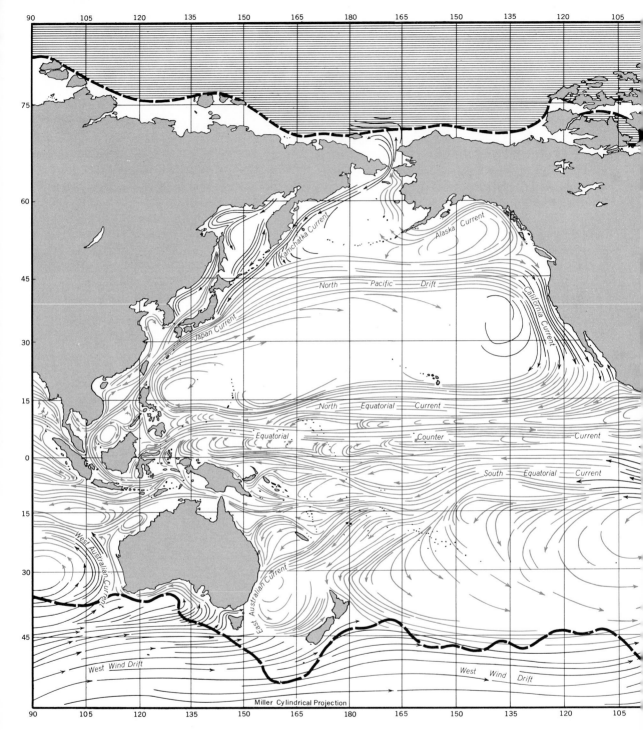

4–6   THE world's major cold and warm ocean currents, which form contrasting patterns in the Northern and Southern Hemispheres, are particularly significant to man in their effects on climate, ship navigation, and commercial ocean fishing. Note the equatorward limits of polar pack ice and icebergs.

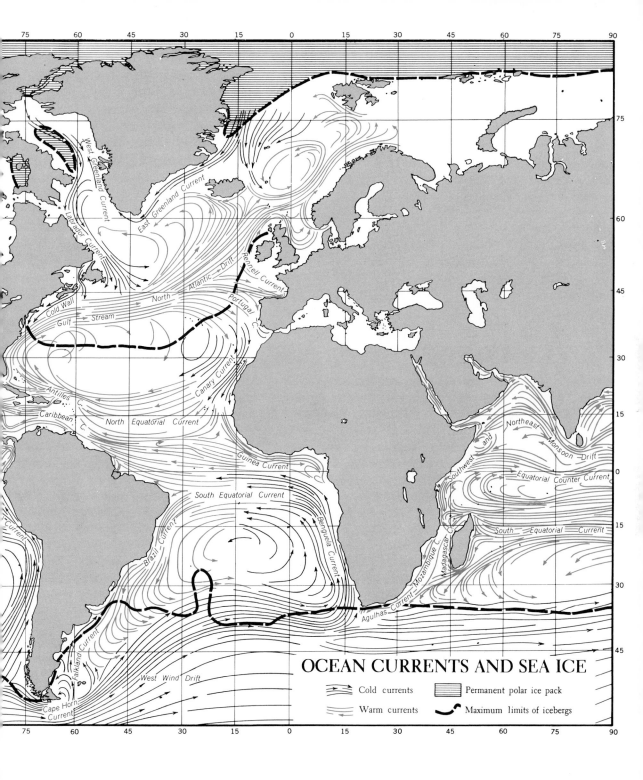

OCEAN CURRENTS AND SEA ICE

⟶	Cold currents	▭	Permanent polar ice pack
⟶	Warm currents	⌇	Maximum limits of icebergs

West Greenland Current

Labrador Current

East Greenland Current

Atlantic Drift

Rennell Current

North

Portugal C.

Cold Wall

Gulf Stream

Antilles C.

Caribbean C.

Canary Current

North Equatorial Current

Guinea Current

South Equatorial Current

Brazil Current

Benguela Current

Northeast Monsoon Drift

Equatorial Counter Current

Southwest and

South Equatorial Current

Agulhas Current

Mozambique C.

Madagascar C.

Current

Falkland Current

West Wind Drift

Cape Horn Current

lantic Drift, the offspring of the Gulf Stream (FIG. 4–6). This current, or slow drift, sends part of its water equatorward as the Canary Current. The latter, in turn, flows into the North Equatorial Current previously mentioned. The other part of the North Atlantic Drift flows in a northeasterly direction between Norway and Iceland into the margin of the Arctic Ocean. It brings relatively warm temperatures to high latitudes and thus accounts for ice-free ports as far north as the Lofotens, off Norway, north of the Arctic Circle. It is responsible for a measurable portion of the climatic mildness characteristic of the British Isles and northwestern Europe in spite of their northerly location.

On the opposite side of the North Atlantic, cold waters from the Arctic Ocean, known as the Labrador Current, hug the eastern edges of the land mass as they move southward to encounter and slide under the warmer waters of the Gulf Stream. Associated with the cold water are the heavy and numerous fogs of the Newfoundland Grand Bank and other nearby areas. The cold waters also bring many types of small marine organisms which help to support fish in the shallow waters of the continental shelf. Unfortunately, the Labrador Current also brings many icebergs to menace the heavily traveled lanes of the great North Atlantic route (FIG. 6–22). Particularly during the summer season, when the bergs are freed from the winter ice lock in Baffin Bay, these floating ice mountains cause trouble. In summer, the shipping lanes are actually shifted a bit farther to the south in order to avoid the areas of greatest berg concentration.

The picture of surface circulation in the northern half of the Pacific is strikingly similar to that of the North Atlantic (FIG. 4–6). However, the near junction of northeastern Siberia and western Alaska does not allow as free an interchange of waters with those of the Arctic Ocean. Instead, there is only a cold water stream passing from the Arctic to the North Pacific through narrow Bering Strait. This current, the Kamchatka, is the Pacific counterpart of the Labrador Current. There are, however, no icebergs, for there is no Greenland glacier to furnish them to the sea waters. Otherwise the two pictures are much the same; the general pattern of *clockwise* circulation occurs in both the North Atlantic and the North Pacific.

The surface currents of the Southern Hemisphere, in the southern parts of the Pacific, Atlantic, and Indian oceans, are essentially the same as those in the northern, but the movement is counterclockwise (FIG. 4–6). There is interchange of polar and tropical waters, westward movement near the equator, poleward movement along eastern coasts, drift across the oceans in the middle latitude positions, splitting of currents in middle latitudes near west coasts, and generally rotary nature of the circulation as a whole.

ICE CONDITIONS • Some small icebergs are derived from local valley glaciers along mountainous coasts, like those of southeastern Alaska, but they are short-lived and few in number. The bergs which are large and numerous come from the Greenland ice and from the vast ice layers of Antarctica. The tabular Antarctic bergs, unlike the jagged Greenland type (FIG. 6–22), do not menace any major shipping lanes, nor do they regularly move as far from points of origin. Only the occasional whaling and scientific exploration vessel must be on guard against them, particularly during fogs or storms. The extreme equatorial limits of icebergs sizable enough to be hazardous are shown in FIG. 4–6.

Most of the ice in ocean waters is pack ice—*floes* (cakes) and *fields* of salt-water ice found in the polar regions (FIG. 4–7). Pack ice is monotonously flat except where the huge cakes have ground against each other and their edges buckled and piled up to form pressure ridges. Because the Arctic polar area is an ocean and the Antarctic a continent, there is more pack ice in the Northern Hemisphere than in the Southern. Arctic pack ice often threatens, entraps, or crushes vessels attempting to develop sea routes and fisheries along the northern continental coasts of North America and Eurasia. Possible future use of the Arctic Ocean is suggested by the under-ice voyages of U.S. Navy submarines.

Some ice of Arctic origin moves into the northwestern portion of the North Atlantic (FIG. 4–6). Packs, or fields, also constitute navigational hazards in the Bering Sea, Baffin Bay, and the Sea of Okhotsk. However, even in the Arctic Ocean, there is always open water. Contrary to popular belief, sea ice there never, even in the height of the coldest season, forms a continuous blanket from shore to shore. Storms, ordinary winds, and currents keep the ice broken up and shifting from place to place. One of the major problems of travel on such ice is the presence of open lanes and areas of water which are difficult for dogs, sledges, half-tracks, and men to cross. Another is that the ice may move at such speed and in such direction that an exploring party toils ahead for many hours, only to find that it is in the same position as before, as though it had been walking on a treadmill.

Lakes

Considering the great size of the seas and oceans, the smaller water bodies seem insignificant. However, significance cannot be measured by size alone. A lake, or group of lakes, may have a local or even an extralocal importance far out of proportion to the area or depth of water involved. Lakes may furnish domestic and industrial water, transportation, fish, and recreational opportunities. In such manner, they may be more truly and directly entwined with the lives of many people than are seas and oceans.

There are major portions of the several continents which do not possess lakes, except, perhaps, for an occasional one created artificially by man. Lakes in South America, at least lakes of any appreciable size, are conspicuously

4–7

U.S. COAST GUARD icebreaker Northwind making its way through floes of salt-water ice en route to Cape Hallett, Antarctica.

rare. The same is true of Australia, most of Africa, and the bulk of Asia. Actually, conditions in nature work against the formation or long-continued preservation of any considerable number of lakes. The existence of a lake demands two things: some sort of basin which has no low-level outlet and enough water to fill such a basin or to flood part of it. Thus, lakes are largely ruled out of the earth's extensive dry lands. Where climates are humid and there are basins present, lakes are soon emptied as gnawing streams cut gorges into their rims and drain away the impounded waters, or they become filled with in-washed sediments and aquatic vegetation. It is possible that lakes are among the most short-lived of the earth's physical features.

In contrast to the vast regions with few or no lakes, there are others in which lakes are numerous. Most of the large regions with numerous lakes are areas of glaciation, chiefly of continental glaciation and to a lesser extent of valley glaciation (FIG. 6–35). In such regions, the characteristic unevenness resulting from both glacial scour and glacial deposition normally results in numerous depressions which have no low-level outlet. It so happens that most such depressions are in humid climates so that there is abundant water to fill them. Streams are busily engaged in cutting through the rims, but there has been insufficient time since the glaciers disappeared for the streams to have drained the lakes of their waters or for the lakes to have become filled with plants and sediment. Some lake regions were not glaciated and lakes in them owe their origin to other causes. A few may be mentioned: the lake country of an appreciable section of equatorial Africa is the result of displacement of the earth's crust and damming by lava flows (FIG. 4–8); that of northern Florida is a result of certain soluble rock conditions; and that of the lower Yangtze Basin is the result of variations in the deposition of river alluviums, plus, in part, some warping of the earth's crust. Beyond these, there are many other occurrences and possibilities of formation, but the original generalization, that lakes are most numerous in glaciated regions, especially those of most recent glaciation, is not invalidated by the exceptions.

THE GREAT LAKES • North America, of all the continents, has the greatest number of lakes, from small and large ones at comparatively low elevations to small ones at mountainous elevations. Of them all, from Canada's Great Bear Lake in the far north to Lake Nicaragua in the tropics, the cluster known as the Great Lakes is the most conspicuous and the most important (FIG. 4–9). Not only does it provide the chief inland waterway of the earth, but it serves many other purposes, from water supply to commercial fishing and recreation.

Lake Superior is the largest of the lakes

4–8

LAKE JIPE, one of the many lakes of the volcanic and block-faulted region of eastern equatorial Africa. (From Focus on Africa, published by the American Geographical Society)

and the most extensive body of fresh water on the globe. It is about 350 miles in length and 160 miles wide. Its deepest section is about 1300 feet, which places its bottom nearly 700 feet below sea level, while its surface is about 600 feet above the level of the sea. With an area of approximately 32,000 square miles, it is large enough to cover all of Belgium and the Netherlands and to extend over half of Denmark as well. A single outlet, the St. Marys river, connects it with Lake Huron. The Soo Canals, paralleling the rapids section of the upper St. Marys, allow vessels to move to and from the Lower Lakes (FIG. 4–10).

Lake Michigan and Lake Huron, lying about 20 feet lower than Superior, are connected by the Straits of Mackinac. The combined flow of Superior, Huron, and Michigan, except for minor diversion through the Chicago Drainage Canal to the Illinois river, moves by way of the St. Clair river into small and shallow Lake St. Clair. That, in turn, drains by means of the

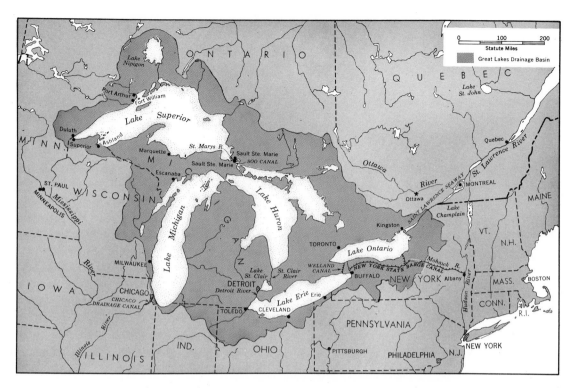

4–9   THE Great Lakes, plus the St. Lawrence River and Seaway, constitute the major inland waterway of the world.

Detroit river into the western end of Lake Erie. At Erie's eastern end, the water forms the Niagara river which tumbles over Niagara Falls on its way to Lake Ontario. The Welland Canal, in Canadian Territory, makes it possible for vessels to move between Erie and Ontario. Lake Ontario is the smallest of the Great Lakes (little Lake St. Clair is not considered one of the Great Lakes), but even it is nearly as large as Massachusetts. From its eastern end pour the waters of all the lakes, waters which form the full stream of the St. Lawrence river. All in all, the Great Lakes cover an area the size of the United Kingdom or an area nearly a third greater than the New England states. The parts of the shorelines which lie entirely in United States territory are longer than the distance from New York to London.

The Great Lakes have been singled out for emphasis here because of their size, arrangement, and commercial importance. With the opening and use of the Great Lakes–St. Lawrence Seaway, the lakes have become of even greater commercial significance. More will be said about the Great Lakes in later chapters in this book. Were space available, it would be pertinent to discuss some of the other lakes of the world, such as Great Bear Lake, which has become famous for the uranium ores located along parts of its shore, or Siberia's deep and crescent-shaped Lake Baikal, or the lake districts of Switzerland and northwestern England, or of Maine. Interesting also would be a discussion of the movements of waters in lakes. Like the oceans, they have their currents, and, again like the oceans, lakes are modifiers of climatic conditions in their shore and near-shore areas.

4-10   HUGE *Great Lakes vessels, the ore boats which carry iron ore "down-lakes" and coal "up-lakes,"*
at the downstream ends of the huge locks of the Soo Canal at Sault Ste. Marie, Michigan. In
the far background at the right is the International Bridge (railroad only), which crosses above
the head of the rapids of the St. Marys river.

DRY LAKES • Maps of the continents and many smaller areas show by names and symbols numerous lakes which are not true and permanent lakes. Some examples are Lake Eyre (Australia), Lop Nor (western China), Shott el Jerid (Tunisia), and Muroc Dry Lake (California). These "lakes which are usually not lakes" are the playas or salars which will be discussed in CHAPTER 6.

STREAMS

THE lines of moving water which thread their way across the surface of the land vary in size from mere rills and brooks to broad, full-flowing rivers. Where land masses and drainage basins are large and precipitation plentiful, streams are numerous and permanent; where drainage basins are small and especially where precipitation is meager, streams are small and intermittent.

The presence or lack of streams affects man's movements and settlements in a wide variety of ways. Primitive man camped at places along or near streams where water and fish were available and where he had a highway for his raft or crude boat. Man, primitive or not, has often settled on islands in rivers where the encompassing water provided a barrier against enemies. River junctions have been strategic points for the control of, and participation in, the trade which moved on the streams. River mouths, making union with the sea, gave access to ocean routes. When industrial centers arose, the riverbank position provided large quantities of water for rapidly growing urban populations and supplied water for power and the processing of materials. In many areas, the fine dark alluviums of river flood plains attracted agricultural populations. In the eastern United States and to a lesser extent in the drier West, the bulk of the westward movement was locally carried and directed by the streams which floated men and their belongings. These are only a few of the ways in which rivers and men have been and, in many ways, still are related.

Humid-land Streams

In regions of humid climate, all except the smallest tributaries are normally permanently flowing waters. Their volumes may vary with seasonal differences in the amount of water available from precipitation, surface drainage, and underground drainage. High and low stages represent ordinary behavior, but the streams are always there. In some streams, there may be little difference between highest and lowest water. This is true particularly where rainfall is of comparatively even distribution throughout the year and where waters are not partly locked up in the form of ice during the winter season. Variations in flow are significant as part of the physical picture of an area, but they are more significant in their relations to man and his activities. It is readily apparent that a permanent stream which is in high flood during part of the year and barely flows at another time is of much less utility than one which maintains a relatively uniform level.

GREAT RIVERS • Each continent except Antarctica has important rivers. All of them have their sources in humid lands, chiefly in rainy and snowy mountains, and most of them flow in humid regions throughout their courses. Exceptions to this latter condition are represented by the Nile and the Colorado, which run in dry areas for most of their lengths.

Streams of this nature, unlike the Amazon and the Mississippi, actually lose volume as they proceed mouthward; however, they receive sufficient water in the wet lands of their origin to carry them through steppes and deserts. Such streams are known as *exotic streams*; at least they are strange, or exotic, in the portions of their courses which extend through climatically dry regions. Exotic streams, like the Nile, Colorado, or Tigris–Euphrates, have played a large part in human history. They have supplied relatively abundant water to regions which otherwise could have supported only small and widely scattered settlements. They have encouraged, even forced, cooperation among peoples using them particularly in connection with the construction and maintenance of extensive irrigation works. Humid-land streams have also played much the same role because the development of river transportation, the control of floodwaters, the generation of power, and the insurance of sufficient and proper supplies of domestic and industrial water have demanded cooperative, rather than individual, activity.

One of the longest river systems is the Missouri–Mississippi. From its source in the northern part of the American Rockies to its mouth in the Gulf of Mexico is a distance of nearly 4000 miles. Among its conspicuous features are a large number of tributaries, broad and fertile flood plains in its lower portion, and the wide delta which it is still building out into the Gulf of Mexico. Nearly as long as the Missouri–Mississippi and greater in volume is the Amazon. From its source in the high Andes, it flows eastward across the full breadth of the Amazon Basin to pour a wide and muddy stream into the Atlantic. So great is the volume and so heavy the load of fine materials that the Amazon can be detected as a dirty fresh-water stream for many miles out into the Atlantic, a sort of river in the ocean. Many large and small islands split its discharge area so that it has several mouths instead of one. The Amazon is the only stream which is

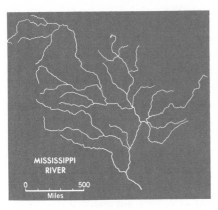
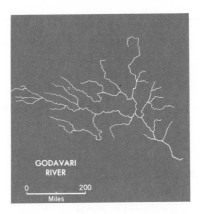

MISSISSIPPI RIVER
0   500
Miles

GODAVARI RIVER
0   200
Miles

TAJIGUAS CREEK
0   1
Mile

4–11   EXAMPLES of the dendritic pattern of drainage in streams of large, medium, and small size.

navigable for ocean vessels for nearly the breadth of a continent; such vessels, except for the larger ones, can travel all the way from the Atlantic to the town of Iquitos in Peru. Should the Amazon Basin ever become highly developed, this river probably will be one of the world's major arteries. The longest rivers of the other continents are the Nile (Africa), Ob (Eurasia), and the Murray (Australia). Australia, with its disproportionate area of dry climates and with only small drainage basins in the sections which are humid, has few large permanent streams.

STREAM PATTERNS • A study of maps which portray the lines of flow of surface waters will indicate many patterns. These are the particular patterns which individual streams have etched into the land as they have carried on their erosive work. That the patterns are very much a part of the actual geographic expression and not just features which have been unduly emphasized on maps is illustrated by almost any view which enables the observer to look down upon the land.

The most common stream pattern is the *dendritic pattern*. The term *"dendritic"* means treelike, and a stream system with this plan possesses a main trunk and branches which join it at acute angles. This pattern develops where the running water is cutting rocks, whether loose or consolidated, which are rela-

tively uniform in their reaction to erosion. Thus, this pattern will occur in a region where streams are running on granite alone, or on a homogeneous sandstone, or wholly on loose clays, and so on. FIGURE 4–11 presents the actual plans of some streams, large and small, which have the dendritic pattern.

Other major stream patterns are the *trellis, radial, annular, braided,* and *glacially deranged.* Over the land surface as a whole, they are much less common than the dendritic pattern, but in areas where they do occur, they are just as observable and significant. The trellis pattern is comprised of relatively straight lines which join each other at right angles (FIG. 4–12). This pattern occurs where there is a definite banding of the rocks or a pattern of structural weakness in the earth's crust. The radial pattern is found where there is a centrally located area of higher land from which the streams flow out in all directions like spokes from the hub of a wheel (FIG. 4–13A). It also occurs in areas where there is a central low section and streams flow in from all, or many, directions. The annular, or ring, pattern occurs most frequently as a result of the erosion of structural domes (FIG. 4–13B). Its plan reflects rock controls which are made operative as soon as the domes have passed the initial stage in their dissection. In a sense, the annular pattern is a curved or bent trellis pattern. The

80 | *The Earth's Waters*

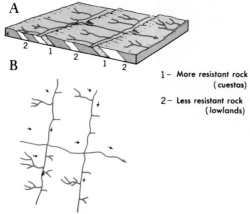

A

B

1 – More resistant rock
(cuestas)

2 – Less resistant rock
(lowlands)

TRELLISED STREAM PATTERN IN RIDGE AND VALLEY AREA

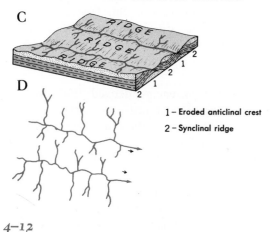

C

D

1 – Eroded anticlinal crest

2 – Synclinal ridge

4–12

TWO *trellis drainage patterns, showing the relation of each to landforms and underlying rock conditions (see the index for references to cuestas, synclines, and anticlines).*

braided pattern, characteristic of streams which are overloaded and have hence dropped materials to clog their former channels, is one of many joining and rejoining lines. FIGURE 4–14 indicates, better than words, the nature of this pattern. The glacially deranged pattern will be discussed in CHAPTER 6 which includes mention of continental and valley glaciation.

Stream patterns are important in many ways. They provide part of the physical plan of a countryside and they affect the distribution of other physical features. One example is seen in the streams of, Kansas; their patterns are largely dendritic and so are the patterns of the accompanying flood plains. Water is more abundant in the flood-plain soils and trees are able to maintain themselves there. Thus, fingers and lines of trees stand out in dendritic pattern and in sharp contrast to the drier, grassy interstream areas (FIG. 4–15). In the ridge-and-valley region of eastern Tennessee, the stream pattern is trellised and this is the key to distribution of the richer bottomland soils, as well as to the location of those types of natural vegetation which require more moisture than do the types on the ridges. These are only two examples, chosen more or less at random, but they serve to illustrate some of the relationships between stream patterns and other natural features.

When man comes to travel across the land, and to inhabit and use it, stream patterns are reflected in still other fashions. In the Amazon Basin, the stream pattern is dendritic and many of the towns and small native villages are located at places along the top edges of valley bluffs. Thus, the population pattern is dendritic, although not solidly dendritic, for settlements are not continuous. It might be described as a broken dendritic pattern. In the northern part of the state of Mississippi, the streams also have a dendritic pattern. The best cornlands are found on the fertile, recent alluvium which borders the stream channels; hence the pattern of corn distribution, at least of heavy corn yields, is the same as that of the streams. An annular pattern is characteristic of much of the drainage system of the Black Hills and the pattern of ranch lands follows in strong correspondence. In a large part of Pennsylvania, chiefly east of the Allegheny Plateau, the stream pattern is trellised and the individual parts of the pattern mark the positions of the more level lands. These are the lands of densest settlement for that portion of the state and the population pattern there is essentially trellised (FIG. 4–16).

There are also significant relationships be-

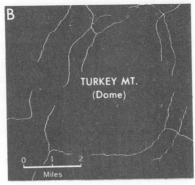

4-13

A. Radial pattern of drainage.
B. Annular pattern of drainage.

tween road patterns and drainage patterns. The problems of road alignment and bridge construction in an area of glacially deranged drainage are very different from the same problems in a region of dendritic stream pattern. Again, the above are only a few examples of the relationships between stream patterns and cultural patterns; they could be multiplied many times.

4-14

BRAIDED channel in the aggraded bed of the Komaktorvik river in northern Labrador. Note the many interlocking stream channels.

WATER POWER • There has been a growing emphasis on the development of power from streams. Particularly is this true of rivers in humid middle latitude regions or those which obtain enough water from humid areas to enable them to continue as streams through dry country.

The use of energy derived from running water is age-old. It began thousands of years ago in such areas as the Nile valley and parts of India and China. Early installations were small and simple. They consisted of some type of wheel equipped with cleats or boards against which the water thrust itself to turn the wheel and its axle. Surprisingly enough, it is the simple type which is most common over the earth as a whole to this very day. With the coming of the Industrial Revolution and its demands for more and more power, much of the energy which at first drove the machines came directly from running water. Later, as man's knowledge of electricity and ways of producing it increased, part of the energy from running water was converted into electricity for driving many of the machines. The large modern water-power establishments do not depend on the simple wheel; instead the water is dropped through huge pipes in which turbines are set. The down-rushing water turns the blades of the turbines at terrific speed and this mechanical energy is used to spin generators which transform the water power into electric power (FIG. 4-17).

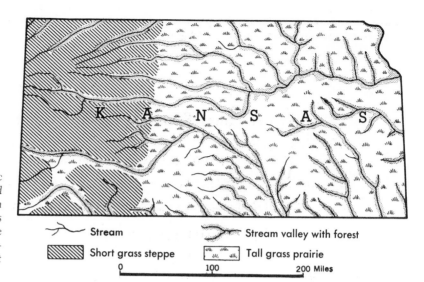

4-15

RELATION *between dendritic stream pattern and pattern and type of natural vegetation in a portion of the interior plains of the United States. Note that forested stream valleys extend through both the short grass and tall grass areas.*

Stream

Stream valley with forest

Short grass steppe

Tall grass prairie

0   100   200 Miles

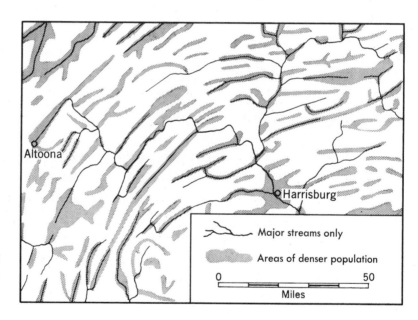

Altoona

Harrisburg

Major streams only

Areas of denser population

0   50
Miles

4-16

RELATION *between trellis pattern of drainage and areas of denser population in a ridge-and-valley area of southern Pennsylvania.*

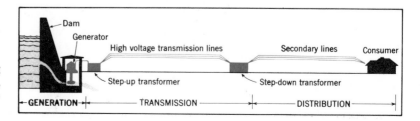

Dam
Generator
High voltage transmission lines
Secondary lines
Consumer
Step-up transformer
Step-down transformer
GENERATION — TRANSMISSION — DISTRIBUTION

4-17

A SCHEMATIC *diagram showing the generation, transmission, and distribution of hydroelectricity.*

TABLE *4*

Water Power Resources—Some Comparisons

I. WORLD WATER POWER

DEVELOPED: 20% (129,718,000 hp)   UNDEVELOPED: 80% (518,902,000 hp)

TOTAL WATER POWER POSSIBLE: 100% (648,620,000 hp)

II. WATER POWER BY CONTINENTS

(% of world total)

Among the continents, Europe, North America, and Asia are the "big three" in developed water power, with Asia a poor third (A). Africa, Asia, and South America lead the continents in water power available for future development (B). If all possible water power should be developed, then Africa, Asia, and North America would lead the continents, with Africa far ahead (C).

A. DEVELOPED		B. UNDEVELOPED		C. TOTAL POSSIBLE	
Europe	42.25	Africa	48.10	Africa	38.58
North America	40.57	Asia	27.12	Asia	24.16
Asia	11.53	South America	11.28	North America	14.20
South America	3.19	North America	7.66	Europe	9.83
Oceania	1.50	Oceania	4.12	South America	9.67
Africa	0.96	Europe	1.73	Oceania	3.56

III. WATER POWER BY COUNTRIES

(Countries with over 3% of world total)

On a country basis the "big two" in water power already developed are the United States and Canada (A). The big two nations in terms of water power still available for development are the Republic of the Congo and the U.S.S.R. (B). If all possible power should be developed, then the big two countries would still be Congo and the U.S.S.R., with Congo holding a considerable edge (C).

A. DEVELOPED		B. UNDEVELOPED		C. TOTAL POSSIBLE	
United States	26.00	Congo (Léopoldville)	25.18	Congo (Léopoldville)	20.04
Canada	12.09	U.S.S.R	13.67	U.S.S.R.	12.02
Japan	7.79	Congo (Brazzaville),		Congo (Brazzaville),	
Italy	7.32	Gabon, and Central		Gabon, and Central	
France	7.24	African Republic	9.44	African Republic	7.49
U.S.S.R.	5.49	India	5.01	Canada	5.65
Sweden	4.47	China	4.23	United States	5.62
Norway	4.00	Canada	3.83	India	4.16
Switzerland	3.57	Brazil	3.35	China	3.54
Germany	3.08	All others	35.29	Brazil	3.23
All others	18.95			All others	38.25

SOURCE: Based on 1955 data from *United States Geological Survey Circular 367.*

4–18 HOOVER (BOULDER) DAM *and part of the downstream portion of the Lake Mead reservoir, in the Black Canyon gorge of the Colorado river, with Nevada at the left and Arizona at the right. The black specks barely discernible along the crest of the dam are automobiles, giving a notion of the gigantic size of this dam.*

At this point, it should be noted that, although important, only a small part of the world's electricity is produced from water power. Most of it is produced by means of coal, petroleum, and natural gas. Even today, hydroelectric energy in the United States supplies only a small part of the total energy used. Further, this part may well be challenged by expansion in the field of nuclear energy.

The United States leads the world in the production of hydroelectricity, although on a *per capita* basis Norway holds first rank. If all possible water power were developed, the political unit of the Republic of the Congo would lead and, among the continents, Africa would hold first place (TABLE 4). So far, the largest and most famous individual power plants are found mainly in the United States, Canada, the U.S.S.R., mainland China, and India. Among them are the plants at Niagara Falls, those of the Tennessee valley, the huge establishment at Hoover Dam on the Colorado (FIG. 4–18), and those at Grand Coulee and Bonneville on the Columbia river. Rapid expansion of hydroelectric production in the U.S.S.R. is evidenced by the plants at Kuibyshev and Volgograd on the Volga, already in operation, and those being built at Bratsk on the Angara and at Krasnoyarsk on the Yenesei. The last named station is claimed to be the largest in the world. In mainland China, the Hwang Ho (Yellow river) complex equals that of the Tennessee Valley Authority. And, in India, the Bhakra Dam (17 feet higher than the Hoover Dam) on the Sutlej river in Punjab State was completed in the spring of 1961.

Beyond engineering know-how, location in reference to markets, size of markets, and the like, the generation of hydroelectricity has certain physical requirements. There must be a large volume of water of relatively steady flow and a sufficient fall of that water. In addition, if artificial dams have to be built to improve natural conditions, there must be sites available where construction is safe and economically feasible. The dams must be located in parts of valleys where sufficient amounts of water can be impounded. Thus, purely physical conditions such as nature of bedrock and shape of valley become significant. The physical conditions requisite to water-power production are most fully met in regions of continental and valley glaciation. Glaciated areas possess many natural reservoirs which insure large volume and steadiness of flow aided, of course, by humid climates. Many falls and rapids are present to insure sufficient water drop. Particularly in regions where glaciers have removed the loose cover from bedrock there are many sites where dams can be easily constructed and safely anchored into the bedrock. Glaciation has helped to make possible the high per capita production of power in Norway. It also largely accounts for the power generated at places along the southern flank of Canada's Laurentian Upland (FIG. 4–19), as well as much of the water power produced in the hilly northeastern part of the United States.

However, optimum physical conditions are no longer so important as they were in the past; greatly increased technical knowledge and abundant capital now enable man to make up in part for certain natural lacks. Hence, tremendous quantities of power can now be pro-

4–19

A LARGE dam, used for purposes of hydroelectric power production, on the Gatineau river in the Laurentian Upland just north of Ottawa, Canada. The sluiceway to the left is to allow floating logs, some of which are visible in the lower left, to bypass the dam on their way to a sawmill downstream.

duced in regions where it would not have been possible, or feasible, a few years ago. Besides, streams today are controlled for other reasons, such as flood prevention, improvement and maintenance of navigation, and insurance of domestic and industrial water supply. Controls of this sort often result in the creation of proper conditions for power production. Thus power can be produced in many places more or less as a by-product of projects which are broader in scope. This is true in the Tennessee Valley, where a separate governmental corporation, known as the Tennessee Valley Authority, was set up to control floods, improve navigation, and, in general, to help rehabilitate the run-down economy of the region. River control for the purposes of flood prevention and navigation entailed many dams and reservoirs (FIG. 4–20). These, in turn, provided several excellent possibilities for the steady generation of hydroelectricity.

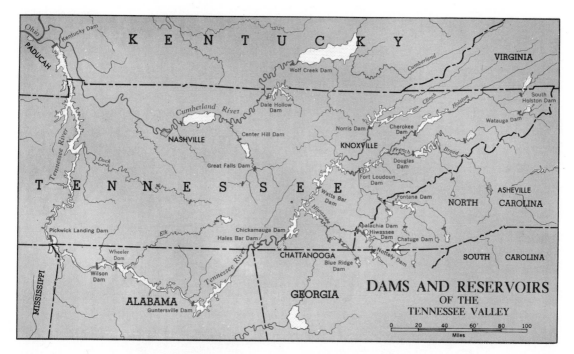

4–20   THE drainage basin of the Tennessee river now has several dams and reservoirs. Many of the dams are multiple-purpose dams, used for flood control and navigation as well as for hydro-electric power production.

Streams in Dry Lands

As we shall see later, stream behavior in regions of arid or semiarid climates is much different from that in humid lands. The streams, except for those which are exotic, are intermittent rather than permanent and they are smaller and less numerous. Yet these intermittent streams present many vexing problems. They pour floodwaters onto settlements and play havoc with transportation systems (FIG. 4–21). Extensive flood prevention works are necessary for the protection of towns and cities, as well as of roads and railroads. It is somewhat paradoxical that floods and flood damage may be as severe in deserts as in lands of plentiful moisture.

The reasons for these difficulties lie basically in the amount and distribution of precipitation; that is, the problems are fundamentally climatic in origin. Because the water does not flow permanently, it drops flood-stage loads and channels are clogged. The next floodwater spreads out over wide areas, carving new channels soon glutted with debris as the water disappears. Except where channels are deeply entrenched, such behavior means that flood areas are usually broad and not too well defined; nevertheless, they are the natural drainways, and man must pay the penalty if he settles in them and builds his transport lines across them. Very often, he seems to know so little about stream behavior under such conditions that he fails to recognize that he is in the natural line of water flow.

4–21   RESULTS of a flood on the intermittent Mojave river in the Mojave Desert, at Barstow, California. Note the breached highway crossing the flood plain and the damaged fields.

GROUND WATER

A PORTION of the moisture derived from the air sinks into the upper part of the earth's crust to become *ground water*. Though not visible, it is just as important as surface water. From it come springs and well water and some of the moisture which is so necessary for the growth of natural vegetation and crops. As water moves downward from the surface, it fills the spaces among soil particles and also the crevices and cracks of the bedrock as far down as such exist in the earth's crust. The zone in which all spaces are filled is the *zone of saturation* (FIG. 4–22). The top of the zone is the *water table*. The water table follows approximately the profile of the land above, al-though it is closer to the surface in low places than in high places. Where it intersects the surface in low spots, the results are swamps, ponds, lakes, or springs. In general, the ground-water table lies closer to the surface in regions of humid climates than it does in the areas of arid or semiarid climates. Even in the latter areas, it may reach the surface in a few low spots and in these, salt marshes are the normal result.

Soil Moisture

The amount of moisture present in the soil is a very critical factor in the growth of natural

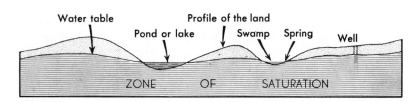

DIAGRAMMATIC *section of the upper portion of earth's crust, illustrating the zone of satura- tion, water table, relationship of water table to land surface, and some possibilities of lakes, swamps, springs, and wells.*

vegetation and crops. Soil moisture is of three kinds: *gravitational water, hygroscopic water,* and *capillary water* (FIG. 4–23). Gravitational water is the water which moves downward, by force of gravity, toward the zone of saturation. If gravitational water is too abundant, soils become waterlogged and useless for crops al- though such drowned soils are still capable of supporting several types of swamp vegeta- tion. Hygroscopic water exists as an extremely thin film around each soil particle, somewhat as though each particle were "wrapped in cello- phane." It is often referred to as "unavailable water" because plants cannot obtain it. Capil- lary water is the water which moves by capil- lary action, or attraction, in the same fashion that spilled ink may be drawn into and among the fibers of a blotter. Its ability to move even against the pull of gravity is significant for, as topsoils dry out, capillary water is drawn to the upper portion of the soil where it supplies the needs of plants. However, if such action is too long continued, particularly if the water is drawn all the way to the surface, soils be-

come either weakly or strongly saline. This oc- curs when the water, drawn to the surface, is evaporated and leaves its minerals behind. If there is insufficient precipitation to wash the minerals, or mineral salts, back down into lower parts of the soil, permanently saline soils are created. If they are mildly saline, a few mineral salt-tolerant crops may be grown; with high salinity, no crops can grow although a few specially adapted types of natural vegeta- tion (halophytes) may be able to exist.

Springs and Wells

SPRINGS • When ground water issues at the surface it creates either springs or seeps. Whether in deserts or in lands of plentiful rain, springs and seeps are very useful to man and animals alike. If they are hot springs or are heavily charged with certain minerals, they may be used for health baths and general resort purposes. A spring in the desert usually makes possible an oasis settlement; and a line of springs, as along the base of a range of hills

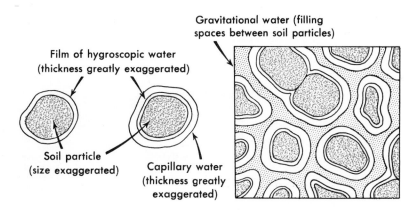

4–23

EXAGGERATED *diagram of the three kinds of soil moisture: gravitational, hygroscopic, and capillary water.*

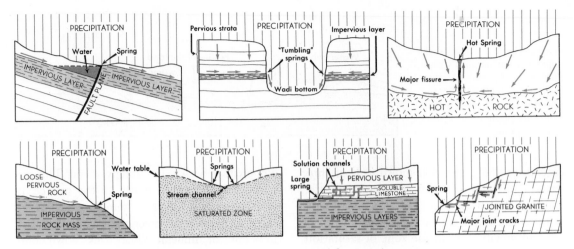

PRECIPITATION

Water   Spring
IMPERVIOUS LAYER   IMPERVIOUS LAYER
FAULT PLANE

Pervious strata   PRECIPITATION   Impervious layer
"Tumbling" springs
Wadi bottom

PRECIPITATION
Hot Spring
Major fissure →
HOT   ROCK

PRECIPITATION
LOOSE PERVIOUS ROCK
Water table
Spring
IMPERVIOUS ROCK MASS

PRECIPITATION
Springs
Stream channel
SATURATED ZONE

PRECIPITATION
Solution channels
Large spring   PERVIOUS LAYER
SOLUBLE LIMESTONE
IMPERVIOUS LAYERS

PRECIPITATION
Spring
JOINTED GRANITE
Major joint cracks

4–24   DIAGRAMS *showing some of the subsurface conditions that lead to the formation of springs.*

or mountains, allows a string of oasis settlements to exist. Springs on farms or ranches may constitute the drinking water supply and may be covered by small structures, called springhouses, to serve as cool, damp places for the storage of milk and other perishable products. While some springs are safe for human use, others, especially those which draw their water supply too directly from local surfaces, may be seriously polluted and may become sources of severe epidemics. The underlying causes of springs are many; FIG. 4–24 indicates a few of the more common possibilities.

ORDINARY WELLS • Wells, with one exception which will be discussed below, do not bring their waters to the surface. Man must dig and drill until he reaches below the water table and then must contrive some method of lifting the water to the surface. Many ways have been devised to bring the water up where man can use it. The problem of water supply from wells is a relatively simple one where the water table is close to the surface, but difficult and expensive to solve where the distance to the zone of saturation is great. The cost of "bringing in" water from a well only 100 or

4–25   DIAGRAM *showing the basic subsurface conditions necessary for the production of artesian well water. In this instance, the aquifer (water-collecting rock layer) has not been filled all the way to the intake area (A), and the aquifer is underlain, as well as capped, by impervious rock.*

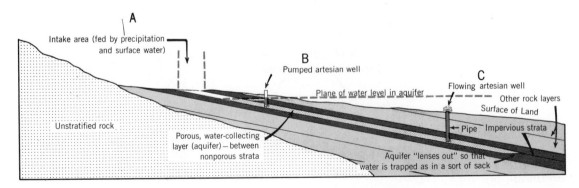

A
Intake area (fed by precipitation and surface water)
B
Pumped artesian well
Plane of water level in aquifer
C
Flowing artesian well
Other rock layers
Surface of Land
Unstratified rock
Porous, water-collecting layer (aquifer) — between nonporous strata
Pipe   Impervious strata
Aquifer "lenses out" so that water is trapped as in a sort of sack

150 feet deep may run into thousands of dollars, and this does not include the cost of pumping, which must continue as long as the well is in use.

ARTESIAN WELLS • These are wells of a special and important category. The conditions necessary for such wells are illustrated in FIG. 4-25. There must be slanting (dipping) layers of rock, the ends of which are exposed at the earth's surface. At least one of the dipping layers must be porous enough to absorb and collect water from the surface, taking the water in at the end which is exposed to precipitation and surface flow. In addition, the porous, water-collecting layer must be capped by a relatively impervious rock layer, otherwise its water will be lost through the several rock layers. As water fills the porous layer, or *aquifer*, considerable pressure is built up in that layer, especially in that part which is far removed from the intake area and is receiving the push of all the water which has collected on the up-slope of the dipping stratum. By drilling into the part of the aquifer where the water is under great pressure, man may obtain a flowing or gushing well (FIG. 4-26). If the pressure is continuous and steady, man receives artesian water without the bother and expense

SIEBENTHAL, U.S. GEOLOGICAL SURVEY

4-26

A FLOWING *artesian well in the San Luis valley of southern Colorado.*

of pumping. However, if the drilling of a well or, perhaps, too many wells causes the pressure to drop, then the water must be pumped to the surface. It is still artesian water, but the well is not a flowing well. Artesian wells occur in many parts of the earth, in dry as well as in humid regions. Obviously, they are apt to be most significant in the dry regions, for they may mean an excellent water supply even in those parts of deserts which are so arid that no springs are present. Australia is particularly famous for its resources of artesian water, the bulk of which lies in steppe and desert.

SOME WATER PROBLEMS

THE preceding discussions have shown that man is confronted with many problems as he attempts to use or to protect himself from the earth's waters. The problems are more numerous and, some of them, more serious than ever before because man himself has created many of them and has often made those of natural origin more pressing.

Oceans

Since the days when trade on the oceans first assumed real importance, there has been an international struggle for control of the sea lanes. History is replete with such references as "Britannia set out to rule the waves," "The War of 1812 was a war for the freedom of the seas," "Mussolini attempted to make an Italian lake of the Mediterranean," "Russia desired access to ice-free ports," or "The Japanese fishermen must be driven from Alaskan salmon waters."

To suppose that the struggle for control of the seas and oceans is over, merely because they are no longer effective defenses against swift ships and supersonic aircraft and rockets, is to be unrealistic. They are still vitally important sources of food and other products of which many nations are growing increasingly aware. The question of how much of the Atlantic should be controlled by the United States, for example, is a vexing one. Should it be the area within 10 miles, or 20 miles, of the shore—or should it be the area within a line drawn from Greenland to include Bermuda and the Caribbean islands and on to northeastern South America? In view of modern weapons, any line drawn for protective purposes may be of no consequence, but how about the resources of the sea and their use in both peace and war? Should the Russians or the British control the Mediterranean—or should control rest in the United Nations? Should fishermen from California have free access to the rich waters which lie off the western coast of Mexico? These and scores of other questions which might be asked present issues that are far from being settled; one can only hope that they will be answered peaceably and that the solutions will bring benefit to the largest possible numbers of the earth's people.

Streams

These are both friend and enemy to man: friend in that they serve so many of his needs; enemy in that they go on rampages of destruction or change their courses and thus confuse property limits and political boundaries, or become polluted and carry filth and disease.

FLOODS • The problem of high water is acute in densely populated regions, especially where the presence of fertile flood plains and strategic trade and manufacturing foci has lured large populations not only into the lower areas but to the very edge of the low-water channels. It has been said that the problem is not so much to keep the rivers away from the people as to keep the people out of the rivers. The magnitude of the problem is partly indicated by the fact that one serious flood

on the Missouri may take scores of lives and cause hundreds of millions of dollars in damage (FIG. 6–5). A major flood on the Hwang Ho, called "China's sorrow," may drown thousands of persons and cause untold damage to fields and sorely needed crops, not to mention the famine and pestilence which ride hard on the heels of such a flood (FIG. 7–15).

The control of river waters to the point of preventing serious floods is neither easy nor inexpensive. Normally it requires careful study and artificial controls of entire drainage basins from uppermost tributaries to stream mouths and the costs run into millions of dollars. Also, it requires the cooperation of many agencies and of the public as a whole. Yet it may be cheaper to pay for proper controls than to pay the bills for flood damage, particularly if man continues to crowd the rivers. Stream control itself is only part of the price man pays for cutting away the forests, breaking the sod of grasslands, running cultivation furrows up and down the slope instead of aligning them with the contours, and settling in the natural drainways. Remedies lie in reforestation, regrassing, contour plowing, strip cropping, construction of large and small dams—in general, in wise land-use policies operating throughout entire drainage areas, including suitable adjustments in the use of areas of flood hazard.

SOIL EROSION • There is always a certain amount of erosion under perfectly normal conditions, but it is seldom, except in dry regions, that normal erosion causes any widespread difficulties. It is when natural balances are upset and waters speed unchecked that erosion rises far above normal, and land, soils, and the works of man are then destroyed. It may be possible to rebuild rather quickly the works of man, whether bridges, highways, or homes, but destroyed soils cannot be replaced for many generations and, in most instances, they are gone for all time. When one realizes that soil is the most valuable of all the resources of the earth—coal, iron ore, and others not

4–27   A SHARP *contrast in land use caused by erosion: badly eroded farmland (especially lower right) and noneroded farmland (top left) near Maysville, Oklahoma.*

excepted—it is startling to learn that we in the United States already have allowed erosion to steal about one third of our best topsoil (FIG. 4–27). That, to use a very trite expression, "is something to think about." It is also a situation to do something about.

SHIFTING COURSES • Streams, regardless of size, are wont to change the positions of their channels unless valleys are of such a shape as to hold them rigidly within bounds, as in normal youthful valleys. In wide and flat valleys or where braided channels are common, shifts in stream courses occur frequently. One common example is the cutting off of a river bend or loop in a valley with alternating flats and steep sides (FIG. 4–28). The stream then flows directly across the neck of the former loop and the land inside the loop finds itself on the opposite side of the river channel. If the water channel is designated, as has so often been the case, as a property line or a political

boundary, disputes arise as to who owns the land and as to its political identity. Or a stream may shift its channel very gradually as a result of lateral erosion; as it eats on one side, it deposits on the other. Again, if the shifting stream channel is a boundary of some sort, arguments arise over land ownership and political position (FIG. 4–28).

The behavior of the Rio Grande in the lower portion of its course created problems international in scope. The lower course crosses a broad floodplain which contains many braided channels. The international boundary between Mexico and the United States had been defined as the main channel of the river, but, under such conditions, which channel is the main one—and where is it located? It was finally necessary for an international commission to study the problem and to reach an agreement on a boundary which would "stay put." The result is a boundary defined by

Some Water Problems | 93

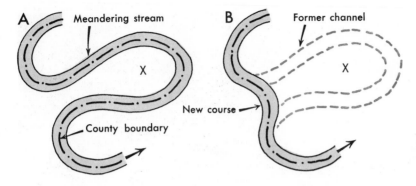

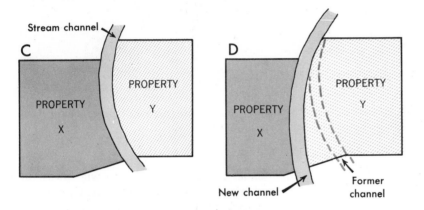

Instance of stream channel designated as a political boundary. After the stream has cut through the meander neck, the land area X lies in a different county.

Instance of stream designated as a boundary between two pieces of property. Lateral erosion has resulted in a shifting stream channel: property Y has gained area at the expense of property X .

4-28

TWO *examples of boundary problems created by shifts in position of stream channels.*

fixed points, on the basis of latitude and longitude, and not by capricious river channels.

WATER RIGHTS · In regions where water is naturally scarce or in humid areas where demands on surface and ground waters are especially heavy, there arise many conflicts over rights to water. The majority of such conflicts revolve around stream water. In the "old days," the disputes were normally settled by force; today they are settled in court and in terms of laws and procedures which have become very complicated. It is not unusual for

litigation of a given dispute to continue for several years, or even for decades. Problems of water rights are particularly complicated in connection with streams which flow through two or more states or in more than one country. California and Arizona are still not in agreement over the disposition of the Colorado river water. Also, many persons and groups in California believe that Mexico has been guaranteed too much of the flow of the Colorado river, especially in view of the fact that there is greater need for the water in California and that the cost of expensive controls, such as Hoover Dam and other works, have been borne by the United States rather than Mexico. There has been, and will continue to be, much argument on both sides.

NAVIGATION • Navigable streams which lie entirely within one country fall under the jurisdiction of the national government of that country. Streams which flow through two or more countries fall under different political control in different sections of their courses, as in the instance of the Rhine and the Danube. Under such circumstances, reciprocal agreements often cover the navigational use of the rivers. For some time, there has been an international agreement on the use of parts of certain rivers like the Rhine, the idea being to provide a "freedom of the rivers" in much the same sense as "freedom of the seas."

Navigable streams present many other problems, most of which are physical in nature. Dams and reservoirs are often necessary to insure a sufficient and steady flow; if the dams are located in navigable sections, they must be equipped with expensive locks to allow the passage of vessels (FIG. 4–29). Channels must be dredged and marked and, usually, artificial embankments must be constructed to prevent shifting of channels. Interestingly enough, portions of some rivers, the Mississippi for example, in its main channel through the delta, are made to dredge themselves. Jetties force the flow of the river through narrower channels, thus increasing the velocity of the water and hence its ability to move its load. The result is that the river literally sweeps its bed clean.

POLLUTION • Countless streams formerly clean and attractive have already been polluted by man. This results not merely from increased loads of sediment coming from man-induced erosion of the land, but also from dumping sewage, trash, and industrial wastes into the nearest convenient stream. The problem has become so serious and widespread that laws to prevent pollution of streams have been adopted in many regions. Such laws are, how-

TENNESSEE VALLEY AUTHORITY

4–29

TOWBOAT and barges (two barges fastened together) "locking through" Fort Loudoun Dam on the Tennessee river, not far downstream from Knoxville, Tennessee. The diesel-powered towboats, like the one shown, actually are "pusher" boats, but the old name remains from the time when many river boats towed, rather than pushed, barges.

ever, too few in number, and they are honored more in the breach than in the practice. Until industrial wastes and domestic sewage are properly treated, far too many of our streams will continue to resemble moving cesspools.

Underground Water

Some of the dangers already noted apply to waters within the earth as well as to those on the surface. The destruction of natural vegetation cover, abnormal erosion, and rapid water loss affect the amount and character of ground water as well as the behavior and nature of streams. When surface waters are not con-

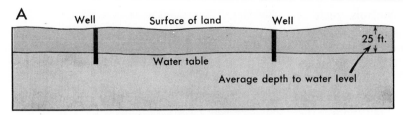

A

Water table little affected by wells.

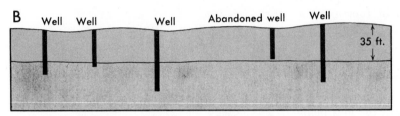

B

Too many wells: withdrawal exceeds natural replenishments.
Water table has dropped slightly.

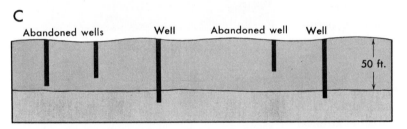

C

Water table greatly lowered: most wells abandoned;
pumping costs very high for wells still in operation.

4-30

A SEQUENCE of changes in the problem of securing water from wells in an area where the withdrawal of ground water exceeds natural replacement. A period as short as 20 years may see the change from the condition shown in A to that shown in C.

served, it is only a short time before the water table is lowered and springs and wells diminish or dry up entirely. Indiscriminate pumping also may drain the ground water reserves and lower the water table to the point where pumping costs are prohibitive (FIG. 4–30). This can happen even in humid areas. In parts of Ohio, the uses of water from the ground have become so heavy and numerous that industrial expansion is severely handicapped. This is no reflection of climate, for the annual rainfall has not changed. What it does reflect is a tremendous withdrawal of water from the ground, followed by discharge of that water into streams which carry it rapidly out of the area. What is seemingly needed is the dumping of used water onto broad "spreading grounds" where it will have an opportunity to sink back into the earth to replenish underground reserves. Another problem is the pollution of ground water. The same practices and lack of foresight which cause stream pollution are apt to render ground water unpalatable and unsafe. This is particularly true in karst regions where water can run "unfiltered" in myriad solution channels (see p. 131).

The Earth's Waters

USES OF WATER
Domestic Use
Industry
Irrigation
  THE SANTA MARIA VALLEY
Power
Transportation
Food and Raw Materials
Recreation

WATER BODIES
Oceans and Seas
  NAMES AND TERMS
  OCEAN BOTTOMS AND DEPTHS
  WATER MOVEMENTS
  ICE CONDITIONS
Lakes
  THE GREAT LAKES
  DRY LAKES

STREAMS
Humid-land Streams
  GREAT RIVERS

  STREAM PATTERNS
  WATER POWER
Streams in Dry Lands

GROUND WATER
Soil Moisture
Springs and Wells
  SPRINGS
  ORDINARY WELLS
  ARTESIAN WELLS

SOME WATER PROBLEMS
Oceans
Streams
  FLOODS
  SOIL EROSION
  SHIFTING COURSES
  WATER RIGHTS
  NAVIGATION
  POLLUTION
Underground Water

• REVIEW QUESTIONS •

1. What "waters" are included in the term "the earth's waters"?
2. List the major uses of water.
3. Why is per capita consumption of water so much greater in urban than in rural areas?
4. Explain the statement, "Heavy use of water for irrigation is not limited to arid and semi-arid regions."
5. What is meant by the statement that water bodies should be considered three-dimensional?
6. What is the landform nature of ocean bottoms?
7. Distinguish between currents, tidal waves, and tsunamis.
8. Discuss the general circulation of major ocean currents. Include causes in the discussion.

9. What would be some of the direct and indirect results if ocean currents moved counterclockwise in the Northern Hemisphere and clockwise in the Southern Hemisphere?
10. Why does the surface of the Arctic Ocean not freeze completely from shore to shore?
11. In what portions of the world are lakes most numerous? Why?
12. Explain the statement, ". . . conditions in nature work against the formation or long-continued preservation of any considerable number of lakes."
13. Determine as many possible origins of lakes or lake regions as you can.
14. What are the component parts, including natural links or connections, of the Great Lakes?

15. Give a number of examples to show relationships between settlements (and spread of settlement) and water features of different sorts.
16. Show that stream patterns affect the distributional pattern of other geographic features.
17. Describe the nature and explain the origin of a trellis drainage pattern.
18. Distinguish between "single-purpose" and "multiple-purpose" control of rivers and drainage basins on the part of man.
19. How do you account for flood damage in arid regions?
20. Distinguish between gravitational, hygroscopic, and capillary water.
21. Why is it that many areas which developed on the basis of artesian water are now suffering water shortages?
22. Certain amounts or degrees of flooding are naturally common to river valleys. What are some of the major reasons for abnormal flooding in areas inhabited by man?
23. What are some of the human implications of shifting stream courses?
24. Give a definite example of a dispute over the control and use of water.
25. What is the nature and degree of seriousness of water pollution in the area in which you live? What are the remedies?
26. Why is it that problems of water supply are serious in many areas of continuously humid climate?
27. The statement, "The world is running out of water," is commonly read and heard today. Is there justification for this statement? How can a world with so much water in it "run out of water"?

5–1

[OPPOSITE, TOP] ONE of the world's most spectacular landforms: the Grand Canyon of the Colorado river, in northwestern Arizona.

5 Introduction to Landforms

UNION PACIFIC RAILROAD

⟨ THE *surface of the earth's crust presents an amazing variety of forms. It has been wrinkled, warped, broken, and worn into many shapes. Such shapes are* landforms, *whether they be small or large, simple or complex. Their enormous variety is barely suggested by such examples as volcanoes, canyons, fiords, sand dunes, plains, tablelands, and mountain ranges. Despite the great proportion of the earth's surface that is covered by water, it is the landforms of the continents and islands that constitute the foundation of man's habitat. No other physical element is, literally, more basic.*

GEOGRAPHICAL SIGNIFICANCE OF LANDFORMS

LANDFORMS are closely and intricately related to man's use and occupation of the land. Hence, even human geography finds landform study essential. In physical geography, landform study is essential in an even more direct sense, for the shapes of the earth's surface comprise conspicuous portions of the natural scene and they are intimately associated with virtually all other physical conditions, from climate and water to soil and vegetation. For such reasons, geography, regardless of the particular portion of its field under investigation at a given time, should not neglect the primary expression of the face of the earth's crust.

In the Human Scene

To illustrate the role of landforms in human geography let us consider the following examples.

The curved island of Honshu, largest of the Japanese islands, both in area and population, is hilly and mountainous to the extent of 85 per cent of its total area. The remaining 15 per cent, comprising small, separated coastal plains and a few flat-floored mountain basins, represents nearly all of the land which can be used readily for buildings, settlements, routes of land travel, and agriculture. On these small portions are packed most of the ninety-odd millions of Japan's inhabitants. The result is that a landform map of Honshu serves admirably as a map of the distribution of population; the predominant hill and mountain country represents blanks, or near blanks, and the scattered and miniature sections of nearly level land represent the densely settled portions (FIG. 5–2). In striking contrast are the northern and central portions of the state of Iowa. Part of an extensive plain which possesses only minor landform irregularities, the surface is such as to allow distribution of population, fields, pastures, woodlands, even the layout of lines of communication and transportation, to be arranged in almost any fashion desired. This is particularly true in the central portion of the state, where the "ups and downs" of the land are decidedly minor. Central Iowa (FIG. 5–3) may not be as flat as a pancake, but compared to Honshu it would seem to be.

As another example of landforms affecting human use of the land, one may think of the westward movement in the course of settlement of the United States. Where hilly or mountainous lands lay athwart migration,

5–2   GENERALIZED landform and population patterns of the island of Honshu and adjacent parts of Japan.

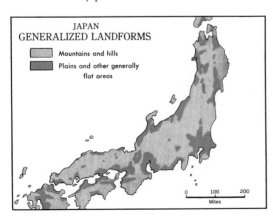

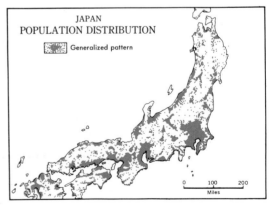

5–3   THE *fertile plains of Iowa, with a spring rainstorm approaching. This area has such low relief that only a virtually ground-level view brings out the slight roll of the countryside.*

travel was difficult and was funneled largely through a few corridors, gaps, and passes, such as the Hudson-Mohawk route in the northeast and Cumberland Gap farther south, or, in the Far West, through high saddles such as Donner Pass in the Sierra Nevada of California (FIG. 5–4). Where landforms were more subdued, as along the Atlantic Coastal Plain or in the vast interior plains of the Mississippi Basin, relative freedom of movement was possible along many lines and in many directions. Another way to show the close association between the lay of the land and human affairs may be indicated by asking a few questions: Why, in both World War I and World War II, did the German forces attack through Belgium rather than directly across the French border? Why is access from the sea easier in Maryland than it is in California? Why is the problem of railroad construction much simpler in Indiana than it is in western Pennsylvania? To answer any of these questions it is necessary to consider the landforms of each area.

In the Physical Scene

As important as landforms are in the human portion of an area, they are even more significant in the physical setting. For one thing, landforms, of and by themselves, constitute a major part of the physical setting (FIG. 5–1). This is true even in plains regions, for the first thing one thinks in examining such areas is, "These are flat countries, aren't they?" (FIG. 5–3). And, in higher and rougher regions, landforms command the view to the initial exclusion of other features. In addition to their importance in the general appearance and first impressions of a countryside, landforms are related to practically all of the other physical conditions, whether in immediately obvious fashion or not.

Geographical Significance of Landforms | 101

5-4

WINTER *scene at Donner Pass in the Sierra Nevada of California, viewed from a bridge on the main highway below Donner Peak. The highway just visible to the left of the bridge railing is part of the same highway that crosses the bridge.*

A bit to the northeast of Knoxville, Tennessee, in the famous ridge-and-valley country which lies between the Cumberland Plateau on the west and the Great Smoky Mountains on the east (FIG. 3–27), is the elongated backbone of Clinch Mountain. On the slopes of this ridge the soils are very thin and stony. This condition is related directly to the landform character, for the slopes are so steep as literally to shed their soils into the valleys which lie to either side. Contrariwise, the soils of the adjacent valleys, lying on nearly level land, are deep and nonstony.

In some areas landforms virtually control local climatic conditions. For instance, the land which lies at the eastern base of the Sierra Nevada is very dry. To the west of it lies the high and startlingly abrupt wall of the mountains. The major winds come from the west. To reach the land east of the mountain wall, the winds must rise over the mountain barrier and then descend 7000 to 10,000 feet. They lose their moisture in the ascent and in the descent they become warm, thirsty winds; and so, instead of dropping moisture, they seek to pick up more of it (FIG. 5–5). The result is a dry climate. If the landform barrier were removed, the moist winds from off the Pacific Ocean would be less modified as they progressed eastward over the land and they would bring considerably more rain. In the same manner, removal of the coastal and near-coastal barrier of the southern Andes would result in more precipitation in the arid and semiarid portions of western and southern Argentina.

Again, to exemplify the relationships between landforms and other physical elements, we may examine the drainage conditions of the Irrawaddy Delta. This large delta, in the southern part of Burma, is a land of sluggish streams, extensive swamps, and many coastal marshes, lagoons, and tidal flats. So low and featureless is the land that the abundant rains and the river waters which come from the north have little chance to drain away. To the west and northwest of the delta is a hilly and partly mountainous region, the Arakan Yoma. There, swamps, lagoons, and other types of "wet spots" are absent even though rainfall is more copious than in the delta lands. Slopes are so steep that the surface waters, whether in thin sheets, tiny rivulets, creeks, or rivers, drain away rapidly to the bordering lower lands.

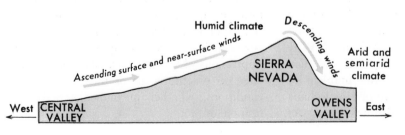

5-5

GENERALIZED *profile across part of the Sierra Nevada, in California, showing effect of the mountain barrier on winds and climates.*

LANDFORM CLASSIFICATION

WHEN one examines the shapes of the surface of the earth's crust, it is not long before he recognizes that some forms are relatively large, or *major landforms*, whereas others are comparatively small, or *minor landforms*. These major and minor landforms of the earth occur in intricate patterns and in nearly an infinite variety of shapes, both over the exposed sweeps of the continents and islands and in the depths of the oceans. Our concern here is primarily with those of the continents and islands, although at times there will be reason to examine those which lie beneath the earth's waters, that is, the *submarine landforms*, as opposed to the *subaerial landforms*. The major landforms of the continents and islands are *plains, plateaus, hills,* and *mountains*. The minor landforms, almost innumerable, are *valleys, ridges, knolls, deltas, mesas,* and like features.

Major Landforms

PLAINS • Plains are comparatively level areas, most of which lie relatively close to sea level (FIG. 5-6). More technically, they normally are regions of low altitude and low local relief. Low altitude means commonly less than 1000 feet above sea level and rarely more than 2000 feet. A few plains exceed the latter altitude figure and they may be distinguished by the term *high plains*, particularly if they represent the continuation, without any major surface break, of plains of lower altitude, as do the Great Plains of the United States (FIG. 5-7). Low local relief means that local differences in altitude are comparatively minor, often less than 100 feet and in nearly all instances less than 500 feet. The Gulf Coastal Plain of the United States (FIG. 5-7), for example, rises very gradually from the edge of the Gulf of Mexico; even at its most northern extent, where it touches southern Illinois, it is less than 500 feet above sea level. At the same time its surface is so nearly level that local differences in altitude (local relief) in excess of 100 feet are unusual. In contrast, in high mountainous regions, such as the Peruvian Andes, altitudes of 13,000 feet or more are attained within a few miles of the coast, and the altitudinal difference from the bottom to the top of a single canyon may be 5000 feet, or more.

PLATEAUS • Plateaus are, in a sense, "plains up in the air." They are *tablelands* characterized by relatively high altitudes, usually in excess of 2000 feet, and, unless their surfaces have been deeply cut by numerous streams, they are relatively level on top (FIG. 5-6). Local relief is usually less than 500 feet. The Colorado Plateau (FIG. 5-7), for example, has an average altitude of 7000 to 8000 feet above the far-away tidewater of the Pacific, but the eye may wander across many thousands of square

5-6 GENERALIZED *theoretical profile, showing the relationships among plains, plateaus, hills, and mountains.*

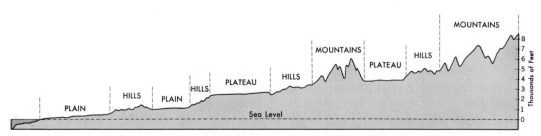

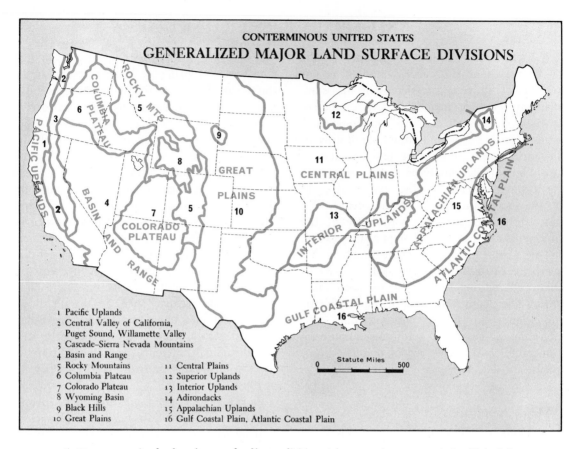

CONTERMINOUS UNITED STATES
GENERALIZED MAJOR LAND SURFACE DIVISIONS

1 Pacific Uplands
2 Central Valley of California,
  Puget Sound, Willamette Valley
3 Cascade–Sierra Nevada Mountains
4 Basin and Range
5 Rocky Mountains   11 Central Plains
6 Columbia Plateau   12 Superior Uplands
7 Colorado Plateau   13 Interior Uplands
8 Wyoming Basin   14 Adirondacks
9 Black Hills   15 Appalachian Uplands
10 Great Plains   16 Gulf Coastal Plain, Atlantic Coastal Plain

5–7 THE major land surface, or landform, divisions of conterminous area of the United States.

miles of its surface without encountering more than minor interruptions in the form of small canyons (FIG. 5–8). In the Grand Canyon section of the Colorado Plateau, the formerly tablelike surface has been cut up into very deep gorges and either flat-topped or knife-edged ridges. This section is a *dissected plateau*. If dissection is fairly pronounced, and local relief exceeds 500 feet a dissected plateau warrants the name of hills. If dissection is extremely pronounced, and local relief exceeds 2000 feet, a dissected plateau warrants the name of erosional mountains. Dissected plateaus, possessing much greater local relief than undissected ones, constitute barriers which are more difficult for man to cross.

Other characteristics of plateaus are found

on their margins. Some, like the Colorado Plateau, have steep cliffs or escarpments on one or more sides but give way to hills and mountains on the other edges. Some, like the Bolivian Plateau or the very high plateaus of Tibet, are completely encompassed by high, rugged mountains.

MOUNTAINS • Mountain country has nothing in common with plains and little in common with plateaus, unless they are extremely and deeply dissected plateaus. Mountainous territory is marked by comparatively high altitudes (about 3000 feet at the minimum), relatively high local relief (usually at least 3000 feet), long slopes, and small summit areas (FIG. 5–6). For example, the previously mentioned Sierra Nevada has crests and peaks

5–8   OBLIQUE *air photo of part of the Colorado Plateau near Winslow, Arizona. This is a tableland, only very slightly dissected. The one canyon that does appear is the famous Diablo Canyon, about 225 feet deep and 500 feet wide in this section of its course.*

which are 13,000 to 14,000 feet, or more, above sea level. Mount Whitney reaches an altitude of 14,495 feet above sea level. From one of the adjacent lower sections, just to the east of Mount Whitney, to the top of the peak itself is a rise of about 11,000 feet (FIG. 5–9).

Another trait is particularly useful in distinguishing mountains from hilly regions. True mountain lands usually are characterized by a marked and readily visible *vertical zonation of landscapes*; hilly lands do not possess this condition. An instance of vertical zonation owing to altitudinal change in mountains is to be seen in the Mount Orizaba area of Mexico. This area lies in the southern part of the Eastern Sierra Madre Range, about on a line between Mexico City and the Gulf port of Veracruz. Much of the land up to an altitude of 10,000 feet is cleared and devoted to agriculture. In the lower parts are crops typical of the rainy tropics: rubber is grown up to 1000 or 1500 feet, sugar cane and bananas up

to some 5500 feet, coffee between 1000 and 5000 feet, and rice up to about 3400 feet. In the upper portion of the agricultural area, or zone, are found crops typical of the mid-latitudes. Their presence is a reflection of the cooler temperatures caused by increased altitude. Wheat is grown from 6000 to approximately 10,000 feet, apples from 6000 to about 8000 feet, and corn and beans are grown up to nearly 10,000 feet. Above the agricultural limits, the land continues upward to 18,700 feet. Here, too, zoning is marked. Forests extend from 10,000 to 13,000 feet, with a transition from broadleaf trees in the lower parts to pines in the upper portion. From 13,000 to about 14,500 feet is a zone of mountain meadows. Above the meadows is the zone of permanent ice and snow. Thus from bottom to top the Orizaba area is one zone after another; an agricultural zone divided between "tropical" and "temperate" crops, a forest zone, a zone of alpine meadows above the

Landform Classification | 105

5–9 THE steep eastern front of the Mount Whitney section of the Sierra Nevada, California. The low, hilly ridge in the middle foreground is completely separate from the Sierra and is a local interruption in the floor of the Owens valley. The immediate foreground shows part of an irrigated ranch being used as a cattle-feeding area.

5–10 GENERALIZED profile of the Ecuadorean Andes at the latitude of Quito (0°13′ S), showing some aspects of vertical zonation in tropical mountains. Information appearing to the right and left of the profile applies to both sides of the mountains. (Diagram based mainly on data supplied by Henry J. Bruman)

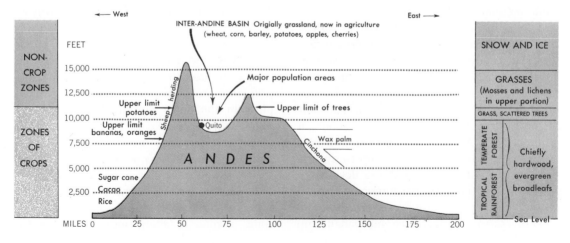

5-11 A

5-11 B

5-11 C

A. Glacially rounded and wooded hill country of northern Vermont.

B. Hilly and forested land along Lake Superior shore, part of the glaciated Laurentian Shield, near Marquette, Michigan.

C. Scrub-covered (chaparral) hills of the so-called Santa Monica Mountains, near Los Angeles, California.

D. Nearly barren desert hills, in the Mojave Desert, near Yermo, California. Creosote bushes dot the alluvial fan slope in the foreground.

A: EAGLE, STANDARD OIL CO. (N.J.)
B, C, D: R. M. GLENDINNING

5-11 D

tree line, and a final zone of snow and bitter cold. It is almost as though one had journeyed from the tropical rainforest, through the mid-latitudes, and on into the polar lands.

In the Ecuadorean Andes, along the equator, is another excellent example of vertical contrast in mountain geography (FIG. 5–10). It will be noted again that there is zonation of crops and natural vegetation alike.

HILLS • Hilly country is, in a loose sense, a "baby" edition of mountain country (FIG. 5–6). Altitude is appreciable (500 feet is an absolute minimum), and local relief is marked but usually less than 2000 feet, though more than 500 feet. Slopes may be as steep or steeper than mountain slopes, but they are much shorter. And often, despite comparatively small summit areas, there is more relatively level land on the ridge tops than is characteristic of mountainous lands. However, there is no readily discernible vertical zonation. The Berkshires of western Massachusetts, the South China hill country, the southern uplands of Scotland, and the ridge-and-valley area of the upper Tennessee Basin are typical examples of what is meant by hilly lands. FIGURE 5–11 provides four views of hilly conditions.

Minor Landforms

The smaller shapes and convolutions of the top of the earth's crust are too numerous to count. It is they, with their host of varying combinations of slopes, which constitute the details of the major landforms and which provide highly localized individuality to the lay of the land. For example, the land which extends a considerable distance north from the Gulf of Mexico is entirely composed of a wide variety of minor forms. Some of them are shore forms built and shaped by waves and currents, such as offshore sand bars, strips of sandy beach, and muddy tidal flats. Others are the low sprawling lands of the Mississippi Delta, marked by islands and tongues of land

which rise barely above sea level and the levels of the many swamps and bayous. Farther up the Mississippi, north of the delta, are the steep but low bluffs which flank the alluvial plain of the valley bottom. Entering the valley bottom plain are many tributary valleys of several different shapes, and in between them are lands which vary from narrow and steep-sided ridges to broad, gently rolling slopes too subdued to call ridges. All of these features are a part of the local individuality which characterizes the surface configuration of the Gulf Coastal Plain.

Another example of local detail in the lay of the land is seen in Norway. This country, with only minor exceptions in the south and far north, is mountainous. Simply to call Nor-

5–12

THE head of Geirangerfiord, one of the many deep fiords on the rocky Atlantic coast of Norway. Note the small area of level or nearly level land and the steep valley sides.

way a mountain country would not bring out the details of the surface which one travels across or sees from a boat offshore or from a vantage point on the land. Many valleys, large and small, lead down and into, even under, the sea. Most of them are overhung by steep cliffs and marked by rocky steps which interrupt the otherwise fairly level valley floors. The lower parts of these valleys are drowned by the in-reaching sea to give Norway its famous fiords (FIG. 5–12). At the heads of the fiords the in-tumbling streams have built little delta plains in the form of gently sloping fans. Between successive fiords rise high, sometimes tablelike, buttresses of solid bedrock. And along the outer coast are hundreds of solid rock islets, shaped much like eggs half-submerged in the salty waters.

SHAPING OF LANDFORMS

Primary Processes

LANDFORMS do not just happen; each shape or combination of shapes, whether it be the Alps or a cluster of sand dunes, is the result of much work. Some landforms are shaped chiefly by processes operating from within the earth, others are shaped mainly by processes and agents working on top of the earth's crust. The shaping which is carried on from within the earth is accomplished by *diastrophism* and *vulcanism*; that carried on from without is the work of *weathering, erosion,* and *deposition.* Processes operating from within are *endogenous* processes, while those operating from without are *exogenous* processes.

Shaping from Within: Endogenous Processes

DIASTROPHISM • The earth's crust is under constant strain and stress. At times, and in certain places, it yields to these forces. When it does, the result is a change, major or minor, slow or cataclysmic, in the shape of its surface.

Under certain conditions the earth's surface wrinkles, or folds, much like the skin of a drying apple. This *folding* may be simple and produce broad and open forms, like those of a gigantic corrugated iron roof (FIG. 5–13A), or it may be complex and result in tight folds, much like those of a closed accordion. In some regions, the folding has been so complex

5–13   A, B. *Two types and degrees of folding of the earth's crust. C. Simple warping of the earth's crust. D. Block-faulting of the earth's crust. Elevated blocks form hills or mountains; depressed blocks form valleys and trenches.*

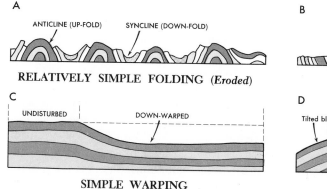

A

ANTICLINE (UP-FOLD)   SYNCLINE (DOWN-FOLD)

RELATIVELY SIMPLE FOLDING (*Eroded*)

B

COMPLEX FOLDING (*Eroded*)

C

UNDISTURBED   DOWN-WARPED

SIMPLE WARPING

D

Tilted block   Down-dropped block (graben)   Up-thrust block (horst)

U N E R O D E D   S U R F A C E

Fault plane

BLOCK-FAULTING

5–14

THE *Hebgen fault scarp which appeared as a result of the Montana earthquake of August 17, 1959.*

that the crustal corrugations have been tipped and laid at an angle on top of one another (FIG. 5–13B). Parts of the Alps show this latter condition, while the simpler type of folding is exemplified in several sections of the Appalachians. Regardless of the degree of complexity, each up-fold is called an *anticline* and each down-fold a *syncline*. Anticlines and synclines, as measured along and at right angles to the folds, may vary from a few feet to many miles in length and breadth.

Parts of the earth's crust yield to stress by *warping*. This is merely a bending or flexing, without folding, of the crustal materials. Ex-

amination of FIGS. 5–13A and 5–13C will indicate the essential differences between warping and folding. Examples of warping on a large scale are found in the North Sea region and in the Lake Superior district. Crustal warping in the former has resulted in the slow drowning of what were formerly low plains. Within the period of recorded history, English shore villages and farms have had to be abandoned to the sea. The Lake Superior basin is being warped in such a manner as to raise the northern shore slowly and lower the southern. These movements are marked on the north by uplifted beaches, and at places along the south shore by submerged tree stumps and drowned river mouths.

When the crust neither folds nor warps, but still gives way to interior stresses, fracturing, or *faulting*, takes place (FIG. 5–13D). It is as though the crust were comprised of large and small earth blocks, each separated from the others by huge cracks along which the blocks are forced to move. Some blocks go up, some go down, and some move sideways. In fact, a given block, or earth compartment, may be moved up and laterally at the same time and another moved both down and laterally during the same disturbance. As one block moves against another, a jarring, irregular set of tremors is induced and transmitted through the earth materials; these are *earthquakes*, the result, not the cause, of earth fracturing. When the movement of an earth block is only slightly upward, only a very minor landform, such as a small *fault scarp*, may be produced (FIG. 5–14); greater movements may result in huge blocky mountains like the Sierra Nevada, or, if the movement is downward, in large trenches in the surface of the earth, like Death Valley.

VULCANISM • The most readily recognized forms produced by vulcanism are volcanoes, especially those like Fujiyama or Vesuvius, which have been built by lavas and ashes into huge conical mountains (FIG. 5–15A). Others, although low and broad, like the dome form

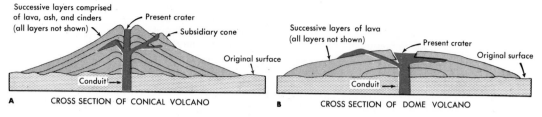

Successive layers comprised
of lava, ash, and cinders
(all layers not shown)

Present crater

Subsidiary cone

Original surface

Conduit

A CROSS SECTION OF CONICAL VOLCANO

Successive layers of lava
(all layers not shown)

Present crater

Original surface

Conduit

B CROSS SECTION OF DOME VOLCANO

5–15   TWO *major types of volcanoes.*

of Mauna Loa in Hawaii, still are conspicuous landform features (FIG. 5–15B).

Vulcanism does not always produce volcanoes. Molten rock may simply issue from great cracks and spread in huge laterally moving *lava flows* across the land. These molten *extrusions* may produce extensive lava caps which cover thousands of square miles, as in the Columbia Plateau of northwestern United States (FIG. 5–7).

In other regions, the molten rock, squeezed under tremendous pressures, may not reach the surface to construct either volcanoes or lava sheets. However, it moves within the cracks and crevices of the crust as *intrusive* materials. Sometimes it is forced as layers, or *sills*, be-

tween the strata of other rocks, or it may rise and fill earth fissures to form *dikes*, or, again, it may simply collect in large subterranean *masses*. The fact that sills, dikes, and masses are not formed at the surface does not necessarily mean that they have no landform significance, for later, as overlying materials are worn away, such intrusive features may be exposed at the surface as definitely visible forms (FIG. 5–16). In the instance of subterranean masses, whether they ever become exposed or not, rock layers above may be deformed by them to create *structural domes*, which do have expression in the surface scene (FIG. 5–17).

It is in such ways that forces working from

5–16   STONE MOUNTAIN, *near Atlanta, Georgia, is a huge mass of gray granite which has been exhumed by erosion to become a prominent minor landform. The rounded form is largely the result of "leafing-off," or exfoliation, of the granite.*

HILLERS, U.S. GEOLOGICAL SURVEY

Shaping of Landforms | 111

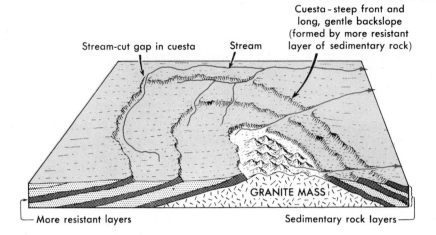

Stream-cut gap in cuesta   Stream   Cuesta - steep front and long, gentle backslope (formed by more resistant layer of sedimentary rock)

GRANITE MASS

More resistant layers   Sedimentary rock layers

5–17

THIS *generalized block diagram of the Black Hills, South Dakota, shows an eroded structural dome.*

below, whether diastrophic or volcanic, or both, change the face of the earth's crust.

Shaping from Without: Exogenous Processes

WEATHERING • Just as paint on the sides of a house or the surface materials of a highway weather under exposure to the elements, so do the materials which comprise the upper portion of the earth's crust. This *weathering* is simply the breaking up of the rocks by chemical and mechanical means. If it is accomplished by chemical actions, it is called *decomposition*; if done mechanically, it is known as *disintegration*. Working together, the two processes change exposed bedrock into pieces of rock, and then further weather the pieces into materials of progressively smaller and smaller size—essentially, it is a business of making little ones out of big ones. The resultant unconsolidated rock material is called *regolith*. It is thus that earth materials are made ready for the erosive agents such as running water, and made available also for evolution into soils.

Decomposition, or chemical weathering, is carried on by *oxidation, carbonation, hydration,* and *solution*. When rocks go to pieces by oxidizing, it is because oxygen in the air unites

with certain elements in the rocks to form oxides. For example, iron may unite with oxygen to form iron oxides giving rise to the familiar rusty color which is seen in many earth materials. As this oxidation takes place, the original material is weakened and rotted. Under carbonation, certain elements unite in new combinations with carbon dioxide, the latter being common in natural ground water in the form of a carbonic acid solution. The element calcium, for instance, may join with carbon dioxide to form calcium carbonate; this chemical reaction weathers the rock apart. Hydration is the taking on of water in chemical combination; the accompanying "swelling," or increase in bulk, causes the rocks so affected to "give" and fall apart. Solution represents the removal of materials which cement rock particles together. These materials, taken into true solution by the water in the ground in the same way that sugar is dissolved in hot coffee, leave behind rocks which are greatly weakened and often porous. Chemical weathering is at a maximum in those parts of the earth which are always hot and moist, such as the Congo Basin. It is least effective in regions marked by extended cold and drought, such as the Bolivian Plateau. While the foregoing processes have been given separate discussion, it must be remembered that they may all go on together in the same rocks at the same time; thus, the rocks of the Congo Basin are acted upon simultaneously by oxidation, carbonation, hydration, and solution.

Disintegration occurs when rocks are broken up by mechanical means. There is actual physical breakage and while the materials are not normally pounded to pieces, as a brick may be broken by a sledge hammer, the results are much the same. Not all aspects of disintegration will be discussed here, but mention will be made of the more important ones. One of the common means of disintegration is *frost action*. Water enters the cracks and crevices of rocks and then, in freezing, expands to pry the rocks apart. If alternate freezing and thawing are the rule, as in high mountains and in polar lands, the amount of regolith produced by frost action is considerable, and it is ordinarily comprised of sharp and angular fragments. Another type of mechanical breakdown is caused by *differential heating* and *cooling*. This results in unequal expansion and contraction of the rocks and causes them to be shattered. For example, a bedrock surface exposed to intense heating by the sun will expand, but the top materials will expand more rapidly than those underneath; something has to "give" and the materials are loosened. At night, or under a sudden, cooling shower, the materials will contract, but, again, the process is differential and the top rock will shrink at a faster rate than the rock directly underneath. Then further breakage occurs. Weathering of this type is not uncommon where rocks are exposed to arid climates, especially if the climate is also hot.

Perhaps the grossest form of mechanical weathering is *diastrophic weathering*. In the formation of a huge anticline, for instance, the rocks at the top of the fold are severely cracked and broken by the stretching incident to the formation of the anticlinal crest; or, in vulcanism, lavas may force their way between rock layers or into cracks and split and pry the rocks apart. All such mechanical breakages as

noted above, abetted by chemical weathering, are constantly at work weathering the bedrock into regolith and weathering the pieces and particles of the regolith into still smaller pieces.

Where plants and burrowing animals are present *organic weathering* operates. Expanding roots ferret out cracks and crevices and split the rocks; burrowing animals wedge, pry, and remove materials: working together, organisms may play a considerable part in rock breakage.

EROSION AND DEPOSITION • Erosion is primarily a process of "pick up and carry" of weathered materials. As earth materials are carried they may be used further as grinding and scouring tools to wear away and break up other rocks; this is *corrasion* or *abrasion*. For example, corrasion occurs when boulders and finer materials are rolled, bounced, and dragged against the bed of a stream and against one another. The *agents of erosion* are *moving water, moving air*, and *moving ice*. Accent is placed on motion, for without it the agents have no power to do work; stagnant water can cut no valleys, still air can carry no dust nor shift any sand, and stationary ice can move no regolith nor cut and scour bedrock surfaces.

Along the continental shores and over the vast stretches of the land, it is moving water which holds first place in erosive activities. This is true even in deserts, as indicated by the very common occurrence of such water-cut or water-deposited forms as arroyos (wadies) and alluvial fans (see pp. 135 and 138). The importance of water is greater in lands with humid climates and hence with a more abundant and reliable supply of water. As moving water carries on its work, it gnaws, batters, and etches the original landforms into new shapes. Following and accompanying such actions, it piles up, or *deposits* layer on layer, the transported materials to create still other shapes. The variety of water-eroded (*degradational*) or water-deposited (*aggradational*) forms may not be infinite, but it often seems so. Water-cut forms vary from wave-eroded cliffs and sea caves to deep canyons and broad, open valleys; water-deposited forms range from deltas and alluvial fans to wide blankets of river floodplain materials and extensive coastal plains. Almost anywhere, either in miniature or in large form, one can see shapes which have been dug out or built up by water "on the move."

Air in motion, or wind, has much less power to transport materials than does water or moving ice. Wind has the ability, however, to pick up fine dusts (*loess*) and, at times, sands. The dusts may be carried to great heights and scattered over extensive areas (FIG. 5–18), but the sands are seldom lifted more than a few feet from the surface over or against which the wind is blowing. In general, coarser materials such as sands or, occasionally, gravels are rolled, bounced, and slid, rather than carried aloft. Yet locally, the forms produced by wind erosion (*aeolian erosion*) and by the deposition of wind-blown materials may be con-

5–18

AN *approaching dust storm in the western United States.*

spicuous and dominant. Rocks are scoured and sandblasted (*wind corrasion*) into new and often fantastic shapes, and materials are removed to create depressions; where materials are deposited, they may form individual dunes or an entire sea of wavelike dune ridges (FIG. 5–19). In several instances it cannot be said

5–19 A   A SHALLOW *basin created by wind erosion in the western Great Plains. The comparative size of the horse and pedestal remnant give an idea of the amount of material removed by the wind in creating this blow-out.*

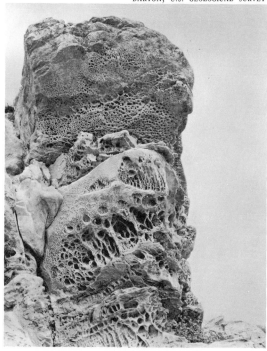

that the results of wind work are merely local. An example is the North China Plain, which has received large loessal accretions for many thousands of years, as well as alluvial materials deposited directly by the waters of the Hwang Ho.

Small cakes of ice, grinding and rubbing against a beach or the base of a rocky cliff, produce minor erosion effects; ice moving in tongues or sheets over the land as a glacier produces both minor and major forms. As soon as glacial ice begins to move, at snail's pace or slower, it carries on two kinds of work—erosion and deposition. Both result in definite landforms. As "scour forms," one may cite the gouged-out valleys (*fiords*) of Norway or the unequally scraped surface of Canada's vast Laurentian Shield (FIG. 5–20). For depositional forms, the curved ridges of loose glacial debris near Chicago or the plains comprised of out-washed materials in parts of southern Wisconsin will serve as examples (FIG. 6–26). Any area which has been "worked over" by moving ice presents a land surface that is drastically modified from its preglacial appearance.

5–19 B

WEATHERED and wind-corraded sandstone bluff near Livingston, Montana.

5–19 C   OBLIQUE air photo of sand dunes in the Colorado Desert, between Yuma, Arizona, and El Centro, California.

Shaping of Landforms | 115

5–20   A GLACIALLY scoured bedrock area in the Labrador section of the Laurentian Shield. Note the many lakes and ponds in the "scour depressions." The sinuous ridge angling across the area is an esker, one of the depositional landforms of continental glaciers. (From The Geographical Review, July 1946, published by the American Geographical Society)

ROCKS

THE earth materials which are deformed by diastrophic movements and distorted and stacked up as a result of vulcanism, are rocks; so are the materials which are rotted and broken up by weathering and cut into or deposited by the agents of erosion and deposition. Over many parts of the continents, loose rocks and bedrock constitute a very conspicuous portion of the landscape, especially in deserts with their scant cloak of vegetation, in high mountains particularly above tree line, and in regions of pronounced glacial scour, where the forest is much broken and even regolith is scarce (FIG. 5–20).

Composition of Rocks

All rocks are comprised of minerals. For example, common limestone is mainly the mineral known as calcium carbonate plus, as a rule, such other minerals as quartz and feldspar. Some rocks are comprised of only one mineral—a piece of quartz, for example.

The minerals which constitute rocks are, in turn, composed of chemical elements. In quartz, two primary elements are involved— silicon and oxygen. Thus quartz is mainly silicon dioxide although, if impure, it may contain such other elements as iron, gold, silver,

◇◇◇◇◇◇◇◇◇◇◇◇◇◇◇◇◇◇◇◇◇◇◇◇◇◇◇◇◇◇◇

TABLE 5

Composition of Rocks

(*Read either from top to bottom or from bottom to top*)

ROCKS
(limestone, granite, sandstone, etc.)

↑
↓

MINERALS
(especially quartz, feldspars, ferromagnesians)

↑
↓

ELEMENTS
(especially oxygen, silicon, aluminum, iron, plus calcium, potassium, sodium, magnesium)

---

and copper. It was noted that a rock may consist of only one mineral; in the same fashion, where elements occur in the free, or pure, state, a rock may be composed of only one element. A piece of pure copper or a gold nugget are examples, for such pieces are rocks, yet contain only one element each. Table 5 shows the relationships just noted and adds certain other information.

Rock Classes

IGNEOUS ROCKS • All rocks are either *igneous*, *sedimentary*, or *metamorphic*. Igneous rocks are those which are molten or have cooled and become solid after being in the molten state. Common examples are granite, syenite (sometimes called "pink granite"), and basalt. Such rocks are formed within the earth, where temperatures are high enough to melt solid rock. These are the intrusive and extrusive materials which were mentioned in the discussion of vulcanism. The intrusives, being buried, cool very slowly. As they cool and solidify, there is time for crystals to grow to relatively large sizes and hence the rocks are usually coarse-grained, like granite. The extrusives, exposed to the air, cool more rapidly and they are normally fine-grained like basalt. If igneous rocks contain a large amount of quartz, they are usually light-colored, like granite. Those which are high in the ferromagnesium minerals are dark, like basalt.

SEDIMENTARY ROCKS • These, as the name implies, are comprised of sediments, or particles. They represent the accumulation through time of layer on layer of deposited materials. Some are carried and laid down by the wind, others by moving water or glaciers. Most of them are finally laid down in the great accumulation basins of the oceans. Each depositional layer is a *stratum*, and a series of them are *strata*; hence sedimentary rocks are normally referred to as *stratified*. The more common sedimentary rocks are sandstone, limestone, shale, and conglomerate. Sandstone is mainly comprised of grains of sand. If the strata are thin and waferlike, the sandstone is said to be *thin-bedded*; if the layers are thick, the sandstone is called *massive*. Limestone is chiefly an accumulation of small limy particles from skeletal remains of small sea organisms. It, too, may be thin-bedded or massive. Shale is a collection of particles of clay and silt, or muds. Conglomerate is, literally, a conglomeration of other rocks. The English refer to it, reasonably enough, as "puddingstone." It is comprised of boulders and gravels set in a filler, or matrix, of sands, silts, and clays. Pieces of it strongly resemble coarse, manmade concrete, both in color and textural variations.

METAMORPHIC ROCKS • These are rocks which have undergone marked change from their original condition. Most of the change is the result of heat and pressure incident to burial within the earth, abetted by the cementing action of underground waters and quite often by crustal deformation. If granite, an igneous rock, is subjected to such conditions over a long enough period, it becomes the metamorphic rock known as banded granite, or gneiss. Sandstone, a sedimentary rock, will change slowly into quartzite, limestone into marble, and shale into slate. Thus, the common slate blackboard has had a long and eventful history. First it was mud; then the mud changed into sedimentary bedrock, or shale. The shale, acted upon over a long period by more heat and pressure, gradually evolved into the metamorphic slate. All this took millions of years; if great crustal deformation took place, the accompanying increased temperatures and pressures resulted in a relative speeding up of the change from shale to slate.

CONSOLIDATED AND UNCONSOLIDATED ROCKS • When earth materials are hard and compact to the point of being solid bedrock, they are called consolidated or indurated. If loose, *they are still rocks*, but unconsolidated or nonindurated. Actually, then, a handful of sand is rock, just as much as a piece of bedrock sandstone or a chunk of granite. In discussing rocks or the landforms which they comprise in part, there is need for careful distinction between the "consolidateds" and the "unconsolidateds." Obviously, it makes a difference whether a given deposit is mud, shale, or slate; it makes a difference whether a hill is a loose collection of sand grains or of massive sandstone bedrock; and, in terms of erosional accomplishments, it makes a difference whether a stream is cutting into loose clays or into solid, massive granite.

LANDFORM ANALYSIS: EMPIRICAL VS. SCIENTIFIC

Types of Analysis

IN DEALING with landforms as part of the fundamental geography of an area, there are two methods of attack. One is simply to describe a given landform as it appears to the eye. This is the *empirical* method. The landform known as a *mesa* may be described as possessing a more or less circular and nearly level top, encircling cliffs, and relatively gentle slopes which lead away from the base of the cliffs (FIG. 5–21A). This method shows the form, but it provides no understanding of how the form got to be that way. It is much as though one described the outer shape of a particular house, but did so with no indication of how that house was built, step by step, from foundation to roof.

Another, and much more meaningful, method is one which not only describes the form as it is at the present time, but indicates how the form was attained. This is the *scientific* method. Using this method, one may point out that the mesa mentioned above was once part of a plateau which possessed a hard cap rock (FIG. 5–21B, part 1). Streams gnawed their way back into the plateau in such a manner as gradually to isolate a portion of it from the rest. This resulted in a flat-topped remnant surrounded by cliffs which marked the existence of the hard cap rock. Materials falling from the cliffs and others washed down by rains slowly built up an "apron" which extended out, at relatively gentle slope, from the cliffs. Thus, the mesa was created (FIG. 5–21B, part 5). Examined from such a point of view, one appreciates that "mesa" is more than a form name; it is also a term which implies a certain kind of origin, or genesis. Involved in its genesis are different kinds and arrangements of earth materials, the processes which shaped them, and a given amount of work accomplished, step by step, by the processes collectively.

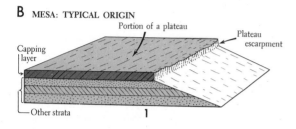

A MESA: TYPICAL PROFILE

Table top — Cliffs — Apron of loose materials

B MESA: TYPICAL ORIGIN

Portion of a plateau — Plateau escarpment

Capping layer

Other strata

1

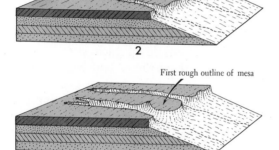

Streams cut canyons into plateau

2

First rough outline of mesa

3

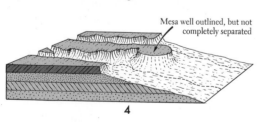

Mesa well outlined, but not completely separated

4

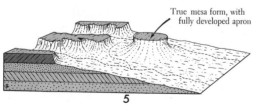

True mesa form, with fully developed apron

5

5-21

A. Typical mesa profile. B. Stages in the origin and development of one kind of mesa.

Structure, Process, and Stage

By means of the scientific method, any landform may be analyzed and comprehended, not only in terms of its present shape, but also in terms of each phase of its evolution. Landform analysis of this sort involves consideration of *structure*, *process*, and *stage*.

Structure refers to the nature and arrangement of the earth materials which are being shaped, whether they are bedrock, unconsolidated rock, or a combination of both. In the instance of the mesa, the structure consists of layers of nearly horizontal sedimentary bedrock with the top layer hard enough to be relatively resistant to weathering and erosion (FIG. 5–21B).

Another example of the meaning of structure is to be seen in the Nashville Basin of Tennessee. Geologically, the region is a broad structural dome. It represents layers of sedimentary bedrock which, under crustal stress, were slowly deformed to create a shape somewhat similar to an inverted bowl (FIG. 5–22). As weathering and erosion went to work on this crustal "blister," they first wore away the higher portion. Working more deeply, they uncovered strata which are comparatively soft. These less resistant rocks (limestones) eroded to form the lowlands. Because the resistant rocks of the domal structure slant (dip) outward from the center, their steep margins form an encircling rim whose edges face inward toward the central portion. Thus, if one begins in the center and travels outward, he crosses a gently rolling plain (softer rocks), climbs up onto a steplike rim (harder rocks), and then, if proceeding eastward, makes another step-

NASHVILLE BASIN — CUMBERLAND PLATEAU

West — RIM — HIGHLAND RIM — East

5-22

A DIAGRAMMATIC cross section of the Nashville Basin, Tennessee, and vicinity (see text discussion).

Landform Analysis: Empirical vs. Scientific | 119

like ascent to a plateau surface (FIG. 5–22). Certainly, in a region of this sort one cannot appreciate the character and geographic pattern of the landforms unless he understands the controlling part played by the underlying structure.

Process refers to all the activities and agents which shape a given structure. To come back to the mesa, the processes involved are weathering, both disintegration and decomposition, and running water. Together, they are the shapers or carvers which have etched out the mesa form from the structure.

Process may also be illustrated by reference to a kind of sand dune. The dune has much the appearance of a breaking wave (FIG. 5–23). It owes its existence to loose sands which have been collected and shaped by winds. The winds slide, bounce, and roll the sand grains up the gentle side of the dune ridge and then drop and collect them at a steep angle in the lee of the wind action. Such action causes the dune to migrate, but it also causes it to retain the same form as it makes its slow journey over the land.

Stage refers to the amount of work accomplished by the processes in the shaping of the structure. Inasmuch as all work cannot be done at once, it is accomplished in sequence, or in "stages." At first the mesa, for example, was only roughly outlined and partly separated from the parent plateau surface (FIG. 5–21B, parts 2, 3, 4). Next, it was definitely outlined and completely separated, as soon as stream valleys had been cut to form parts of its margin and tributary valleys had been etched out "behind" to complete the isolation. Finally,

the isolated and cliffed form was modified by regolith falling and being washed from above (FIG. 5–21B, part 5). Thus there are, in a sense, three *major* stages which may be distinguished in the evolution of the mesa.

Further ramifications of the concept of stage may be illustrated by a stream valley created in a region of humid climate and hence by permanently running water. Let it be supposed, in this example, that the structure is uniform, that all the materials into which the stream is cutting are essentially the same from top to bottom. At first, the stream will erode vertically to carve a valley which, in profile, has the shape of a **V**. The stream is greatly aided by the work of rainwash, which widens the valley by wearing away the slopes. This is the first major stage. When the stream has cut vertically as far as it can, it erodes sideways, or laterally. The lateral erosion widens the valley. The bulk of the lateral cutting takes place on the outside of each stream curve; deposition, marking the earliest beginnings of a river plain or a valley bottom plain, occurs on the inside of each curve. The cutting produces a bluff and the deposition creates a small valley flat. A valley which has attained this stage might be called a bluff-and-valley-flat valley. Further lateral erosion and rainwash, accompanied by more deposition, slowly create a relatively wide valley which possesses a definite and comparatively broad plain. This is the final stage in the genesis of the valley form. It might be called a river-plain valley (FIG. 5–24).

In the next chapter, where landforms and the agents of erosion are treated in some de-

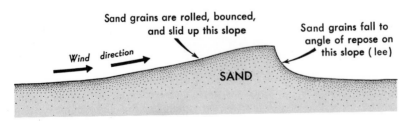

Sand grains are rolled, bounced, and slid up this slope

Sand grains fall to angle of repose on this slope (lee)

Wind direction

SAND

5–23

PROFILE of a "wave" dune. The angles of the slopes are somewhat exaggerated.

5-24 AN example of a "river-plain" valley—a view of the Connecticut river valley in Massachusetts.

tail, more will be said about stages of development of particular landforms and landform groups. Then, in CHAPTER 7 is presented a discussion of the major landforms of the continents, their patterns of distribution, and their significance to man.

ROCKS
Composition of Rocks
Rock Classes
    IGNEOUS ROCKS
    SEDIMENTARY ROCKS
    METAMORPHIC ROCKS
    CONSOLIDATED AND UNCONSOLIDATED ROCKS

LANDFORM ANALYSIS: EMPIRICAL VS. SCIENTIFIC
Types of Analysis
Structure, Process, and Stage

• REVIEW QUESTIONS •

1. Choose two examples, if possible from your own experience, to illustrate relationships between landform conditions and human conditions and activities. Discuss the relationships.

2. Choose two examples, from your own experience if possible, to illustrate relationships between landform conditions and other physical conditions.

3. What is the distinction between the terms "major landforms" and "minor landforms"? What is the difference in meaning between "major landforms of the earth" and "major landforms of the continents"?

4. Name some typical minor landforms in the area in which you live.

5. In general, and in simple words, state the differences among plains, plateaus, hills, and mountains.

6. What processes account for the shaping of landforms "from within"? "From without"?

7. Draw cross-section diagrams to show the difference between a structural basin and a structural dome.

8. What is the end result of weathering? Where-in is decomposition different from disintegration?

9. Name the chief agents of erosion.

10. Suggest what evidence there is to support the contention that, even in desert regions, moving water is the chief erosive agent.

11. Which of the following landforms are degradational and which aggradational: a sea cliff, the Grand Canyon, a delta, a gully, a sand dune, a loess plain, a fiord, an alluvial fan?

12. Give an example of a rock that is composed of one mineral; an example of a mineral that is composed of one element.

13. What is the difference between an igneous and a metamorphic rock? Give common examples of each.

14. Thinking of the rocks of the earth's crust as a whole, what are the most important chemical elements which compose them?

15. Give examples, from your own experience if possible, of: (a) landforms of different structure, (b) landforms shaped by different processes, (c) landforms in different stages.

6–1

[OPPOSITE, TOP] "HIGH *country*" *in southwestern Colorado—part of the San Juan Mountains. Some of the peaks have altitudes in excess of 14,000 feet above sea level.*

6 Landforms and the Agents of Erosion and Deposition

CROSS, U.S. GEOLOGICAL SURVEY

⟨[THE *agents of erosion and deposition help to shape the land surface in two major ways. First, they carve much as a sculptor cuts into stone. Second, they create new forms by piling up materials which they have transported. The first activity is essentially one of removal; the second is one of addition or accretion. For example, the deep gorge of the Grand Canyon and the low and nearly level delta of the Mississippi are both the result of work by running water; the gorge was created by erosion, the delta by deposition, layer on layer, of water-borne materials. Similarly, moving ice may scour out a valley to produce a fiord, such as the famous Stavanger Fiord of southwestern Norway, or it may lay a blanket of loose earth debris over the land, as in the glacial plains of Illinois. And, when wind carries on its work, one may find basin-shaped depressions, as among the knolls of the Sand Hills of Nebraska, or closely packed mounds and ridges, as occur in the White Sands of southeastern New Mexico.*

In addition to the two ways in which each of the agents of erosion and deposition acts, it should be realized that each one creates its own distinctive forms. Often, too, several agents act collectively or in sequence. Thus there is created almost infinite variety in landform detail.

THE WORK OF MOVING WATER

THE accomplishments of moving water are dominant over most of the earth's surface. Almost anywhere one looks, one sees water-cut or water-deposited features, whether it is the valley course of the Amazon, the gorges of the Yangtze, the Nile Delta, or the alluvial plains at the northern base of the Pyrenees. Even in the deserts and the semideserts, lands of little rain, the work of moving water is attested to by the presence of many landforms resulting from erosion or deposition by that agent.

The Work of Streams

As rain falls and snow melts, water begins to move over the land. At first it moves down the slopes in thin sheets, but soon it is concentrated in small rills and creeks and, later, in large streams and full-flowing rivers. As soon as there is any degree of movement, there is capacity to do work. When there is only slight motion and little water, only the finest materials, such as clay and silts, can be transported; when volume is greater and movement faster, coarse materials, such as sands, gravels, and boulders, can be moved. In extreme instances, huge boulders weighing many tons are shifted from one place to another, although their transportation is by sliding, bouncing, and rolling rather than by being picked up and carried.

VELOCITY • The ability of water to shape the land depends chiefly, though not entirely, on its velocity. Even a slight increase in velocity is accompanied by greatly increased power to do work. To put the matter technically, the transporting power of moving water varies as the sixth power of its velocity. This means that if the velocity of a stream is doubled, its capacity to transport sediment is increased sixty-four times! Knowing this, one can appreciate why flood damage by streams may be surprisingly great, even though the speed of the water may seem to have increased only slightly. Likewise, it is possible to understand why a minor increase in velocity results in a markedly greater ability to pick up and carry earth materials (TABLE 6).

The velocity attained by a stream depends on several factors; chief among them are *slope*, *volume*, and *load*. Slope is the angle, or gradient, down which water is moving. Volume is the amount of water which is "on the move." Load is the amount of material carried by moving water. Greatest velocities are attained when there is a large volume of water flowing with only a slight load down a very steep gradient. Conversely, the smallest velocities occur when a small volume of heavily loaded water is moving down a very gentle slope. Any change in one or more of the factors will immediately modify the rate at which the water moves. If a stream is flowing over solid bedrock and then, without any change in slope, flows across loose, easily eroded material, it will pick up more load and its velocity will decrease. If a stream issues from a steep mountain canyon onto a gentle plain, the change in slope will check its velocity, perhaps to the point where it will have to drop part of the load it carries. If a rain swells the volume of a stream, slope and load remaining constant, the water in the stream will move at a faster rate. Such changes, in affecting the velocity, produce significantly different effects on landforms. When the velocity is great, much material is trans-

TABLE 6

Relation Between Stream Velocity and Ability of Stream to Move Materials of Different Sizes

STREAM VELOCITY	SIZE OF MATERIALS MOVED
⅓ miles per hour	as large as sand grains
¾ miles per hour	as large as gravels
3 miles per hour	as large as small stones (2 to 3 inches in diameter)
6 miles per hour	as large as large stones (10 to 11 inches in diameter)
20 miles per hour	as large as huge boulders (16 to 17 feet in diameter)

ported, or at least the stream has a large capacity to carry materials; the result is normally an active cutting into the land surface. When velocity is slight, capacity to carry load is small and built-up surfaces usually result. Thus the velocity of a stream may determine whether it cuts a valley or lays down a blanket of alluvial material.

VALLEY STAGES • A stream which is cutting a valley cannot do its work all at once but instead works in sequence or in stages. Each stage is marked by a particular valley shape. At first, the stream is attempting to cut its bed to the level of the body of water into which it flows. This level is called *base-level*. In its effort to reach base-level, the stream erodes vertically; then, when it has cut vertically as far as it can, it erodes laterally. As long as vertical erosion occurs, one type of valley shape exists; when lateral erosion becomes dominant, new shapes slowly emerge. Thus, there is an "erosion cycle," each stage of which is characterized by a typical valley form.

The first stage of the normal valley cycle is called *youth* and the valley is termed a *youthful valley*. A valley in this stage is recognized readily by the V-shape of its profile; sides are very steep, there is no level land in the valley bottom, the stream occupies the entire lower part of the V,

and the valley follows a relatively straight course across the land (FIG. 6–2A). Its shape shows clearly that the stream is still cutting vertically and has not yet reached the condition where valley widening by means of lateral erosion is possible nor the condition where rainwash down the valley sides has had the opportunity to widen the valley appreciably. As examples of such a valley type, one may turn to any ordinary small gully or, on a much grander scale, to any typical mountain gorge.

A *mature valley* represents the second major stage in valley shape. The original V-shape has been modified by lateral erosion so the valley has the asymmetrical profile shown in FIG. 6–2B. Lateral erosion occurs on the outside of each curve of the stream where it produces a definite *undercut bluff*. On the inside of each curve, part of the load of the stream is deposited to form an arc-shaped *valley flat*; this marks the very beginning of a river plain. As a result of cutting on the outside of each bend and deposition on the inside, the stream widens its valley bottom and it curves, or *meanders*, more and more as time goes on.

The third major stage in valley form, an *old valley*, exists as soon as the work of lateral ero-

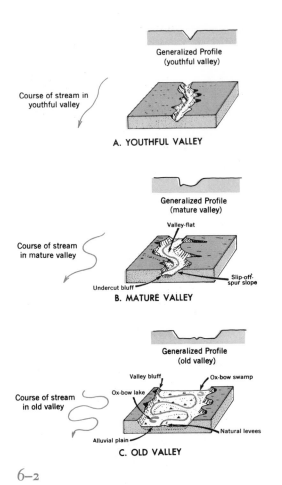

Generalized Profile
(youthful valley)

Course of stream in
youthful valley

A. YOUTHFUL VALLEY

Generalized Profile
(mature valley)

Valley-flat

Course of stream
in mature valley

Undercut bluff

Slip-off-
spur slope

B. MATURE VALLEY

Generalized Profile
(old valley)

Valley bluff   Ox-bow swamp

Ox-bow lake

Course of stream
in old valley

Natural levees

Alluvial plain

C. OLD VALLEY

6–2

DIAGRAMMATIC *illustration of the erosion cycle of a valley in a region of humid climate.*

almost enclosed by the meander loops and the low, smooth forms of the natural levees. These wet spots are called *back marshes*, whether they occur back near the bluffs or in back of the natural levees. Old meander loops mark former positions of the stream channel within the flood plain; if they are largely filled with vegetation and in-washed sediments, they are termed *ox-bow swamps*; if they are unfilled, except by water, they are *oxbow lakes* (FIG. 6–3).

Thus, from the first small notch of youth to the broad plain of old age, valleys undergo drastic changes in form as streams cut their way into the land—first vertically and finally in large meander sweeps which plane away the land and create broad alluvial plains.

SIGNIFICANCE OF VALLEY SHAPES • Whether a given area possesses youthful, mature, or old valleys, or a mixture of all three, makes a considerable difference in its appearance. More significantly, it makes a great deal of difference to man if he is attempting to live there. If there is a large number of youthful valleys, there is no level valley land available for use. If such valleys are so numerous as to lie extremely close together, there is practically no level upland in among them (FIG. 6–4A). In either instance, both travel and the transportation of goods are difficult and expensive.

If valleys are largely of the mature type, and especially if they are deeply entrenched, the same difficulties of movement of man and his goods are present. Routes are still faced with steep valley-sides and stream crossings, and they may have to follow even more devious lines than is true in an area of youthful valleys. This latter condition reflects the fact that the undercut bluff portions of mature valleys are too steep for roads or railroads; thus a given route will have to proceed down the more gentle side onto one of the valley flats, then turn, either upstream or downstream, to cross the river to the next valley flat, and then continue up another comparatively gentle slope. However, mature valleys provide more level land for man's use than do youthful valleys; at least there is level land in the form of

sion, rainwash, and deposition has created a comparatively wide river plain, or *flood plain.* The flood plain is bordered by steep, but low, *valley bluffs.* These are steepest where migrating meanders are actively undercutting them, or where such undercutting has recently occurred (FIG. 6–2C). Within the flood plain, the stream swings in tightly curved meander loops which wander as though lost in the alluvial materials. Along the immediate banks of the stream channel are *natural levees* built up by successive deposits during times of flood. Swampy spots are common in the lowest places, near the valley bluffs or in the very shallow basins which are

6–3   AN oxbow lake in the flood plain of the lower Rio Grande valley in Texas.

the small valley flat which occurs on the inside of each river bend (FIG. 6–4B). Such features normally support one or more farms, depending on the size of the flat.

In an area of old valleys, there is a great deal of nearly level land. This is particularly true where flood plains are very broad and spaced closely together (FIG. 6–4C). Valleys of this sort, climate allowing, ordinarily support large farming populations, for the alluvial soils are normally of high productivity and they extend over many square miles with little interruption. However, there are some drawbacks; many sections of the flood plain are too swampy to use for crops although they may produce swamp forests and their margins may grow lush grasses suitable for feeding domestic animals. Moreover, there is the ever-present danger of floods, floods which may spread from one valley bluff to the other and destroy crops, settlements, roads, and railroads, even the inhabitants themselves (FIG. 6–5). Because of flood conditions, man often distributes many of his crops and settlements along the natural levees in the hopes that these slightly higher sections may stay above the floodwaters.

INTERFLUVE STAGES • At the same time that valleys are being etched into the land, areas between valleys are undergoing change. These areas are the ridges, or *interfluves*. Like valleys, certain normal interfluve types develop in definite sequence, each with its own characteristic form.

The first stage in the normal erosion cycle of ridges is the *youthful interfluve*. Interfluves in this stage are characterized by a nearly level top and steeply sloping sides. The top is part of the original upland surface, as yet little eroded; the sides are those of the adjacent valleys (FIG. 6–6A). The exact condition of the sides will depend on whether the adjacent valleys are youthful, mature, or old. If they are youthful the sides of the youthful interfluves are, automatically, the steep sides of the V-shaped youthful valleys.

By the time weathering, soil creep, rainwash, and stream erosion have eaten into and sharpened the original youthful ridges, *mature interfluves* are created. At first such ridges are very narrow and sharply crested. The form is essentially that of a steeply pitched roof. A bit

The Work of Moving Water | 127

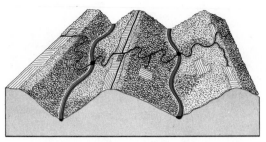

A. YOUNG VALLEYS

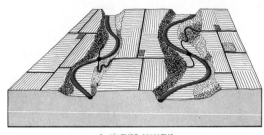

B. MATURE VALLEYS

C. OLD VALLEYS

Stream Settlement Bridge or ferry
Woods Main road Pasture or cropland

6–4

SOME effects of different valley shapes on land use in an area of humid climate.

later the sharp crests are rounded as a result of weathering and rainwash, but they are still relatively narrow (FIG. 6–6B).

With continued wearing away, the pronounced ridge forms of maturity become *old interfluves*. Now they are so low and comparatively broad that they can hardly be called "ridges," but they still are "interfluves" (FIG. 6–6C). The lowness and smoothness are further enhanced by downwash and the slow creep of soils until old interfluves are only gentle swells in the land surface. However, steep slopes may occur at places on their lowest and outermost

margins where laterally eroding stream channels create abrupt drops. If, for example, two valleys adjacent to an old interfluve are in the stage of old age themselves, then the outermost edges of the old interfluve are the short, steep bluffs of the old valleys (FIG. 6–7).

SIGNIFICANCE OF INTERFLUVE SHAPES • As with the typical valley forms produced by running water, the type or types of interfluves in a given region affect the general appearance of the land and are important in determining its use by man. Where broad youthful interfluves are numerous, there is much nearly level land available for agriculture, settlements, and routes of travel. Transport lines can be laid out in almost any fashion desired (FIG. 6–8A).

A countryside comprised largely of mature interfluves is quite another matter. The interfluves provide practically no level land. If slopes are utilized for crops, great care is needed to prevent the soils, loosened by cultivation, from being washed away into the valleys. Where there are many people to feed, such slopes may be terraced to provide level land not available under natural conditions. This is common practice in densely settled portions of the Orient. In general, mature ridges are best used for forest or for permanent scientifically managed pasture. The same conditions which limit agricultural use make the laying out of routes difficult. Quite commonly, the major roads, as well as the distribution of dwellings, follow the crests of the narrow ridges (FIG. 6–8B).

In areas of old interfluves, there is relative freedom from limitations imposed by landforms. The gently rolling condition allows cropland to be widely spread. There is land suitable for villages, towns, and cities, and routes can be distributed in almost any pattern. In these respects, areas of old interfluves closely resemble those of youthful interfluves: both have a considerable amount of nearly level land, although there normally is more "roll" to the surface where interfluves are old (FIG. 6–8C).

VALLEY AND INTERFLUVE COMBINATIONS • The foregoing discussion dealt largely

6–5 FLOODWATERS of the Missouri river surge through a break in an artificial levee at Kansas City, Missouri. Note the breaching of the railroad along the levee.

with valleys and interfluves as though they occurred without association with one another. Actually, they are inseparable and they occur in manifold combinations. Through use of the various terms which are applied to valleys and interfluves of differing stage and shape, a simple and meaningful description of local landforms becomes readily possible. Specific illustrations will serve to clarify what is meant.

There is a portion of the Cumberland Plateau in eastern Kentucky in which the landforms may be described simply and concisely as consisting of youthful valleys and mature ridges. This immediately gives a picture of a countryside with a surface profile somewhat like that of the teeth of a saw—the V's of the youthful valleys and the inverted V's of the mature ridges (FIG. 6–8B). In this instance, the saw-tooth profile is not on a mountainous scale, for the vertical distance from ridge top to valley bottom is measured in hundreds instead of thousands of feet. Yet nearly all

the land is steeply sloping and the relatively sparse agricultural population is forced to use sidehill fields, in addition to what meager level land occurs along the narrow ridges and in the equally narrow creek beds.

In a similar fashion, the landforms of another area may be described as comprised of old valleys and old interfluves. Such a description brings to mind an entirely different kind of countryside than the one mentioned above. It is a countryside with very little "up and down" to it; valleys are nearly level and relatively broad, the interfluves low and gently sloping (FIG. 6–7). It is an area where, as far as the dictates of surface are concerned, man has relative freedom to settle and work. Parts of the inner, and older, portion of the Atlantic Coastal Plain of the United States (see FIG. 5–7 for location) are thus hospitable to man.

There are, of course, many other possibilities of valley and interfluve combinations. Some of

The Work of Moving Water |

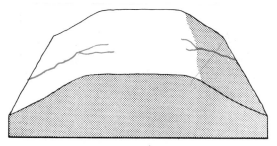

A. YOUTHFUL INTERFLUVE

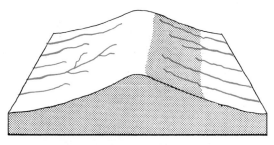

B. MATURE INTERFLUVE

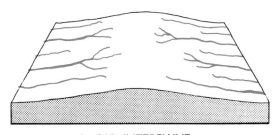

C. OLD INTERFLUVE

6–6

EROSION cycle of a normal interfluve in a region of humid climate.

these may be envisioned by means of a few questions. What would be the landform appearance of an area comprised of youthful ridges and youthful valleys (FIG. 6–8A), or one with youth-

ful valleys and old interfluves—or mature valleys and youthful interfluves (FIG. 6–4)?

STREAM-DEPOSITED FORMS • Not only does running water help to create landforms by carving valleyways and eating into and modifying interstream areas; it also produces new forms by actual construction. Some depositional forms have been noted already in connection with the formation of valley flats in mature valleys and flood plains in old valleys. Other common examples, ones in which the entire form is depositional in origin, are the small cones and fans of alluvial material built up at the mouth of almost any little gully. On a much grander scale is the mammoth alluvial fan deposited at the northern base of the Pyrenees in southern France known as the Lannemezan Plateau. Another example is the almost unbelievably level land called the North China Plain, where the silt-laden waters of the Hwang Ho filled in and built up an extensive plain in the shallow waters of a former sea. Other instances are to be seen in the large "birds-foot" of the Mississippi Delta, which the muddy Mississippi river is still actively building into the waters of the Gulf, or in the arcuate delta which the Nile has constructed in the southeastern corner of the Mediterranean Sea.

The Work of Solution

Some landforms owe their existence and nature to solution by moving water. Solution goes on, as was mentioned in the discussion of chemical weathering, in practically all earth materials, both at the surface and to considerable depths. However, production of definite landforms by solvent action demands what might be considered as wholesale removal of materials by solution. Enough material has to be removed to affect the lay of the land. Accompanying such

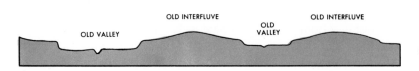

OLD INTERFLUVE   OLD VALLEY   OLD INTERFLUVE

OLD VALLEY

6–7

PROFILES of old interfluves in an area where the valleys are also in the old-age stage.

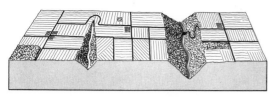

A. YOUTHFUL INTERFLUVES

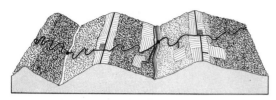

B. NARROW MATURE INTERFLUVES

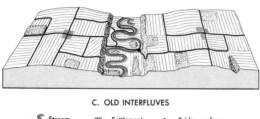

C. OLD INTERFLUVES

〰 Stream   ⧣ Settlement   ● Bridge or ferry
▨ Woods   ⊥⊤ Main road   ▥ Pasture or cropland

6–8

SOME *effects of different interfluve shapes on land use in a region of humid climates.*

removal is the development of subterranean forms. These are not landforms, but, as the name indicates, forms which occur *under* the land. Regions in which solution proceeds to a major degree are known as *karst* regions—areas which are directly underlain by soluble or partly soluble rock. The name derives from the Karst Plateau of Yugoslavia. Here both subterranean and surface forms of solution are highly developed, and here some of the more significant early studies of karst conditions were made. Other famous karst areas include the peninsula of Yucatan, the Mammoth Cave section of Kentucky, the Shenandoah caverns of Virginia, and the Carlsbad Caverns of New Mexico.

EVOLUTION OF KARST FORMS • As water works its way down the cracks and between the layers of soluble rock, it dissolves and carries away some of the rock materials. In time the vertical and oblique cracks, as well as the horizontal ones which separate the rock layers, are enlarged until they become small *solution channels*. As further work of solution takes place, small channels become large ones and rock members are honeycombed with a completely developed, three-dimensional system of passageways. Here and there, where rock is more soluble, channels are expanded into *caverns*; these are the famous limestone caves. When caverns are numerous, and when they occur in lines at different levels, they are referred to as *galleries*.

By the time caverns are well formed, particularly near the surface, the work of solution is reflected in the landforms. As near-surface cavern roofs collapse, either slowly or suddenly, depressions called *sinkholes* are formed in the land. These are circular or oval in ground plan and vary in size from a few feet to perhaps hundreds of feet across. In general, there are two types of sinkholes: one is funnel-shaped and is called a *doline* (FIG. 6–9A); the other is shaped more or less like a well and is known as a *ponor* (FIG. 6–9B). Where they are numerous, entire areas are pock-marked with large and small depressions. If several caverns collapse along the same line or if the roof of an underground stream falls in, trenchlike forms are produced. These are *uvalas*; like sinkholes, they may be relatively small or may extend for several hundreds, or even thousands, of feet (FIG. 6–9C). Some of the uvalas in the karst of Yugoslavia are large enough and have sufficient soil accumulation on their floors to contain entire agricultural settlements.

After solution has continued for some time, the layers of soluble rock are almost entirely removed. If this has happened, there is a new level to the countryside, lower than the original surface and marked by hilly or moundlike remnants of the soluble rock. Such remnants are greatly honeycombed and are known variously as *haystacks*, *hums*, or *magotes* (FIG. 6–9D).

A. DOLINE

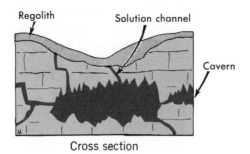

Regolith   Solution channel

Cavern

Cross section

Edge of doline   Mud flat or temporary pond   Gentle slopes

Top view

B. PONOR

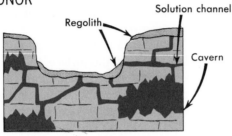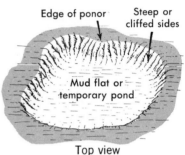

Solution channel

Regolith

Cavern

Cross section

Edge of ponor   Steep or cliffed sides

Mud flat or temporary pond

Top view

C. UVALA

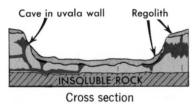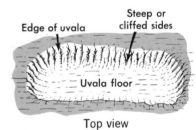

Cave in uvala wall   Regolith

INSOLUBLE ROCK

Cross section

Edge of uvala   Steep or cliffed sides

Uvala floor

Top view

D. MAGOTES

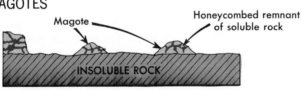

Magote   Honeycombed remnant of soluble rock

INSOLUBLE ROCK

6–9   DIAGRAMMATIC *illustration of some typical karst features.*

DRAINAGE IN KARST • Conditions of drainage are normal in the initial phases of karst development. Of the moisture which falls from the skies, some sinks into the regolith, some evaporates, and some collects and runs along low lines in the surface to form streams. But as soon as solution channels, caverns, and sinkholes appear, the drainage condition is greatly modified. Water sinking into the regolith and on into the bedrock moves downward very rapidly through the honeycombed strata. Surface waters travel only very short distances before they disappear into the sinkholes and the underground channels which drain them. The lack of definite streams and the rapid removal of water to lower levels may actually produce "droughty" soils in regions which are climatically humid; in lands with arid and semiarid climates, the karst condition produces extreme dryness, often so dry as to leave the surfaces bare of all vegetation.

Some karst regions, depending largely on their degree of development, possess numerous small lakes and ponds. These usually reflect the blocking of sinkhole outlets so that each one acts as a reservoir to entrap local surface flow. Such ponds or lakes may drain away overnight if the outlets into the subterranean channels are freed of earth materials which block them. Thus, detailed maps of karst regions may show ponds and lakes which no longer exist, and fail to indicate those which have come into being since the maps were made (FIG. 6–10).

By the time the soluble rocks which comprise the karst are largely removed, drainage is again back at the surface and more or less normal drainage patterns are present (FIG. 6–10C). It is almost as though karst conditions had never existed in the region. As usual, there may be exceptions to this. For example, the soluble rocks in a given area may extend below sea level. If this is true, the final stages of karst witness extensive surface water channels and numerous ponds and lakes which are flanked and dotted with the remnants of the original rock.

STAGES IN KARST • The foregoing discussion of karst landforms and karst drainage shows a definitely sequential development of conditions. It shows, in a sense, the major steps in what may be termed "the karst erosion cycle." Obviously, the cycle is very different from that which occurs in connection with the evolution of stream-cut valleys and interfluves, but it is, nevertheless, a matter of stages. It is often convenient to distinguish three major stages in the karst erosion cycle.

Youthful karst is characterized by a few sinkholes and predominantly surface drainage. *Mature karst* is marked by the presence of numerous sinkholes, a few or many uvalas, and drainage which is almost entirely subterranean. In the third major stage, *old karst*, drainage is back on the surface again, and all that remains to mark the area as karst are the scattered knobby and hilly remnants of the soluble rock. Each of these stages is represented in FIG. 6–11, a study of

6–10   SKETCH *maps showing conditions of drainage in karst areas in different stages of development* (compare with FIG. 6–11).

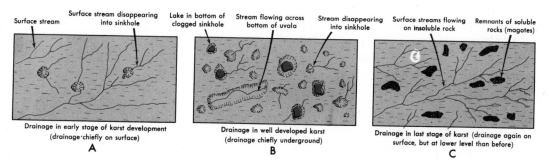

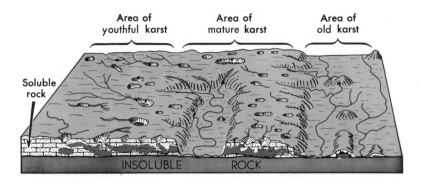

Area of youthful karst

Area of mature karst

Area of old karst

Soluble rock

INSOLUBLE ROCK

6–11

TYPICAL surface forms, subterranean forms, and drainage conditions in different stages of the karst erosion cycle.

which will show how different a given karst area is from one stage to another.

SIGNIFICANCE OF KARST • In terms of human habitation of an area, it makes a great deal of difference if it is a karst region, and whether it is in a youthful, mature, or old stage. In youthful karst, assuming a humid climate, water is abundant. Streams are on the surface and underground channels have not developed to the degree that they quickly rob the soils of necessary moisture. In addition, sinkholes are few and thus there are only minor interruptions to the surfaces of fields and only slight controls placed on the pattern of land routes.

By the time uvalas and numerous sinkholes develop, habitat conditions are modified. Despite humid climate, water becomes a problem. There are no surface streams and soils may be deficient in moisture. This condition may be offset partly by the use of sinkhole ponds and lakes as sources of water for domestic animals. However, such water is of little use for man himself because it is usually polluted, stagnant, and unsafe to drink. In most karst areas, man has to collect rain water from the roofs of dwellings and store it in surface containers or in underground cisterns. Soils may be so dry as to support only drought-resisting crops or to demand special dry-farming methods. Moreover, the

countryside is much interrupted by depressions, which affect the amount of land available for crops and exert strong limitations on the alignment of routes. Where sinkholes are of the doline type, more land is available for agricultural use; for example, the sides of the dolines may be used for pasture, and the ponds in their bottoms for water for stock, including such domestic animals as ducks and geese. If the sinkholes are ponors, much land is wasted. The sides, usually cliffed, are too steep to use and any impounded water is not accessible to livestock. More than this, it is often necessary to construct fences around the ponors to prevent stock from falling in. Dolines place fewer limitations on the patterns of roads and railroads than do ponors; in fact, where dolines are very broad and relatively shallow they produce no more than a gently rolling country.

Areas which have reached the stage of old karst are little affected by karst conditions. Only remnants are left of the original soluble rocks. Streams are again on the land and soils are not losing their moisture to subterranean solution channels. However, in places soluble rock remnants may be so numerous as to interfere with the use of fields and to cause marked deviation in the alignment of roads.

THE WORK OF MOVING WATER IN DRY LANDS

THE surface features of the world's dry lands, like those of humid regions, are the result of the combined efforts of diastrophism, vulcanism, weathering, erosion, and deposition. By and large, they consist in forms ordinarily referred to as *hamada, erg, reg,* and *mountain-and-bolson.* A *hamada* is a rocky desert (FIG. 6–12A), often representing layers of sedimentary bedrock which have been uplifted sufficiently to provide a sort of slightly elevated benchland. Much of northern Libya is hamada. An *erg* is a sandy desert, best described as a sea of sand dunes (FIG. 6–12B), as in the Grand Erg Oriental of the Sahara, south of the eastern portion of the Atlas Mountains. A *reg* is an exceedingly level plain surfaced with gravels; it is a gravelly or pebbly desert, as opposed to a rocky or sandy one (FIG. 6–12C). Many large sections of the heart of the Sahara are of this nature. A *mountain-and-bolson* area is one of large and small basins which are rimmed and bordered by hills and mountains (FIG. 6–12D). Most of the state of Nevada is like this, and so is much of the Mojave Desert of California.

While the major landforms referred to above comprise the broader view in dry lands, the closer and more intimate scene consists of much smaller forms, most of which owe all or part of their characteristics to the work of moving water. As stated previously, it is true, even in the regions of dry climates, that running water is the chief agent of erosion. The valley forms which thread hamadas and cut the surfaces into isolated segments are carved by water. The hills and mountains which encircle bolsons are lined and marked with deep canyons and sharp ridges which have been etched out by stream action. Ergs and regs are laced and intersected by usually dry stream courses. In lower portions of the drainage ways, other forms which have been built up by materials transported and dropped by water are common. Many of the differences in appearance between the landforms of dry lands and those of humid regions result directly from the difference in the behavior of running water. In the dry lands, it is a case of "feast and famine," of freshet waters or no waters at all. In the western United States, one hears often about cloudbursts. Of course, clouds do not burst, but the fall of rain is commonly so heavy as to give that impression. Downpours of this sort create flash floods. Stream courses suddenly become raging torrents and then, almost as suddenly, dry up. Floodwaters carry heavy loads and exert a strong scouring action; then, quickly, as the waters dwindle and disappear, the loads are deposited.

Water-cut Landforms

No attempt will be made here to discuss all the surface features which are shaped entirely, or in part, by the intermittent waters of the dry regions. Instead, some of the more typical forms to be seen in all deserts and semideserts of any appreciable extent will be described.

WADIES • *Wadies* are the typical stream-cut valleys of the dry lands. They are known also as *washes, arroyos,* and *barrancas,* although the term wadi is most usually applied to them. A wadi may be shallow or deep, narrow or wide, but it is marked always by steep, normally cliffed sides and a nearly level bottom (FIG. 6–13). The shape is a direct consequence of the intermittency of water flow. When running water is present, it carves a more or less V-shaped valley at first, like the youthful valley of humid areas. As water disappears, the load is dropped to fill in the lower part of the V and create a level bottom. Succeeding water encounters a channel which is glutted with previously dropped materials; the flood spreads out over the wadi floor and actively undermines and steepens the valley sides. This procedure is repeated over and over again. Each freshet relays material farther downstream, leaves other material in its place, and erodes the banks to push them farther and farther apart.

6–12 A

OBLIQUE air view of a small hamada in southern Nevada. The table-top surface is the remnant of a once more extensive hamada.

6–12 B

AN erg in the central portion of the floor of Death Valley, California.

6–12 C

TYPICAL reg (gravelly desert) in the desert of South-West Africa.

6–12 D

OBLIQUE air view of part of a mountain-and-bolson area in southern Nevada. The light colored portions in the bolson floor are playas which are being encroached upon by the alluvial-fan piedmonts built out from the higher lands.

For these reasons a wadi, large or small, is maintained constantly with steep sides and level bottom. For the same reasons, its shape is different from that of the normal youthful valley in any humid area.

Where wadies are broad, their bottom lands sometimes attract agricultural use under irrigation, and even settlements. The results are often disastrous, for the wadi bottom is the natural floodway, and fields, buildings, domestic animals, and human lives are apt to be wiped out by suddenly appearing walls of water. The fact that wadies are so numerous in dry regions also creates problems for builders of highways and railroads. Road builders must construct many expensive bridges or else expect to have sections of highways temporarily blocked by floodwaters and deposited earth debris. Railroad builders have no alternative; they must build sound bridges, and even then one of the large items of expense is the repairing of washouts and the clearing of debris from the channels underneath the bridges.

MESAS AND BUTTES · *Mesas* are etched out and separated from tablelands by streams which dig valleys around them (FIG. 5–21A). The same is true of many *buttes*, for they are often only the remnants of former mesas (FIG. 6–14). However, they may consist of the weathered and pointed "plugs" which remain after conical volcanoes have been almost destroyed by weathering and erosion; an example of this

6–13

ONE type of wadi, or arroyo, in the Mojave Desert in California. Note the steep sides and the gravel-and-boulder-strewn floodway of the intermittent stream which "dug" the wadi.

is to be seen at Shiprock, New Mexico. The more common type, usually representing the "dying stages" of mesas, occurs in large numbers in the famous Monument Valley region of northeastern Arizona, as well as in many other dry areas of the world. A region marked with numerous mesas and buttes is like no other land surface expression, whether in dry or humid regions. The "monuments" dominate the scene, and whatever travel there may be must usually thread its way along their flanks and in among them, despite risk in follow-

6–14

TWO common origins of buttes.

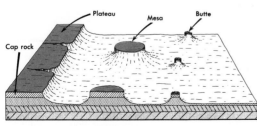

Buttes as remnants of mesas

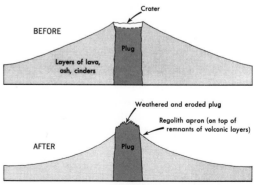

Butte formed by weathering and erosion of a conical volcano (more resistant plug becomes core of butte)

The Work of Moving Water in Dry Lands | 137

ing wadi-bottom trails and roads which are sandy and at the mercy of every flash flood.

PEDIMENTS • Many desert regions are of the mountain-and-bolson type. This means that there is much sloping land which is located along, or is comprised of, the bases of the hills and mountains. As floodwaters pour from hill and mountain canyons, they often spread out to carry on considerable lateral, as well as vertical, erosion. If they do not spread out, but follow rather definite courses, the results are still much the same. A given channel becomes glutted as the floodwaters recede, and the next waters seek new channels and, hence, carry on further lateral erosion. Given sufficient time, the waters plane away the slopes to create a gently sloping *pediment* or *rock pediment* which descends, strewn with boulders, sands, and gravels, to the lower portion of a given area. Pediments become more extensive with time, for, as hills and mountains are worn down and their fronts are planed away, the pediment sections grow in the direction of the higher crests (FIG. 6–15).

Water-deposited Landforms

Landforms of water deposition in dry lands are not necessarily separate from those which are water carved. A wadi is primarily an erosional form, yet its floor is the result of deposition; a pediment, created by lateral cutting, is veneered usually with materials dropped by freshets. However, there are several characteristic landforms which owe their existence and shape to deposition alone.

ALLUVIAL FANS • If one had to choose the most characteristic minor landform developed under dry climates, it would be a toss-up between the wadi and the alluvial fan. In most sections one might, finally, choose the alluvial fan, because it is normally much more extensive than a wadi and, being a built-up form, it is more readily visible.

The alluvial fan is well named for it is comprised of layer on layer of alluvial material and, when viewed from above, it has the shape

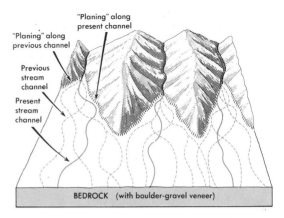

6–15

DIAGRAMMATIC *illustration of the development of a pediment (foreground). Only a few of the former stream-flow lines are shown on the pediment surface.*

of a fan (FIG. 6–16). If the waters which created it were permanently running, there usually would be no fan; instead, the materials would be carried into larger streams and eventually into the bodies of water into which the streams flowed. Again one sees the significance of the fact that dry-land waters are intermittent.

The origin of all alluvial fans is essentially similar. When floodwaters issue from a steeply

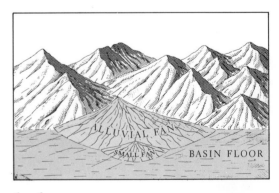

6–16

AN alluvial fan *constructed at a canyon mouth. Some of the lines of intermittent water flow are shown on the fan surface. Notice the recent, subsidiary fan.*

sloping area such as a hill canyon, their velocity is suddenly checked by the change in gradient and they drop their load of fine materials, sands, gravels, and boulders. Loss of water by evaporation and sinking into the ground further decreases the ability to carry load. A channel followed by water from a given flood is filled in and somewhat elevated when materials are dropped; the succeeding waters seek a new, lower line of flow and then drop their load along it. The same thing happens over and over again; slowly but surely the alluvial fan takes shape as materials are deposited by channels which swing through an arc of about 180 degrees as water issues, flood by flood, from the canyon mouth (FIG. 6–16). In general, finer materials are carried to the lower margins and the coarser left near the apex. However, some floods are more intense than others, and coarser materials are carried farthest at times when water is greatest in volume and velocity. Because of the manner in which deposition occurs, soils vary greatly, even within distances of a few feet. However, it is generally true that the bulk of the finer soils is to be found near the lower margin of the fan and the coarser on the upper portion.

The slopes of alluvial fans are normally quite gentle. It is seldom that they exceed 3 or 4 per cent grade (3 or 4 feet of total vertical rise or fall in 100 feet of horizontal distance).

Water may be diverted from the upper points of alluvial fans through about 180 degrees of arc, by means of simple and cheap gravity flow. For such reasons, alluvial fans are often used for irrigated farm or ranchlands. If water from the drainage basin in the higher area is abundant, an entire fan may be irrigated. If water is relatively scarce, irrigation is limited to the apex portion of the fan, and there may be enough of it to support only one farm. Of course, if the supply is too meager, no permanent use is possible. Moreover, some fans are too bouldery to use, and all of them are subject to torrential floods. In areas of dry climate, however, their importance

PIPER, U.S. GEOLOGICAL SURVEY

6–17

A playa *in the Harney Basin of Oregon, east of the Cascade Mountains. Beyond the shore zone (foreground), the playa surface is almost mathematically flat.*

is great, for they are the places where water is most likely to be found.

PLAYAS · *Playas* are the beds of lakes which are dry most of the time. In southwestern United States, they are referred to commonly as *dry lakes*. A playa is comprised of fine silts and clays which are washed into the lowest spots in desert basins. During the short periods when lakes exist, the fine materials are uniformly deposited. Then, as the lakes dry up, they are exposed as extremely flat surfaces (FIG. 6–17). As long as the materials remain wet, they are very muddy, but when thoroughly dry, they become much like concrete floors. In this latter condition, they are useful as landing fields for aircraft and for automobile races and speed trials. Playa materials are high in mineral salts, so much so that their soils are useless for agriculture. Some playas contain so much mineral salt that they are completely surfaced with gleaming white salt crystals, as are the Bonneville Salt Flats to the west of Great Salt Lake in Utah and in the Devil's Golf Course of Death Valley in California. Playas of this particular type are usually termed *salars*.

The Work of Moving Water in Dry Lands |

The Dry-Land Erosion Cycle

It is both possible and useful to distinguish an erosion cycle in arid and semiarid lands. The *youthful stage* of this type of erosion cycle is marked by unfilled basins or bolsons and by sharp, angular hills and mountains, as shown in FIG. 6–18A. The *mature stage* is characterized by considerably worn down hills and mountains and appreciably filled basins. In this stage, alluvial fans are numerous, and large and small fans have joined one another laterally to form continuous *piedmont alluvial plains*. Out in the central portions of the bolsons, fans advancing from opposite directions are practically touching along their lowest margins. In the lowest spots between advancing fan fronts are numerous playas. The indices of maturity are illustrated in FIG. 6–18B. The *stage of old age* represents the work of dry-land weathering, erosion, and deposition, nearly completed. All that is left of the higher lands are rocky platforms, or hamadas. The former depressions are now almost completely filled with alluvial fan materials. Here and there are sand dune areas, as well as playas. This third stage, shown in FIG. 6–18C, has been described, and aptly so, as a "wind-swept desolation of hamada and erg." Dry lands in the stage of old age are normally exceedingly dry. There are few of the comparatively wetter hill and mountain regions present to furnish water to the lower sections, and what moisture does fall on the general surface is quickly lost in the loose, porous regolith of the filled basins.

Such dry lands have exceedingly little to offer man, in terms of habitat value.

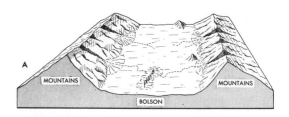

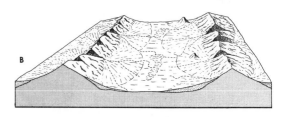

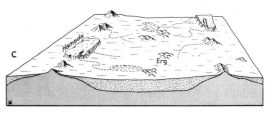

6–18

BLOCK *diagram series showing stages of erosion in a region of dry climate. A. Youthful stage: mountains are bold; depression is only slightly filled. B. Mature stage: mountains considerably worn and dissected; depression-filling is prominent, alluvial fans have coalesced laterally to form continuous alluvial-fan piedmont plains. C. Old age stage: only remnants of mountains remain; depression is filled; this stage is often referred to as the panfan stage.*

THE WORK OF WAVES AND CURRENTS

THE preceding discussion dealt primarily with moving water which "runs." There is other water which is "on the move," but is not running—the water of waves and currents. Because it moves, it, too, has the ability to do work, and it affects the shores of humid lands and dry lands alike, whether the shores of Lake Michigan, the coast of Oregon, or the western edge of the Sahara. Given sufficient time, without any complicating movements of sea level or of the earth's crust, it actually would plane away the exposed land

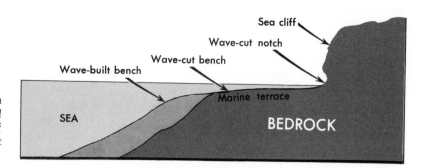

6-19

CROSS *section of seashore area showing typical sea cliff and marine terrace comprised of wave-cut and wave-built benches.*

masses until the latter were no more than slightly submerged marine platforms. It is interesting to speculate on what sort of a world would then exist.

Erosional and Depositional Forms

SEA CLIFFS AND MARINE BENCHES • As waves roll and pound against a bold coast, they slowly eat their way into the land. Active removal of materials produces steep, usually vertical, forms called *sea cliffs* or *wave-cut cliffs*. The famous cliffs of Dover owe their shape to wave erosion. Portions of cliffs which are more resistant to wave action are isolated in forms of *stacks*. Other portions, much less resistant, develop *sea caves*, such as the famous Blue Grotto of the island of Capri near Naples, Italy. As the waves cut into the land, they also create slightly submerged platforms at the base of the sea cliffs (FIG. 6-19). These are *wave-cut benches*. Some of the materials re-

moved from the land are deposited directly adjacent to the wave-cut bench. They comprise *wave-built benches*. The two together constitute the typical *marine terrace*, as illustrated in FIG. 6-19. Other materials are carried by shore currents out into deep water or are moved along the coast, often to be deposited in bays which lie between rocky headlands.

BARS AND SPITS • Many coasts, instead of being bold and rocky, are low and subdued, and the waters offshore are shallow. This results in the development of quite different forms. Prominent among them are the various types of *bars* and *spits*, which represent the combined action of waves and currents. As waves break in shallow waters, they drag bottom to pick up materials which are then dropped as the waves break and topple over. This creates *offshore bars* behind which are *lagoons* (FIG. 6-20). Where bays are present, materials may be carried by shore currents and heaped up by wave action to create *bay-mouth*

6-20

SKETCH *map showing some of the more typical depositional forms that develop along subdued coasts with shallow offshore water.*

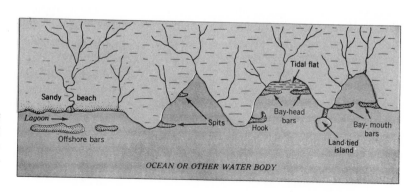

The Work of Waves and Currents | 141

bars or *spits*. Other currents, moving within bays, create spits in several bayshore positions. Where spits develop curved ends, they are known as *hooks*. These are only some of the forms to be seen commonly along subdued coasts; some others, as well, are illustrated in FIG. 6–20.

Significance of Shore Forms

The general type of coast and the individual coastal forms play a large part in the appearance of the margins of the land masses and they decisively affect human activities. One extreme is comprised of prominent, rocky cliffs interspersed with only limited beaches, and perhaps no bays for the use of ships. Access to the land is difficult. Another extreme, marked by shallow waters, bars, wide beaches, and lagoons, may offer much for resort purposes and for small, shallow-draft vessels, but little for easy use by large, ocean-going ships. In between such extremes are many other combinations. One very useful one is the coast with prominent headlands and numerous deep and broad embayments. The headlands provide protection from storms and are often of such beauty as to attract vacationists. The bays provide deep anchorages for ships and reach far enough into the land, often into wide rivers, to tie the business of the sea and the land together. Then, too, many parts of the bay areas are ideal for resorts as well as for ports.

THE WORK OF MOVING ICE

ICE, like water, has to be moving in order to take part in the creation of landforms. Also like water, its movement results in two kinds of work, erosion and deposition, each with its own particular set of landform features. A little ice "on the move" will not transform a countryside, but comparatively large ice masses will eradicate or drastically modify previously existing landforms and substitute new and very different ones. Such masses are known as *glaciers*. The largest of them, like those in Greenland or Antarctica, are *continental glaciers*; smaller ones, in valleys in Switzerland or the Rockies, for example, are *valley glaciers*. This twofold classification does not include all types of glaciers which may be distinguished, but for our purposes it is sufficient.

Continental Glaciation

GLACIER ORIGIN AND MOVEMENT • Contrary to popular belief, a glacier is not the result of water freezing into a large sheet of ice. Instead, glaciers are born of snow. When more snow falls during the colder season of the year than melts during the warmer season, the result is an annual increment of snow crystals. As the older layers of snow become buried and are pressed down by newer layers, they slowly change into a coarse, granular snow. In time the granular snow itself is transformed into solid glacial ice. If one visits the vast ice plateau of Greenland (FIG. 6–21), he sees little except mile after mile of snow, but digging into the snow a few feet reveals the coarse granular material and, below that, the ice mass itself.

When appreciable thicknesses of ice have accumulated, movement begins. In continental glaciers, the motion takes place outward in all directions from the center. It is almost as though sand were being shoveled onto a pile and each successive shovelful forced the mass to move toward the outer edges of the pile. The movement is very, very slow, a snail's pace or less, because ice cannot flow like water even though in large amounts it does possess sufficient plasticity to acquire a creeping and ponderous motion. Continental ice sheets which are still "alive" and advancing push their edges forward only a few feet each year. Even then, there are times when the rate of melting equals the rate of advance and the line of the "front" becomes stationary. There are other periods when the front retreats, *even though the ice itself is still moving forward.* This condition reflects a melt rate which is greater than the rate of forward motion of the mass. Still another situation arises when the supply, in the center of the accumulation area, is no longer sufficient to cause forward motion; then the ice merely lies in place until melting destroys it. Its last vestiges are to be seen in the places where it was thickest, or where great chunks of it were buried and insulated by earth debris.

If ice moves into the sea, its front breaks off, or *calves,* to form icebergs. Where it descends into the sea from considerably higher and rougher lands, as in Greenland, the resultant bergs are sharply jagged in appearance; where it moves in a thick, nearly horizontal sheet into the sea waters, as it does along much of the Antarctic shore, the bergs are flat and tablelike (FIG. 6–22). The flat bergs, moved by winds and currents, menace only occasional whaling vessels and the ships supplying Antarctic scientists, but the Greenland bergs, carried southward by the Labrador Current, menace the shipping of the world's busiest oceanic trade route—the North Atlantic.

LANDFORMS OF GLACIAL EROSION • When a continental glacier moves its billions of tons of ice across the land, it does an almost unbelievable amount of work. Loose soil or other regolith is picked up and carried in the subglacial ice and is used as scouring and grinding material to plane away and gouge into solid bedrock. Because the rock varies in hardness from place to place and because the local velocity and thickness of ice also vary, the stripping and scouring action is uneven. In some spots the ice scours deeply, in others it merely scrapes a bit at the uppermost materials. Thus, when an ice mass has done its

F. ALTON WADE

6–21

TEMPORARY camp of a scientific party in the interior of the vast snow-covered ice plateau of Greenland. (From The Geographical Review, July 1946, published by the American Geographical Society)

work and has disappeared, the resultant lay of the land is a series of "smoothed" ups and downs—pronounced if the countryside was formerly hilly, subdued if the former surface was a plain (FIGS. 5–20 and 7–14).

The most conspicuous landform of glacial scour is the *roche moutonnée* (FIG. 6–23), a type of hill which has been shaped from solid bedrock by the erosive action of moving ice. On the side from which the ice approached (the stoss, or struck, side) it has a smoothed and relatively gentle slope; on the opposite end (the lee side) it is rough and steplike. The steplike condition is the result of a plucking action whereby the lower ice carried away blocks of bedrock of different size, later to become glacial boulders. *Roches moutonnées* occur in many sizes; some would fit into a small room while others are hundreds of feet in height and several miles in length. Regardless of size, their frequent occurrence gives a unique expression to a whole region. Less readily visible is another ice-shaped landform known as a *scour basin.* It has been scooped out of solid bed-

6–22   AT the top is an example of the Greenland type of iceberg. Below, a new tabular Antarctic type iceberg breaks away from shelf ice.

rock and its surface is just as hard, and sometimes as barren, as that of the *roche moutonnée*. However, because it is a depression instead of a hill, its surface is often partially buried by a thin veneer of loose glacial debris or covered by the water of a lake or the thick growth of a brush or tree swamp. The third of the more common landforms of glacial scour is the *glacial trough*, a gigantic groove which may extend across country for many miles. It usually marks the course of a former stream-cut valley which ran with the axis of ice motion. When this form is drowned, as where a trough enters the sea, it is known as a fiord; however, fiords are more common in connection with valley glaciation than with continental glaciation.

LANDFORMS OF GLACIAL DEPOSITION • The materials which are picked up and carried in the lower portion of the ice are eventually spread over the land in many forms. In some areas, the debris is laid down so thickly that all previously existing landforms are completely smothered and bedrock lies at considerable depths; in others, the debris blanket is thin and patchy, and bedrock, smoothed and grooved by ice scour, sticks through the unconsolidated materials. In general, the debris,

Stoss (struck) side   Lee side
                       (staircase)
SOLID ROCK

A   B

Longitudinal section of a roche moutonnée

C   SOLID ROCK   D

Transverse section of a roche moutonnée

Direction of ice motion →

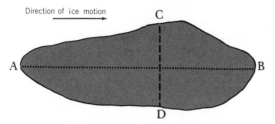

C

A · B

D

Typical shape when viewed from directly overhead

6-23

SKETCHES of surface profiles and ground-level contour showing the general nature of a roche moutonnée.

_____

or *glacial drift*, is thinnest toward the centers of ice accumulation and thickest near the margins of the farthest advance of the ice.

Some of the more common and more readily visible features which have been shaped from the glacial drift are the *morainal forms* (FIG. 6–24). They are comprised of a helter-skelter mixture of transported regolith which ranges from fine clays and silts on through sands, gravels, and boulders. In places, these unassorted materials have been deposited in the form of low rounded ridges which curve across country for many miles; in others, they comprise no more than gently and smoothly undulating plains. The occurrence of a morainal ridge marks the line along which the glacial front remained stationary for some time. The forward-moving ice carried debris to this line and stacked it up to form a ridge. Because the front of the ice had a scalloped or arc-shaped pattern, the morainal ridge took the same arrangement (FIG. 6–25). Moraines of this type, which were laid down at the line of

6-24 A

Morainal ridges *deposited in a basin area by valley glaciers issuing, in the past, from the mountains in the background.*

6-24 B

VALLEY glaciers *in Glacier Bay National Monument, Alaska. Note the burden of morainal material carried by Ferris Glacier in the center. Pick out the characteristic features associated with mountain glaciation.*

The Work of Moving Ice | 145

farthest advance of the ice, are known as *ter-minal moraines;* those laid down elsewhere, each marking a stage in the recession of the line of the glacial front, are called *recessional moraines.* The only difference between them is a matter of geographical position, for they were formed in the same manner and from the same types of materials. Between the ridges of terminal and recessional moraines, or between two recessional moraines, the ice front was retreating and as it retreated it dropped a gently rolling carpet of *ground moraine.* Like the ridge moraines, it is comprised of materials ranging from silts to huge boulders.

Another landform fairly common in regions of glacial deposition is the *outwash plain.* It is well named, for it consists of debris which was washed out from the glacial front by meltwater and deposited, layer on layer, to form a plain of very low relief (FIGS. 6–25, 6–26). Such plains may cover an area the size of a few city blocks or several square miles. Tucked here and there against the outer edges of the morainal ridges, they present a sudden change in the lay of the land, even though the drop from the top of a moriainal ridge to the surface of an outwash plain is usually only a few feet—perhaps 20 or 30 feet in some instances or as much as 75 or 100 feet in others. Outwash plains are notably sandy. Evidently the meltwater which flows more or less in a sheet from the ice front is not powerful enough to handle gravels and boulders, but it does have the ability to pick up and transport the silts, clays, and sands. As its power lessens, it drops the sands to build the outwash plain, while the finer clays and silts are carried on into the courses of glacial streams which lead out, at places, from the plain's margin.

Another important type of plain also occurs in glaciated areas. It owes its being to the previous existence of a glacial lake and is therefore called a *glaciolacustrine plain* (FIG. 6–27). A very large and famous plain of this sort occupies most of southern Manitoba province in Canada and extends in an ever-narrowing finger across the border into northwestern Minnesota and the eastern edge of North Dakota. This area was once covered by the cold waters of glacial Lake Agassiz, waters which were caught between the wall of the ice front to the north and slightly higher land to the south. As long as the ice dam existed, materials, particularly fine materials, were washed into the lake's shallow waters and distributed very evenly over the lake floor. Later, when the ice dam disappeared, Lake Agassiz drained away to Hudson Bay, leaving behind a lake bed which is nearly as flat as a billiard table and which constitutes some of the most productive soils of the world. These soils, fine textured and fertile, have proved capable of

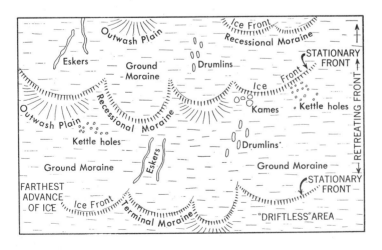

6–25

DIAGRAMMATIC *sketch map showing the kind and characteristic location of typical landforms of glacial deposition, as deposited by a continental ice sheet. The symbols shown in the pattern of arcs and lobes mark successive positions of stationary ice front.*

growing several varieties of high-grade wheat in tremendous quantities, and they comprise the basic resource of much of the major agricultural region known as the *Spring Wheat Belt* of the United States and Canada. The remnants of old Lake Agassiz are to be seen in the cluster of lakes which includes Lake Winnipeg and Lake Winnipegosis.

Leading out from temporary glacial lakes, and hence from the low featureless plains which they left behind, are the ribbonlike forms of *glacial spillways*. These used to be the outlets for surplus lake waters; today some of them are valleys for streams, but others are simply elongated depressions floored with alluvial material. Because they form low corridors, their courses are often used as routes for highways, railroads, and canals.

In addition to the major landforms already discussed, there are several minor features worthy of mention. In some areas, these are so numerous as to affect the general appearance of the land, as well as its use by man. One of these is the *drumlin* (FIGS. 6–25, 6–28). A drumlin is a small hill shaped like an egg which has been cut in two longitudinally. The end pointing in the direction from which the ice came is usually blunt and steep; the other, somewhat narrower, end is more gently sloping. Drumlins were formed underneath the ice sheet and their unconsolidated materials are normally high in clay content. They commonly occur in groups, and from high in the air they resemble schools of half-submerged whales moving over the glacial plains.

Other minor forms include *eskers, kames,* and *kettle holes* (FIG. 6–25). An *esker* is a low,

6–26

THE *smooth surface of a glacial plain with a low ridge of glacial debris in the background.*

sinuous ridge which winds across country for a few rods, or, in some instances, for several miles (FIG. 6–29). The esker evidently represents a portion of a subglacial tunnel which was blocked with stream-borne materials; after the ice melted away, the mold of the tunnel was left behind as a low ridge. Because it is well drained, an esker often serves as a route for a trail or road. *Kames* are small, knobby hills; in single occurrence they are seldom conspicuous, but, when they occur in tightly packed groups, they create a sort of miniature hill country. *Kettle holes* are small funnel-shaped depressions. They mark places where blocks of ice were buried in glacial debris. As the blocks melted, the materials covering them dropped lower and lower until pits were created. They may be found almost anywhere in glacial debris. There are pitted outwash plains, pitted morainal ridges, pitted ground moraines,

6–27

CROSS *section representing one type of origin of a glaciolacustrine plain. Following the disappearance of the ice dam and the glacial lake, the lake-bed deposits are exposed as a plain of extremely low relief.*

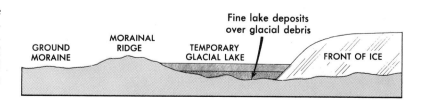

GROUND MORAINE

MORAINAL RIDGE

TEMPORARY GLACIAL LAKE

Fine lake deposits over glacial debris

FRONT OF ICE

The Work of Moving Ice | 147

and the pits, or kettle holes, may be found in among clusters of kames (FIG. 6–30). Kettle holes, because of their shape, are often mistaken for sinkholes, but obviously there is no connection between a glacial kettle hole and a karst sinkhole.

GLACIAL DRAINAGE • When continental ice masses "work over" a region, they change more than the landforms. From the preceding discussion, it is evident that soils are vitally affected, as in the instance of a sandy outwash plain, an old lake bed, or a bouldery and gravelly ground moraine. Evident, too, is the effect of the distribution of landforms on the pattern of routes. Even more important is the effect on conditions of drainage, for glaciation plays complete havoc with pre-existing stream patterns and stream behavior.

Whether in areas of scour or deposition, a *glacially deranged pattern* of drainage is created. The pattern is well named, for it is a "crazy" pattern without apparent rhyme or reason (FIG. 6–31). Lakes and ponds are numerous. They lie in the depressions created by unequal scour and by uneven deposition. Scattered among the lakes and ponds are many swamps, some of them representing former lakes and ponds which have been filled with inwashed materials and by the growth of dense swamp vegetation. Connecting lakes, ponds,

6–29

AN esker *traces its sinuous course across an area of ground moraine near Fort Ripley, Minnesota.*

and swamps are many large and small streams. They wander in a willy-nilly fashion as running water seeks the low lines in the glaciated surface and follows the varying tilt of the land. Their wanderings reflect the lack of sufficient time since the ice disappeared in which to carve definite and coordinated channels and patterns of drainage. Falls and rapids are the rule rather than the exception, although they are shorter-lived where streams are eating into loose glacial drift than where they are attempting to cut into solid bedrock.

SIGNIFICANCE OF CONTINENTAL GLACIATION • The achievements of the great ice sheets affect the appearance and nature of several million square miles of the earth's surface. FIGURE 6–32 shows that the glaciers of Pleistocene times (the most recent great ice age) covered truly huge areas and that their much shrunken remnants are still present, chiefly in Antarctica and Greenland.

In Europe, the center of ice accumulation was on the edge of the Fenno-Scandian Shield, chiefly in what is now the mountainous backbone of Norway. From this elevated and somewhat elongated area, the ice pushed out in all directions. Much of it went out to sea, but at least half of it moved in such directions as vitally to affect the character of land. The

6–28

A drumlin. *The steep front end (direction from which the ice moved) has been left in woods, while the less steep portions have been almost entirely cleared and put to pasture and crop use.*

British Isles were glaciated as far south as London, and the Continent was covered as far south as a line extending from the mouths of the Rhine through central Germany and southern Poland, and on in a northward curving arc through the center of the Russian Plain to the lower valleys of the Ob and Yenesei rivers in northwestern Siberia.

An even larger area was affected in North America. Here there were four centers of ice action. One, the Labrador center, lay about midway between the eastern shore of Hudson Bay and the coast of Labrador, and another, the Keewatin, was about midway between the western shore of Hudson Bay and Great Slave Lake. Along the "height of land," or drainage divide, between Lake Superior and the southern margin of Hudson Bay was the Patrician center. Far to the west, in the crest areas of Canada's high mountains and on into Alaska, was the elongated Cordilleran center. From these four centers, the ice moved out in all directions until, at one stage, it covered prac-

6-30

THIS is a "kame and kettle" surface in a glacial depositional area in Pennsylvania. The knobby hills are kames and the depressions are kettles.

tically all of Canada, parts of Alaska, and a considerable portion of the northern United States. The last was glaciated as far south as a line extending roughly from Long Island across to the headwater section of the Ohio river, then along the Ohio and Missouri rivers

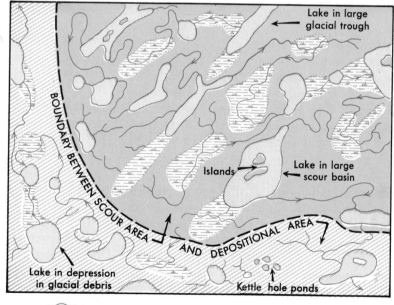

6-31

GLACIALLY deranged pattern of drainage in area of glacial scour (above dashed line) and in area of glacial deposition (below dashed line).

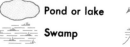

The Work of Moving Ice | 149

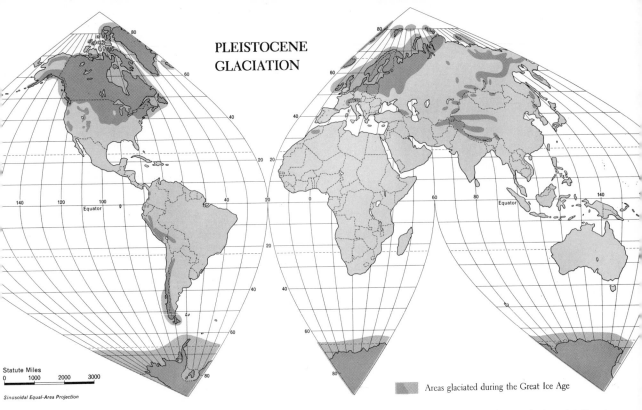

PLEISTOCENE
GLACIATION

Statute Miles
0   1000   2000   3000

Sinusoidal Equal-Area Projection

Areas glaciated during the Great Ice Age

6–32   APPRECIABLE *portions of the earth's surface were affected by continental glaciers during the Great Ice Age of Pleistocene times, especially in North America, Europe, and Antarctica. Large remnants of these continental glaciers still cover most of the areas of Greenland and Antarctica.*

to the northern portions of Montana, Idaho, and Washington. By the time the ice wasted away, it left nearly half of North America an inheritance of glacial landforms, glacial soils, and glacially deranged drainage. In terms of earth history, this legacy is so recent that it is as though the bequest had been made only yesterday. Only at the outermost margins of the oldest deposition has there been sufficient time for normal stream erosion largely to restore ordinary drainage conditions and create new, nonglacial landforms.

Elsewhere in the Northern Hemisphere (FIG. 6–33), ice sheets covered most of Greenland and Ellesmere Island, the Brooks Range of northern Alaska, and smaller areas in the American Rockies, the Cascades, and the Sierra Nevada. In Europe and Asia, they cov-

ered parts of the Alps, Pyrenees, Caucasus, and many of the ranges which stretch from the Pamir mountain hub to northeastern Siberia. Noteworthy is the fact that most of Siberia was not then, and never has been, glaciated. Off the shores of parts of Europe and Asia, the ice affected, on more than local scale, such islands and island groups as Iceland, Svalbard (Spitzbergen), Novaya Zemlya, and the New Siberians.

In the Southern Hemisphere, the ice smothered Antarctica and pushed on into the sea, representing a glacial mass at least twice the size of the United States. South America's ice sheets, affecting only a relatively small part of that continent, lay mainly in the southern Andes with smaller occurrences in the central and northern Andes. Elsewhere in the world,

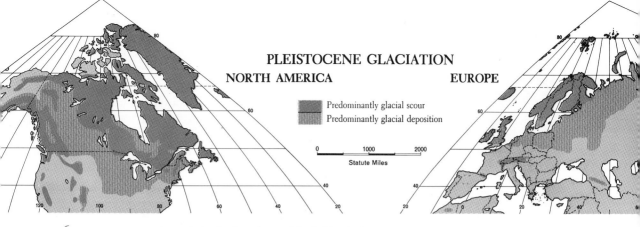

PLEISTOCENE GLACIATION

NORTH AMERICA   EUROPE

Predominantly glacial scour
Predominantly glacial deposition

0   1000   2000
Statute Miles

6–33   LARGE portions of the land surfaces of both North America and Europe were affected by continental glaciation in Pleistocene times in two different ways: (1) by glacial scouring, and (2) by
glacial deposition.

small masses covered much of South Island,
New Zealand, portions of Tasmania, and the
southern part of Australia's Great Dividing
Range. In Africa, there were minor glaciers
in the higher levels of the central highland
and lake district and, far to the northwest, in
the High Atlas.

Even this brief discussion makes clear that
the modifications wrought by continental glaciers are much more than matters of local
geographic concern. It can be appreciated,
also, that the present geography of Greenland
and Antarctica, more than 6 million square
miles of the earth's surface, is essentially an
"ice geography"; in those regions there remains
a "laboratory" for the study of the nature and
behavior of continental ice sheets like those
which moved over so much of the world during Pleistocene times.

Valley Glaciation

Quite in contrast to the extensive ice
blankets of continental glaciers are the much
smaller masses and tongues of valley ice (FIG.
6–24B). Each is born in a high valley head in
those parts of mountains where more snow
falls in winter than melts in summer. As soon

as the accumulating snow has been transformed into ice and the ice has acquired sufficient mass to move, the glacier begins its slow
journey down the valley. Again, motion means
power to do work; by the time the work is
finished and the ice gone, the typical V-shaped
mountain valley has been changed to the typical U-shaped form of valley glaciation, the
crestline sharpened and made more irregular,
and much of the whole preglacial surface
greatly modified (FIG. 6–34).

TYPICAL LANDFORMS AND DRAINAGE
CONDITIONS • The first major job accomplished by valley ice is the creation of a cirque.
This form is shaped in the valley head, where
the glacier is born and where its ice is thickest. By a combination of scour and frost action, the valley head is carved into a type of
small basin which has the form of an amphi-
theater, or of half of a bowl (FIG. 6–34). It is
very steep on three sides and the fourth side is
open in the down-valley direction. Where two
or more cirques are formed close together in
adjacent valley heads, the divides between
them are sharpened into knife-edge ridges, or
arêtes. If the ridges are lowered, mainly by
frost action and the removal of materials at
their bases by ice plucking, they become sad-

The Work of Moving Ice | 151

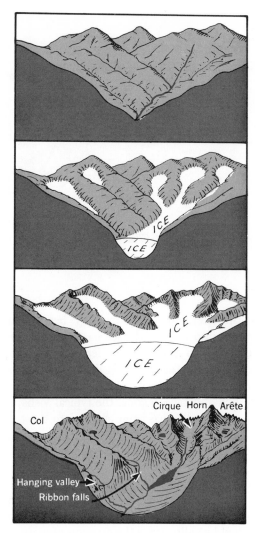

6–34

A PORTION of a mountain region before, during, and after valley glaciation. Notice how greatly this process of valley glaciation has modified the landform and the drainage conditions in the region.

As the glacial tongue moves down the valley from the cirque basin, its strong erosive action steepens the valley sides and somewhat deepens the valley bottom, thus changing the V to a wide and irregularly shaped U. Also, there may be streams of ice in tributary valleys which are creating U-shaped valleys of their own and which add their ice to the main glacial tongue. As a rule, the ice in tributary valleys, being less in volume and power, does not cut as deeply as the main ice flow and, hence, *hanging valleys* occur (FIG. 6–34).

Valley ice also builds landforms of deposition (FIG. 6–35). If the ice traveled the full length of the valley and emerged to fan out on a piedmont plain, a terminal morainal ridge is present. Because of its shape, it is called a *horseshoe moraine*. With retreating front, ground moraines are laid down, some of them out on the piedmont and some in the valley floor. Successive stages of stationary front are marked by the damlike forms of recessional moraines. Along the valley sides are hummocky ribbons of glacial debris in the form of *lateral moraines*. Where two valley glaciers join, the lateral morainal material which unites at the junction appears later as middle moraine, or *medial moraine*, in the main valley floor (FIG. 6–35).

A great part of the beauty of a glaciated valley results from glacially deranged drainage. The uppermost drainage feature is the *tarn*—a small lake which occupies the lowest portion of the cirque basin and sends its waters tumbling over the rocky edge of the cirque into the valley below. The lake waters are clear and cold and they make a perfect mirror which reflects the jagged pinnacles of the arête that stands against the sky hundreds of feet above. Farther down-valley, there is normally a series of small and shallow lakes which lie in local scour basins or are dammed behind deposits of morainal debris. Out on the piedmont, if the glacier went that far, there is usually a marginal lake impounded by the curve of a horseshoe moraine (FIG. 6–35). Connecting all the

dles, or *cols*, which mark low places in the mountain crests and which may be used as pass routes. Where at least three cirques have been created in a local area, the land between may be sharpened into a pyramidal peak, known as a *horn* (FIG. 6–34), such as the famous Matterhorn of the Swiss Alps.

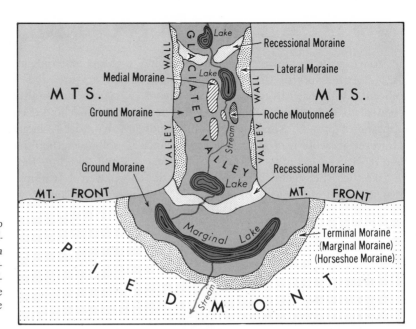

A DIAGRAMMATIC *sketch map showing the characteristic landform and drainage features in the lower portion of a completely glaciated mountain valley (in this instance the ice fanned out partially on the piedmont).*

lakes, from tarn to piedmont, are the alternately swift and sluggish waters of the valley stream. Where hanging valleys are present, the streams from them leap into space as misty ribbons of white water. A famous example of such *ribbon falls* is Bridalveil Fall in the glacial trough of Yosemite (FIG. 6-36).

SIGNIFICANCE OF VALLEY GLACIATION • This type of glaciation has affected much smaller portions of the land surface of the earth than has continental glaciation. Yet it occurs in hundreds of places, from the high mountain valleys of South Island, New Zealand, and the southern Andes to those of the Brooks Range of Alaska and the Stanovoi Range of Siberia. It is to be found in such well-known alpine regions as the Rockies and Sierra Nevada of North America and the Alps, Pyrenees, and Caucasus of Europe.

Many of the earth's glaciated valleys, as in Switzerland, are intensively utilized by man.

The valley ice created more level or nearly level land than was present before, thus providing more land suitable for crops, pasture, and settlements (FIG. 7-5). The glacially deranged drainage provides many natural reservoirs as well as falling waters to aid in the generation of hydroelectric power. And the total condition, marked by such features as tarns, arêtes, horns, hanging valleys, and ribbon falls, provides a scenic beauty which is the chief resource for recreational and resort industries. Perhaps it should also be pointed out that glaciated mountain valleys are important to lands which lie below, and sometimes miles away. The valleys, with their many natural reservoirs, collect waters which they release slowly. This not only minimizes dangers from floods in lower areas, but also insures a steadier supply of water for piedmont settlements, or, if the piedmont areas are in the dry lands, for irrigation.

THE WORK OF WIND

COMPARED to moving water and moving ice, the work of wind is relatively insignificant. Wind has carved no Grand Canyons, created no vast plains, nor changed the basic appearance of any Norways or Switzerlands. However, its work is of great local significance and it affects a few areas of appreciable size.

Like the other agents of erosion, wind does two jobs: one is the work of scour and transportation, the other the work of deposition.

6-36

BRIDALVEIL FALLS, one of several ribbon falls which plunge from tributary hanging valleys into the main portion of Yosemite Valley in part of California's Sierra Nevada.

Most materials moved by wind action are fine in texture and light in weight. These are mainly dusts, although at times of high velocity sands and even gravels are moved. The last are moved chiefly by sliding, bouncing, and rolling, rather than by large-scale picking up and carrying, for wind does not constitute a powerful working stream in the same sense as a stream of water or a moving ice mass. As would be expected, wind accomplishes most in regions of dry climates. In these regions, the regolith is usually dry and subject to easy blowing, and it is not held firmly in place by the scant vegetation. Thus some of the better places in which to examine the achievements of wind are in such areas as the Sahara, the Gobi of inner Asia, the deserts of Arabia, or the Great Plains or the Mojave Desert of the United States.

There are places in humid lands, however, in which the work of wind is locally pronounced, mainly along the edges of bodies of water where wind sweeps across the water surfaces to blow sands and to shape dunes along the shore and near-shore sections. A good example is to be seen in the Indiana Dunes located at the southern margin of Lake Michigan. Also, there are many other spots where man has overcultivated, or otherwise abused, the land, in which soils blow badly during the drier periods of the year.

Erosional Work

Those unused to dry-land conditions often complain more of the wind than they do of dryness and high temperatures. Wind seems ever-present and is most noticeable, as a rule, during the daylight hours. It dries the skin and nasal passages and it makes the eyes smart. It whips dust into the air and moves the sands (FIG. 5–18). During storms, as much as 16,000 tons of dust may be contained in one cubic mile of air; a storm covering an area 100 miles long and 50 miles wide has been estimated to pick up and carry some 20,000,000 tons of loess!

DEFLATION • The removal of materials from a surface by wind action is called *deflation*, or *eflation*. If a given region were always subjected to large-scale deflation, its entire surface would be considerably lowered, perhaps even changed into a large and ever-deepening basin. However, deflation surfaces are more apt to be local and somewhat temporary. The winds which rob them of fine materials also bring replacement materials from other areas, and a reversal of wind direction may result in the return of dusts which were removed previously. Of course, an area which is so constituted and situated as ultimately to lose more than it gains becomes a more or less permanent deflation surface. Regs, mentioned earlier, represent one type of deflation surface. In them, the finer materials have been removed and the coarse pebbles and gravels have been left behind to comprise a "gravel desert" (FIG. 6–12C).

Depressions known picturesquely as *blowouts* represent another type of deflation surface. Usually circular or oval in plan, they are formed by the blowing out of sands and finer materials from a given section until a type of basin results (FIG. 5–19A). In southeastern Wyoming and adjacent parts of Nebraska, for example, they are sufficiently numerous to affect the general appearance and the use of the land. Blowouts may vary in size from a few feet in diameter to those which are large enough to contain a cluster of buildings eight or ten stories in height. They are marked commonly by strings of sand dunes which lead away from them on their lee sides.

SCULPTURE AND POLISH • Where rocks, boulders, or the bases of cliffs are exposed to sandblast, the softer materials are worn away and the harder left in place. The results are pockets, caves, flutings, and other intricately etched forms. Similar action, operating over finer materials and more level surfaces, scours and buffs rocks and pebbles until they acquire a high degree of *desert polish*. The smoothness and shininess of the pebbles or other rock material is enhanced by the dry air drawing moisture and dissolved chemicals from the inside to the outside surfaces; this moisture, in evaporating at the surface, leaves the chemicals behind as a crust which is baked by the sun and polished by wind-blown sands and dusts.

Depositional Work

Sands and dusts carried by winds are deposited in many different forms and at varying distances from points of origin. Sands, which normally do not travel far, are shaped into several types of dunes; fine dusts, which may be transported hundreds or even thousands of miles, are laid down in thin sheets which take the mold of the land on which they settle, or, if in large amounts, create extensive loess plains which are independent of the terrain smothered by them.

DUNES • Dunes assume many different shapes. Some of them are merely veneerlike sheets, or *sheet dunes*, which are spread over a surface like a blanket. They occur most commonly on flattish areas, but in places they are to be seen extending up the slope of a desert hill or draped over the nose of a ridge (FIG. 6–37). Because of their light color, they then may be seen for long distances. Other dunes may be no more than small knobs, or *hillock dunes*, formed where sands have collected around obstacles such as clumps of desert brush. If the brush succeeds in keeping its head above the sand, the queer appearance illustrated by the Devil's Cornfield of Death Valley is provided (FIG. 6–38). Some dunes, called *barchans*, are crescent-shaped in ground plan, very strongly resembling crescent moons superimposed on the general surface. Perhaps the most common type of dunes are those in the form of wavelike ridges, the ridges being oriented at right angles to the major winds. Such *ridge dunes* may be a few feet high and long, or they may loom as high as 100 feet or

6-37   A sheet dune *in the Colorado Desert in southeastern California. At times of stronger winds, sand is blown from the hillock dune area in the foreground and strewn as a sandy veneer, or sheet dune, up the side of the rocky ridge.*

6-38

Hillock dunes in the Devil's Cornfield, in central portion of Death Valley, California. Tough desert shrubs trap and collect some of the moving sand. As the sand accumulates, the shrubs must grow above it, thus producing the appearance of shocks of corn.

more and extend in unbroken ranks for several miles. Where dunes cover many square miles, they comprise typical erg areas (FIG. 6–12B); where locally developed, they may be thought of as miniature ergs.

Many dunes and dune regions pose problems for man. Their coarse sands provide no resource and their disconcerting habit of moving slowly and inexorably across a countryside often results in the covering and abandonment of man's establishments. Scores of oases, and the buildings on them, as in Arabia and northern Africa, have been overwhelmed by marching lines of *active dunes*, although later, after the dunes moved by, they may be reoccupied—even the same buildings as used previously. In humid lands, migrating dunes are sand-fed from shores and river beds; fields, orchards, buildings, and even railroads and major highways may be smothered, or kept clear only at considerable expense.

LOESS DEPOSITS • Loess is fairly common in either small or large deposits throughout most of the dry lands. Strangely enough, many of the truly extensive loess deposits are to be found in regions of humid climates. Outstanding examples are found in parts of the Mis-

FREDERICK G. CLAPP

6–39

BADLY eroded loess deposits in part of Shansi Province, China.

sissippi valley, the North China Plain, and the Argentine Pampas. Large loess deposits are actually worth more than gold mines for they are highly productive, especially if they occur where nature supplies enough water for normal crop growth. In steppe regions, as the southern part of the Russian Plain, their inherent fertility warrants the use of dry-farming practices, at least temporarily. Moreover, loessal soils are comparatively retentive of moisture so that they are not as "droughty" under semiarid conditions as one might expect.

There is some argument as to the source or sources of the fine wind-blown dusts which have created the world's major loessal plains. It was thought formerly that they were derived entirely from steppes and deserts. Now much evidence has been gathered to show that a great deal of the loess originated within humid lands, particularly where broad river plains furnished winds with abundant fine material and, more especially, where rivers carried exorbitant loads of fine glacial outwash which, after deposition, became important sources of supply of fine dusts. In any event, these wind-worked materials have provided man with several large, and many small, fruitful plains.

In a dissected area, the presence of loess deposits is indicated not only in the soil characteristics but also in very steep valley slopes. The bluffs at Council Bluffs, Iowa, are loessal, and they are so steep as to form palisades. In the loessal hills of China, just west of the North China Plain, many of the roads lie in the bottoms of loessal trenches. For countless years, turning wheels and animal hoofs have stirred up the dust and the wind has blown the dusts away. Thus the roadways have sunk slowly into the loessal deposits. In the same area, man long ago wiped out the forests and allowed the summer rains to gully and channel the land; today, there are *badlands* which cover hundreds of square miles, and the inhabitants become more and more desperate as they attempt to find and maintain enough level land for the production of vital crops (FIG. 6–39).

The Work of Wind | 157

Landforms and the Agents of Erosion and Deposition

• REVIEW QUESTIONS •

1. Distinguish between sheet erosion and rill erosion.
2. Explain why a slight increase in stream velocity results in greatly increased ability to move materials.
3. What is meant by base-level?
4. Account for the shape of a youthful valley.
5. Explain the formation of valley flats in a mature valley.
6. Draw a surface profile to illustrate the landform nature of an area comprised of youthful valleys and youthful interfluves; of mature valleys and youthful interfluves.
7. If you were in a typical karst area, what criteria would you use to determine whether the area was young, mature, or old?
8. Explain the development of galleries in karst.
9. If you were a farmer whose land was pitted with numerous sinkholes, would you prefer the sinkholes to be of the doline or ponor type? Why?
10. What is the basic reason for the differences in valley forms in dry lands as compared to those in humid lands?
11. Why is it that, even with continued erosion, wadies tend to maintain steep sides and essentially level bottoms?
12. Restate the following quotation in simple

language: "The hamada margin contains many deep wadies and its former extent is marked by numerous mesas and buttes. Nearby, in a lower area, are several small playas separated by miniature ergs."

13. Explain the origin of an alluvial fan.
14. What will a mountain-and-bolson region look like by the time it attains the stage of old age?
15. Discuss some of the problems of the engineer whose job it is to construct a modern highway across a large mountain-and-bolson region, or across a succession of ergs and hamadas.
16. Describe the landforms which are normally found along subdued, shallow-water coasts.
17. Consult a modern geology textbook for discussions of the theories of ice motion in glaciers.
18. Explain the origin of the Greenland icecap.
19. List as many reasons as possible why it makes a great difference whether a region was glaciated or not.
20. Distinguish between: (a) morainal ridge and ground moraine; (b) drumlin and *roche moutonnée*; (c) outwash plain and glaciolacustrine plain; (d) kettle hole and sinkhole.
21. Compare central Indiana with the central portion of Ontario in terms of landforms, drainage, and soil conditions.
22. Describe the succession of landforms and drainage features which you would expect to see in traveling from the head to the mouth of a typical glaciated valley.
23. Just how has glaciation made certain rugged mountain regions more habitable and more useful?
24. What is meant by a surface of aeolian deflation?
25. Distinguish between loessal dunes and sand dunes.
26. Two areas are "covered" by sand dunes; one has a barchan surface, the other has a wave dune surface. What is the difference in appearance of the two areas?

7 The Landforms of the Continents

UNITED NATION

⟪ THIS *chapter focuses attention on the continental patterns of the earth's major landforms. These are among the more basic of geographical patterns and, because of this, are described and discussed in the text, as well as depicted on the maps. Moreover, the chapter, by example and reference, emphasizes the important fact that parts of the earth are mountains or plains while other parts are plateaus or hills. In addition, the chapter gives wide sampling of the many different types of mountains, plains, plateaus, and hills.*

MOUNTAINS

OUNTAINS cover very appreciable portions of the earth's surface (FIG. 7-2). Because so many of us live in lowlands far removed from most of the earth's mountainous regions, we may not be aware of the extent, pattern of distribution, or variety of the world's highest and most rugged areas. Because of inadequate surveys, no one knows exactly what proportion of the land surface is truly mountainous. However, a study of the world map of mountains will show that they occur in many and extensive areas, and that some continents are more mountainous than others. For example, Asia, despite vast areas of plains, hills, and plateaus, has hundreds of thousands of square miles of mountain lands—enough, in fact, to equal the size of Europe. On the other hand, mountains are almost nonexistent in Australia; only a small section in the southeast is sufficiently high and rugged to be considered mountainous. Perhaps it would be safe to say that at least 10 per cent of the exposed face of the earth's crust is mountainous. This may not sound like a great deal, but it means that at least one out of every ten square miles of land is mountainous. In addition, there are the millions of square miles of mountains which are drowned by seas and oceans. All except the completely submerged mountains stand as barriers to the movement of man and his goods, although most of them serve, at least to some degree, as human habitats.

The Pacific Ring

One of the conspicuous parts of the world pattern of mountains is the "ring" which encircles the Pacific Basin. If one examines the Pacific Ocean on a physical globe, he sees a rim of high, rugged country which practically encompasses the broad Pacific waters. Tracing from the far south, the jagged and nearly ice-drowned mountains of Antarctica are first. Then, on the western margin of South America, other mountains extend high and unbroken from Tierra del Fuego and the Strait of Magellan to the shore of the Caribbean Sea. These are the famous Andes, the longest and most continuous belt of high country on earth (FIG. 7-2). Possessing no low passes, the Andes constitute a physical barrier which even modern aircraft cross with difficulty. To this day, they act as a "separator" between the limited lowlands of the west coast and the major part of the continent. Were it not for the floors of occasional high-level basins which are tucked within the Andean ranges, no more than foothill portions of the Andes would be populated.

From South America, the Pacific ring continues in the mountains of the Central American backbone. Fortunately, this portion is broken by plains and hills, as in Panama and Nicaragua, and in Mexico's Isthmus of Tehuantepec, so that the barrier effect is less pronounced than in the Andes. Again there are some intermountain basins to serve as human abodes. These are welcomed not only because of the presence of comparatively level land, but because they are sufficiently high to provide more comfortable and healthful living conditions than are to be found in the adjacent hot and damp tropical lowlands.

Northwest of the Isthmus of Tehuantepec is a major mountain knot which splits to form Mexico's Eastern Sierra Madre and Western Sierra Madre ranges, between which lies the Mexican Plateau. Because the heart of Mexico, in the sense of numbers of people and governmental establishments, is in the southern part of the plateau, the two Sierras act as barriers between the most densely populated area and the outside world. The Western Sierra rather effectively isolates the northwestern part of

7-1

[OPPOSITE, TOP] NEPALESE *porters against the backdrop of the crestline of 18,480-foot Gangja La in the Himalayas.*

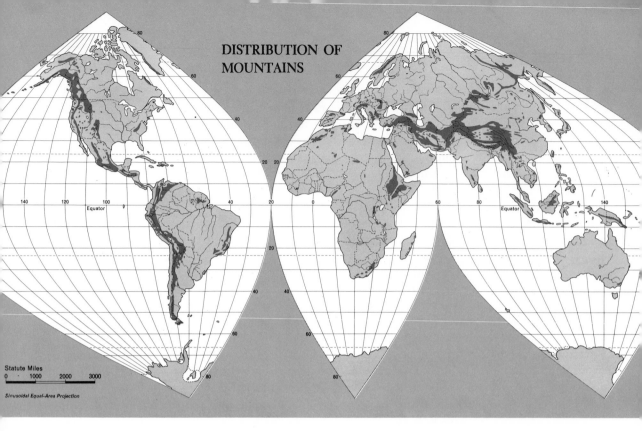

DISTRIBUTION OF
MOUNTAINS

Statute Miles
0 · 1000 2000 3000

Sinusoidal Equal-Area Projection

7–2   THE world patterns of mountainous areas extend to every continent and every major country, with
the greatest mountain masses lying in the Americas, Europe, and Asia. Antarctica's mountains
are almost drowned by ice, which transforms the continent into a plateau (see FIG. 7–16).

the country from Mexico City. After a break in portions of northern Mexico and the southwestern United States, high country again rises to form the Rockies and, closer to the ocean, such ranges as the Sierra Nevada (FIG. 7–3), the Coast Ranges, and the Cascades. In addition to being "broken" in the south, the American Rockies are sufficiently separated in the Wyoming Corridor to allow routes to pass through without too great difficulty. The southern "break" allowed the development of the Santa Fe Trail and the more modern transportation lines which were to follow; the Wyoming Corridor has played a similar role in connection with the Oregon Trail and today's highway and railway lines. Within the Rockies themselves, many valleys and local basins have become ranchlands and, here and there, in the

higher sections, lumbering and recreation have become important. In some ways, the Sierra Nevada–Cascade backbone is much more of a barrier than the Rockies (FIG. 7–2). Its eastern face is very abrupt and there is no easily crossed pass all the way from the southern part of California to the gorges of the Columbia river.

Farther north, the Canadian Coast Ranges and the Canadian Rockies form a continuous series of unbroken barriers all the way to southern Alaska. There the Coast Ranges merge, without any easily crossed passes, with the great arc of the Alaska Range. The Alaska Range, with its 20,320-foot-high Mount McKinley (FIG. 7–4), rises as a complex wall between the Pacific and the interior of Alaska, thus making transportation difficult between such places as Seward and Fairbanks, as well

162 | *The Landforms of the Continents*

7-3

THE *sheer face of Half Dome in the Sierra Nevada looms over part of the Yosemite valley, California.*

as walling off the interior from moderating marine air masses. The western part of the Alaska Range slowly drowns itself to become first the Alaska Peninsula and later the Aleutian Islands. North of the Yukon country, the east-west trending Brooks Range stands as a continuous wall between the Arctic Coastal Plain and the interior. Because of mountains and their particular trends, the heart of Alaska is most accessible, in terms of ease of construction of land routes, from the east, and in terms of sea and land routes, from the west (FIG. 7–2). However, the isolation of northwestern Canada and of the Bering Sea have not encouraged the development of the routes which are easier from the standpoint of landform conditions.

The remainder of the Pacific ring lies on the western side of the Pacific. It extends, interrupted by drownings and by nonmountainous sections, from Kamchatka through the islands of Japan, Taiwan, the Philippines, New Guinea, and New Zealand, and back to Antarctica. The mountains on the western side of the Pacific are much less continuous and barrierlike (FIG. 7–2), but, in general, they represent, latitude for latitude, the same radical changes from other landform conditions as are found on the eastern side of the Pacific. In islands such as Honshu, New Guinea, and South Island of New Zealand, the mountains bulk large in the total geography, as scenery, as habitats, and as determiners of climatic distribution.

The Pamir Mountain Hub and Its Spokes

The complex mountain node of the Pamirs, often referred to as the "roof of the world," lies in the extreme northerly tip of Pakistan and adjacent parts of the U.S.S.R., Afghanistan, and China. From it extend three broad and partly broken spokes which reach for thousands of miles across the earth (FIG. 7–2). This "hub" with its "spokes," together with the Pacific ring, completes the general plan, or pattern, of world mountain distribution. One spoke, trending northeasterly, stretches across the heart of Asia to farthest northeast Siberia. It includes such famous mountain lands as the Tien Shan, the Altais, Sayans, Yablonois, and the Stanovois. Beginning at the Pamirs, one could follow, with short interruptions, high mountain crests for a distance of nearly 5000 miles. Actually there are a few breaks, as between the Tien Shan and the Altai Mountains and between the Sayans and the Yablonois, and these breaks long have been followed by caravan routes. To this day, the only rail line which crosses the "ridgepole" is the Trans-Siberian, which takes advantage of the break in the mountains near and southeast of Lake Baikal. Of course, the long-continued isola-

7-4   MOUNT MC KINLEY, *highest peak (20,320 feet) in North America, tops the snowy and icy wastes of the Alaska Range. Note the many valley glaciers.*

tion of inner Asia reflects many things, such as great distances, scarcity of water, unfriendly tribesmen, political affiliations, and so on, but much of it results from the presence and alignment of great mountains.

Another spoke, broader and more complex than the first, extends southeasterly from the Pamirs. It includes the highest ranges on the earth's surface. Among them are the Karakoram, the Kunlun, the Altyn or Astin, and the famous Himalaya (FIG. 7–1). Along with others which reach to the edge of China's extensive hill lands, these ranges form the world's most impressive mountain bulwark. For some 2000 miles, numerous peaks and crests attain altitudes of 27,000 to 29,000 feet. Between them, the lower parts are only com-

paratively lower, for there is no easily crossed pass from the Pamirs in the west to the edge of China proper in the east. Thus, interior Asia and India are effectively separated from each other, almost as though they lay in different continents. In addition, the bulwark blocks the movement of moisture-laden air masses from the south and thereby plays an important part in the creation of the "dry heart of Asia" to the north. Farther east, as well as southeast, less continuous mountains occur here and there in Burma and Indochina and form the backbones of Sumatra and Java.

The third of the spokes which lead out from the Pamir hub extends to the west (FIG. 7–2). As far west as Turkey and southern Russia, there is no major break for the north-south flow of man and his goods. The lands of the Persian Gulf and Mesopotamia are separated from Russian Turkestan and southeastern Russia nearly as effectively as India is shut off from inner Asia. Scores of ranges comprise this vast mountain country, among them the Hindu Kush, Elburz, and Caucasus. West of Turkey and southeastern Russia, there are many large and small mountain regions. However, they lack the pronounced continuity noted in the high, rugged areas of Asia and Asia Minor. Among them and along their borders are plains and lowland corridors leading in many directions (FIG. 7–2), and well within them are numerous fertile valleys quite in contrast to the arid conditions that border the major mountain regions of so much of Asia. Chief among the mountainous regions west of Turkey—that is, in southern Europe—are the Rhodope, Balkans, Pindus, Dinaric Alps, Carpathians, Alps, Apennines, and Pyrenees. The farthest west extension is found in the High Atlas Range of northwestern Africa. Many of these regions, such as the Alps and the Carpathians, offer favorable human habitats in lower- and middle-level valleys (FIG. 7–5) and all of them are conspicuously tied into the life of adjacent lowlands—whether in connection with passes or with such activities as summer grazing, lumbering, mining, recreation, or the generation of hydroelectric power.

Other Mountain Regions

In addition to the Pacific ring and the Pamir hub with its three major spokes, there are other mountain areas scattered widely over the earth's surface (FIG. 7–2). However, they are not as extensive or numerous as those already noted. In North America, comparatively small sections of the Appalachians constitute true mountain country, as in the Great Smokies of eastern Tennessee and the western Carolinas, in a part of the Adirondacks in New York, and in portions of north-central New England. The northern part of the rocky coast of Labrador is

SWISSAIR

7–5

AN *inhabited glaciated valley (the Lötschental) high in the Swiss Alps. Note how the villages, to the left of the river, stand out in the winter scene. Note, also, the marked difference between the sunnier side (adret) of the valley, to the left, and the shadier side (ubac), to the right.*

mountainous, as is much of the ice-free section of western Greenland. The Caribbean region, particularly in extreme southeastern Cuba and much of western Haiti, has a taste, here and there, of the earth's high and rugged lands. In South America, far east of the Andes, there is a considerable mountain cluster in eastern Brazil and one in and just south of the Guianas. In Europe, far north of most of the mountain areas of that "continent," occur the Norwegian mountains. Between Europe and Greenland, minor spots of mountain country appear in Iceland and Svalbard (Spitzbergen). The broad continent of Africa has comparatively few mountains. The High Atlas has been noted above, as the end of the complex mountain spoke extending westward from the Pamirs. In addition, there are the mountains of Ethiopia (Abyssinia), the scattered mountains of eastern equatorial Africa, southern Africa, and the heart of the Sahara, and a few others. Australia has only one truly alpine area; this occurs in the southeast and it represents the highest and most rugged portion of the otherwise hilly Great Dividing Range.

Mountain Types

Mountains are not "just mountains," for, like other landforms, or like human beings, they have their own individual characteristics. Some mountains are narrow and jagged, some broad and generally rounded, some are blocky, and others are comprised of sharp, conical peaks. While they are all mountains, their individual characteristics help to provide great variety in the physical scene and are strongly reflected in human activities as man attempts to live in parts of them or to build his lines of transport and communication across or around them. There are many shapes, or forms, to be seen in mountainous regions, but four types stand out particularly: *folded mountains, fault-block mountains, dome mountains,* and *volcanic mountains.*

FOLDED MOUNTAINS • Mountains of this type have the general aspect of a corrugated iron roof expressed on a grand scale (FIG. 7–6). As was pointed out earlier, the earth's crust is under great strain and stress. In some regions, the stresses result in the folding of the crust into a series of mammoth anticlines and synclines (FIG. 5–13A). Such diastrophic activity does not necessarily produce alpine forms; it may not be pronounced enough to provide the required high elevations, but instead may result in hilly lands or nothing more than appreciable undulations in a plains country. However, when diastrophism occurs on a grand

scale, and when uplift more than keeps pace with down-wearing, folded mountains are the result. Such mountains are represented by the Juras and the Alps, although the Alps as a whole look less like a series of great folds than do the Juras. The fact that certain mountains are classified as "folded" does not mean that other types of deformation are not present. It means simply that folding has been the dominant process in their formation. Where dissection, as by running water, has created many deep canyons and sharp ridges between canyons, folded mountains have lost much of their corrugated appearance even though the underlying bedrock, wherever exposed, shows the familiar upbends of anticlines and downbends of synclines.

FAULT-BLOCK MOUNTAINS • The origin of mountains of this sort is portrayed clearly in their outward appearance. They actually look like huge and jumbled blocks (FIG. 7–7). One can appreciate readily from their shape that the earth's crust where they occur has broken into mammoth blocklike compartments, some of which have been heaved slowly upward and, as a rule, tilted from the horizontal (FIG. 5–13D). There is no better example of this type of crustal disturbance than a mountain region which has been mentioned previously—the Sierra Nevada of California (FIG. 5–9). This entire range has the outward appearance of one huge block which has been upthrust and slightly tilted. The steep face of the block is toward the east and the gentle face toward the west. Just as folded mountains have undergone more than folding alone, so has the Sierra Nevada block been intricately folded and intruded with volcanic materials, but, nevertheless, the dominant mountain-building process responsible for its present form is block-faulting. Other samples of fault-block mountains are found in the Charleston Mountains (Spring Mountains) near Las Vegas, Nevada; the Panamints, which border the western edge of the hot, arid trench of Death Valley; and several of the mountains of equatorial Africa.

7–6   ONE *type of folded mountains: the ridges rise like waves in the surface of the higher Appalachians in the eastern United States.*

DOME MOUNTAINS • The well-known Black Hills of South Dakota and Wyoming represent a doming of the earth's crust which has been pronounced enough to create a small area of mountain condition (FIG. 5–17). As their name implies, most of them are hills; but, in the central and higher section, one sees all the earmarks of mountain geography, including the characteristic vertical zoning of landscape. The Black Hills are not primarily folded or faulted, although both folds and faults may

be seen in places where the bedrock has been exposed by weathering and stream erosion. Instead, they owe their existence and general shape to forces which produced a broad dome in formerly horizontal layers of sedimentary rock. Underneath the sedimentary strata is a mass of igneous rock which, in its upsurge, may have been the cause of the blisterlike form. Down-wearing has exposed the igneous core and local dissection of the core has created high relief. Dissection of the domal structure

Mountains | 167

7–7 A COMPLICATED, *tilted block of the earth's crust forms an individual fault-block mountain in the Amargosa valley area of southern Nevada.*

as a whole has produced roughly concentric rings of in-facing ridges, or *cuestas*. The latter are typical of dissected domes, whether of mountainous scale or not, and each one marks the exposure of a dipping rock layer which is more resistant to wearing away than are the adjacent layers (FIG. 7–8).

Doming on a huge scale occurs in the Rockies, as, for example, in the San Juan Mountains of southwestern Colorado. Here the doming has been both broad and high. The result is that some of the higher spots, despite long exposure to the agents of degradation, are 13,000 to 14,000 feet above sea level

and 4000 to 5000 feet above adjacent lower areas. Examination of the rock structure of the San Juans indicates that rock members comprising the broad dome are intricately faulted and folded, but that the major action was domal upheaval; hence, the mountains are essentially domal, rather than folded or faulted.

VOLCANIC MOUNTAINS · One type of volcanic mountain is the cone-shaped volcano, like Fujiyama or Vesuvius. This type owes its being and form to the piling up of successive layers of materials which have issued from the earth by way of pipelike vents (FIG. 5–15A). The superheated materials, comprised of lavas,

7–8 AN *oblique air view of a small, eroded structural dome adjacent to Sinclair, Wyoming. Note the encircling and in-facing cuestas.*

BALSLEY, U.S. GEOLOGICAL SURVEY

gases, and steam, are exuded into the open air, often with tremendous explosive force. . At times of most violent eruption, gases, steam, and rocks are hurled high into the air. The larger pieces fall as "volcanic bombs," while the smaller rock particles—the volcanic ashes —sift slowly downward. At the same time, flows of molten rock issue from the main vent, or subsidiary vents, and move over the surface. It is the alternate layers of lava and ash which, through time, build up the conical form (FIG. 7–9). If volcanic activity is sufficiently common, the cone may be built up to truly mountainous proportions. Occasionally, the conical type of volcano is so violently eruptive as practically to destroy itself. In 1883, Krakatoa, a conical island between Java and Sumatra, suddenly exploded with almost unbelievable force. Within a short time, only a blasted stump remained and the surrounding sea was thickly blanketed with ash and pumice. Volcanic dusts were hurled into the upper atmosphere where they circulated slowly around the earth. Very red sunrises and sunsets, resulting from the dust, occurred in places as far away as London, England. The noise of the blast was heard 2000 miles away and great sea waves swept onto the beaches of neighboring islands to cause a loss of life estimated at 35,000 persons. Even when less violently active, the conical type of volcano may destroy life and property in surrounding areas, as have the many eruptions of Vesuvius, particularly the eruption which destroyed the cities of Pompeii and Herculaneum, and much of the nearby countryside, in 79 A.D.

The other major type of volcano is known variously as the *shield type, caldron type, quiescent type,* and *dome type.* "Dome type" perhaps best describes its form (FIG. 5–15B). Each dome volcano represents a nonexplosive accumulation of lavas, sheet on sheet and flow on flow, which has created a great mass in the form of a huge inverted bowl. In the upper portion of each dome occur one or more shallow craters, or "caldrons." The lavas boil and bubble in

7–9

CINDER cone, ash, and lava accumulations of the recent, active volcano Paricutín, about 190 miles west of Mexico City.

these caldrons. At times of pronounced activity, they boil over and lavas move in fiery tongues down the flanks of the dome, there to cool and harden and thus add another bit to the mass of the volcano. The Hawaiian Islands themselves are excellent and famous examples of dome volcanoes. The islands owe their very existence to lava flows which have piled up on the bottom of the sea and then, with further addition, have pushed above the waters of the Pacific. On the island of Hawaii itself, the higher points are about 13,000 feet above sea level—but more than 20,000 feet above the sea floor where the initial construction began! Haleakala, on the island of Maui, is known to thousands of tourists from all parts of the world (FIG. 7–10).

7-10   SMALL cinder cones and "ropy" lava (foreground) within the wide crater of Haleakala, on the island of Maui, Hawaii.

The occurrence of volcanic mountains, especially those of the conical type, is surprisingly widespread. They are most numerous in regions of very active diastrophism, particularly along the crests of sharply folded mountains. There, they arrange their steep cones in "marching" lines along the higher crests. Along such crests, the rocks of the earth's crust are being stretched and broken and it is relatively easy for the volcanic materials to escape. Typical "strings" of volcanoes are to be found over nearly the full extent of the Andes, the folded mountain section of Honshu, the alpine backbones of Java and Sumatra, the Alaska Range, and the island arcs of the Aleutians, Kurils, and Philippine group. Considerable numbers also are to be found in southern Europe, east-central Africa, Asia Minor, and the mountain heart of Asia, as well as in Iceland.

PLAINS

IN TURNING from a discussion of mountainous lands to plains, one goes from the most conspicuous to the least conspicuous of the major landforms. Plains occur in all the continents except Antarctica (FIG. 7-11). Some of them are small and some are extremely large; but, whether small or large, they are generally the earth's most productive, most easily traversed, and most densely populated regions. So large a proportion of the earth's inhabitants live in plains that the number supported in plateau, hill, and mountain country is comparatively negligible. Most of the land, and even air, routes over which man moves himself and his goods lie on and over plains. What has just been said does not mean that all plains

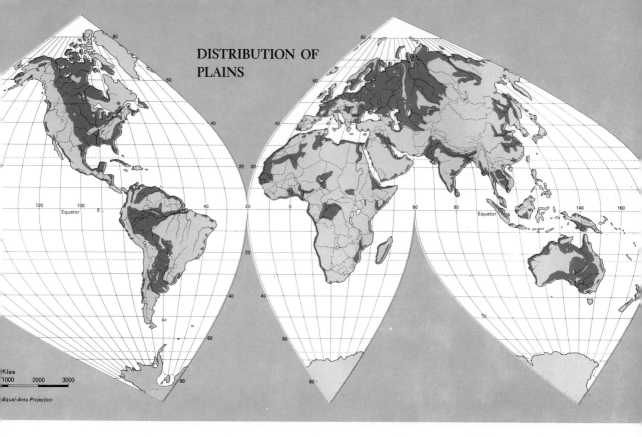

7–11   THE *world patterns of plains areas spread over vast portions of all the continents except Antarctica. It is in plains areas that are found most of the great concentrations of the world's
population.*

are highly productive, readily habitable, or easily traveled. For example, most of the extensive plains of Australia are deserts and semideserts; the Arctic Coastal Plain of Alaska is so cold so much of the time that it can hardly be called a readily habitable land; the low plain of western Siberia is so swampy as to make widespread use difficult. Yet, by and large, it is the plains regions which have had and will undoubtedly continue to have the greatest significance for mankind as a whole.

North American Plains

Except for Europe and Australia, North America has proportionately more area in plains than has any other continent. The largest plain of North America sweeps all the way from the subtropical shore of the Gulf of Mexico to the cold waters of the Arctic Ocean, a distance of nearly 3000 miles (FIG. 7–11). On the west, this vast interior plain is flanked by hills, plateaus and, most of all, by high mountains. On the east, in the southern portion, it reaches to the Atlantic and sends an ever-narrowing finger northeastward as far as southern New England. Farther north, the main mass of the great interior plain is largely cut off from the Atlantic by the Appalachian uplands and the higher and rougher portion of the Laurentian Upland. A notable corridor of appreciable width, the St. Lawrence Lowland, breaks through the eastern barrier to join the Great Lakes region with the Gulf of St. Lawrence. However, from the Gulf of Mexico to the Arctic Ocean, the plain is only slightly interrupted, even by low hills, and one may travel from the delta lands of the Mississippi to those of the Mackenzie without being forced to climb higher than 900 feet above sea level.

North America contains many lesser plains, some of them of considerable size. The low, swampy plain of western Alaska is as large as Ireland. Alaska's Arctic Coastal Plain is nearly as large as Finland. Other plains, smaller, but much more hospitable to man than the two just noted, occur in the Puget Sound–Willamette Valley sections of Washington and Oregon, the Central Valley and the Coachella–Imperial Valley of California, and the lowland sections of Mexico and Central America. There are still others such as those of Nova Scotia, New Brunswick, and Newfoundland.

All in all, North America is fortunate in its possession of so much territory that is easy to lace with routes, grow crops on, build great cities on, and, in general, to spread out on. To be sure, much of the plains land is a bit too dry, other parts are too swampy, and still others are cold and isolated. But there is plenty of good usable plains land left. If one thinks only of the major agricultural regions of the United States, he will realize that nearly all of the Cotton Belt, all of the Corn Belt, and all of the Winter Wheat and Spring Wheat Belts spread over hundreds of thousands of square miles of easily cultivated plains. Our resource of plains is of inestimable value. How different the United States would be if mountains, hills, and plateaus swept unbroken from the Atlantic to the Pacific!

South American Plains

In South America, as in North America, the lowlands are mainly interior plains. Their greatest extent is north-south (FIG. 7–11); they are walled in to the west by high mountains and to the east by other types of uplands, chiefly hill and plateau combinations with some comparatively minor occurrences of

mountains. The largest interior plain includes the Pampas and the Great Plains of Argentina and extends northward through the Paraná Lowlands to join with the widest portion of the Amazon Plain. A relatively narrow lowland corridor connects the larger part of the Amazon Plain with the Atlantic. By following the course of this interior plain, one can travel from Buenos Aires to the mouths of the Amazon without ascending more than 900 feet above sea level at any point. Most of the plain is more isolated than the interior plain of North America. Part of this isolation, or comparative isolation, reflects such items as great distances, unfavorable or relatively unfavorable climates, several occurrences of huge swamps and marshes, and lack of government control in far interior holdings. The general isolation reflects, moreover, the landform conditions to the west and east. The Andes constitute a much higher and more continuous barrier than do the Rockies. Also, the eastern uplands are broader and less broken than those in North America. From Rio de Janeiro to the nearest part of Brazil's interior plain is 800 miles; from Rio to the Amazon Plain proper is nearly 2000 miles—in between is little more than sparsely populated, undeveloped hill and plateau country.

The second largest continuous plain in South America is that of the floor portion of the Orinoco Basin. This extends from the Orinoco to the foot of the northern Andes, a distance of 1000 miles. It is largely shut off from the Caribbean by the eastward arc of the Andes and from the Amazon country by the generally hilly and incompletely explored Guiana Highlands. Within itself it is handicapped by a type of climate which is too dry at one season and too wet at another.

The remainder of South America's plains are small and scattered. Those which lie outside of the hot, wet tropics have proved, at least so far, easier to live in and develop. The Central Valley of Chile and the coastal plain of Uruguay are instances.

7–12 A SEA *of wheat in a sea of plain: wheat harvesting in the Krasnodar territory of the southern Russian Plain.*

European Plains

The major plain of Europe is very wide in the east and narrow in the west (FIG. 7–11). Its wider portion, known as the Russian Plain, extends from the Black and Caspian Seas to the Arctic Ocean. South of the hilly lands of the Urals, the Russian Plain merges with the plains of Russian Turkestan and the southern end of the West Siberian Plain. While certain portions of the Russian Plain are arid and semiarid (in the extreme south and southeast) and other parts are cold and appreciably swampy (in the north), most of the plain is highly productive. This plain furnishes the Soviet Union with the bulk of its great agricultural strength (FIG. 7–12) and provides easy access to the Baltic and the Black Sea regions, as well as to Asia and the Arctic. The plain narrows westward in Europe. Part of it en-

circles the Baltic Sea and its fingerlike, westernmost extension curves through the Low Countries and western France to the base of the abruptly rising Pyrenees. The lack of mountains and any considerable hilly country between this latter portion and the Atlantic insures western Europe easy access to the sea. It also allows marine air masses to penetrate readily, thus providing relatively moderate, moist climates many miles inland.

Elsewhere in Europe are smaller plains important out of all proportion to their size. Among these are the plains portions of the British Isles, the plains of the Po river in northern Italy, the highland-enclosed basin of Hungary, Romania, and Yugoslavia, and the Walachian Plain of Romania. Others include the Rhône valley of France and the Spanish plains in Aragon and Andalusia. Many minute plains lie between the sea and encroaching

Plains | 173

hills and mountains in Italy and Greece. On these sea-fronting plains developed the civilizations of Greece and Rome and the nuclei of empires.

African Plains

Such a small percentage of the total surface of Africa is plains that it might be referred to as the "plains-poor continent." However, Africa is a large continent, and its plains, which appear insignificant, actually cover several hundred thousand square miles (FIG. 7–11). Perhaps the most famous of African plains is the floor of the Congo Basin which covers an area larger than France. Set well into the interior of the continent, the Congo Plain is surrounded by tablelike uplands which are in turn surrounded by hilly country. This situation, coupled with its hot, wet climate and dense forest growth, has caused it to be more than a little isolated. It reminds one, in many ways, of the wider portion of the Amazon Plain. Another large plain, of which little is heard, occurs in the western part of northern Africa. It extends along the coast for 1500 miles, from the edge of Morocco into Portuguese Guinea. Inland, it sends an angling and branching finger well into the Sahara. Rocky and, in part, sandy, this arid and windswept plain has little to offer man except for the petroleum deposits so recently brought into production.

The remaining plains of Africa are smaller and much more elongated than the two noted above. Most of them occupy narrow coastal lowlands and send tentacles for various distances toward the interior. Some of them are dry lands, such as those of southern Tunisia, Somalia, and South-West Africa; others are hot and steamy, like the Niger Delta. Most famous of them all is the plains area of the delta and lower valley of the Nile. Here, under desert conditions ameliorated by irrigation water from the Nile, flourished one of the earliest civilizations; here, today, is the densest population of all Africa.

Asian Plains

Asia, largest of the land masses and nearly twice the size of North America, possesses one truly vast plain. This extends from the Caspian depression to the Arctic, a distance equal to the east-west extent of the United States (FIG. 7–11). It varies greatly in width, being widest in western Siberia and along the northern edge of the continent. Its southern portion is handicapped by aridity and its northern part, in addition to its long and severe winters, contains what is probably the most extensive swamp area on earth. In between, along and south of the Trans-Siberian Railway, the plain is more favorable to settlement, and development is being pushed rapidly by the Soviet government.

Next in order of magnitude are the plains of India. These surround the triangular, generally hilly upland of the Deccan. The Ganges–Brahmaputra Plain, humid and fertile, sweeps from the head of the Bay of Bengal to the margin of the Punjab Plain of northern West Pakistan. Cradled between the towering Himalayas and the much lower hill lands to the south, this plain supports more millions of persons than any other single physical division of India. Another major plain extends from the Arabian Sea northward nearly to the base of the Pamir mountain hub. This plain, usually referred to as the Indus Plain, is comprised of hot desert in the southern half and semiarid lands in the northern. The northern part, often designated as the Punjab Plain, merges with the plain of the Ganges. The Indus Plain allows relatively easy connection between the sea and the Punjab wheat region. Now, with more water available for irrigation, it might develop high population densities like those of the Ganges Plain. The plains of peninsular India are narrow but highly productive; population densities are comparable to those of the Ganges region. On the west is the lowland ribbon which lies between the Western Ghats and the Arabian Sea. Its southern part is the

Malabar Coast, famous as the section of India first brought into contact with Europe by the Portuguese explorers in the early sixteenth century. On the eastern side is a somewhat wider plain, from the southern tip of India to the Ganges Delta. Its coast, the Coromandel, is famous as the scene of the eighteenth-century struggle between the British and the French for the control of southern India.

The plains of southeastern Asia lie chiefly in Burma, Thailand, and Cambodia. Less densely populated than those of India, they represent some of the few areas of the continent which can probably support much greater populations than are now present. In southwestern Asia are the anciently settled plains of Mesopotamia, most of them located in the present country of Iraq. They suffer from insufficient water, although the Tigris and Euphrates rivers bring water from the Turkish mountains to modify the condition and allow irrigated areas to exist.

The major lowlands of eastern Asia lie in the northern portion of China proper and Manchuria. Although fertile, they are largely overpopulated. And, while they connect with the sea, they do not form great corridors extending into the heart of the continent. One of these plains is a series of basin floors reaching from the mouth of the Yangtze to the Yangtze Gorges at Ichang. Another, the extremely level North China Plain, arcs around the hilly land of the Shantung Peninsula and extends inland to the North China hill country. A third begins as a corridor-plain connecting with an embayment of the Yellow Sea and then widens to form the bulk of the Manchurian Plain. The northern part of the Manchurian Plain is the only portion of Greater China which offers any appreciable room for further settlement. Its gentle surface and rich grassland soils make it a much coveted area.

Plains of Australia and New Zealand

Australia has more plains than it has higher and rougher lands. One continuous plain crosses Australia from the shores of the Great Australian Bight in the south to the Gulf of Carpentaria in the north, and other plains occur along the eastern and western coasts (FIG. 7–11). However, this condition is not as favorable as it sounds, for most of the plains, square mile after square mile, are either arid or semiarid. Australia has plenty of low and nearly level land, but far too much of it is dry country.

In New Zealand, hill and mountain country predominates, but there are limited plains on both North Island and South Island. Each has encouraged considerable settlement for there is no major problem of water supply.

Types of Plains

Like mountains, the many large and small plains of the earth are of several types. Some of them are the result of the wearing down accomplished by erosion while others are the result of the building up, layer on layer, of deposited materials. The former may be called *erosional plains*; the latter, *depositional plains* (FIG. 7–13).

EROSIONAL PLAINS · Erosional plains occur in all continents except Antarctica. Two examples, in the Americas, will suffice to show what is meant. More than half of the ancient hard-rock area which curves in a wide arc

7–13   A SIMPLE expression of the basic difference between an erosional and a depositional plain.

EROSIONAL PLAIN

BEDROCK

DEPOSITIONAL PLAIN

Depositional Material

BEDROCK

7–14

VERTICAL *air photo of the ice-scoured bedrock plain of part of the Laurentian Shield west of Hudson Bay—a "world" comprised mostly of smoothed rock, lakes, ponds, and swamps.*

around Hudson Bay and reaches to the Arctic is an erosional plain. Within it there are some depositional plains, but it was formed mainly through the lowering and smoothing of a formerly higher and rougher surface by erosive action. First, stream action wore the surface down by picking up and carrying weathered materials. Next, within comparatively recent times, it was smoothed by the glaciers—the great ice sheets of the Pleistocene Age. The combination—running water and moving ice —produced the erosional plain which exists today (FIG. 7–14).

In the broad plain of the western part of the Amazon Basin, we find another low and relatively smooth land which owes its form to erosion. Here, moving ice has played no part. Rather, running water, aided by weathering, has created the extensive plain. The streams cut their ways into the land and carried off the materials; rainwash ate at the sides

of the ridges which the streams had created by digging their valleys and thus the interstream areas were lowered; the result is the plain of western Amazonia. The amount of the erosional accomplishment is shown by several higher remnants, known technically as *monadnocks,* which stand conspicuously above the stream-eroded plain. As the eye draws a line from the top of one monadnock to another, a line marking the general level of the former surface, one can begin to appreciate the tremendous erosional job done over the region as a whole.

DEPOSITIONAL PLAINS • Lowlands resulting from deposition are large and small and of many types. A very famous one, already mentioned, is the North China Plain (FIG. 7–15). It is mainly the creation of the silt-laden waters of the Hwang Ho (Yellow river). These waters, flowing from the mountains, plateaus, and hills to the west, have dumped their loads, century after century, into the shallow Yellow Sea and the Gulf of Po Hai. There the materials have collected, layer on layer, to create slowly a low, featureless plain

7–15

OBLIQUE *air photo of part of the North China Plain during a major flood of the Hwang Ho. In a plain of such low relief, even shallow floodwaters cover vast areas, almost like water spreading over a floor.*

built up from sea bottom. The river has been aided in its job of plain-building by annual accumulations of fine wind-blown dusts (loess) from the lands to the west. Another example of a river-built plain is found in the lower course of the Nile valley. This plain is a long ribbon of alluvial material in the bottom of the Nile trench and to either side of the Nile channel. It represents layers of silt deposited by many thousands of Nile floods.

A different type of depositional plain may be seen in Illinois and the states which border it on the east, west, and north. This gently rolling plain owes its existence to the work of glaciers. The glaciers dropped and spread a thick carpet of glacial debris over the entire region (FIG. 5–3). Glacially carried clays, silts, sands, gravels, and boulders smothered the previously existing landforms and produced a new kind of plain comprised of sandy flats, muddy swamps, low curving ridges of greatly mixed debris, and, here and there, small knobby hills.

The Atlantic Coastal Plain of the United States resulted from materials carried into and dropped in the shallow waters of the ocean. There they were spread and smoothed by waves and shore currents to produce an underwater surface of very low relief. Later, with slow uplift of the land, this smooth surface emerged to become the plain.

Another example of a depositional plain is the triangular delta of the Irrawaddy river in southern Burma. It has grown and is still growing into the shallow waters of the Gulf of Martaban. The copious, mud-laden waters of the Irrawaddy provide a steady stream of materials for the job of delta-building. As the waters enter the gulf, their velocity is checked and the load is dropped at and near the seaward edge of the plain; as this goes on and on, the delta slowly pushes its marshy fringes farther and farther out to sea. In addition to those mentioned, there are several other types of depositional plain. For example, an alluvial fan (FIG. 6–16) is a type of depositional plain; so is a loessal plain.

PLATEAUS

PLATEAU lands are few and far between in some parts of the earth, as in Europe, but numerous and rather closely spaced in other parts, as in Africa (FIG. 7–16). Plateaus in Africa are so large, and cover such a major portion of the land mass, that any discussion of the world distribution of plateaus should begin there.

African Plateaus

From north to south and from east to west, the African continent is mainly one huge upland platform. There are, as pointed out previously, a few large plains and many small ones, as well as a relatively small area of mountains (FIG. 7–2). In addition, large parts of the continent are chiefly hilly regions. However, as a study of the map (FIG. 7–16) will indicate,

Africa has about as much land in plateaus as it has in all other major landform types combined.

At this juncture, it is necessary to recall once more that a general, broad uniformity in landform condition does not mean geographical sameness or monotony. Nor does it signify an equality of habitat value. Some of Africa's plateaus are wind-swept, hot, and dry; others are hot and only semidry; still others are seasonally wet and dry grasslands or perennially damp rainforests.

In general, the African plateaus range from 2000 to 5000 feet in altitude. Some sections, as around the floor of the Congo Basin and in the Sahara, are lower than 2000 feet and others, as in Tanganyika, are higher than 5000 feet. Most of the vast plateau area of northern Africa is comparatively low. Throughout, it is

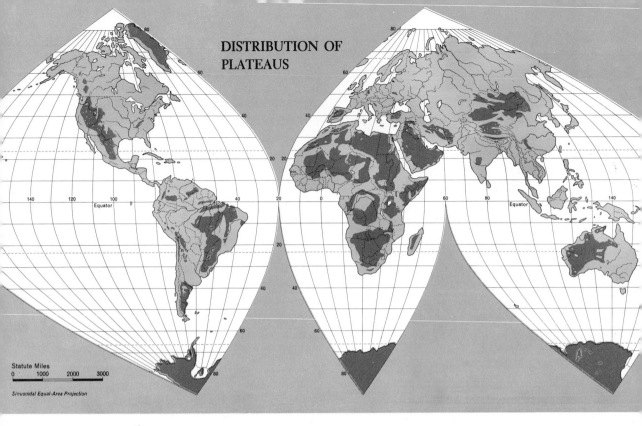

Statute Miles
0   1000   2000   3000

Sinusoidal Equal-Area Projection

7–16   THE world patterns of areas which are predominantly plateaus (tablelands) include considerable expanses of intermont basins. Africa has the largest area of land plateau of all the continents; Greenland and Antarctica are almost completely ice plateaus.

mainly desert and semidesert and has little to offer man. Its interior portion is very isolated— an isolation resulting primarily from aridity and great distances. Most of it receives less than 10 inches of average annual precipitation; its central section is nearly 2000 miles from the Atlantic Ocean and the Red Sea and nearly 1000 miles from the Mediterranean. The central African plateaus fringe the Congo Plain and encircle Lake Victoria. Those of the Congo are hot and wet, with dense rainforests. Those around Victoria are high, comparatively cool, extensive grasslands. The latter comprise much of the famous "big game country" of Africa. The South African plateaus cover much of the Republic of South Africa, all of Bechuanaland and Southern Rhodesia, nearly all of Northern Rhodesia, and at least half of South-West Africa. They are relatively high plateaus.

To the west, they are mainly high grasslands, and to the east they are upland, as opposed to lowland, savannas. Partly tropical and partly subtropical, they offer, especially in the east, considerable opportunity for further settlement. They are high enough so that temperatures are comparatively cool, droughts are somewhat less severe, and conditions in general are relatively comfortable and healthful. The eastern and southeastern portions of the South African plateaus have been mentioned several times as possible resettlement areas for some of the "war-displaced" populations of Europe.

Plateaus of Europe

In sharp contrast to Africa, the plateaus of Europe are few and small (FIG. 7–16). Actually there is only one of appreciable size, the Spanish Meseta, which occupies the upland heart of the Iberian Peninsula. On most of its margin it gives way, downward, to hilly lands, but to the north and northwest it is flanked by abruptly rising mountains. The central part of the Meseta is semiarid, but the margins are humid. The Meseta's interior position and the surrounding rougher lands engender a degree of isolation from the Atlantic and Mediterranean seaboards.

Elsewhere in Europe, small plateaus occur in eastern France, in western Germany and part of eastern Belgium, and in western Russia just northeast of the Carpathian Mountains. Other European uplands which are sometimes designated as plateaus, such as the Massif Central of France and the Bohemian Massif of Czechoslovakia, are so broken and dissected as to have the characteristic appearance of hill, rather than plateau, lands.

Plateaus of Asia

In southwestern Asia are three famous plateaus. The largest—rocky, sandy, and arid—is the Arabian Plateau (FIG. 7–16). It tilts from a higher edge adjacent to the Red Sea to a lower, more or less cliffed, drop-off which fronts partly on the Persian Gulf and partly on the lowlands of Mesopotamia. Like its North African counterpart, it is sparsely populated and its interior is isolated. Next in size is the mountain-walled Plateau of Iran (Persian Plateau), which extends from Iran into both Afghanistan and West Pakistan. Its encompassing mountains make it a dry and greatly isolated region. The third of the major plateaus of southwestern Asia is that of Turkey, or Anatolia. While the central part is semiarid, most of it is sufficiently watered to support much denser populations than are found in Arabia or Iran. It has access, between individual mountain areas and through bordering hilly lands, to the Black Sea and the Turkish Straits and the Aegean Sea. On the east and south, however, it is confronted with high and unbroken mountains.

Much of the heart of Asia is plateau (FIG. 7–16). Moreover, nearly all of it is desert and the remainder, semidesert. Again, the combination of aridity, great distances, and hilly and mountainous borders means a land of few people and little connection with the outside world. The central Asian plateau extends from the eastern base of the Pamir mountain hub to the big bend of the Hwang Ho and the western border of Manchuria. This is a distance equivalent to that from Los Angeles to New York City. Within it is the Takla Makan (desert) of the Tarim Basin and the broad desert and semidesert of the great Gobi. To the south of the Tarim Basin, but separated from it by some of the world's highest and most rugged mountains, is the plateau—or, perhaps more accurately, the several plateaus—of Tibet. Here are the most elevated tablelands on earth. They range in altitude from 10,000 to 15,000 feet above sea level, but even so, they are completely surrounded by mountains which rise from 10,000 to 15,000 feet higher. The high altitude of these plateaus, abetted by the moisture-excluding effect of the high mountains, makes them most inhospitable. They are so high as to have polar temperatures and so dry as to be deserts. The expression "frozen desert" comes close to describing them.

The remaining plateaus of Asia are comparatively small. One of them lies in the northwestern part of the Deccan and the other in China's Yunnan province. The former is humid and quite fertile, and supports a dense population. The latter, humid but much higher and more isolated, supports populations of medium density.

Australian Plateaus

Most of the portion of Australia which is not plains is low plateau with several patches of interior high plateau (FIG. 7–16). Nearly all of the huge plateau region is hot desert, from

7–17 A SMALL *intermont plateau (intermont basin) set high in the Andes of Colombia. The plateau and the city of Bucaramanga are here viewed from the Cordillera Oriental.*

near the shore of the Indian Ocean to the geographical center of the continent, and from near the Great Australian Bight to the northern part of the country. There are no extensive plateaus in the islands to the north, the East Indies, nor in those to the east, including New Caledonia and New Zealand.

Plateaus of the Americas

Plateaus are well represented and well scattered in South, Central, and North America (FIG. 7–16). Some of them are intermixed with mountains, as is true of most of the Asiatic plateaus, and some of them stand more or less by themselves, as in Africa and Australia. The largest plateau areas of South America are in Brazil and Argentina. Those of Brazil extend from the lower Amazon region to the southern boundary of the country and into the central part of Uruguay. About half of the great triangle ordinarily designated as the Brazilian Uplands is plateau. To the north and west

the plateau regions are comparatively low; to the east and south, they are much higher. The lower parts are mainly sparsely populated rainforests and tropical grasslands; the higher parts support larger populations and are more in the nature of upland grasslands, with scrub or thorn forests and, farthest south, pine forests and prairies. Argentina's major plateau is that of Patagonia. It extends from the Andean wall to the Atlantic and is a cold, windy desert of low habitat value. Other South American plateaus east of the Andes are in the heart of the isolated and little-known Guiana Highlands and in the equally isolated interior of southern Colombia.

The remaining plateaus of South America lie chiefly in the Andes (FIG. 7–16). Mostly small, but some comparatively large, they extend from central Colombia to northern Chile and Argentina. Largest and highest is the Plateau of Bolivia. The greater part of it is dry and wind-swept, much like the Plateau of Tibet. These plateaus were the centers of set-

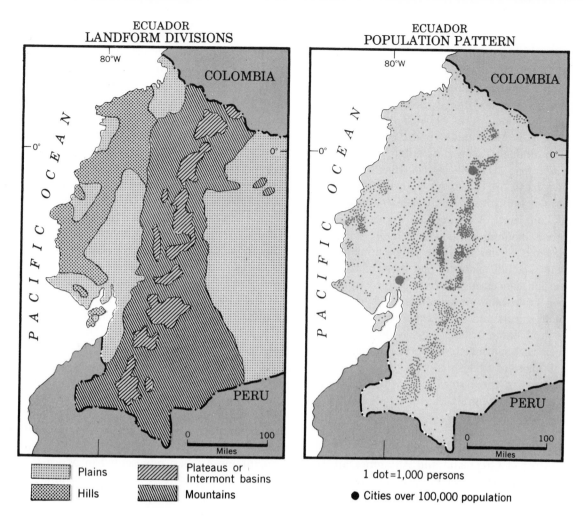

ECUADOR
LANDFORM DIVISIONS

ECUADOR
POPULATION PATTERN

Plains
Hills
Plateaus or Intermont basins
Mountains

1 dot = 1,000 persons

● Cities over 100,000 population

7–18   COMPARISON *of the landform divisions and population pattern of Ecuador brings out the close correlation between intermont plateaus and population density.*

tlement and culture for the Indians of the tropical Andes, perhaps because they were cooler and more comfortable than the lowlands to the west and east. When the Spaniards appeared, they naturally set up their seats of government where most of the native populations lived (FIG. 7–17). To this day, a map of these intermountain plateaus is essentially a map of major human activities and of the distribution of population (FIG. 7–18).

North America's most extensive tableland stretches from Mexico City almost to the Canadian border, a distance of more than 2000 miles (FIG. 7–16). It is chiefly semiarid with patches of true desert. Many small mountain districts interrupt its surface. Here and there, great canyons have been cut into it. The Mexican Plateau portion is closed in on the south, east, and west by mountains. The portion in the United States is mountain-locked on the north and west, and nearly so on the east, but relatively open on the southwest. With minor exceptions, it has remained an area to get across rather than to settle in— much of it is still part of "the wide open spaces." Different names are applied to its major parts. To the north it is called the Columbia Plateau, to the south and west, the

Great Basin, and to the east, the Colorado Plateau.

In Canada, between the Coast Ranges in the far west and the Rockies, are three other plateaus (FIG. 7–16). The southerly one lies mainly in the middle portion of the Fraser river drainage area; the central one partly in the upper drainage area of the Skeena river and partly in the upper drainage area of the Fraser; the third in the upper drainage of the Yukon river. All three are "pocketed" in a broad mountain region and their isolation is extreme. So far, they are either unmapped or very sketchily mapped, and most of the information concerning them is derived from trappers' tales and meager reports from government agents and a few explorers.

From the distribution given above, it can be seen that southwestern North America has its full share of plateau country. This is in sharp contrast to the eastern part, where major plateaus are lacking.

Polar Plateaus

Most of Greenland and Antarctica are covered by another kind of plateau, the ice plateau. The Greenland ice plateau smothers valleys, ridges, and mountains alike (FIG. 6–21). Its snow-veneered surface extends mile after mile without perceptible slope. Only by careful measurements can it be shown that the surface does slope from its central area to outer edges; there it drops precipitously to the sea or to narrow margins of ice-free land along the coasts. Antarctica presents much the same wintry aspect, except that a considerable number of barren mountain backbones rise above the sea of ice to break the monotonous flatness.

Plateau Types

Plateaus may be classified in several ways. The particular classification used at a given time depends largely on whether one wishes to emphasize geographical location, bedrock structures, or stage of erosional evolution.

LOCATIONAL TYPES • In terms of geographical position, including extent and relation to other surface features, there are three chief plateau types. These are *intermont* or *intermountain plateaus*, *piedmont plateaus*, and *continental plateaus*. The Bolivian Plateau is an example of a relatively large and high intermont plateau (FIG. 7–19). It is hemmed in between the eastern and western ranges of the Andes. A much smaller example is the small intermont plateau in northeastern Colombia in which the city of Bucaramanga is located (FIG. 7–17). It, too, is completely surrounded by high mountain lands. In Asia, the Yunnan Plateau is a piedmont plateau, for it lies in a piedmont, or foot-of-the-mountain, position in relation to the mountains of southern China. The plateau which extends eastward from the base of the Andes in southern Colombia is another example. The continental plateaus, so named because of their great extent and the fact that they represent "continental platforms" largely unassociated with mountains, are best represented in Africa. The South African Plateau is a good example. In South America, the plateau portion of the Brazilian Uplands is another good example. A given plateau region may happen to be included in more than one of the locational categories just mentioned. For instance, the vast plateau area of western United States may be termed intermont, because it lies between the Rockies and other mountains to the west; it may be called a piedmont plateau, because many of the marginal portions are at the foot of mountains; or, because it is so extensive and platformlike, it may be considered a continental plateau. The choice of term depends on where one wishes to place emphasis for a given purpose.

STRUCTURAL TYPES • If a plateau is underlain by layers of bedrock which lie at or near the horizontal, it may be termed a *horizontal-rock plateau* (FIG. 7–20A). Examples are

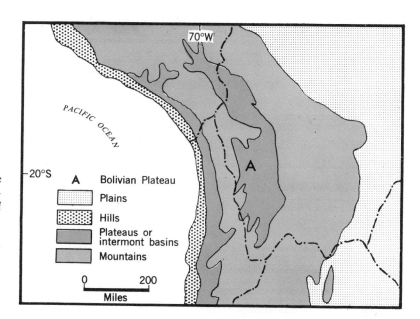

THE *Bolivian Plateau (A on the sketch map) is completely encompassed by high, rugged ranges of the Andes. Although this plateau (altiplano) has an average altitude of about 12,000 feet, it is surmounted by mountain crests and peaks which reach above 21,000 feet.*

A Bolivian Plateau
Plains
Hills
Plateaus or intermont basins
Mountains

0   200
Miles

the Colorado Plateau and the Arabian Plateau. If tablelands are comprised of greatly deformed rocks which have been virtually beveled by erosion (and uplifted afterward), they may be called *deformed-rock plateaus* (FIG. 7–20B). The greater part of the Ardennes region of southeastern Belgium is a good example. In other regions, lavas have welled up through large earth fissures and spread over entire countrysides, thus smothering existing landforms and rock structures and creating *lava plateaus* (FIG. 7–20C). The Colombia Plateau is such a one; so is the Paraná Plateau of southern Brazil.

DISSECTED PLATEAUS • There are many large and small sections of the earth which were formerly plateaus, but which have been changed in form by weathering and erosion until they no longer reasonably fit the plateau concept; no longer are they tablelike uplands

of relative smoothness. Instead, they have been so deeply cut and etched by streams that their relief is marked. They are *dissected plateaus*, such as the Grand Canyon section of the Colorado Plateau. In some of them the pronounced ridges between canyons are still flat-topped and might be called miniature plateaus in themselves, but, in many others, the ridges have been sharpened until they resemble inverted wedges or steeply pitched roofs. Often the dissection has produced relief characteristics of hills or, if the relief so produced is extraordinary, mountains—hills and mountains created by erosion instead of by crustal deformation. For example, the so-called Allegheny Plateau of the eastern United States has been so greatly dissected that, for all practical purposes and in terms of appearance, it is a hilly region rather than a plateau (FIG. 7–21).

7–20   PLATEAU (tableland) *surfaces may develop on either simple or complex geologic structures, or they may result from extensive and thick lava flows (as in C).*

HORIZONTAL-ROCK PLATEAU   DEFORMED-ROCK PLATEAU   LAVA PLATEAU

A   B   C   LAVA

HILLS

THE discussion of the major landforms of the continents has progressed from those which are highest and most rugged (mountains) to those which are lowest and least rugged (plains), and from there to the landforms which are comparatively high but nonrugged (plateaus). There remain extensive regions which are not plains, plateaus, or mountains. These are the earth's hill lands. Within these regions, both elevation and ruggedness are moderate, and most of the land is conspicuously sloping.

J. L. RICH

7-21

HILLY country in West Virginia. Although commonly labeled "plateau," this area, in any real geographical sense, is about as hilly as an area can be. (From The Geographical Review, Vol. XXIX, no. 4, October 1939, published by the American Geographical Society)

Hill Regions of North America

Study of the map (FIG. 7-22) will show that the hills of North America occur in many places from the Isthmus of Panama to the Arctic and from the Atlantic to the Pacific. There are others too small to show on a map of this scale.

The great bulk of the North American hill region is in the east. As settlement crept inland from the Atlantic seaboard of what later became the United States, hills, rather than mountains, stood in the way. A few passes became funnel lines, witnessing the first trickles and, later, the full surge of the westward movement. Very important among them were the Hudson–Mohawk, the Potomac–Ohio, and the Cumberland Gap routes (FIG. 7-23). Farther north, the St. Lawrence corridor served as another way through the hills, particularly for Canadian settlement. Otherwise, a broad hilly barrier stretched from central Alabama to the Hudson Bay entrance and beyond that to the far Arctic. To be sure, there are many local valleys within the hills, and scores of them served as new homes for the pioneers. But, by and large, the hill country was something to get through in order to reach the rich plains lands of the interior. It may seem strange to emphasize the barrier nature of hills inasmuch as they are lower in relief than are mountains. However, hill slopes are numerous, many of them are as steep or steeper than some mountain slopes, and they are just about as difficult to cross as are mountain

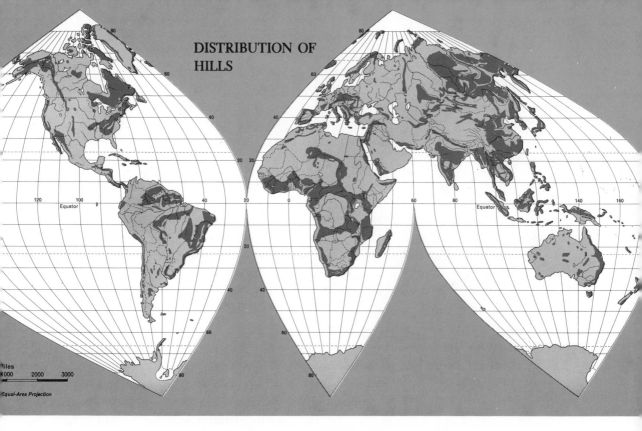

7–22   THE *world patterns of areas which are predominantly hilly.*

slopes (FIG. 7–21). To this day, there are only a few major routes across this eastern hill country of the Appalachians.

In the west, hills lie along the eastern foot of the Rockies and continue northwest and, finally, west to occupy the wide interior of Alaska. Along the Pacific coast, the land is mainly hilly from the tip of the peninsula of Lower California to northwestern Washington. Aided here and there by mountains, the hills provide a bold coast (FIG. 7–24), and one which has few gaps or routes to the immediate interior. The "break" through the Golden Gate is the only major one from the Tropic of Cancer to Puget Sound (FIG. 7–22). Another extensive hill area lies west of Mexico's Western Sierra Madre and reaches northwest into southern Arizona and southeastern California. Unlike those mentioned so far, this region is greatly handicapped by aridity. All of North America's western hill regions are closely associated with mountains and, in places, with high tablelands. The total combination has played a large part in separating the East from the West.

Hill Regions of South America

Like its sister continent, South America has most of its hills in the east (FIG. 7–22). The various hill regions extend chiefly from Uruguay to the Orinoco river and are greatly interrupted by broad plateaus. To the north of Rio de Janeiro and in the Guiana Highlands, they are interrupted to some degree by mountains. The corridor of the lower Amazon is the only lowland pass in a north-south distance of 3000 miles. Together with plateaus and some mountains, the eastern hill lands tend to separate the interior plains from the Atlantic even

Hills | 185

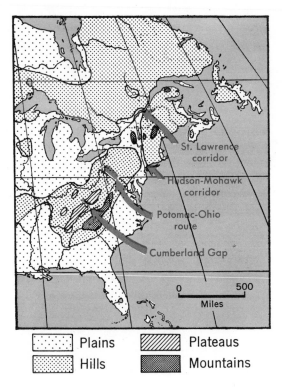

Plains ∷∷ Plateaus ▨ Hills ▦ Mountains ■

St. Lawrence corridor

Hudson-Mohawk corridor

Potomac-Ohio route

Cumberland Gap

0   500
          Miles

7-23

THE *predominantly hilly lands of eastern North America form a barrier between the east coast and the interior. Only the St. Lawrence and Hudson-Mohawk routes follow lowland corridors through the upland barrier.*

more effectively than in North America. They are dominantly tropical regions and most of their territory is grassland with some rainforest and scrub forest. Except near the coast, the hill regions are sparsely settled and largely unexplored and unmapped.

In western South America, hills are prominent along the coast of Chile and on north well into Peru. Ecuador and Colombia have sizable hill regions which also lie close to the coast. Like the hills of the west coast of North America, those of western South America are caught mainly between the ocean and high mountains and they, too, provide an essentially bold coast with few harbors.

Hill Regions of Europe

Outside of the Russian Plain, hills are prominent features in Europe (FIG. 7-22). Because most of them are neither too cold nor too dry and because of population pressure, they are used and permanently inhabited to a greater degree than in the Americas. In the British Isles, hills cover Scotland and Ireland (except for central lowlands), most of northern and western England, all of Wales, and small sections of Cornwall. Partly forested and partly in grass and shrub, they furnish some lumber and large areas of sheep-grazing land. Being relatively steep lands in a humid climate, they also supply considerable water power to the lower areas, many of which are highly industrialized.

On the Continent, most of the hill regions lie in the south. They extend, interrupted by mountains and plains, from the Atlantic to the Aegean and Black Seas and from the shores of the Mediterranean to central Germany and southern Poland. It is pertinent to note that the territories of several nations, such as Portugal, Italy, Yugoslavia, Greece, Bulgaria, and Czechoslovakia, are comprised more of hills than any other type of surface. Some of these nations also contain much land that is mountainous. With only constricted lowlands, nations of this sort have been forced to the development of "hill-land economies" marked by intensive use of valleys within the hills and by grazing and forestry on the slopes and ridge tops. Fortunately, the greater portion of the hill regions of southern Europe has a sufficiently mild and humid climate to allow such utilization. In many places, the lower parts of hills have been terraced in an attempt to provide level agricultural land where nature neglected to do so (FIG. 7-25). A person from the hill regions of the eastern United States is usually amazed at the high degree of utilization of most of the hill country of Europe, whether in Greece, Italy, the Massif Central of France, or the southern half of Germany.

7-24   OBLIQUE *air photo of part of the bold and hilly coast of southern California. Steep slopes, land-slides, and wave erosion make the coastal highway difficult to build and maintain.*

Northern Europe's hills are mainly in Sweden and parts of Norway and Finland. They form a long belt between the Norwegian Mountains and the Baltic Plain. Except in the southern part, they are less used than the hills of southern Europe. With their northern forests, numerous lakes and streams, and long cold winter, they remind one of the hill regions of eastern Canada, north of the Great Lakes and the St. Lawrence.

In eastern Europe, the long north-south stretch of the Urals forms a hilly "separator" between the Russian Plain and the plain of western Asia.

Hill Regions of Asia

Asia has more than its share of hills, just as it has more than its share of mountains. The hills of Asia extend from near the equator to the Arctic Ocean and from the Pacific to the far interior (FIG. 7–22). In a broad sense,

they form a ring, only slightly broken around the mountain and plateau core of the Asiatic land mass. Because of their great extent, both latitudinally and longitudinally, they present many different aspects and degrees of habitability. Some are bleak tundras, others are part of extensive northern forests, others practically barren deserts, and still others savannas and tropical forests. In general, the warmer and wetter ones, such as the rolling hills of peninsular India and the knobby hill lands of southern China, support dense populations. Those which are dry or cold support only sparse populations. In eastern and southern Asia, where most of the plains are crowded with people, the hilly regions have been populated much more than they would have been if the plains with their resources had not been used completely. Again, as in parts of southern Europe, the people have terraced many of the lower slopes, in an attempt to provide "plains in hills."

Hills | 187

7-25 MAN-MADE *terraces provide the only land level enough for agriculture in the hilly lands along the middle course of the Douro river in Portugal.*

Hill Regions of Africa

The hilly areas of Africa are rarely associated with mountains. Mostly, they join plateaus. In fact, the portions of this plateau continent which are not plateaus are mainly hills. Most of the hill regions of this continent occur south of the Sahara where they usually surround extensive interior plateaus (FIG. 7–22). The vast Saharan tableland is invaded by a curved finger of hills as a sort of hill-bridge which connects central Sahara with the hills which rim the northern margin of the Congo Basin. Northwest of the Sahara, hills are mingled with the plateau and mountain complex of the Atlas region. Among other hills are those which separate the Nile valley from the Red Sea and those which extend from the

mountains of Ethiopia to the northeastern "horn" of Africa.

Africa's hills, like those of other continents, vary in climate and vegetation cover. For example, the hilly lands to the east and north of the Congo Basin are rolling grasslands. Those to the south are a part of extensive tropical scrub forest. Those to the west are clothed with dense, wet, tropical forest. Quite in contrast, the hills of desert regions rise gaunt and barren above equally barren plateaus.

Hill Regions of Australia and New Zealand

Most of Australia's hill land is in the far east of that continent (FIG. 7–22). It acts as a separator between the humid east coast and the dry interior and forms the well-named Great Dividing Range. A few hilly areas lie to the west, partly in the interior plain and partly in the central and western plateau. These are semidesert and desert hills, as opposed to the eastern hills, which are cloaked with a mixed forest. Tasmania is almost entirely hilly. Several hill regions occupy the bulk of North Island, New Zealand, as well as the northern end and southwestern corner of South Island.

Hill Types

It has been noted that there are different types of mountains, plains, and plateaus. The same is true of hills: they, too, possess individuality. While such regions as South China and eastern Kentucky are both hilly, the hills differ sufficiently in shape and arrangement to provide a different cast to the particular surface configuration, even before we consider the changes brought about by their differing utilization by man.

STRUCTURAL HILLS • In some sections of the earth, the form and pattern of the hills reflect direct and strong bedrock control. For example, much of the hill country of Tennessee is underlain by strongly folded layers of sedimentary rocks whose axes have a pronounced northeast-southwest trend (FIG. 7–26). As weathering and erosion have worked on these materials, the hard-rock portions have produced ridges and the soft-rock portions have become narrow lowlands. The result is a hill country comprised of nearly parallel ridges and valleys with a northeast-southwest arrangement—the hill country resembles a series of huge "marching" waves. In an area of this sort, the pattern of land use is belted—strips of agricultural land occupy the valleys and strips of forest, the ridges. Travel is easy in the valleys, but difficult across the ridges; only where streams have cut narrow gaps, or passes, through the ridges is travel easy from one valley to another.

EROSIONAL HILLS • The patterns of many hill regions show no immediate control by the underlying structure. This is particularly true where the rock layers are horizontal or where the "underlay" is comprised of masses of relatively homogeneous rock. The hill country of eastern Kentucky is the result of valley cutting by numerous streams in nearly horizontal rocks. So many streams have become estab-

E. N. TORBERT

7–26

THE *ridge-and-valley region northeast of Knoxville, Tennessee. Narrow cultivated valleys lie in between steep, largely forested ridges.*

lished and have cut their valleys that virtually all the land between them has been sharpened into steep-sided ridges (FIG. 7–21). The stream patterns are treelike and hence so are those of the valleys. The ridges between the valleys merely fill in the areas between the trunks and branches of the streams. Along the southeast coast of Brazil, especially at and near Rio de Janeiro, are the famous "sugar-loaf" hills. They are much different than the hills of eastern Kentucky. They represent hill types commonly produced in humid regions as a result of the weathering and erosion of granite. Their forms are knoblike and there is commonly level land around and among them. Despite their abruptness and steepness of slope, they do not constitute barriers as do hills which are primarily ridges. On the other hand, their slopes are so steep that they do not support forests, let alone "side-hill" farms.

Still another type of hill country is seen in some of the regions which were "worked over" by continental glaciers. A typical section is the edge of the Laurentian Upland to the north of the St. Lawrence valley (FIG. 7–27). Here are many ancient hills that have been shaped from solid bedrock partly by normal stream erosion and, more recently, by moving ice. Between the hills are broad troughs and shallow basins which also represent the erosional accomplishment of glacial ice. The result is a

7–27

PART of the ancient, glacially rounded bedrock hills of the Laurentian Shield, in the area between Quebec City and the Saguenay river.

strongly rolling surface with enough irregularity to create a hilly condition.

The foregoing discussion of different types of hills, or hill regions, is far from complete; it is not an attempt to classify and describe all hill types which might be distinguished. The chief point is that within the many hill regions of the earth there are several types of expression and condition, each having direct reflections in the form of the land and in the use of the land by man, and each adding another element to the infinite variety of the face of the earth.

• CHAPTER OUTLINE •

The Landforms of the Continents

Types of Plains
EROSIONAL PLAINS
DEPOSITIONAL PLAINS

PLATEAUS
African Plateaus
Plateaus of Europe
Plateaus of Asia
Australian Plateaus
Plateaus of the Americas
Polar Plateaus
Plateau Types
    LOCATIONAL TYPES

STRUCTURAL TYPES
DISSECTED PLATEAUS

HILLS
Hill Regions of North America
Hill Regions of South America
Hill Regions of Europe
Hill Regions of Asia
Hill Regions of Africa
Hill Regions of Australia and New Zealand
Hill Types
    STRUCTURAL HILLS
    EROSIONAL HILLS

• REVIEW QUESTIONS •

1. What is meant by the term "intermont basin"? Why are intermont basins apt to be comparatively more significant within the tropics than elsewhere?

2. "In some ways, the Sierra Nevada–Cascade backbone is much more of a barrier than the Rockies." Explain this statement.

3. Do mountain barriers act as barriers to other movements besides those of man and his goods? Justify your answer.

4. Sometimes the same mountain region acts both as a barrier and as an important human habitat. Locate such a mountain region and discuss its dual function.

5. Account for the fact that active, or recently active, volcanoes are most numerous in such areas as the Andes, Japan, and Java.

6. Why does man live chiefly in plains areas? Does this mean that all plains are readily habitable? Discuss.

7. Both North and South America have extensive interior plains. Suggest why those of North America are characterized by greater populations and by a greater range of human activities than those of South America.

8. What might be some of the results if the plains of western Europe were walled off from the Atlantic Ocean by a high, continuous mountain region stretching from northern Norway to southern France?

9. The expression "Alpine Europe" includes what areas? What areas are included in "Plains Europe"?

10. Demonstrate that the importance of a plain is not necessarily dependent on large size.

11. What are the major handicaps for human use of Asia's largest single plains region? Are the handicaps ones which can be overcome? Discuss.

12. The North China Plain and the plains of Illinois are both depositional plains. If one were attempting to interpret these two areas to another person and were restricting the discussion to landforms alone, what else could one say about them?

13. Does the statement, "Africa is essentially a plateau continent," mean a general uniformity in Africa's geography? Discuss.

14. In what ways are the Bolivian Plateau and the Colorado Plateau dissimilar?

15. How was the westward movement in the United States affected by hilly regions? Do the same hilly regions still affect the movement of men and goods? Illustrate.

16. Granting major settlement from the Atlantic seaboard, how do you think the penetration and settlement of the United States would have been affected if the major landform divisions of the country had been reversed so that the Appalachian Upland was in the Far West and the mountain, plateau, and hill complex was in the East?

8 | Elements and Controls of Climate

❰ THE existence of a blanket of atmosphere about the earth is the basic essential for all forms of life. So far as we are aware, no other planet has just the exact gaseous mixture to support not only man, but other animals and plants as well; nor is there another planet known upon which the heat and moisture conditions are such as to be capable of supporting similar life forms. The individual gases which are present, the states in which they exist, and the controls to which they are subject are all vital to man's very being. Climate does not "make the man," but it does play an important part in his life.

COMPOSITION OF THE ATMOSPHERE

THE atmosphere is a mechanical mixture of gases and finely divided solid impurities. The dominant gases in terms of volume are nitrogen and oxygen. In dry air, nitrogen makes up about 78 per cent of the total and oxygen, by far the most important ingredient since it maintains human respiration, about 21 per cent. Both nitrogen and oxygen remain in relatively fixed proportion throughout the lower atmosphere; only at heights over 40 miles do scattered measurements indicate any appreciable change in proportion. This statement may seem to contradict ordinary experience in mountain climbing or in high-altitude airplane flight; actually, it does not. True, there is a smaller amount of oxygen at high altitudes, but so is there a smaller amount of all other gases. The air becomes "thinner" with altitude. Yet the proportion of oxygen remains essentially the same.

Of the other gases present in dry air, carbon dioxide, necessary to plant life, is perhaps the most important. The proportion of this gas is very small and slightly variable, between .025 and .03 per cent by volume.

Water vapor, source of the world's precipitation, is always present, physically mixed with dry air in the *lower* atmosphere. The proportion varies markedly from place to place and from time to time. In the hot and humid tropics, it approaches 4 per cent by volume, but it is commonly much lower.

The solid impurities include smoke, chemical salts, microorganisms, and dust. They are likewise concentrated in the lower portion of the atmosphere. There the finest particles, some so small as to be invisible even under a microscope, aid in the process which changes water vapor to liquid water. The impurities are present in amounts which vary both from time to time and from place to place.

ELEMENTS AND CONTROLS OF CLIMATE

Climatic Elements

THE atmosphere is a mobile and constantly changing body. The detailed analysis of its composition and motion are properly the field of meteorology. Nevertheless, a recognition of certain of the basic elements, of their controls, and of the nature and distribution of the combinations resulting from the action of these controls is essential to the full appreciation of the world in which we live.

Why is one area forest-covered and another grass-covered? Why are the common trees of eastern Canada, like pine, hemlock, and spruce, lacking in the Great Plains of the United States? Why are red soils, like those of Georgia and Alabama, unknown in Iowa? Why does the house-builder of the tropics keep his dwelling open to the winds while the northerner strives to make his dwelling as windtight as his culture allows? These are only a few of the more obvious questions whose answers depend on the average state of the atmosphere in different parts of the world.

TEMPERATURE AND PRECIPITATION • The most commonly appreciated climatic elements are heat and moisture, or *temperature* and *precipitation*. The degree of heat and the moisture content of the atmosphere affect pro-

---

8–1

[OPPOSITE, TOP] THE *blanket of atmosphere that surrounds the earth is a basic essential for all life. This bank of cumulus clouds over the plateau region in the southwest United States evidences the condensation of moisture in the atmosphere.*

foundly the way man feels and acts. An oppressively sticky, steamy, summer day like one in southern Illinois, with its afternoon thunderstorm interlude bringing temporary lowering of temperature, makes one long for the sparkling days and chilly evenings of fall. The bitterly cold, blustery, snowy day of a northern New England winter makes one shudder at the thought of leaving the warm protection of a well-heated house and wish devoutly for the balmy days of summer. Both the sullenness of the pre-shower hours of a summer day in Illinois and the frigidity of the New England winter day are typical conditions of that portion of the atmospheric shell closest to the earth's surface. Without really seeing it, we are continuously affected by the atmosphere about us.

People of primitive cultures were governed by the major climatic elements in matters of clothing and shelter. Prehistoric man sought shelter in caves as protection against the frigid blasts from retreating ice sheets. Later, with the disappearance of the ice, he came out from the caves to occupy rock shelters such as those that line the valley sides of the Vézère river in southwestern France. Similarly, the placing of primitive settlements near sources of water and the avoidance of waterless areas suggest their complete dependence on natural moisture.

Peoples with the most advanced cultures (according to Western, or Occidental, standards) attempt to regulate both temperature and moisture, at least inside homes and other buildings. Air conditioning, house insulation, and centralized heating are all attempts on the part of man to control the effectiveness and the actual distribution of heat and moisture. The practice of adjusting the distribution of water, either on the surface, as in the irrigation projects of the Nile valley in Egypt or the Imperial Valley of southern California, or in the air, as in the humidification of cotton-spinning mills in the Carolinas, testifies to man's recognition of atmospheric limitations.

Temperature is commonly measured in degrees on either the Fahrenheit or the centigrade scale; the former is the English system of measurement and the latter, the metric system. Precipitation is measured in inches or in millimeters. *Unless otherwise specifically indicated, this book uses the Fahrenheit scale for temperature and inches for precipitation.*

PRESSURE • Much less commonly appreciated as a climatic element is *atmospheric pressure.* Even air has weight, and atmospheric pressure is the force exerted against a surface by that weight. At sea level the pressure exerted by the air on the earth's surface averages 14.7 pounds per square inch.

But pressure varies from place to place and from time to time at any one place. For any given volume, warm air is lighter than cold air. Consequently, if the temperature of the air is high, pressure is low; if the temperature is low, pressure is high. In addition, increase in elevation above sea level brings about decrease in pressure because the volume of air above a point at high altitude is relatively small, so that it weighs less and is able to exert less pressure at that point. The decrease of pressure with increased altitude proceeds slowly at low altitudes and more rapidly at higher ones. At 18,000 feet elevation, pressure averages slightly less than half that at sea level (FIG. 8–2).

While the slight changes of pressure common at low altitudes are seldom sensed by human beings and are thus insignificant climatic elements, the human body is not properly adjusted to the very low pressures of high altitudes. Pressure there becomes a vital element, especially in air travel. At high altitudes, the human body finds difficulty in securing enough oxygen. Oxygen, which makes up about ⅕ of the whole atmosphere, exerts about ⅕ of the total atmospheric pressure, and near sea level, the pressure and the amount of oxygen are such that the human body functions at its best. With the decrease in total pressure incident to increased altitude, there is a decrease in oxygen pressure.

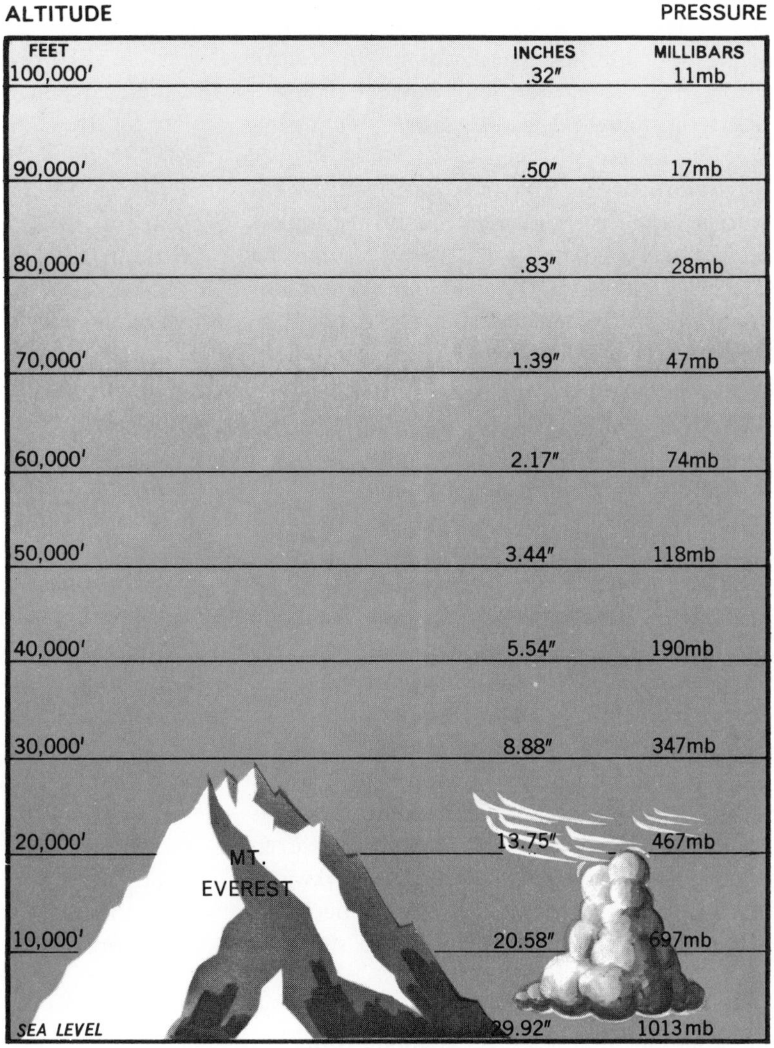

ALTITUDE	PRESSURE	
FEET	**INCHES**	**MILLIBARS**
100,000'	.32"	11mb
90,000'	.50"	17mb
80,000'	.83"	28mb
70,000'	1.39"	47mb
60,000'	2.17"	74mb
50,000'	3.44"	118mb
40,000'	5.54"	190mb
30,000'	8.88"	347mb
20,000'	13.75"	467mb
10,000'	20.58"	697mb
SEA LEVEL	29.92"	1013mb

MT. EVEREST

8–2

THE lower part of the earth's atmosphere has become well known to man. Within it, atmospheric pressure decreases with increase in elevation above sea level. Note the average height of the cumulo-nimbus cloud—the type with the greatest vertical development—and the height of Mt. Everest, the world's highest mountain peak.

A deficiency of oxygen results in damage to the brain. Consequently, oxygen must be supplied artificially. The danger point is usually considered to be 20,000 feet elevation, though prolonged flight above 15,000 feet requires additional oxygen supply.

WIND • For general purposes, a region or center of *high* pressure (pressure above sea-level average) may be thought of as a sort of hill in the atmosphere while a region of *low* pressure (pressure below sea-level average) may be thought of as a basin, or trough. Much

as water runs downhill into a valley or surface basin, so air flows from high to low pressure centers. Such a movement of air, essentially a horizontal one, is spoken of as *wind*. Obviously, the speed of flow is closely related to the rate of pressure change, or the *pressure gradient*. Wind is not a startling climatic element except when it reaches speeds capable of material destruction, as in a tropical hurricane striking Florida's east coast near a city like Miami, in a typhoon like those which lash China's southeast coast, or in the whirling fury

Elements and Controls of Climate | 195

of a Kansas tornado. Its effects, as well as those of pressure, are most significant in the control which they have over temperature and precipitation, for wind is the carrier of temperature and moisture.

MEASUREMENT OF ATMOSPHERIC PRESSURE • Pressure is measured by an instrument called a *barometer,* a word derived from the Greek *baros.* meaning "weight." In its simplest form, this instrument consists of a glass tube filled with some liquid and then inverted in a cup of the same liquid. If the tube is long enough, the liquid will fall away from the top, creating a vacuum. The height of the liquid in the tube is directly proportional to the atmospheric pressure exerted on the uncovered surface of the liquid in the cup.

Early barometers used water. It was found that water stood about 34 feet up the tube on the average. This meant that the atmospheric pressure was equal to that of a column of water 34 feet high. Obviously an instrument over 34 feet long was very unwieldy. Hence a heavier liquid, mercury, was substituted for water. Even with mercury, the column is about 30 inches high when measured at sea level. A mercury barometer is delicate and awkward, but very accurate measurements can be made with it. Hence it has remained the standard for pressure measurement.

Since the column of mercury supported by the atmosphere at sea level is about 30 inches high on the average, it has become customary to say that normal sea-level pressure is 30 *inches.* A newer unit, common in meteorological work, is the *millibar.* It is sufficient for our purposes to know the approximate relationship: 30 inches (of mercury) equals 1016 millibars. Exact standard sea-level pressure is 29.92 inches or 1013.3 millibars. These pressures are often translated into pounds per square inch, but the use of that unit of measure has become less and less common.

Because the mercury barometer is so delicate and so awkward, another type has come into more common use. Essentially, it consists of a metal box with a flexible lid. A vacuum is created in the box. For this reason, the lid responds to changes in pressure. The fluctuations of the lid's position are conveyed to a scale by means of a pointer. (The scale is in inches or millibars or both.) This type of instrument is known as an *aneroid,* meaning "without fluid."

MEASUREMENT OF WIND • Two measurements are common in wind observation, direction and velocity. Direction is determined by a weather vane. A rod, with a pointer at one end and a relatively wide vertical surface or plate at the other, is mounted so that it can rotate freely about a perpendicular shaft. Indicators of direction are fixed accurately on the shaft. As the wind blows, the pressure which it exerts on the vertical surface of the vane causes the pointer to swing around into the direction *from which* the wind is blowing. Thus, a *west* wind is a wind blowing *from* the west. By reference to the direction indicators, the direction of the wind can be ascertained.

Wind velocity is measured by an *anemometer,* from the Greek word *anemos,* meaning "wind." One of the most common types consists of three or four light metal cups mounted on a horizontal frame which rotates easily at the end of a vertical shaft. The difference in the effect of pressure on the inside and outside of the cups as the wind blows causes the frame to rotate. By counting the rotations, the speed of the wind can be determined in miles per hour. There is a standardized scale of wind velocities called the *Beaufort scale,* after the man who devised it.

Climatic Controls

There are many controls which act upon the climatic elements and, in so doing, produce characteristic combinations which are known as *climatic types* (TABLE 7). Of the many controls, those of recognized world magnitude are seven in number. They are (1) latitude, (2)

TABLE 7

Relation of Climatic Types, Controls, and Elements

		CLIMATIC CONTROLS		CLIMATIC ELEMENTS
World's climatic types	result from the action of	latitude land and water distribution ocean currents altitude mountain barriers pressure and wind storms	upon	temperature precipitation pressure and wind

land and water distribution, (3) ocean currents, (4) altitude, (5) mountain barriers, (6) pressure and wind, and (7) storms. The temperature and precipitation conditions of a place are affected by each. Pressure and wind, as elements, are acted upon by the other six controls. The resulting combinations are visibly observable in the forms of the land surface, the soil, the vegetation cover, and even in the features of the human scene. Numerous examples are given in later chapters. The climatic types and their distribution thus offer clues or guides to many other distributions over the earth. Before the fullest meaning of these types can be understood, the individual elements of which they are constituted, and the controls to which those elements are subject, must be examined in their broader aspects.

ATMOSPHERIC TEMPERATURE

Source of Atmospheric Energy

THE sun is the only significant source of atmospheric energy. In the form of both light and heat, that energy is essential to all life on this planet and, indirectly, to many inanimate objects as well. The sun radiates energy from its surface in all directions out into space. The planet earth is a relatively small body at a considerable distance from the sun. Hence only a very small portion, estimated at one two-billionth of the total output of solar energy, is intercepted by it. Yet that small portion is fundamental to the production of air temperatures in which living things can exist and of the light which is so essential to their growth.

Insolation

The solar radiation which is received at the surface of the earth is called *insolation*. It varies in amount from place to place over the earth's surface and from time to time at any given place. Differences in temperature and, through them, other differences in climate are thereby produced.

While the amount of insolation varies first of all with output of energy by the sun, changes resulting from this factor may be considered nonessential for our purposes in this book. The extreme variation so far observed is barely more than one per cent of the total. Similarly, variation is induced by the seasonal change in distance of the earth from the sun. The earth in January is some three million miles nearer the sun than it is in July. This causes a difference of about one per cent in the intensity of radiation, computed for the outer edge of the atmosphere, from one season to the next in any one year.

The truly significant factors are the angle of the sun's rays and the length of the daylight period. The rays of the sun which reach the earth are essentially parallel to one another. Any specific group of rays striking the earth near the equator spreads over a smaller area than another group (FIG. 8–3, left) striking the earth near the poles. But the amount of energy is the *same* in both groups of rays. Since this energy is concentrated in the first instance and spread out in the second, the insolation *per unit of surface area* will be greater near the equator than near the poles.

Both concentration and diffusion of the sun's rays are illustrated in another way in FIG. 8–3, right. There, A represents a group of rays striking the earth from overhead at noon and B represents the late afternoon position of the same rays. It is a common experience to look directly at the sun just before it sinks below the western horizon; it is difficult without blackened glass to look directly at the sun at noon. In the evening, no sensation of great heat is experienced even on a clear midsummer day; at noon the sensation of scorching heat accompanies the glare. The spread of the rays over a larger surface area when they come from a low angle accounts for part of the difference in effect. The thickness of atmosphere through which they penetrate is also an important factor. That thickness is about 12 times as great when the rays come from just above the horizon as it is when they come from directly overhead. Not only are the rays spread over a larger surface; they are scattered, absorbed, and reflected to a greater degree when they pass

8–3   THE *effect of angle of the sun's rays on insolation. Left: High-latitude rays at A versus low-latitude rays at B. Right: Noontime rays at A versus late afternoon rays at B.*

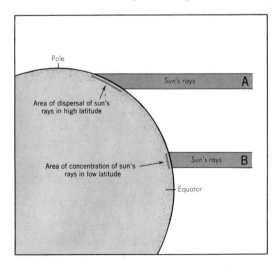

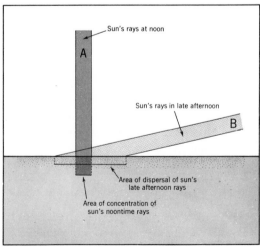

through a greater depth of atmosphere. Consequently their effectiveness when they reach the earth's surface is much diminished.

Of equal significance with the angle of the sun's rays is the length of the daylight period. Because of the movements of revolution and rotation and because of the inclination of the earth's axis, there is variation in the length of the daylight period in the course of the year. Along the equator, day and night are equal in length throughout the year; elsewhere over the globe, day and night are approximately equal only at the time of the equinoxes, which occur about March 21 and September 21. In the Northern Hemisphere, the days are longest in late June, shortest in late December; in the Southern Hemisphere, the dates are reversed (FIG. 8–4).

At the period of longest day, the sun is highest in the noon sky. This means that the rays are most directly received during the same period that the sun is longest above the horizon. As a consequence, insolation during the summer months, or high-sun period, is considerably greater than during the winter, or low-sun period. The farther from the equator, the more pronounced is the seasonal rhythm insofar as it is produced by insolation.

Distribution of Insolation

EFFECT OF LATITUDE • The net effect of all the foregoing factors of variation is an exceedingly complex distribution of insolation. In a general way, the annual total for any one latitude is constant and there is a decrease from low latitudes to high latitudes. TABLE 8 shows observed values at the surface of the earth. These are maximum values; actually they may be from 30 to 70 per cent less, depending upon the degree of cloudiness. The greater surface insolation at 10° latitude than at the equator is primarily a result of the drier air which persists there. Drier air permits a greater portion of the rays to penetrate to the surface without loss of energy on the way.

TABLE 8

Observed Values of Insolation at the Earth's Surface

(In thousands of calories per square centimeter)

LATITUDE	INSOLATION
0	186
10	187
20	183
30	171
40	152
50	124
60	110
70	91
80	77
90	68

SOURCE: From a table in Helmut Landsberg, *Physical Climatology*, School of Mineral Industries, Pennsylvania State College. Copyright, 1941, by Gray Printing Co., Du Bois, Pennsylvania. Reprinted by permission of Gray Printing Co.

EFFECT OF DIFFERENTIAL HEATING OF LAND AND WATER • Second to latitude as a determinant of the amount of heating of the earth's surface is the nature of the surface itself. Not all materials heat at the same rate or to the same degree. The land heats very rapidly and to a high temperature since it is composed of solid materials. Common experiences on a hot summer day offer fine examples. A tar road surface which is firm and, to all appearances, quite solid in the early morning hours becomes a sticky semifluid by midday.

In contrast, the water of a lake exposed to the same sun for the same length of time is warmed only slightly. It is fluid and heats more slowly and to a lesser degree than a solid. The relief brought by an afternoon swim after

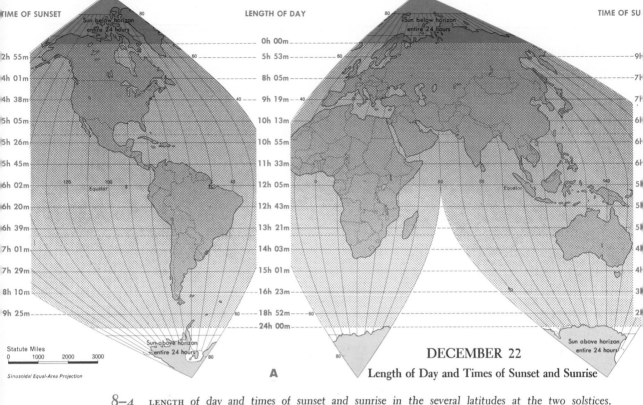

DECEMBER 22

Length of Day and Times of Sunset and Sunrise

8–4 LENGTH of day and times of sunset and sunrise in the several latitudes at the two solstices. (Source: Nautical Almanac for 1961, U.S. Naval Observatory, Washington, D.C.)

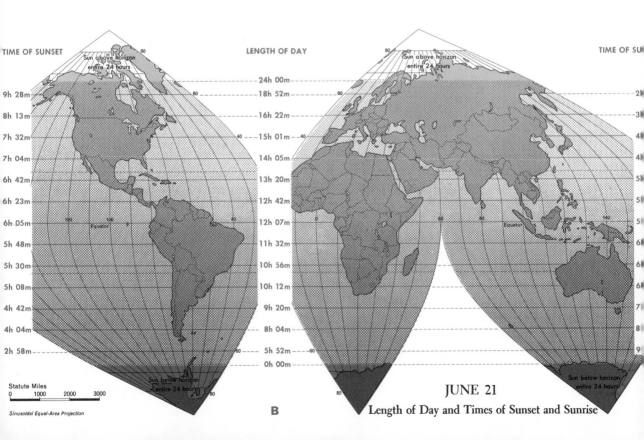

JUNE 21

Length of Day and Times of Sunset and Sunrise

a day of high temperature offers support. If the water of the lake heated to the degree that the tar pavement did, swimming would certainly be far from the pleasant pastime that it is. In part, this difference in heating results from the fact that energy received at the surface is distributed downward through a relatively thick layer of water while it is confined to a very shallow layer of the solid body. A greater volume of the water is available to absorb the energy, and, hence, there is less energy per unit of volume.

At one extreme in the scale is dry sand or bare rock; at the other, a large and deep body of water. Between these are all the variations in plant cover of the land surface and all the variations in size and depth of water bodies from the great oceans to the shallow, small-area ponds.

As a result of the differential heating and cooling of land as compared with water, the oceans of the world heat up less in summer than the land masses in the same latitudes. Likewise, in the winter, the oceans remain relatively warmer than the adjacent land masses. Air assumes the temperature of the portion of the surface above which it lies. Consequently, the regular decrease of temperature from the equator to the poles, which might be expected solely on the basis of the angle of the sun's rays and the length of the daylight period, is upset. While it is generally true that the highest temperatures occur in the low latitudes and the lowest occur in the areas nearer the poles, the pattern is not uniform.

How the Air Is Heated and Cooled

As solar energy passes through the atmosphere, only a small part of it is absorbed to warm the air. Actually, the air is heated mainly from the earth by the processes known as *radiation, conduction,* and *convection.* The same processes also operate to cause cooling of the air. In addition, there is what is known as the *adiabatic process* of heating and cooling.

RADIATION • The energy received at the earth's surface as insolation is short-wave energy which passes readily through the atmosphere. Upon reception this energy is transformed into long-wave energy which can be absorbed readily by the atmosphere. The earth's surface becomes a radiator which heats the air. This process is known as *terrestrial radiation.*

Just as the air nearest the radiator in a cool room warms most, so the air nearest the earth is heated to the greatest degree. With increased distance from the surface, the effectiveness of radiation declines. Hence, the air at low elevations is relatively warmer than that at some considerable distance above.

On the average, temperature decrease is about 3.6° F. for every 1000 feet increase in altitude. Anyone who has been in an unheated airplane recognizes decrease of temperature with increase of altitude. While it may be very hot near the ground, it will be cold enough to require the heaviest clothing at 15,000 feet altitude. Similarly, a climb into a high mountain area in summer brings one to levels where snow remains unmelted (FIG. 8–5). In part, lower temperatures experienced in mountains result from the smaller amount of surface exposed to solar energy, but primarily they are the consequence of distance from the main mass of the "radiator" and of the "thinner" atmosphere at high altitudes.

Regular decrease of temperature continues for approximately 10 miles upward over the equator and 5 miles upward over the poles. At those elevations, a level, or a series of step-like levels, is reached beyond which there appears to be no appreciable drop in temperature for from 12 to 15 miles farther upward. Above this, temperatures increase to levels far higher than those experienced at the earth's surface. Most of the air, by weight, is in the lowest zone, where are also the greater part of the water vapor, the carbon dioxide, and the solid impurities.

The lowest zone is called the *troposphere*

8–5

MONTREUX, *Switzerland, near the eastern end of Lake Geneva, basks in the warm sun while snow still covers the higher elevations of the Dents du Midi (10,600 feet).*

(FIG. 8–6). The stage at which temperatures cease to drop with increased elevation is called the *tropopause*, and the zone above is called the *stratosphere*. In the stratosphere, very low temperatures (approximately −130° F. near the equator) prevail, there is little water vapor or dust, and the air movement appears to be nearly horizontal. There is little upward or downward movement to cause irregularities like those common within the troposphere. Beyond the stratosphere, upward from about 45 miles above the earth, is the *ionosphere*. In this uppermost layer temperatures increase with distance away from the earth, but the rate of increase, its regularity, and the maximum attained are still controversial. Electrical phenomena like the *northern lights*, or *aurora borealis*, occur in the ionosphere.

CONDUCTION • The second type of heat transfer from the earth to the atmosphere is *conduction*. When two bodies of different temperatures are in contact, there is a flow of heat from the warmer to the cooler until the same temperature is attained by both bodies or until the contact is broken (FIG. 8–7). Again, this is a common phenomenon to most people. When a silver spoon is placed in a cup of hot coffee, the handle of the spoon becomes too hot to hold comfortably. It is warmed by conduction from the hot coffee. When one dives into relatively cool water, the sensation of cold is in part a matter of flow of heat from the body to the water. After one has been in the water a short while, a balance is reached between skin temperature and water temperature, and the sense of cold disappears. In comparison with other heating processes, conduction plays only a small part in the heating of the atmosphere; it is significant only in that portion of the atmosphere which is in direct contact with the earth's surface.

CONVECTION • *Convection* is the third process in the heating of the atmosphere. When air is heated it expands in volume and, as a consequence, overflows aloft. This reduces the pressure which the air exerts on the heated surface and, at the same time, increases the pressure exerted by adjacent cooler air. The heavy, cooler air flows in along the surface toward the warmer, lighter column forcing the latter upward (FIG. 8–7). Such a circulation is called a convectional system.

On a miniature scale, convection can be observed by any smoker sitting near a lighted electric lamp. The bulb warms the air in contact with it. The air expands and overflows near the ceiling of the room increasing the weight of the air not directly in contact with the lamp or just above it. The heavier air settles in toward the lamp carrying the smoke with it. Contact with the lamp warms the air and it, in turn, moves upward only to settle back away from the column just above the lamp. The only function of the smoke is to make the air movement visible.

The boiling of water illustrates the same type of circulation. Water in a teakettle is heated by conduction from the bottom of the kettle. As it is heated, it expands and becomes lighter. The heavier water near the top sinks

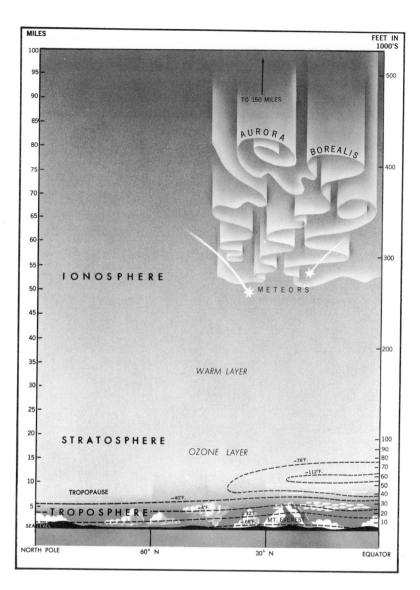

8–6

GENERALIZED cross section of the lower portion of the atmosphere. In the troposphere, temperature decreases with increased altitude; within the stratosphere, vertical temperature changes are less marked; and at the base of the ionosphere, temperature begins to increase with increased distance from the earth's surface.

along the sides of the kettle and pushes the heated water upwards. Fireplaces, likewise, offer excellent examples of convectional circulation. Who has not felt the draft across the floor toward the fireplace when a fire is first lighted in a cold room?

It is by means of convectional circulation that much heat *transfer* in the atmosphere is accomplished. As a process of atmospheric heating, convection is limited to the troposphere.

Just as the processes of radiation, conduction, and convectional circulation are the major controls of air heating, so they are the main controls of air cooling. During the night when there is no receipt of solar energy at the surface, the process of earth radiation continues. The earth's surface is cooled by the continued radiation until it becomes slightly colder than the air above it. When this occurs, the air begins to lose heat to the ground as well as to outer space. Likewise, the bottom zone of air

Atmospheric Temperature | 203

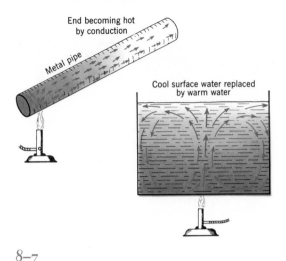

End becoming hot
by conduction

Metal pipe

Cool surface water replaced
by warm water

8–7

HEAT *transfer by* conduction (left) *and by* convection
(right).

in direct contact with the cooling earth's surface becomes cooled by conduction. Where inequalities of cooling exist, convectional currents form and cool or cold air is thus imported
from adjacent colder regions.

ADIABATIC HEATING AND COOLING • Inequalities in the earth's surface may cause a
further type of heating or cooling in moving
masses of air. When air is forced to descend,
as down the slope of a mountain range, it
moves from a region where the weight of overlying air is low to one where it is high. This
movement is accompanied by compression in
volume, which heats the air mass. Similarly,
when air is forced upward, it moves into regions where the weight above is less. Consequently, it expands and becomes cooler. The
downward movement of great masses of air is

a far more commonly observed phenomenon
than the upward movement.

The famous *chinook,* a wind moving with
great speed down the east face of the Rocky
Mountains, and the *foehn,* a down-mountain
wind in the Alps, bring excessively high temperatures to the lowlands onto which they
blow. Not only are they warming, but they
are drying winds and they may do great damage
because of this feature. In many of the Swiss
valleys, it is considered a criminal act to build
a fire, indoors or out, even for cooking when
the foehn is blowing. In our own Great Plains,
the chinook played no small part in the parch-
ing and blowing of soil in the Dust Bowl
storms of the late 1930's.

Atmospheric Heat Balance

The total heat energy of the atmosphere
remains constant even though the processes
just described produce a wide variety of temperatures over the face of the earth. Just as
much energy is returned to space as is received
from space. There is constant loss from both
the atmosphere and the earth itself, principally by reflection and by radiation. There is
constant gain in the form of insolation. The
loss and the gain just balance one another.
Were it not for this interchange, the atmosphere would become progressively hotter or
colder. The details of the interchange are complex and, since they are properly matters of
atmospheric physics, they need not be entered
into here. What is significant is recognition
that a balance exists. Because of this as well as
because of the particular composition and physical state of the atmosphere, life can exist on
the earth.

ATMOSPHERIC MOISTURE

Humidity

THOUGH the water present as a vapor in the atmosphere constitutes only a small and variable percentage of the whole, yet that small amount is a very significant portion for life on this planet. Most of the gases which make up the atmosphere are present in fairly constant amounts near the earth's surface. With the exception of water vapor, the mixture of gases over the Sahara is much the same as that over the southeastern United States. The amount of water, however, varies constantly from place to place and from time to time at any one place. Further, most of the water vapor in the total atmosphere is concentrated in the troposphere. As an invisible gas in the atmosphere, water cannot be used directly to any considerable extent by life upon the earth's surface, but when *condensation* and *precipitation* take place it does become available. Its amount, its distribution through the year, and its dependability all combine to place definite limits upon habitability from place to place over the land surface of the earth.

SOURCE OF ATMOSPHERIC MOISTURE • By far the largest part of the moisture which is present in the atmosphere as water vapor derives from the great oceans that cover so large a portion of the earth's surface. By air movements, moisture evaporated from the oceans is carried over the land masses and there, under certain conditions, is condensed and precipitated upon the surface. Of the water thus supplied to the land some runs off directly to the sea, some is intercepted by the vegetation, another portion sinks into the ground to become soil moisture and ground water, and part is lost by evaporation. The moisture which falls on the land supplies plants, lakes, streams, and man himself. The moisture which is evaporated from lakes and streams and from plants may be dropped again on the land or carried by the winds to fall over the oceans and thus aid the interchange of water between the oceans and the continents (FIG. 8–8).

ABSOLUTE AND RELATIVE HUMIDITY • There is a certain fixed maximum amount of water vapor which the air can contain at any given temperature. This amount changes with any change of temperature as is indicated in TABLE 9.

The air is said to be *saturated* if it contains all of the water vapor possible at any given temperature. It should be noted that the capacity of the air for water vapor increases with an increase in temperature and that this capacity becomes greater at an increasing rate.

Two measurements of the moisture in the atmosphere are commonly made. There is the measurement of the actual amount or weight of water vapor per cubic foot of air; this is known as the *absolute humidity*. The other measurement is the statement of the proportion of water vapor actually present to the

TABLE 9

Water Vapor Capacity of Air at Different Temperatures

TEMPERATURE (°F.)	WATER VAPOR (grains per cubic foot)
100	19.7
90	14.7
80	10.9
70	8.0
60	5.7
50	4.1
40	2.9
30	1.9

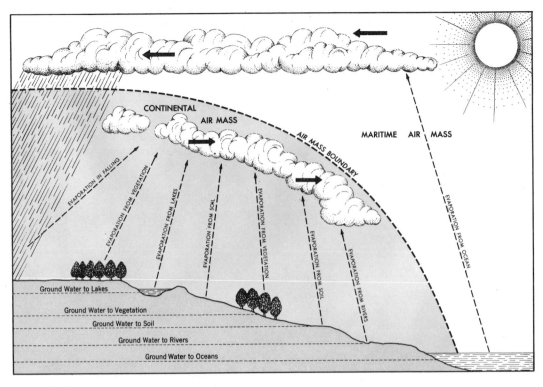

8–8 THE *hydrologic cycle. The oceans are the ultimate source of all precipitation. Moisture is evaporated from the oceans, carried inland, and precipitated. It is carried back to the oceans by evaporation, air-mass movement, and later precipitation, and by running off the land as surface water and by movement as ground water.*

maximum amount possible at a given temperature; this is known as the *relative humidity.* Relative humidity is always stated in per cent. By definition, *saturated* air has a relative humidity of 100 per cent.

The meaning of these various terms may be made clearer by specific examples. Suppose the temperature of a given air sample is 70°. A cubic foot of this air could hold 8 grains of water vapor (TABLE 9). A measurement of the actual amount in a cubic foot of the sample air shows, however, that there are only 4 grains present. Under these conditions, the *absolute* humidity is 4 grains per cubic foot; the *relative* humidity is 50 per cent—that is, 4 (the amount actually present) divided by 8 (the maximum amount the air could hold at that temperature). The air is not saturated, for it does not

have in it as much water vapor as it could possibly hold at the temperature of 70°.

Absolute humidity, unlike relative humidity, does not change unless some vapor is added to the air or some is taken from it. Temperature changes do not affect it *unless* there is a lowering to the point where the air becomes saturated. This point is known as the *dew point* and it is always expressed in degrees of temperature. When the dew point is reached, some of the vapor has to be removed either by deposition on some object with which the air is in contact or by condensation and precipitation.

For example, suppose the absolute humidity is 4.1 grains per cubic foot and the temperature 80° F. If no more water is added to the air but the temperature rises to 100° F., the absolute humidity remains 4.1 grains per cubic foot. If the temperature drops to 50° F., the absolute humidity is still 4.1 grains per cubic foot, but this is all that the air can hold. Air at 50° F. with an absolute humidity of 4.1 grains per cubic foot is saturated, as a reference to TABLE 9 will show. Any further drop in temperature would force some of the vapor to condense and either be deposited or precipitated. The dew point of this particular sample of air is 50° F.

Generally speaking, absolute humidity is highest near the equator and over the oceans. It decreases toward the poles and toward the interiors of the large land masses. Air over the Sahara may have an absolute humidity higher than that in the British Isles, yet no surface moisture may result from it because of the high temperatures of the Sahara as opposed to the relatively low ones of the British Isles. It ,is likewise generally true that summer absolute humidities are higher than those of winter, for, as we have seen, air at high temperatures can hold more water vapor than can air at low temperatures.

Relative humidity varies greatly with temperature. A reference to TABLE 9 will show that air at 30° F. can hold only 1.9 grains of water vapor per cubic foot. If 1.9 grains are actually present in air at that temperature, the absolute humidity is 1.9 grains per cubic foot; the relative humidity is 100 per cent. Now suppose that the temperature is raised to 40° F. At that temperature, the air could hold 2.9 grains of water vapor. If no water has been added, the relative humidity at the new temperature is 66 per cent—that is, 1.9 (the amount actually present) divided by 2.9 (the amount which the air could hold). If the temperature rises to 50° F. and no more water is added, the relative humidity becomes 1.9 divided by 4.1, which is 46 per cent. On the same basis the relative humidity at 60° F. would be 33⅓ per cent; at 70° F., 24 per cent; at 80° F., 17 per cent; at 90° F., 13 per cent; and at 100° F., only 10 per cent. Thus relative humidity varies inversely

with temperature; an increase of temperature brings about a decrease in relative humidity and a decrease of temperature brings about an increase in relative humidity. This relationship holds only when no additional water vapor becomes available through increased evaporation.

Condensation

PROCESS • When air is cooled, its ability to contain water vapor is reduced, or, in other words, its relative humidity is increased. Continued cooling will bring it sooner or later to a condition of 100 per cent relative humidity or saturation. If the cooling continues beyond this point, the excess of water vapor over the amount which the air can contain at the new temperature is thrown off as minute particles of water or of ice, the former if the temperature is above 32° F. and the latter if the temperature is below 32° F. This process is called *condensation* if the change is from the gas to the liquid, and *sublimation* if the change is from the gas directly to the solid form.

The amount of condensation depends upon the degree of cooling and upon the absolute humidity of the air which is being cooled. Saturated air at 90° F. contains 14.7 grains of water vapor per cubic foot. Air which is 10° F. cooler can hold only 10.9 grains per cubic foot. If the saturated air at 90° F. is cooled to 80° F., then 3.8 grains of water vapor must be condensed from each cubic foot of air. If a further cooling of 10° F. takes place, another 2.9 grains must be condensed. With still further lowering of temperature, increasingly smaller amounts are removed. It becomes obvious then that cooling of warm, moist air provides more water than that of cooler, drier air. It is for this reason that hot summer air has greater potentialities for the production of abundant precipitation than does cold winter air.

DEW AND WHITE FROST • On clear, cold nights, radiation from the earth's surface proceeds at a very rapid rate and the ground soon reaches a temperature below that of the air lying immediately in contact with it. The air in turn is chilled by radiation and conduction from it to the colder ground. When the temperature of the lower few inches of the air is brought below the dew point, condensation of moisture takes place. If the dew point is above 32° F., the condensation appears as little droplets of water and is called *dew*; if the dew point is below 32° F., moisture removed from the air appears as minute ice crystals and is known as *white frost*. Both dew and white frost collect on cold objects at the surface of the earth.

FOG • Another form of condensation is *fog*. This is no more than a mass of fine water droplets suspended in the air close to the earth's surface; in a sense, it is cloud near the ground. The water particles are condensed, but are too light to fall to the earth; rather, they float in the air and are moved about by such light winds as may occur. Condensation to form fog is brought about either by the lowering of temperature below the dew point or by the addition of water vapor so that the dew point temperature is raised. The cooling processes which cause fog are those of radiation, conduction, and mixing of warm and cold air.

CLOUDS • When the lowering of temperature to the dew point occurs mainly through movement of the air upward from the surface of the earth, the condensed particles become visible as clouds. Their forms are almost infinite and they change constantly. Yet they are good indicators of the state of the atmosphere. With increased use of the lower zones of the atmosphere by man, the study of clouds has come to be recognized as of great significance. Only a suggestion of their importance can be made in this book.

Basically, there are three major cloud forms; these are *cirroform*, *stratiform*, and *cumuliform*. Cirroform clouds are the filmy or feathery, wispy clouds that appear at great heights. They are usually composed entirely of ice crystals. They are fair weather clouds when scattered irregularly over the sky and, in the sunlight, they appear dazzlingly white against a deep blue. When they are arranged in regular bands and appear to be heavier, they usually presage the coming of stormy weather. Stratiform clouds are sheetlike, almost without individual shapes, and usually dull gray in color. They cover the sky in a uniform layer. They are the typical winter cloud of the middle latitudes, often remaining as a leaden-gray cover over the whole sky for days at a time. They are low lying and are remarkably uniform in thickness. Neither the base nor the top of the cloud layer shows much unevenness. Cumuliform clouds are massive, rounded clouds typical of the middle-latitude summer days. The base is usually quite even and of low elevation while the top is cauliflower-like and may reach elevations normal to cirrus clouds (FIG. 8–1). Usually, the cumulus cloud is a fair weather form, but when, on a hot, sultry, summer afternoon, it grows to great height sending up great bulbous projections or flattening off at the top and the bottom to assume the shape of an anvil, it is the indicator of sharp showers or squalls. In common parlance, it is the "thunderhead."

An international classification of clouds has been adopted by most countries and is here given for reference. The classification recognizes ten distinctive combination forms divided into four families:

FAMILY A. High clouds—usually at elevations above 20,000 feet
    1. Cirrus
    2. Cirro-cumulus
    3. Cirro-stratus

FAMILY B. Middle clouds—elevations between 6500 and 20,000 feet
    4. Alto-cumulus
    5. Alto-stratus

FAMILY C. Low clouds—elevations from close to the surface up to 6500 feet
    6. Strato-cumulus
    7. Stratus
    8. Nimbo-stratus

8–9   A WELL-DEVELOPED *roll cloud preceding a thunderstorm.*

FAMILY D. Clouds with great vertical development—bases averaging 1600 feet and tops as high as 40,000 feet

     9. Cumulus
     10. Cumulo-nimbus

Each of these types gives definite indication of the condition of the atmosphere (FIG. 8–9). For example, cirro-cumulus and cirro-stratus both occur typically ahead of a storm center and denote its approach. Nimbo-stratus is associated with steady rain or snow; it produces low ceilings, poor visibility, and icing conditions so that air travel is greatly handicapped. Cumulo-nimbus, the thunderhead or overgrown cumulus, is associated with violent vertical air movement, often exceeding 100 miles per hour within the cloud; it produces tremendous downpours of rain with sharp, brilliant lightning and heavy thunder, and with frequent falls of hail. The storm which accompanies it may cause great destruction and the extreme turbulence of the air within it prevents air travel or renders it extremely hazardous.

Precipitation

FORMS OF PRECIPITATION • In a meteorological sense, the term precipitation includes all forms of condensed water vapor which "fall" to the earth's surface from the atmosphere. Condensation produces six main forms of moisture in the air: dew, white frost, fog, hail, snow, and rain. Only the last three are spoken of as precipitation for they are the only ones which actually fall to the earth's surface.

Dew, white frost, and fog are of some significance as sources of usable moisture. The accumulation of water from the first two of these three forms is sufficient in many places to make a notable contribution to successful agricultural land use, but by themselves these forms are very minor sources of moisture. Likewise, fog, through contact with the surface and with objects on it, does provide some moisture; far more important, however, is the handicap which fog offers to navigation, both of the oceans and of the air, and to movement overland. As producers of usable moisture, fog,

Atmospheric Moisture | 209

dew, and white frost may have local but hardly world-wide significance.

Hail is always associated with extreme air turbulence characteristic of thunderstorms. It is rare in polar regions and in the tropics. In the former areas, thunderstorms are uncommon and hence the conditions for the formation of hail are lacking. In the tropics, it is likely that such hail as may be formed in the thunderstorms melts before it reaches the ground. Hail consists of ice pellets formed in concentric layers alternately of clear hard ice and of soft white ice in which there are air bubbles. The pellets are formed in the higher parts of a cumulo-nimbus cloud. As the frozen drops fall through the cloud, they collect a coating of water. Because of the terrific updraft of air in the cloud, the water-coated pellets are tossed back upward and the water is frozen to form a concentric layer about the original nucleus. The opaque nature of the new coating results from extreme rapidity of freezing. As the heavier pellet drops back again toward the earth, it collects still more water on its surface and the freezing process is repeated. Thus the hailstone grows larger until its weight overcomes the lifting power of the upward-moving air within the cloud. Then it falls from the cloud toward the earth. Its size when it reaches the surface depends in large part upon the temperature and relative humidity of the air through which it falls; sometimes it melts entirely and at other times it may reach the surface still of sufficient size to do great damage. Hailstones of four inches diameter and with a weight of one pound have frequently been recorded, but more commonly they are of smaller size. As a major source of moisture, hail may be overlooked, but as a destructive agent, particularly of crops, it is important. Since it is an accompaniment of thunderstorms, it is largely significant as a summer phenomenon of the middle latitudes.

It is from *rain* and *snow* that the greatest amount of moisture is supplied to the earth's surface. Rain results from the coalescence of water droplets within clouds. The individual droplets are so light that they float within the cloud, but when they are combined the weight becomes sufficient to make them drop toward the earth. Temperatures in the air through which they fall may be high enough to cause their evaporation before they reach the surface. This phenomenon is quite common in deserts where the very low relative humidity of the air gives it the power of rapid evaporation and there may be "rainstorms without rain." In humid lands, the air is more frequently near the saturation point and, consequently, the rain once formed normally falls to the surface of the earth.

Snow results from the condensation of water vapor at a temperature below 32° F. Minute ice particles thus formed unite to produce snow crystals which have sufficient weight to fall from the cloud. If the air through which the flakes descend does not have a temperature near freezing, they may be melted and reach the surface as rain.

Ordinarily about twelve inches of snow provides the same amount of moisture as one inch of rain. If the snow is very fine and powdery, more will be required, whereas if it is large-flaked and moist, even partially melted as it falls, as little as four inches will provide the equivalent of one inch of rain.

MAJOR CAUSES OF PRECIPITATION • Precipitation in any form results only when air has been cooled *below* the dew point and *after* condensation has occurred. Stated simply, precipitation is caused by *any sufficient cooling* of a large volume of air. In the form of rain and snow, moisture falls to the earth's surface from clouds. Clouds result from the condensation of moisture in air which is at a considerable altitude. In other words, rain and snow can occur only as the result of cooling which takes place when a large volume of air rises from the surface of the earth. There are three ways in which this can happen. These are by convection, by the opposition of air masses of different temperature, and by the imposition of a barrier across which wind must blow. As has previously been stated, air moving upward in a convectional system expands. This expansion is accompanied by cooling. If the cooling is sufficient, condensation occurs and precipitation results. When two masses of air of different temperature come in contact with each other, the cooler mass tends to stick to the surface because of its greater weight and the warmer mass is forced to move up over it. Again the upward movement brings about expansion and cooling of the rising air. If these processes continue long enough, precipitation results. Finally, if air moves against a mountain range, it is forced to rise with accompanying expansion and cooling. Precipitation results if the cooling is great enough. These three types of precipitation are called respectively *convectional, cyclonic* or *frontal,* and *orographic.*

The amount of precipitation caused by these three major forms of rising air depends upon the moisture content of the air, its temperature when it begins to ascend, and the height to which it is forced to rise. Warm, moist air is buoyant. It can therefore be forced upward more easily and when it does rise, the dew point is quickly attained. Thus, warm, moist air provides greater possibilities of heavy precipitation than does cooler, drier air.

Because of the rapidity with which air rises in a convectional system, the precipitation which results is usually more torrential than any other type. Since convectional systems are rarely very extensive, convectional precipitation is usually local and of short duration. Thunderstorm rain is frequently, though not always, of this type. The type is most common in the tropics and in the continental interiors of the middle latitudes. Both of these locations are areas of intense surface heating. In the tropics, intense heating persists throughout the year, but in the continental interiors of the middle latitudes it is restricted to the summer season.

Cyclonic or frontal precipitation is usually less heavy within short periods of time than is convectional. The rise of warm air over cold commonly proceeds less rapidly than that in a convectional system. At the same time, the area over which this type of rising persists is usually greater and consequently the precipitation is usually more widespread. And it persists for longer periods of time. It is this type of rain which is most common in the middle latitudes, for reasons which will be amplified in a later chapter.

Orographic precipitation is local or widespread, largely depending upon the size of the barrier which is encountered and the steadiness of the winds which cross it. In the tropics, where winds are dominantly from the east, this type of precipitation is most common on eastern coasts and on east-facing mountain slopes; in the middle latitudes, it is most common on west coasts and west-facing mountain slopes because the winds of these latitudes are dominantly from the west.

· CHAPTER OUTLINE ·
Elements and Controls of Climate

COMPOSITION OF THE ATMOSPHERE

ELEMENTS AND CONTROLS OF CLIMATE
  Climatic Elements
    TEMPERATURE AND PRECIPITATION

PRESSURE
WIND
MEASUREMENT OF ATMOSPHERIC PRESSURE
MEASUREMENT OF WIND
Climatic Controls

Atmospheric Temperature

Source of Atmospheric Energy
Insolation
Distribution of Insolation
    EFFECT OF LATITUDE
    EFFECT OF DIFFERENTIAL HEATING OF LAND
       AND WATER
How the Air Is Heated and Cooled
    RADIATION
    CONDUCTION
    CONVECTION
    ADIABATIC HEATING AND COOLING
Atmospheric Heat Balance

Atmospheric Moisture

Humidity
    SOURCE OF ATMOSPHERIC MOISTURE
    ABSOLUTE AND RELATIVE HUMIDITY
Condensation
    PROCESS
    DEW AND WHITE FROST
    FOG
    CLOUDS
Precipitation
    FORMS OF PRECIPITATION
    MAJOR CAUSES OF PRECIPITATION

• REVIEW QUESTIONS •

1. Why should geography concern itself with the elements and controls of climate?
2. Give some examples from your own experience of the appreciation of climatic elements by the ordinary person.
3. Suggest some ways in which atmospheric pressure is important in everyday life.
4. What causes wind?
5. How do climatic controls differ from climatic elements?
6. Explain why insolation varies in amount from place to place over the earth's surface and from time to time at any given place.
7. In what way does the distribution of land and water affect insolation? How is this significant to the ordinary person?
8. How do the troposphere, stratosphere, and ionosphere differ from one another? Of what significance are these differences to man? To space exploration particularly?
9. Discuss the whole process of heating of the earth's atmosphere.
10. How does adiabatic heating differ from other kinds of heating?
11. Explain how the chinook played an important part in the Dust Bowl storms of the 1930's.
12. What is the source of atmospheric moisture? Since the source is a single one, suggest some of the reasons why water is abundantly available in some parts of the world and not in others.
13. From the point of view of human beings, which is most noticeable, absolute or relative humidity? Why should this be so?
14. Tell how temperature change affects relative humidity. Give examples from your own experience.
15. How is the water which exists as vapor in the atmosphere made available for use by man? In this connection, what is the basic idea behind rainmaking experiments of the present day?
16. Of what conceivable use is dew? Explain.
17. What is the difference between fog and cloud?
18. Suggest some ways in which cloud forms may be good indicators for weather forecasting.
19. What matters help to determine whether precipitation will be in the form of hail, snow, or rain?
20. Can one expect hail to be more common during one season of the year than during another? If so, why? If not, why not?
21. During any period of precipitation, what might indicate whether the precipitation was convective, cyclonic, or orographic?
22. What kind of atmospheric condition is most likely to produce precipitation? In arriving at and stating your answer, consider *all* the climatic elements.

9–1

[OPPOSITE, TOP] STORMY *winds roughen the ocean surface. The sea is one of the greatest of the controls of climate.*

9 Climatic Elements over the World

PHILIP GENDREAU

⟨ THE *distribution and interaction of climatic elements over the earth result in a great variety of habitats. Some places, like the lowlands of Indonesia, are hot the year round; other places, like much of the United States, are hot during part of the year and cold during the rest. Similarly, some places, like the coast of British Columbia, are very wet, and other places, like Sonora in Mexico, are very dry. A knowledge of the distribution of the climatic elements over the earth, along with some consideration of the causes of this distribution, is essential to an understanding of the human habitat.*

WORLD DISTRIBUTION OF TEMPERATURE

Isothermal Maps

THE best means of showing the distribution of temperatures over the earth is the *isothermal* map. An isotherm is a line connecting points of equal temperature. The temperatures shown may be those for any specific time or they may be averages or means for any stated period. A commonly used period is the month. Means for January and July offer a measure of temperatures at the height of opposite seasons of the year. Hence, they illustrate the extremes of the year from place to place over the world. In addition, they may be used to indicate the effects of some of the climatic controls.

Effects of Some Climatic Controls upon Temperature Distribution

MEAN MONTHLY TEMPERATURE DISTRIBUTION: JANUARY AND JULY • FIGURE 9–2 is a world isothermal map showing actual mean temperatures for January; FIG. 9–3, for July. On both of these maps, the isotherms are seen to follow roughly an east-west direction. In other words, temperatures are arranged generally in belts of latitude with highest averages near the equator in Middle and South America, Africa, Arabia, India, the East Indies, and Australia. Averages become progressively lower both northward and southward from those areas. Essentially, the control of *latitude* is that of determining the amount of insolation. As we have seen, the angle of the sun's rays and the length of the daylight period combine to make insolation greatest in the low latitudes and least in the high latitudes. If there were no other variables, no other climatic controls, this would result in a regular gradation of air temperatures from the equator to the poles.

The greatest departure from the regular east-to-west trend of the isotherms occurs where they pass from the land to the sea. This is primarily a reflection of the control of *land*

and water distribution. The differential heating of those two kinds of surface is responsible for air temperature differences.

On the January map (FIG. 9–2) it can readily be seen that the highest temperatures occur over the land masses lying across the equator or in the Southern Hemisphere. During that month, the greater part of Australia falls within the area having temperatures over 80° F.; in the northwestern part of that continent, a small area actually averages over 90° F. Two areas in the interior of South America and a small area on the "nose" of that continent exhibit temperatures over 80° F. In Africa, a narrow strip along the Guinea coast and another along the central eastern coast likewise have a monthly mean over 80° F.

During the same month, extremes of low temperature are found over the Northern Hemisphere land masses. Northeast Asia exhibits the lowest mean with a considerable area where the temperature is actually below −40° F.! Over the Greenland icecap and over the far northern portion of North America, subzero temperatures are the rule.

On the July map (FIG. 9–3) notable changes are evidenced. The highest temperatures are no longer mainly in the Southern Hemisphere but over the Northern Hemisphere instead. Northwestern Mexico and adjacent sections of the southwestern United States stand out as a hot zone in the Americas, along with the southeastern United States, the Caribbean, and the east coast of Middle America. Through most of the Sahara and on eastward through lowland Arabia, most of India, the coastal districts of southeastern Asia, and the nearby islands stretches a like zone of great heat. Regions of intense cold have all but disappeared from the Northern Hemisphere, only interior Greenland remaining as a cold center; and Antarctica appears as the center of the cold zone of the Southern Hemisphere, much colder than it was in January. Migration of the temperature belts with the seasons is thus demonstrated. The controls of *latitude* and of *land and water distribution* are evident.

Another fact of distribution is illustrated by the course of the isotherms. In the Northern Hemisphere, the January map shows the distinct equatorward bend of the isotherms over the land masses and the July map shows the distinct polarward bend. In the Southern Hemisphere, the patterns are reversed. Also, extremes of temperature, no matter what the season, always occur over the land masses. Here again, the facts are primarily reflections of the control of *land and water distribution*.

The effect of *ocean currents* upon temperature is also demonstrated. The distinct poleward bend of the isotherms off *higher latitude* west coasts, especially off the coast of southern California during July (FIG. 9–3), are indicators. Off the British Isles and the Norwegian coast, the Gulf Stream, or the North Atlantic Drift (FIG. 4–6) as it is known in those latitudes, carries relatively warm water well northward of its usual position. Relatively high air temperatures are thus maintained. Similarly, off the California coast, the California Current brings relatively cold water southward from the North Pacific and air temperatures are consequently lowered.

Finally, regardless of season, there is less deviation from the latitudinally arranged belts of temperature in the Southern Hemisphere than in the Northern. The Southern Hemisphere is chiefly water and this condition makes for greater uniformity. If it were all water, the deviation would be still less. Again the control of *land and water distribution* is evidenced.

SEASONAL AND HEMISPHERIC TEMPERATURE DIFFERENCES • To illustrate some of the changes from season to season and some of the differences between the hemispheres, certain isotherms should be followed in detail. The one indicating the average of 32° F. brings out the essentials. On the western side of North America, the January map shows that the mean of 32° F. for that month is encountered first

of all well out along the chain of the Aleutian islands (FIG. 9–2). From that position, it bends slightly northward across the Gulf of Alaska to intersect the coast just north of Sitka. The January mean temperature at Sitka is 32.4° F. A pronounced southward bend brings the isotherm well within the United States, around the southern end of the Rocky Mountains. On the eastern plains it passes a little south of St. Louis, where the January average is 31.6° F. Toward the east coast, the isotherm turns slightly northward again to leave the continent just south of New York, where the January average is 30.6° F. Once off the land, the course of the isotherm is turned sharply northeastward over the Atlantic to cut just south of Iceland and to strike the European coast north of 60° latitude. On the land, the direction is again changed; the isotherm bends southward through coastal Norway, Denmark, Germany, and into southeastern France. There, it assumes an eastward direction through northern Italy, along the Dalmatian coast, through the Balkans, and across the northern part of the Black Sea. It passes a little south of the center of the Caspian Sea, and so on still eastward to the coast of China. It leaves this coast just south of Tsingtao, where the January mean is 31.7° F. Once again the isotherm has a northeasterly trend across southern Korea and the northern end of the largest part of Japan, the island of Honshu, and on across the North Pacific to the outer Aleutians.

This isotherm sets the pattern for all winter isotherms in the Northern Hemisphere. Over the continents, it bends southward or equatorward; over the oceans, it bends northward or poleward. This characteristic is in part explained by the differential heating of land and water; the large areas of land in these latitudes of the Northern Hemisphere become very cold during the period of least insolation, while the water bodies retain heat. The very pronounced poleward bends off the west coasts, like those along the western coast of Europe or the Alaskan–British Columbian coast of North

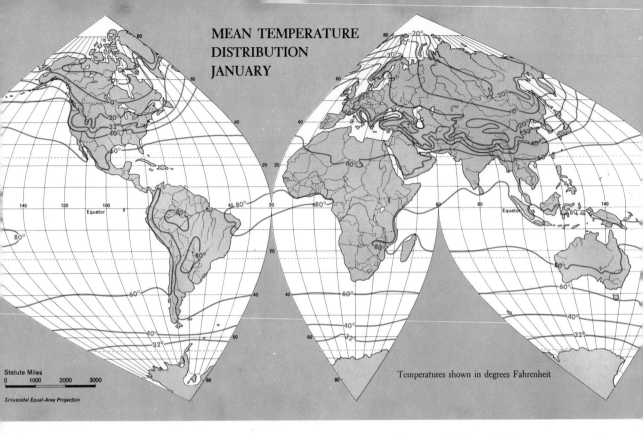

MEAN TEMPERATURE DISTRIBUTION JANUARY

Statute Miles
0   1000   2000   3000

Sinusoidal Equal-Area Projection

Temperatures shown in degrees Fahrenheit

9–2   ACTUAL *mean temperatures are arranged generally in latitudinal belts, with the warmest near the equator. In January the warmest temperatures occur over land masses immediately south of the equator.*

America, are in large part accounted for by the flow of warm ocean currents. These currents have a considerable warming effect upon the air which moves over them; the higher temperatures of low latitudes are thus carried well northward along the courses of the currents.

· At the opposite time of year, the individual isotherms in the Northern Hemisphere show quite a different pattern. The isotherm of 60° F. for July illustrates the characteristic behavior (FIG. 9–3). Beginning near the west coast of North America almost at San Francisco, where the July average is 58.9° F., this isotherm trends sharply northward, parallel to the coast and only a short distance inland, to reach well into northern Alberta and Saskatchewan in Canada. There it reverses its direction and

extends southeastward across the rest of the continent to leave the coast in the Gaspé peninsula. Offshore, it makes a sharp loop southward off the New England coast. It follows a nearly true east-west course across most of the width of the Atlantic along the 50th parallel of latitude. Through the British Isles and onto the Scandinavian peninsula, it reaches to higher and higher latitudes until, across most of Siberia, it follows nearly along the Arctic Circle. From this northernmost position, it turns abruptly southward to leave the Asiatic land mass just north of the mouth of the Amur river. Another abrupt southward curve brings it across Hokkaido, the northernmost island of Japan. Over most of the Pacific, the isotherm assumes an east-west trend along the 40th parallel of latitude until, some distance

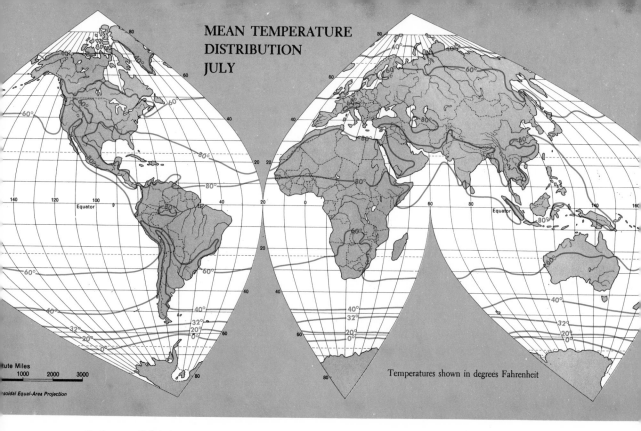

Temperatures shown in degrees Fahrenheit

9–3   IN *July the warmest temperatures occur over land masses immediately north of the equator.*

off the California shore, it makes a final south-ward bulge before turning northward onto the land.

The summer isotherms of the Northern Hemisphere bend well northward or poleward over each of the land masses; over the oceans, they are relatively straight. The pattern over the land is the reverse of that of the winter period. Over the seas, where there is any departure from an east-west line, that departure is toward the equator. This is likewise the reverse of the winter tendency. The higher temperatures, latitude for latitude, over the land in this season are the result mainly of differential heating of land and water. The sharp equatorward bends of the isotherms over the oceans, like that off the New England shore (FIG. 9–3), result primarily from the presence of cold currents. These cold currents are found off west coasts in the latitudes between 20° and

40° and off east coasts poleward of 40° (FIG. 4–6).

In the Southern Hemisphere, it should be noted that the isotherms have a more nearly constant east-west trend regardless of season. Tendencies toward an equatorward bend over land in winter and a poleward bend over land in summer are best evidenced in Australia. Africa and South America show some of the same trend especially in July, their winter period. Neither of those continents imposes any considerable width to interrupt the great expanse of water in the Southern Hemisphere. There is more uniformity of heating surface in that hemisphere and hence the ordinary contrasts of differential heating of land and water are masked by other controls of temperature.

SEA-LEVEL EQUIVALENT TEMPERATURE • In order to demonstrate more clearly some of the controls of temperature distribution, it is

World Distribution of Temperature | 217

sometimes desirable to construct isothermal maps on the basis of temperatures reduced to sea-level equivalents. This procedure does away with temperature differences which are caused by altitude changes from place to place. Effects of other controls, like latitude, land and water distribution, and ocean currents, in determining the distribution of temperature are emphasized.

An example of the use of sea-level temperatures instead of actual ones is shown in FIG. 9–4. On the left side, the January sea-level isotherms are shown for a portion of North America; on the right is a map of the actual January averages taken from FIG. 9–2. Notice that on both maps the isotherms bend generally equatorward as they cross the continent. They appear as smoothly bending lines on the map showing temperatures reduced to sea level equivalents, but on the map of actual temperatures they are irregular in detail. The effect of altitude is clearly shown both in the Rocky Mountain area and in the much lower Ap-

palachian zone in the east. On the sea-level temperature map, the 20° F. isotherm never reaches as far south as the 40th parallel of latitude. Actual temperatures show an average of 20° F. well southward along the Rocky Mountains into New Mexico. On the sea-level map, the isotherm of 60° F. crosses through Lower California, northern Mexico, and south-central Florida, but on the map of actual temperatures, that temperature is carried southward around Lower California and around the highland area of Mexico.

Though sea-level equivalent temperatures sharpen the demonstration of temperature controls, they fail to show the real climatic state. Their use geographically is thus extremely limited.

TEMPERATURE RANGE • Isothermal maps showing actual temperatures for January and July (FIGS. 9–2 and 9–3) make clear the fact that seasonal changes in temperature vary markedly over the world. The difference in degrees between the average temperature of the

9–4   COMPARISON of the pattern of actual isotherms and that of sea-level equivalent isotherms in North America. Note the greater irregularity and the more southerly position of the isotherms showing actual temperatures, especially in the western part of the continent where altitude is greater and is, therefore, a more prominent control.

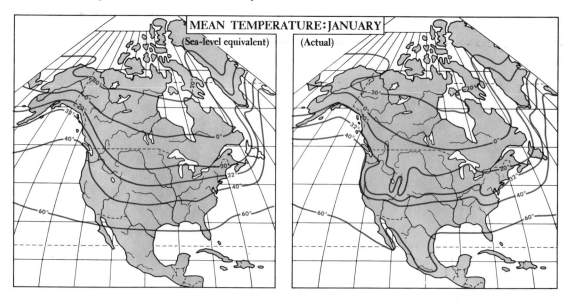

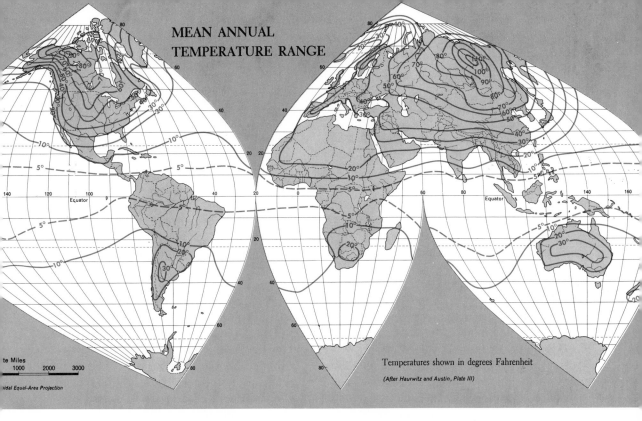

MEAN ANNUAL TEMPERATURE RANGE

Temperatures shown in degrees Fahrenheit

(After Haurwitz and Austin, Plate III)

te Miles
1000   2000   3000

idal Equal-Area Projection

9–5   MEAN annual temperature ranges are generally smallest near the equator and at high latitudes, while the largest ranges are found in the interiors of the great land masses of the Northern Hemisphere. Note that the belt where the range is 5° F. or less is set off by dashed lines.

warmest and that of the coldest month of the year is called the *average annual temperature range*.

Smallest ranges between warmest and coldest months are encountered near the equator (FIG. 9–5) and at high altitudes. Largest ranges are encountered at low elevations in the interiors of great land masses in the higher latitudes. The greatest seasonal temperature differences occur in the Northern Hemisphere because of the great extent of land in the higher latitudes of that hemisphere. The smallest temperature differences on land occur along windward coasts near the equator and in tropical high

mountains. In the latter locations, the effects of nearly constant insolation the year round and of high altitude are both operative. Over large water bodies the temperature range is relatively low; where winds blow onshore from the oceans the tempering effect of large water bodies is found to exist not only along the immediate shore but also for varying distances inland.

Specifically, ranges vary from less than 5° on the equator to over 110° in interior Asia. For example, the range at Manaus, on the Amazon in Brazil, is about 3°; that at Verkhoyansk in northeastern Siberia is nearly 119°.

World Distribution of Temperature | 219

Major Function of Wind

Wind is significant among the climatic elements because it is an agent of transport. In any part of the United States a south wind is associated commonly with warmth; a north wind is associated with cold. This is true throughout the Northern Hemisphere. Conditions are reversed in the Southern Hemisphere; there, a south wind is relatively cold and a north wind, relatively warm. Wind, the horizontal movement of air, is thus recognizably an agent in the transport of temperature. In a similar fashion, people in the eastern United States usually associate an east wind with rain. Thus, the function of wind as a transport agent for moisture is exemplified. Without wind, tropical areas would become intolerably hot, areas in the higher latitudes extremely cold, and continents moistureless. The cause of wind is difference in atmospheric pressure between adjacent regions. Hence, before any detailed understanding of wind systems can be acquired, the generalized distribution of pressure over the earth must be sketched.

World Distribution of Pressure

ISOBARIC MAPS • As was explained previously, pressure tends to be lower than normal in areas of great heating and higher than normal in areas of little heating. While this is not the only factor in pressure determination, it is one of the most important. The distribution of pressure over the earth is best shown by maps similar to those presenting the distribution of temperature. Like isothermal maps, they may be drawn for any particular period or for any one time. The lines which appear on a pressure map connect points of equal pressure. They are called *isobars*. Since there is such a close relationship between temperature and pressure, it is desirable to consider isobaric maps for the January and July periods as was done for isothermal maps. These are FIGS. 9–6 and 9–7. On both maps, sea-level equivalents of pressure are shown.

WORLD PRESSURE BELTS • On both isobaric maps, it will be noted that a zone of low pressure exists generally along the equator. This corresponds closely to the zone of greatest heating. The low pressure can be ascribed completely to the high temperatures which exist throughout the zone. Near the margins of the low latitudes, it can be seen that there exists either a series of high pressure zones over the oceans or a continuous band of high pressure linking together the oceanic highs and widening materially over the continents. Closer examination will reveal that the highs exist separately over the oceans during the period which is summer in their hemisphere and are linked together across the land during the winter.

In addition to the seasonal change just suggested, it should be noted that the pressure belts shift slightly equatorward in the winter and slightly poleward during the summer. For example, the January map (FIG. 9–6) shows that the belt of high pressure over the North Atlantic centers about 30° N whereas the July map (FIG. 9–7) indicates a center at nearly 40° N. This seasonal shift of pressure belts corresponds moderately closely with seasonal changes in heating which result from the migration of the sun's vertical rays.

The existence of the highs over the oceans near the margins of the low latitudes cannot be accounted for solely on a basis of temperature. They are partially the result of earth rotation. But the connecting wide bands over the land areas in winter are essentially the result of continental cooling at that season and the lows which separate the oceanic highs during summer are essentially the result of continental heating in that season.

Still farther poleward, there is a second zone of low pressure. This is much more intense in the Southern Hemisphere than in the North-

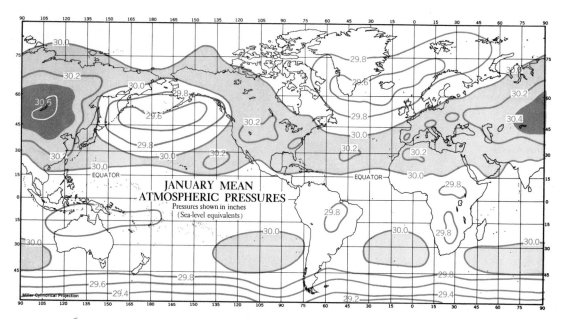

9–6   MEAN monthly atmospheric pressures (sea-level equivalents) are generally lowest near the equator and in the higher latitudes. In January the highest pressures occur generally over the interior of the great land mass of Asia in the Northern Hemisphere. Areas of high pressure are shaded.

9–7   IN July the highest pressures occur generally over the oceans near the margins of the low latitudes in both hemispheres. Areas of high pressure are shaded.

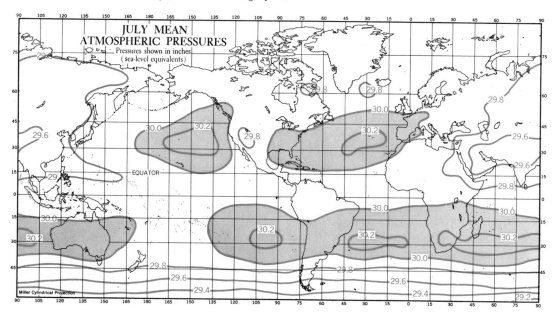

World Distribution of Pressure and Wind | 221

ern, largely because in that hemisphere there is no alternation of land and water in these latitudes.

There are thus five general belts of definitely low or high pressure: (1) an equatorial belt of low pressure, (2) a northern and (3) a southern subtropical high pressure zone; and (4) a northern and (5) a southern subpolar low pressure zone. In addition, about the poles, there are subsiding eddies creating high centers which expand in area in winter (in January in the Northern Hemisphere and in July in the Southern) and contract in summer. Along any one meridian, the lows can be thought of as troughs and the highs as ridges. The slope from any high to an adjacent low brings about a flow of air from the ridges into the troughs, and thus definite wind belts may be distinguished.

World Wind System

From the subtropical highs, in both Northern and Southern Hemispheres, surface air moves toward the equator and toward the subpolar lows. Surface air flows toward the subpolar lows from the polar eddies. There are thus created three wind belts in each hemisphere. These are the *Trade Winds*, the *Prevailing Westerlies*, and the *Polar Winds*.

Between the Trades and the Prevailing Westerlies in each hemisphere, there is a zone of light, variable winds and calms known as the *Horse Latitudes*. Between the Trades of the Northern Hemisphere and those of the Southern Hemisphere lies another belt of light, variable winds and calms known as the *Doldrums*.

There are in all, then, nine wind belts. These are indicated in TABLE 10.

CORIOLIS FORCE • If pressure differences alone controlled wind directions, the winds flowing from the subtropical highs toward the equator would be directly from the north in the Northern Hemisphere and directly from the south in the Southern Hemisphere. The

TABLE 10

Wind Belts of the World

APPROXIMATE LATITUDE	WIND BELT
90°–60° N	Polar Winds
60°–35° N	Prevailing Westerlies
Centering on 30° N	Horse Latitudes
25°–5° N	Trades
5° N–5° S	Doldrums
5°–25° S	Trades
Centering on 30° S	Horse Latitudes
35°–60° S	Prevailing Westerlies
60°–90° S	Polar Winds

rotation of the earth, however, exerts a deflective force on all moving bodies on its surface. That force is exerted to the *right of the direction of movement* in the Northern Hemisphere and to the *left of the direction of movement* in the Southern Hemisphere. It is commonly called the *Coriolis force* after the French mathematician who first formulated a statement of it.

MAJOR WIND BELTS • As a result of the Coriolis force, winds moving toward the equator in the Northern Hemisphere are northeasterly or easterly rather than northerly. In the Southern Hemisphere, since the deflection is opposite to that in the Northern Hemisphere, that is, to the left instead of to the right, similar equatorward moving winds are dominantly southeasterly. There are two belts of equatorward moving winds, one in each hemisphere. They are known as the *Trades*, or *Trade Winds*. They are the least interrupted of any of the world wind belts and are consequently the most regular and persistent of any winds.

The winds flowing from the subtropical highs to the subpolar lows in each hemisphere are the *Prevailing Westerlies*. In the Southern Hemisphere, where practically uninterrupted ocean circles the globe in the latitudes where these winds blow, they are persistent throughout the year and they blow from nearly a due west direction. Any description of "rounding the Horn" at the southern tip of South America and Antoine de Saint-Exupéry's marvelous description of air flight off the Patagonian coast in his book *Night Flight* attest to the wildness and storminess of this wind belt. In the Northern Hemisphere, where large land masses break the continuity of the subpolar low and impose frictional blocks to the clean sweep of these winds, the Westerlies are much more variable both in strength and in direction. During the winter months when the subpolar lows are best developed over the North Atlantic and the North Pacific, storminess on those bodies approaches the ferocity of the southern belt of Westerlies.

The *Polar Winds* of each hemisphere are less well-known. Since they move toward the equator, rotational deflection makes "easterlies" of them. Their strength and blusteriness are attested by frequent references in all accounts of polar exploration and by motion picture record. The films taken in the Antarctic during the International Geophysical Year and since indicate, in a manner that leaves no doubt, the intensity and persistence of these winds.

OCEANIC WIND CIRCULATION • Deviations from this simple belted arrangement are so numerous as nearly to obscure the whole pattern. During the summer in each hemisphere, the subtropical belt of high pressure is broken; oceanic high pressure and continental low pressure centers take its place. From the highs, winds blow outward in all directions. The Coriolis force converts the outward draft into a huge whirl about the ocean basins. These whirls proceed in a clockwise direction in the Northern Hemisphere and in a counterclockwise direction in the Southern Hemisphere.

Actually, the half of the whirl toward the equator is the zone of Trades while that toward the poles is the zone of Prevailing Westerlies. Thus during the summer season there is a continuity between the two belts which is absent in the winter half of the year. On the western sides of the ocean basins, winds flow from the Trade Wind belt generally poleward, deflecting more and more until they become the Westerlies. On the eastern sides of the ocean basins, the Westerlies turn more and more equatorward until they eventually become Trades. Low pressure developed over the continents during summer has the general effect of bringing about an indraft of air toward the continent and, thus, of strengthening the continuity between Trades and Westerlies.

The actual prevailing winds over the oceans for the months of January and July are shown on FIGS. 9–8 and 9–9. In these figures the arrows point in the direction toward which the wind is blowing. The length of the arrows indicates the relative persistency of the wind and the thickness indicates the relative strength. It should be noted that the Trades are generally persistent in both seasons and that the Prevailing Westerlies are strongest in the winter season.

MONSOONS • Where a continental mass is sufficiently large, the tendency toward air movement inland during the summer becomes so strong as to upset the Trade Wind and Prevailing Westerly circulation completely. Asia offers the best example. On that continent, the most intense of all continental lows develops during the April-to-September period. Opposite Asia in the Southern Hemisphere, at the same season, is an intense subtropical high. Winds coming off the Southern Hemisphere high and flowing toward the equator start as southeasterly Trades (FIGS. 9–8 and 9–9). The pressure gradient toward India is sufficiently great to cause a flow of these Trades across the equator. When they move from the Southern Hemisphere into the Northern Hemisphere, the Coriolis force upon them is re-

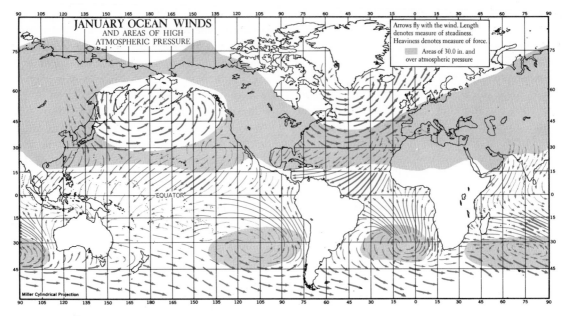

9–8   THE actual prevailing winds over the oceans in January show a well-developed counterclockwise circulation over the Southern Hemisphere oceans, and also a strong development of the Prevailing Westerlies in the Northern Hemisphere.

9–9   THE actual prevailing winds over the oceans in July show a well-developed clockwise circulation over the Northern Hemisphere oceans.

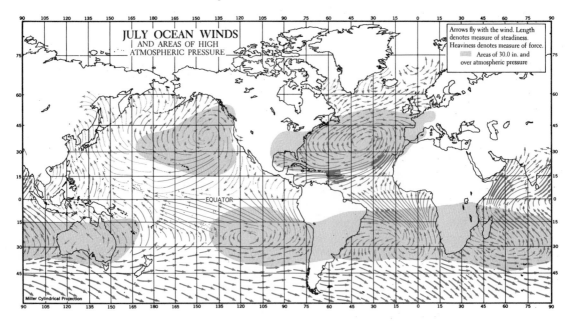

versed. The winds curve to blow in toward India from the *southwest* where ordinarily the *northeasterly* Trades would be expected. During the winter season, the strongest high pressure system in the world is built up over Asia; it is opposed by an intense low over northern Australia and Indonesia. The pressure gradient is southward across the equator and the out-blowing northeasterly winds from India are moved into the Southern Hemisphere. Their deflection is reversed and they become *north-westerlies* where the belt of *southeasterly* Trades would be expected.

The seasonal indraft or outdraft of winds from a continent, like those over southern and eastern Asia, is known as a *monsoon*. Monsoons are well developed only along the southern and eastern Asiatic coasts, Indonesia, northern Australia, and the westward bulge of Africa. Elsewhere, the upset to general atmospheric circulation is not sufficiently intense or sufficiently persistent to warrant recognition as a monsoon. All continents cause a monsoonal tendency, but seldom does that tendency dominate the air movements for a whole season or for the year.

THE INTERTROPICAL FRONT • Between the belts of Trades in each hemisphere, there is a zone of very light and irregular surface winds and calms. This is known as the *Doldrums*. It is in this zone that air is rising from the surface, partially as a result of the high temperatures which exist near the equator, and partially as the result of slight differences between the masses of air flowing in from the northeast and from the southeast, the Northeast and Southeast Trades. Slight inequalities in heating, and hence in density, cause one mass to be forced upward over the other. Where active rising, or pushing upward, of air is going on, there exists what is frequently called the *intertropical front*.

The term *front* is used to mean the surface between bodies of air of observably different quality, as for example between a body of cold, dry air containing little dust and another con-taining very warm, moist air with many dust particles. In a sense, a front in the atmosphere is like the surface which divides oil from water when those two liquids are poured into the same container. They do not mix, but a contact surface is formed with water on one side and oil on the other. Whether the rising of air in the zone between the Trade Wind belts is convectionally induced or whether it is brought about by action along an intertropical front, the end result is an upward movement leading to expansion, cooling, and condensation with attendant clouds and precipitation.

THE POLAR FRONT • In the middle latitudes, there are two belts of opposing winds, the *Westerlies* and the *Polar Winds*. In this instance, there is direct opposition, for the former are from a westerly direction and the latter from an easterly direction. In addition, the Westerlies are relatively warm since they come from the low latitudes, while the Polar Winds are cold. A distinct front, called the *Polar Front*, is formed.

Lack of constancy of either the Westerlies or the Polar Winds causes a wavelike fluctuation in the position of the Polar front; at one time, the Polar Winds are stronger and a mass of cold air pushes well equatorward into the Westerlies; at another time, the Westerlies may be stronger, and a mass of warm air pushes well poleward. When the cold air is advancing equatorward, the front is spoken of as a *cold front*; when the warm air is advancing poleward, the front is spoken of as a *warm front*. On a weather map a cold front is always represented by a line to which are attached triangles pointing in the direction of movement. A warm front is represented by a line to which are attached semicircles rounded in the direction of movement (FIG. 9–10). Along both types of front, air is being forced upward with the end result of cloud formation and precipitation of moisture.

During the winter when the Polar Winds blow farther equatorward than at any other period of the year, cold front conditions carry

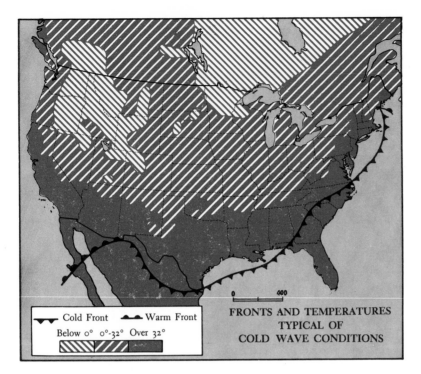

Cold Front   Warm Front
Below 0°   0°–32°   Over 32°

FRONTS AND TEMPERATURES
TYPICAL OF
COLD WAVE CONDITIONS

0   400

9–10

DURING *the winter season when a cold front pushes its way southward across Canada and the United States into the Gulf of Mexico, the low temperatures in back of the front produce what is called a cold wave. (Based on the U.S. Daily Weather Map for December 6, 1949)*

freezing temperatures south into the Gulf of Mexico (FIG. 9–10). The newspapers tell of the cold wave and thus emphasize the role of the polar portion of this zone of opposition. In summer, the similar emphasis upon the warm front conditions draws attention to a heat wave (FIG. 9–11). Both elements are present in both seasons, but the fluctuation seasonally of the position of the Polar Front makes people in the United States more subject to the effects of one side of the front at one season and the other side at the opposite season. This shift is far more marked than that of the Intertropical front and it therefore affects a wider zone of the earth's surface.

THE HORSE LATITUDES • There remain only two sections of the world wind system to consider. These sections are those between the Trades and the Westerlies in each hemisphere. The central part of the zone of subtropical high pressure is a region of very light, shifting, irregular winds or of calms. This zone is known as the *Horse Latitudes*. The lack of wind results primarily from the lack of appreciable pressure

gradient. Generally the zone of calms is more pronounced in mid-ocean, for it is there that high pressure dominates throughout the year. In the winter period, the oceanic high is extended landward over the continents on either side; with this expansion comes spreading of the belt of calms. As the high retreats to its oceanic position during summer and as lows begin to form over the continents on either side, a flow of air becomes noticeable on the continental fringes. At that time, the belt of calms is confined to the ocean centers.

UPPER-AIR WINDS • So far the discussion has been concerned essentially with surface winds. To complete the general picture of atmospheric circulation, it is necessary to suggest the movements above the earth, at least in that zone with which man is mainly concerned. Along the zone of greatest heating, air is rising away from the earth's surface. As has been suggested previously, there is a flow of air poleward from the top of the rising column. In the Horse Latitudes, the poleward current descends toward the earth's surface. Part of the

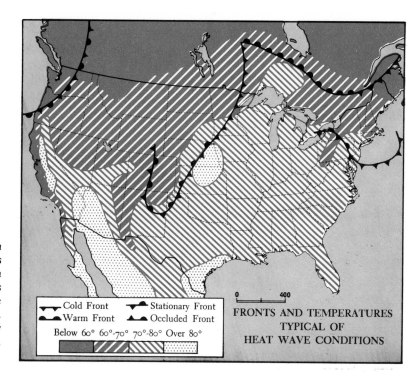

DURING *the summer season
when a warm front pushes its
way northward into southern
Canada, the high temperatures
in back of the front produce
what is called a heat wave.
(Based on the U.S. Daily
Weather Map for July 26,
1949)*

| Cold Front | Stationary Front |
| Warm Front | Occluded Front |

Below 60° 60°-70° 70°-80° Over 80°

0   400

FRONTS AND TEMPERATURES
TYPICAL OF
HEAT WAVE CONDITIONS

descending air moves equatorward at the surface as the Trades and part of it moves poleward as the Prevailing Westerlies. In the middle latitudes, the surface Westerlies are forced to rise over colder Polar Winds. Aloft, it is believed that a portion of this rising air continues to move poleward, descending to the surface well within polar regions. Another portion moves back toward the equator (FIG. 9–12).

In addition to the poleward and equatorward movements of air, there appear to be broad flows moving from west to east at high speeds near the tropopause. These "rivers of air" move essentially horizontally. They are spoken of as *jet streams*. Typically, they meander through the belt of Prevailing Westerlies, edging equatorward and dying out when they move into the subtropical high pressure belt. Usually they persist at very high elevations, but at least occasionally they descend to as low as 6000 feet. The actions and consequences of these jet streams are not well understood, but it is certain that they are re-

sponsible for great energy exchanges throughout the atmosphere as a whole.

The details of circulation are certainly much more complex than might be concluded from this brief statement. So far as upper air circulation is concerned, man is now only in the exploratory stage of investigation. So far as surface winds are concerned, there is an assumption in the scheme here presented that the pressure belts are continuous and static. This we have seen is not true. Lack of continuity and mobility, particularly seasonal shifts of position, change the location of ascending and descending air currents and are, thus, effective climatic controls.

SEASONAL SHIFT OF WIND BELTS • The wind belts migrate latitudinally with the passage of the seasons. The cause of the shift is, basically, seasonal change of insolation. This is reflected in the change of position of pressure belts and, consequently, of the winds.

During the Northern Hemisphere winter, the zone of maximum insolation lies south of the equator. Consequently, the equatorial belt

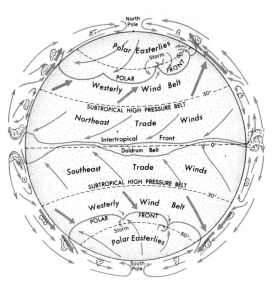

9-12

SCHEMATIC *diagram showing the world's major wind belts, the frontal zones, and the vertical circulation within the troposphere.*

of low pressure is somewhat south of the equator also. In response to this, the Northern Hemisphere Trades move farther toward the equator than at any other season. All of the other wind belts of the Northern Hemisphere shift equatorward also. Likewise, the Southern Hemisphere wind belts are displaced southward.

In the Northern Hemisphere summer, maximum insolation is received north of the equa-

tor. Hence, the equatorial belt of low pressure is developed somewhat north of the equator. All of the Northern Hemisphere wind belts migrate northward, which is poleward for them; the Southern Hemisphere wind belts move northward, but this is equatorward for them. In other words, the wind belts of each hemisphere migrate equatorward in winter and poleward in summer.

Over the oceans, the migration is through 10 to 15° of latitude; over the land masses, it may amount to as much as 35°. In addition, the shift over the oceans usually lags behind the movement of the sun's vertical rays by a month or two, while over the land there is usually no lag. Both of these effects are closely related to the different heating qualities of land and water.

The areas most affected by these shifts are those that lie near the margins of the wind belts. This is well illustrated by the Mediterranean area of Europe and Africa. The Mediterranean basin lies in the general zone of the Horse Latitudes. During the summer when all wind belts move poleward, the Mediterranean comes under the partial influence of the Trades. In winter when the wind belts move equatorward, it lies just within the Westerlies. Since the Trades blow generally off the land toward the Atlantic, they bring little moisture; summer drought results. The Westerlies, blowing in off the Atlantic, carry both the moisture and the mechanism—cyclonic storms—to make the winters rainy.

WORLD DISTRIBUTION OF PRECIPITATION

Mean Annual Precipitation

As with temperature and pressure, maps are constructed to show precipitation amounts both seasonally and annually. The lines which connect points of equal precipitation are called *isohyets*. FIGURE 9–13 indicates

mean annual precipitation for the world. While annual amounts are subject to year-by-year fluctuation, nevertheless certain areas stand out as excessively moist and certain others as excessively dry. Almost without exception, equatorial areas belong among the wettest areas of the world and polar regions among the driest.

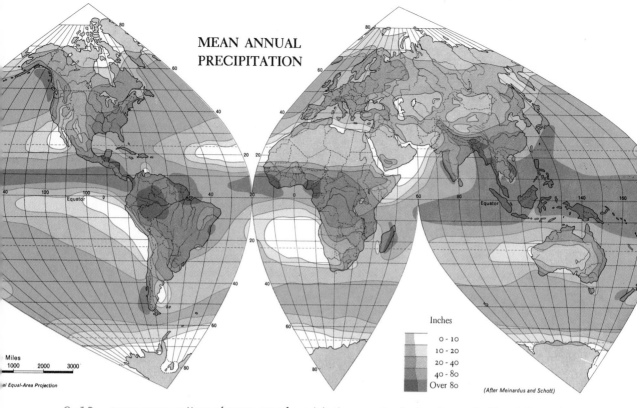

MEAN ANNUAL PRECIPITATION

Inches

0 - 10
10 - 20
20 - 40
40 - 80
Over 80

Miles
1000   2000   3000

...al Equal-Area Projection

(After Meinardus and Schott)

9–13 GENERALIZED *pattern of mean annual precipitation over the land and water bodies of the world.*

Evident as areas of dryness are the low latitude west coasts and the continental interiors. Elsewhere, precipitation is intermediate in amount.

EQUATORIAL AND TROPICAL ZONE • If the discussion of the major causes of precipitation is recalled, this broad pattern can in part be explained. It is largely a question of knowing where moist air is rising and where air, whether moist or not, is settling toward the earth. As has previously been pointed out, air is rising in a broad zone along the equator. So long as the air contains a large amount of water vapor, precipitation results. Since air at the high temperatures common to equatorial regions is capable of holding large amounts of water vapor and since the Trades and monsoons of equatorial regions flow over large expanses of warm ocean, the moisture which they carry produces more ample precipitation than is to be found anywhere else in the world. Where onshore winds and rising air combine most effectively in this

zone, tremendous amounts of rain fall to the surface. The highest mean annual rainfall in the world is recorded on the windward slopes of mountains in the Trade Wind belt. Mount Waialeale in the Hawaiian Islands has a seven-year uninterrupted record showing an average of *476 inches per year*; Cherrapunji on the windward southern slope of the Khasi Hills in the face of the summer monsoon has recorded *366 inches in one month*; and Baguio on Luzon in the Philippine Islands has received *46 inches in one twenty-four-hour period*.

LOW LATITUDE WEST COASTS • The decline in amount of precipitation away from the equator and on the continental west coasts may be coupled with the existence of the subtropical belt of high pressure. Winds in these latitudes strike the east coasts; the west coast areas are regions of offshore winds. In addition, air in these latitudes is settling toward the surface, as described in the discussion of major wind belts. There is therefore no adequate source of moisture nor is there the mechanism necessary for condensation and precipitation of such moisture as may be available. While there is no absolute evidence that any one part of the earth's surface is absolutely rainless, yet there exist, for the low latitude west coast zones, several records of rain gauges which have seldom been wet from rain or snow, as at Iquique and Calama in northern Chile. In these and similar locations, as in the coastal desert of southern Peru, dew contributes appreciable amounts of usable moisture. Usually, the precipitation is below 10 inches per year, as throughout the whole Sahara, and what does fall occurs at irregularly spaced intervals.

MIDDLE LATITUDES • Through the middle latitudes, a moderate amount of precipitation is common, though parts of the continental interiors are characteristically dry. This is the zone in which cyclonic storms, or frontal activity, are linked to the zone of rising air between the Prevailing Westerlies and the Polar Winds. Here precipitation amount depends largely upon distance from the source of moisture, the oceans. Onshore winds carry much moisture toward the continents and orographic or cyclonic conditions bring about its precipitation. In either event, most of the moisture is removed from the air relatively near the continental margins and only a small portion of it penetrates to the interior.

Study of the map of average annual precipitation in the United States (FIG. 9–14) illustrates the contrast between continental margins and interiors. Large amounts of precipitation are seen to occur on the Pacific coast, especially in Oregon and Washington. Decrease is very pronounced eastward. Here the control is in large part orographic. Along the Atlantic coast, precipitation is moderately heavy. Decrease toward the interior is again noticeable though it is more gradual than that near the Pacific coast. The Great Plains are dry largely because rain-bearing winds from the Gulf of Mexico do not regularly penetrate northwest-ward into the continental interior and those from the Pacific lose much of their moisture in passing over mountains before reaching that far east.

HIGH LATITUDES • In the polar regions, air is settling toward the surface and, in addition, it contains little moisture. The ability of cold air to contain water vapor is very low and the mechanics by which that small amount might be condensed and precipitated are usually lacking. Hence the fall is light. In this instance, the amount of precipitation is of little significance, for temperatures are always low. Few measurements have been made for this reason. Upernivik, Greenland, has an average of only 9.2 inches despite its marine position and Point Barrow on Alaska's north coast has only 5.3 inches.

SEASONAL DISTRIBUTION OF PRECIPITATION • Not only the total yearly precipitation, but its seasonal distribution are important in a discussion of climate. This distribution is represented by the isohyetal maps for January and July (FIGS. 9–15 and 9–16). On them, it can be noted that there is a shift of rainy and dry zones comparable with the shift of wind belts previously described. For example, almost all of the area in central Africa receiving over 2 inches of rain during January lies south of the equator. This is the season when the zone of greatest heating and the Intertropical front occupy their farthest south position. In the opposite period of the year, July, most of the area receiving over 2 inches during the month lies north of the equator. This, in turn, is the season when the vertical sun is well north of the equator, as is also the Intertropical front.

Similar shifts may be seen in the middle and high latitudes. Almost without exception, the shift parallels that of temperature and winds which have been described previously. The specific variation in any one particular place may not correspond to the general world pattern, but the broader picture reflects the influence of the climatic controls upon precipitation as well as upon temperature.

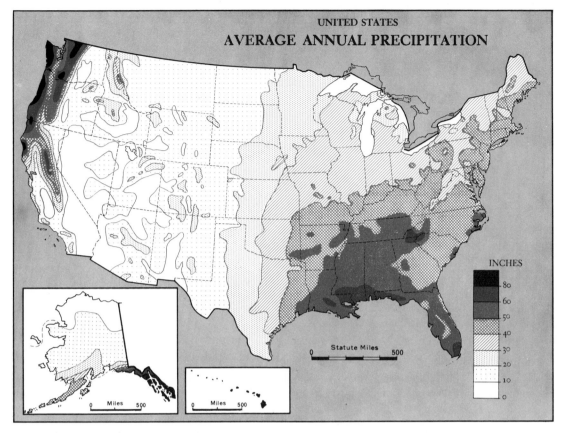

9-14   GENERALIZED map of average annual precipitation over the United States. (After Goode's World Atlas, 1961, and others)

Precipitation Variability

Mean annual or mean monthly precipitation data provide valuable measures of comparison between various parts of the world. Nevertheless, it must be remembered that the total for any one place may vary widely from the mean. Over the period from 1888 through 1938, Amherst, Massachusetts, had a mean annual precipitation of 43.70 inches. In 1938, the amount was 59.00 inches, 35 per cent above the mean; in 1908, the total was only 30.68 inches, nearly 30 per cent below the mean.

When the period is shorter than a year, even greater variability can be observed. September is usually the wettest month at Amherst with an average of 4.24 inches. September of 1938

recorded 14.55 inches, nearly three and one-half times the mean. Yet in 1914, that month had only .52 inch, less than one-eighth the mean amount.

Though variability is encountered everywhere, it is generally true that areas of little precipitation are subject to greater fluctuation than those with heavy precipitation. This can be illustrated by comparison of FIGS. 9-13 and 9-17.

Middle Latitude Storms

In the zone of contact between the Prevailing Westerlies and the Polar Winds, there is a constant variation of weather. Drizzly rain of three or four days' duration gives way to dry,

World Distribution of Precipitation | 231

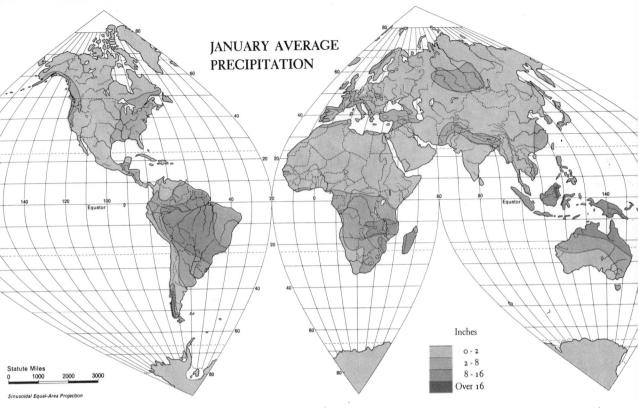

Inches

0 - 2
2 - 8
8 - 16
Over 16

Statute Miles
0   1000   2000   3000

Sinusoidal Equal-Area Projection

9–15   AVERAGE *precipitation over the land areas of the world during January shows a concentration south of the equator.*

clear, cloudless days. The hot mugginess of summer days contrasts vividly with the biting cold of winter days. Though a certain temperature may be characteristic, sudden sharp drops in spring or sudden sharp upward swings in fall bring "unseasonable" spells of cold or of heat. The weather is constantly changing; there is no monotony to it. This is the zone of middle latitude cyclones and anticyclones.

Where the Polar Front (the contact between the Prevailing Westerlies and the Polar Easterlies) exists, there is produced a stream of eastward-moving eddies of air. These eddies are in reality the moving rising-air centers, or the *cyclones*, of our mid-latitude weather. They are the main source of precipitation in the middle latitudes. Between the eddies of rising air are tongues of cold polar air flowing toward the equator. These are the *anticyclones* which are commonly associated with clear, cloudless weather in the same zone.

An eddy in the Polar Front becomes more prominent as it moves along eastward. It forms at first a sort of crest to a wave (FIG. 9–18A). Ahead of this crest, the relatively warm air from lower latitudes is pushing poleward actively, trying, as it were, to push colder polar air out of its way. Thus a portion of the Polar front bends poleward and assumes a shape more or less like that of a scythe blade (FIG. 9–18B). Since warm air is the active force, this section is called a *warm front*. Back of the crest, cold air from higher latitudes pushes actively in behind the warm air so that this portion of the Polar Front assumes a shape like that of the handle of a scythe. This section is called a *cold front* because cold air is the active force. Middle latitude cyclonic storms, then, have both warm front and cold front parts.

WARM FRONT WEATHER • Since middle latitude cyclonic storms move eastward and since the warm front is that portion ahead of

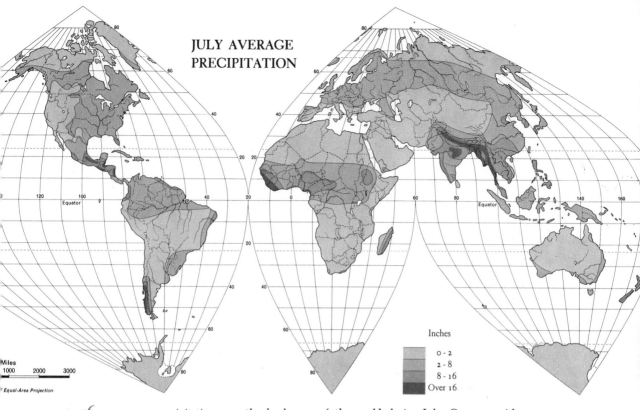

Inches

0 - 2
2 - 8
8 - 16
Over 16

Miles
1000   2000   3000

Equal-Area Projection

9–16   AVERAGE *precipitation over the land areas of the world during July. Compare with* FIG. 9–15,
noting especially the seasonal shift of wet and dry conditions.

the wave crest in the Polar Front, it is that section of the storm which passes any given point
first. Along a warm front, warm air glides up
over cold along a slope which is relatively
gentle, between 1 in 100 and 1 in 300. In other
words, 100 miles ahead of the line along which
the front meets the *ground*, the frontal surface
lies from 1700 feet to 1 mile above the ground
(FIG. 9–19B). The warm air slips gently but
steadily up this surface, forming cirrus-type
clouds well out ahead of the front. These are
followed shortly by the lower alto-stratus and
possibly a few very low strato-cumulus clouds.
Gentle rain or snow begins, increasing in intensity as the front approaches any specific
place. Frequently, just before the front passes,
fog or very low black clouds form with the continued light drizzly rain. As the front moves
past, the clouds become higher, precipitation
ceases, and temperatures rise. The wind usually
shifts from easterly or northerly directions to

southerly or southeasterly ones. The period of
precipitation is usually long-continued; it covers
a wide area, but the fall is usually gentle.

COLD FRONT WEATHER • Along a cold
front, warm air is forced up over cold along a
slope which is relatively steep, anywhere from
1 in 25 to 1 in 100; that is, 100 miles from the
line where the front meets the ground, the
frontal surface may be anywhere from 1 mile
to 4 miles high (FIG. 9–19A). Cloud formation
is delayed almost to the time of the passage of
the cold front *on the surface*. Precipitation begins either just before or almost immediately
after the passage of the front on the ground
and, though heavy, is usually of short duration
followed by relatively rapid clearing. Before the
passage of the front, warm moist air flows in
from a southerly or easterly direction, and
being forced to rise rapidly, forms clouds almost above the location of the front on the
ground. With the coming of cloudiness, there

World Distribution of Precipitation | 233

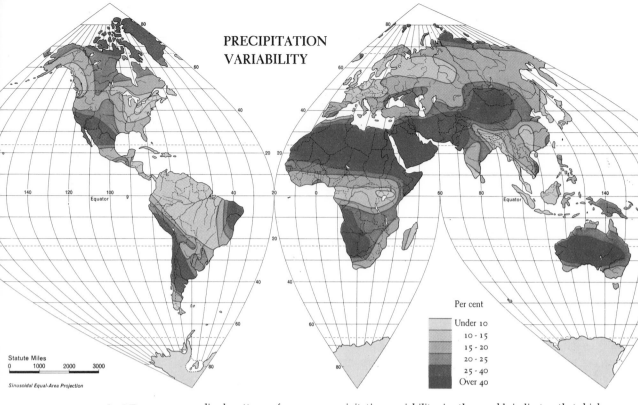

Per cent

Under 10
10 - 15
15 - 20
20 - 25
25 - 40
Over 40

Statute Miles
0   1000   2000   3000

Sinusoidal Equal-Area Projection

9–17   THE *generalized pattern of average precipitation variability in the world indicates that higher variability is generally more common in areas of light precipitation than in areas of heavy precipitation.*

is a shift of wind to a westerly direction and an accompanying drop in temperature. After the passage of the rain or snow belt, there is a marked drop in relative humidity.

The evenness of progress of the storm depends upon the rate and continuity with which the front is moving. It may vary irregularly or it may remain constant. As yet, it is impossible to determine accurately the regularity with which a front moves. Consequently, any forecast of the changes is subject to many qualifications. If the front moves evenly eastward, the time of passage can be calculated and an accurate forecast of the sequence can be made. If the front becomes stagnant, the sequence may be held up at any point. The sequence of weather remains the same; the time element changes.

Ordinarily, cold fronts move with greater

steadiness and speed than do warm fronts. Thus, the blade and handle of the scythe, the warm and cold fronts, are folded in upon one another. When a cold front finally overtakes a warm front, the condition is known as an *occlusion*; an *occluded front* is formed (FIG. 9–18D).

OCCLUDED FRONT WEATHER • If the air back of a cold front is of a lower temperature than that which lies ahead of the warm front, the cold front will push in under the warm front, forcing it aloft. This is known as a *cold front occlusion* (FIG. 9–20A) and is commonest on the eastern sides of continental areas. If the air back of the cold front is warmer than that ahead of the warm front, the cold front will be forced aloft in a *warm front occlusion* (FIG. 9–20B). This type of occlusion is commonest on continental west coasts.

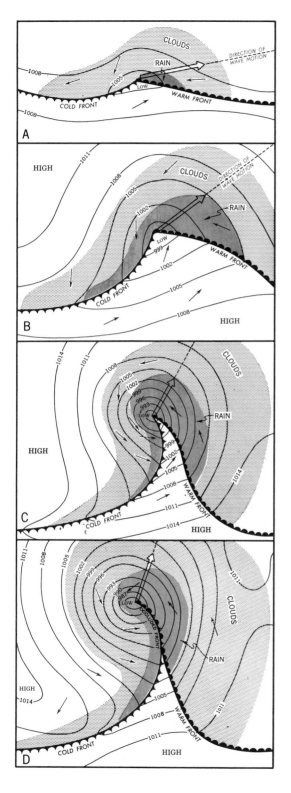

The weather which is associated with occlusions combines the features of both types of frontal storms. Since the occlusion takes place near the center of the cyclone, bad weather is widespread, particularly at the time when occlusion begins. The length of the period of bad weather and its intensity depend again upon the rate at which air is forced upward. Eventually, if the air is forced high enough so that temperature differences are dissipated, low pressure will disappear. Air which was relatively warm and light will have been replaced by that which is colder and heavier, and the cyclone will have disappeared.

It is through the agency of cyclonic storms that the greater part of the precipitation in the zone of Prevailing Westerlies is derived. Warm, moist air from the low latitude oceans provides water; colder, drier air from polar regions and from the far continental interiors provides the power which forces condensation of the vapor.

Because there is seasonal migration of the zone of contact between warm and cold air masses, there are some areas which are always under the influence of middle latitude cyclonic storms and other areas which experience their influence during only part of the year. Further, it appears certain that shifts in the position of the Polar Front jet stream, in terms both of altitude and of latitude and in terms of intensity, have profound effects upon the detailed nature of middle latitude cyclonic storms.

THUNDERSTORMS AND TORNADOES • Within the middle latitudes, especially during the summer months, two kinds of violent atmospheric disturbances of small size occur. These are *thunderstorms* and *tornadoes*. Both of them

9–18

SCHEMATIC vertical views of the development of a cyclonic storm as a wave along the Polar Front in the Northern Hemisphere. A. Incipient. B. Actively developing. C. Well developed. D. Final. Note patterns of rain, clouds, pressure (figures in millibars), and winds (small straight arrows). North is at the upper edge of each diagram.

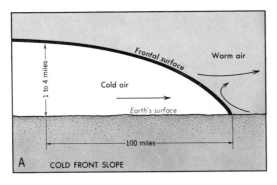
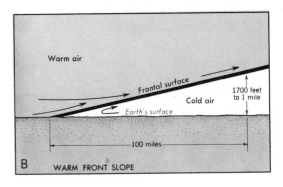

9-19   CHARACTERISTIC *profile slopes along (A) cold and (B) warm fronts. Note that warm air is actively forced steeply upward along the cold front but glides smoothly upward along the warm front.*

exist within the general framework which has just been described.

When, for one cause or another, masses of warm, moist air are forced to rise very rapidly and to very high levels, they are cooled excessively. Moisture in the air is condensed to form massive, vertically extensive clouds, heavy rain, and sometimes hail. Descending columns of cold, dry air spill downward from the tops of the clouds which often build up to an altitude of over 20,000 feet. The vertical downward movement of cold air in some parts of the storm contrasts sharply with vertical upward movement of warm air. Within these currents, velocities of over 100 miles per hour are characteristic. Electrical differences are developed, and there are electrical discharges between cloud and cloud and between clouds and the ground (FIG. 9-21). The sound produced as a result of the passage of one of these charges through the atmosphere is thunder.

Thunderstorms are seldom more than a few miles in diameter, though a whole series of them may follow one after another. They always occur within a warm air mass, but the force which starts the upward movement of air may be the result of a number of different factors. Sometimes thunderstorms are convective, the result of local differences in atmospheric heating. At other times, they may be orographic, the result of movement of air up a mountain slope. And at still other times, they may result from the passage of air mass fronts. Regardless of the starting force—the *trigger action*, as it is called—the air that is displaced upward must be warm and moist if a thunderstorm is to develop.

Another striking type of storm of small diam-

9-20   CROSS *sections through air-mass occlusions. A. Cold front occlusion. B. Warm front occlusion. In both diagrams, the black line represents a cold front and the double line represents a warm front.*

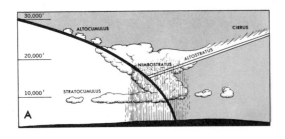
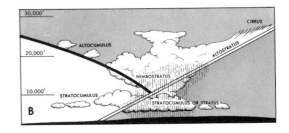

9–21

BRILLIANT, and often destructive, lightning accompanies the heavy downpour of rain in a thunderstorm.

eter which occurs in the middle latitudes especially during the summer months is the tornado. The diameter of the tornado at the ground varies between 10 and 500 yards. A funnel-shaped cloud reaches down from low, heavy cumulo-nimbus and twists erratically along the surface (FIG. 9–22). This cloud represents the center of very low pressure and, about it, air spirals inward and upward at rates well over 100 miles per hour. Along its path, such a storm is terrifically destructive, but it has little effect beyond its immediate locale. A tornado is in reality a "thunderstorm run crazy."

Other Storms

Cyclonic storms also occur in the tropics. Many of them are nonviolent—similar in many ways to the middle latitude cyclonic storms. They originate along the Intertropical Front and move generally westward, carried along by the drift of the Trade Winds. As they move onto land and thus increase their distance from a source of moisture, they tend to become less intense and finally to disappear altogether.

Quite frequently in their westward path, tropical cyclones veer toward the margins of the middle latitudes. When their path is over water, as for example over the Caribbean Sea, they sometimes become violent. Such violent tropical storms are spoken of as *hurricanes* when they occur off the east coast of North America, or as *typhoons* when they occur in the same latitudes on the east coast of Asia. They are inward and upward spirals of air about a low pressure center. Their diameters are usually between 100 and 400 miles. At the center, there is a relatively calm, cloudless, and rainless zone, known commonly as the *eye*. Around the edge of the eye, wind velocities may exceed 120 miles per hour (FIG. 9–23). The passage of a hurricane or typhoon brings a deluge of rain. Since these storms originate over the ocean, they cause serious damage to shipping as well as great destruction in coastal districts onto which they move.

The havoc wrought by small-area storms like thunderstorms, tornadoes, hurricanes, and typhoons far surpasses that resulting from the larger, less violent middle latitude or tropical cyclonic storms. But the smaller types are all limited in their occurrence both as to area and as to time. Their very infrequency makes them subject to specific study and comment; as origins of precipitation or as agents of temperature change, they are not significant from a world point of view. They are important in their limited distribution, but they are far less significant in the world as a whole than the more extensive cyclones which develop along either the Polar or the Intertropical Fronts.

World Distribution of Precipitation | 237

9-22   THE development of a tornado near Gothenburg, Kansas. Note how the funnel cloud reaches down and eventually makes destructive contact with the ground.

9-23   HURRICANE Debbie (September 13, 1961, at 9:16 A.M. E.S.T.) as seen from a Mercury spacecraft 12 minutes after its launching. Note the eye of the storm.

CONCLUSION

WHAT has been said in this chapter gives only a suggestion of the almost infinite variety of combinations of climatic elements which occur at or near the earth's surface—in the zone where man's activity goes on. Understanding of the major elements—temperature, precipitation, and pressure and wind—and of the controls which are active upon them pro-vides a basis for understanding the variety of the physical setting in which man lives (TABLE 7, page 197). From this point, it is possible to proceed to a systematic study of the major combinations of climatic elements and to the distribution of these combinations over the face of the earth.

· REVIEW QUESTIONS ·

1. Present a logical argument, supported by specific illustrations, as to why the distribution of climatic elements over the earth is signifi-cant to man.

2. How is an isothermal map constructed? Of what specific use is an isothermal map?

3. In what specific ways do isothermal maps show the effects of the climatic controls upon

temperature distribution over the continents? Over the oceans?

4. Why are January and July isothermal maps better for general study of temperature distribution over the earth than those for March and September?

5. Explain why some of the lowest temperatures on the earth are experienced in northeastern Asia.

6. Why is it that sea-level equivalent temperatures are often used instead of actual temperatures in constructing world isothermal maps? Why are maps made by using actual temperatures more significant geographically?

7. Suggest ways in which average annual temperature range is important to human beings.

8. Distinguish between wind and air currents. In what ways may wind be considered essential to man?

9. For what purposes might it be more satisfactory to use actual observed atmospheric pressures rather than sea-level equivalent pressures in constructing an isobaric map?

10. Give some reasons why a knowledge of the world pressure belts contributes to an understanding of the world climatic pattern.

11. Why is it that the Trade Winds in the Northern Hemisphere are generally northeasterly winds?

12. Is there any difference in the persistence and direction between winds, like the Trades and Prevailing Westerlies, over oceans and the same winds over land areas? Explain.

13. Explain the conditions under which a monsoon develops. How does a monsoon affect the general world wind belts?

14. In what way is the Intertropical Front important climatically?

15. How does the Intertropical Front differ from the Polar Front? Are the differences significant to man? If so, in what ways?

16. Suggest reasons for and the major results of the seasonal shift of the world wind belts.

17. What is a jet stream? In what ways may jet streams be of major climatic importance?

18. What are the major reasons for differences in the seasonal distribution of precipitation from place to place over the earth?

19. Give some of the reasons for differences in amount of precipitation from place to place over the earth.

20. What are warm fronts and cold fronts? How can one tell when a warm front or a cold front passes? If possible, give examples from your own experience.

21. Why should Florida be more subject to "cold waves" then southern California?

22. Why should Chicago be more subject to "heat waves" than San Francisco?

23. Explain the higher frequency of thunderstorms in Mississippi, for example, than in coastal California.

24. In what parts of the world do hurricanes or typhoons occur? What is their significance to man?

25. Are cyclonic storms encountered in the low latitudes? If they are, how do they differ from those in the middle latitudes; if they are not, why are they absent?

10—1

[OPPOSITE, TOP] ANGULAR *landforms and sparse vegetation characterize regions of arid climate like those of the southwestern United States.*

10   Climatic Types: The Tropical Moist and the Dry Climates

JOSEPH MUENCH

⟨⟨ FROM *earliest times, students of man's habitat have attempted to classify climatic elements so as to provide a means of comparison between one land and another. The early Greeks established one such classification based largely upon the single element of temperature. They knew the climate of the area in which they lived, with its hot, dry summers and mild, rainy winters, with its clear summer skies occasionally blurred by the fine particles of dust blown northward from the great desert of Africa, and with its cloud-filled skies of winter. They realized fully the vital importance of securing additional water for agriculture during the summer, but beyond this, the climate of the area in which they lived posed few problems of sustenance and fewer still of shelter and clothing. To them, it was the ideal climate—the* Temperate Climate.

Their knowledge of the burning desert to the south led them to believe that even hotter lands lay beyond, lands where the sun was so hot as to burn a man's skin to a blackish color, hot enough to be uninhabitable by civilized peoples. This was their concept of the Torrid Climate. *In a similar manner, they deduced the opposite extreme. The occasional cold, north winds of the Aegean Sea in winter, the skin clothing of the few northern peoples who penetrated the Grecian world, and the stories of the hardships of travelers to the north combined to lead to the concept of an area too cold for human habitation, at least by civilized peoples like themselves. This was their* Frigid Climate.

Almost on the basis of temperature alone, they erected this threefold climatic classification which, even to this day, remains in the frequent reference to Torrid, Temperate, and Frigid Zones. But this classification is not adequate. It recognizes fully only one of the climatic elements. While there is an approach to truth in such a system, it does not really reflect the actual combinations of climatic elements known to exist over the face of the earth.

CLASSIFICATION OF CLIMATIC TYPES

Purposes of Classification

CLASSIFICATION is a tool, not an objective in itself. Many systems have been devised for the orderly grouping of individual climatic phenomena into major complexes. These systems have been used to serve two main purposes; they have provided means of systematic, meaningful comparison, and they have been used as implements in the determination of a basic world pattern.

SYSTEMATIC COMPARISON • When we hear the comedian's overworked remarks about the "heavy dews" of the California winter, we are hearing a reference, in a loose way, to winter rains. It has been observed that winter rain is a recurrent feature in that part of the world. But such a statement is hardly adequate to allow comparisons between California and other parts of the world where characteristic winter rains have also been observed. The problem is to define precisely what is meant by winter rains.

Equally common is the expression, "Hot for this time of year, isn't it?" Such a remark points to an everyday recognition of the factor of temperature and to the recurrence of certain temperatures at certain times of the year. We cannot use such everyday remarks as the basis for definite comparison. Precisely how hot is it during a particular season and at a particular place?

While there is great variety in the possible combinations of climatic elements, certain broadly similar ones have been observed to recur frequently throughout the world. Such combinations are the basic climatic types. Each type can be given exact quantitative, rather than mere qualitative, definition. On the basis of these definitions, a system or classification can be erected. Such a scheme not only defines each of the types, but indicates, in terms of observable and measurable amounts, the relationships between them. Through the use of such a classification, descriptive statement is made exact. No matter who may use the classification, or to what part of the world it may be applied, the meanings are standard. It is possible to state whether or not one area exists under essentially the same combination of climatic elements as another.

DETERMINATION OF A BASIC WORLD PATTERN • In another way, climatic classification makes possible the determination of the pattern of climate over the world. For any chosen area, observed records of as many places as possible can be classified. The location of each place, with the climatic type represented by its record, can be plotted on a map. Then lines can be drawn in such a way as to separate the places with one type of climate from those with another. The result is a climatic map of the area. The lines on such a map are primarily indicators of direction of change. That change is greatest at right angles to the lines and least along them or in a direction parallel to them. If the same process is followed for the whole earth, one of the basic world patterns is obtained (PLATE IV).

The distribution of climatic types, or the climatic pattern, is basic to an understanding of the human habitat, because of the close relationship between climate and the many other elements of that habitat. Visible forms of the physical setting, like landforms, vegetation, and soil, are all greatly modified by the climate under which they exist. A hot, rainy climate produces certain characteristic forms of the actual surface, of the cover of plants on that surface, and of the soil in which the plants grow. These forms are quite unlike those produced under a cold, dry climate.

To be sure, there are many influences other than that of climate involved in the shaping of the earth's surface. However, climate does impose general differences from place to place. Sharp, angular landforms are common through the arid southwestern United States. More subdued, rounded landforms characterize the rainier eastern part of the country.

While variable supplies of water available for plant life may cause local differentiation in vegetation, over and above that, vegetation existing under one climate is notably different from that found under another. For example, the sparse, drought-resistant vegetation of much of Arizona contrasts vividly with the forests of the Pacific Northwest.

Similarly, while local soil types may reflect certain differences in the rock materials from which they are formed, on the whole, given the same basic materials, the soil developed under one climate is vastly different from that formed under another. The reddish and yellowish soils of Georgia are a far cry from the deep black and dark brown ones of Iowa.

Even the forms of human utilization of the physical setting are affected by climate. The type of building admirably suited for human use in the constantly hot, wet climate of an equatorial forest is hardly adequate protection against the severe winters of northeastern Siberia. That cotton should dominate the agriculture of the southeastern United States and be absent from that of the New England states is primarily a reflection of climatic difference. The contrast between the intensive use of the lowlands of Japan and the near emptiness of the lowlands that face upon the Arctic Ocean is, in part, the result of the respective climates of these two areas. To much that man does in the land in which he lives, climate is a limiting force either directly or indirectly. Consequently, the distribution of climatic types over the world, the climatic pattern in other words, is the key to the arrangement of many other features of man's habitat. From this point of view, climate classification is a tool; it is *not* a desired end in itself.

Plan of Classification

To serve the purposes just stated, the climates of the world are grouped into categories based upon the two elements which are most significant to man as he attempts to live and work on the face of the earth. These two elements are temperature and precipitation. Long-time records of each are available for numerous and widely scattered places on the earth. When these records are analyzed, it is found that certain outstanding combinations regularly occur. For example, some places show a combination of "hot and moist," others are "hot and dry," still others are "cold and moist," and so on through many temperature and moisture combinations.

There are five major categories of specific climatic types. These are as follows:

1. Tropical Moist (or A) climates
2. Dry (or B) climates
3. Moist, Mild Winter (or C) climates
4. Moist, Severe Winter (or D) climates
5. Polar (or E) climates

In addition there is one general category of undifferentiated climates—the Mountain (or H) climates. Each of these broad categories is subdivided to indicate further significant climatic differences from place to place within any wide zone. For example, within the Moist, Mild Winter climates, there are some places that have summer drought, like the San Joaquin valley of California; other places in the same broad class have characteristic winter drought, like parts of southern China; and still other places are moist the year round, like Washington, D.C.

Still further subdivision is possible and, for some types of climate, essential. In the Moist, Severe Winter climates, for example, there is a great difference between the climate of Chicago with its hot summers and that of, say, Quebec, where the summers are shorter and warm rather than hot.

This classification is essentially the one known as the Köppen system. The Köppen system uses letter symbols rather than descriptive names to represent the various climatic types, and each letter has a specific definition. Thus, a Moist, Mild Winter climate in which the summers are characteristically droughty is known as a *Cs* climate. If such a climate has hot summers, it is known as a *Csa* climate; if the summers are warm rather than hot, it is known as a *Csb* climate. And each of these terms, like "hot" or "warm" or "droughty" or "mild winter," are defined in exact temperatures or amounts of precipitation. In mountain areas, the distribution of specific climatic types is so spotty that it is impossible to differentiate between one type and another on a world scale. Consequently, all are grouped together, with definition stated principally in terms of elevation.

In what follows, the descriptive names will be used and the Köppen equivalent letter symbols will be added in parentheses. *For general purposes*, it is unnecessary to follow the great detail of the Köppen system in its entirety. That detail is stated in terms of specific definitions and their use in Appendix B.

THE TROPICAL MOIST (A) CLIMATES

Characteristics

THE climates which prevail in equatorial areas and throughout much of the low latitudes are those which are hot throughout the year and are moist enough to support a dominantly forest vegetation. Within this broad pattern of similarity, however, there are significant differences. It is to the characteristics of these climates, both their similarities and their differences, that attention is now directed.

TEMPERATURE • The common characteristic of all Tropical Moist (A) climates is constant high temperature. In the definition of these types, an average temperature for the *coolest* month is specified as a limit. Such a temperature is an indication of whether or not a season exists in which truly tropical vegetation cannot flourish—a period of plant rest induced by relatively low temperatures. The average of 64° F. for the *coolest* month is taken as the limit of the A climates. This temperature corresponds closely with a notable change in vegetation type. When cool month averages are below 64° F., trees like the palm begin to drop out of the forests and their place is taken by types like the oak. Other features of the physical setting also are markedly affected, as will be illustrated in later chapters.

On some tropical uplands, as in southeastern Africa and southeastern Brazil, elevations are great enough to reduce temperatures somewhat below 64° F. Except for this one item, however, the climate of these uplands is very like that of Tropical Moist (A) lowlands. For general purposes, tropical uplands may therefore be considered to have a climate which is a variant rather than a distinctive type.

In the heart of the zones having Tropical Moist (A) climates, monthly averages are in the 70's and 80's, and the ranges between the average for the coolest month and that for the warmest month are very small. The graph of the statistics for Singapore in southeastern Asia (FIG. 10–2A) indicates these two conditions. Here the coolest month average is 78° F. while the average for the warmest month is 81° F.—a difference of 3°. This is typical of the most pronounced of the Tropical Moist (A) climates. Often the differences between day and night are far greater than those between the coolest and warmest months. A daily range of as much as 15° is not unusual. At Singapore, the average daily range varies between 12° in July and 15° in March. Monotony is the key word for such a temperature condition and monotony prevails throughout the heart of all Tropical Moist (A) climatic regions.

As one proceeds toward the margins of the Tropical Moist (A) climatic regions, greater range between coolest and warmest month averages is encountered. This tends to make the daily range less significant and to emphasize the seasonal quality of the climate. The graph of the statistics for Corumbá in Brazil (FIG. 10–2B) illustrates this condition. There, the coolest month average is 70° F. while the warmest month average is 80° F.—a difference of 10°. The average daily range is approximately 20°. Other factors, particularly moisture differences between these two places, tend to emphasize the differences shown in temperature. But the monotony so pronounced at Singapore is greatly modified at Corumbá.

PRECIPITATION • It is in the amount of precipitation and in its distribution through the year that the greatest contrasts between the various phases of the Tropical Moist (A) climates are to be noted. All phases are sufficiently moist to be included in the wet climates; in many places, there is excessive wetness. But there the common quality ends. Some of the Tropical Moist (A) climates have rainfall distributed evenly throughout the year, or, if they do show any period of appreciable dryness, that period is relatively short. Frequently the precipitation during the greater part of the year is very high and never is there a true season of drought. When there is no drought, the climate is of the *Tropical Rainforest (Af)* type, as in Singapore (FIG. 10–2A).

In other areas of Tropical Moist (A) climate, intense drought during one season alternates with heavy rain during another. Where such a condition prevails, as in Corumbá (FIG. 10–2B), the climate is of the *Savanna (Aw)* type. It is obvious that the transition from one extreme to the other is gradual and, consequently, that the definition of any divide between Tropical Rainforest (Af) and Savanna (Aw) types is arbitrary.

Intermediate between these extremes is the rainfall type encountered along parts of the southern and southeastern coast of Asia, where

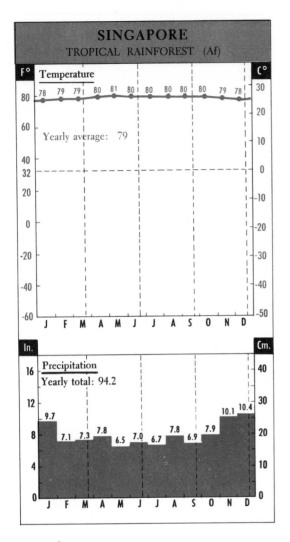

SINGAPORE
TROPICAL RAINFOREST (Af)

Temperature

Yearly average: 79

78 79 79 80 81 80 80 80 80 80 79 78

Precipitation
Yearly total: 94.2

9.7 7.1 7.3 7.8 6.5 7.0 6.7 7.8 6.9 7.9 10.1 10.4

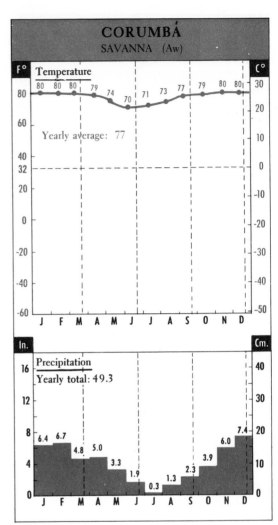

CORUMBÁ
SAVANNA (Aw)

Temperature

Yearly average: 77

80 80 80 79 74 70 71 73 77 79 80 80

Precipitation
Yearly total: 49.3

6.4 6.7 4.8 5.0 3.3 1.9 0.3 1.3 2.3 3.9 6.0 7.4

10–2 A

CLIMATIC *chart and statistics for Singapore, Malaya.*

10–2 B

CLIMATIC *chart and statistics for Corumbá, Brazil.*

excess of precipitation at one time of the year compensates for lack of it at another. There, where monsoons are most typically developed, a characteristic distribution of rainfall through the year occurs. This distribution is shown on the graph of the climatic statistics for Akyab in Burma (FIG. 10–2C). It is similar to that in areas of Savanna (Aw) climate—there is a rainy season and a dry season—but the rainy season is generally longer and the dry season shorter

than those in Savanna (Aw) zones. In addition, the amount of rain which falls during the rainy season is tremendous. While this rain cannot be as effective, coming during a relatively short period, as it would be if spread through the year, it is still effective enough to prevent a complete cessation of growth processes and hence to produce a setting more nearly like that encountered under a Tropical Rainforest (Af) climate than that of a Savanna (Aw) cli-

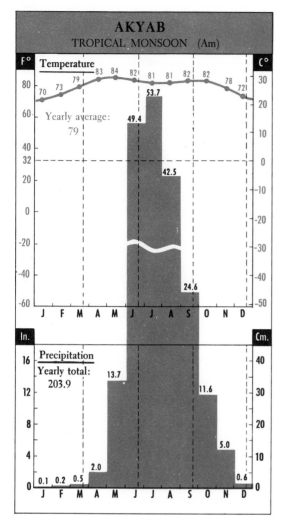

AKYAB
TROPICAL MONSOON (Am)

10–2 C

CLIMATIC chart and statistics for Akyab, Burma.

line along which a change from the year-round rain of the Tropical Rainforest (Af) climate to the alternating rainy and droughty seasons of the Savanna (Aw) climate is experienced, in some areas, the so-called Tropical Monsoon (Am) climate represents a transitional type between extremes rather than a type indicative of monsoonal circulation.

The relationship between the total precipitation for the year and the amount which falls during the driest month determines which of the three varieties—Tropical Rainforest, Tropical Monsoon, and Savanna (Af, Am, and Aw) —is represented by any one set of precipitation statistics. This relationship is mirrored in the native vegetation. Tropical Rainforest (Af) climate, in which there is no season of rest for plant growth, supports a heavy forest. Savanna (Aw) climate, in its drier phases, supports a mixed cover of sparse grass and thorny bushes which, though lush and green during the rainy season, is dull, brown, and lifeless during the height of the dry season. Again, in the intermediate position, Tropical Monsoon (Am) climate supports a light forest with heavy undergrowth rather than the heavy forest of Tropical Rainforest (Af) climate or the grass and bush cover of the drier Savanna (Aw) climates. In Tropical Monsoon (Am) forests, relative dryness rather than absolute drought is characteristic. It must be noted, however, that one type of vegetation merges gradually with another; there is no sharp line between one type and another.

Subdivisions of the Tropical Moist (A) Climates

TROPICAL RAINFOREST (Af) CLIMATE • For direct comparison of the extremes to be found within the Tropical Moist (A) climates, we may refer again to the graphs for Singapore, Corumbá, and Akyab (FIG. 10–2). Singapore has a yearly precipitation of 94.2 inches. The driest month is May, during which 6.5 inches fall; the wettest month is December, in which

mate. This type is the *Tropical Monsoon (Am)* type.

The intermediate type of rainfall just described is commonly associated with areas in which a monsoonal circulation is present. There are some situations, however, in which other causes, such as local exposure to rain-bearing winds during one season and shelter from them during another, may produce this rainfall pattern. And since there is no precise

10–3   A HEAVY *cover of vegetation clothes the surface in areas of Tropical Rainforest (AF) climate, as here in Urundi, in central Africa. Note the fog collecting in the valleys.*

10.4 inches fall. In no conceivable way can it be said that Singapore has a dry season. Accompanying this constantly high rainfall in an area of high temperatures, there is naturally continued high relative humidity, frequently in excess of 90 per cent. Even though the temperature may drop slightly from the high 70's, there is little or no relief from the steamy, sticky feel of the air. Seldom if ever does the thermometer register 100° F., a figure common enough in the central United States, but seldom is the heat dry. Humidity is man's greatest problem in the areas of extreme Tropical Rainforest (Af) climate (FIG. 10–3).

SAVANNA (Aw) CLIMATE • At Corumbá, the total yearly precipitation is 49.3 inches. The driest month is July with an average of .3 inch; the wettest month is December with an average of over 7 inches. The graph (FIG. 10–2B) shows the pronounced nature of the dry season. When this is coupled with the temperature curve, it is evident that the period of greatest dryness comes when the temperatures are

lowest. The doubled effect of seasonal difference is thus made the more noticeable. Relative humidity is less than at Singapore and shows considerable fluctuation through the year. The average for December, the rainiest month, is 84 per cent and that for August, one of the drier months, is 68 per cent. The wet season approximates the characteristics of the Tropical Rainforest (Af) climate; the dry season approximates the climate found along the margins of the moisture-deficient or Dry (B) climates farther away from the equator.

TROPICAL MONSOON (Am) CLIMATE • The graph for Akyab (FIG. 10–2C) shows a temperature curve similar to that of the other Tropical Moist (A) climates with the slight exception that the highest temperatures come in the months just preceding the maximum rainfall. The precipitation distribution through the year suggests the characteristics of the Savanna (Aw) climate. The amount of rain which comes during the rainy season, however, is much greater than that at Corumbá. The total

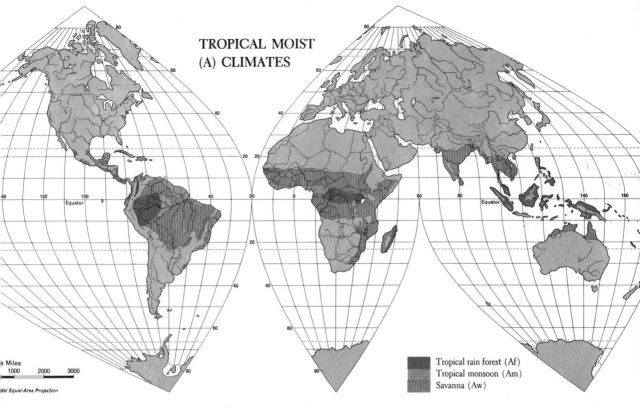

TROPICAL MOIST
(A) CLIMATES

Tropical rain forest (Af)
Tropical monsoon (Am)
Savanna (Aw)

Miles
1000   2000   3000

idal Equal-Area Projection

10—4   WORLD distribution of Tropical Moist (A) climates.

for the year at Akyab is 203.9 inches; of this, over one-quarter, 53.4 inches, comes during the single month of July. This amount is sufficient, along with the amounts during the other months of the rainy season, to prevent long-continued drought fully comparable in terms of intensity with that of the Savanna (Aw) climate. This is true despite the fact that each of four months from December through March receives less than one inch of rain. As is true in the Savanna (Aw) climate, seasonal change is quite pronounced. Temperatures throughout most of the dry season are appreciably lower than those during the rainy season. Just at the end of the dry season, high temperatures do occur. Relative humidity averages about 70 per cent through most of the dry season; it averages in excess of 90 per cent from May through September. In terms of human reactions, there are really three seasons in such a climate: the cool (relatively), dry season;

the hot, dry season; and the rainy season. This climate represents a kind of merging between the extremes of the Tropical Rainforest (Af) and the Savanna (Aw) climates, partaking as it does of certain of the features of both.

Distribution

FIGURE 10–4 shows the actual distribution of the Tropical Moist (A) climates for the whole world, distinction being made among the three subdivisions: Tropical Rainforest (Af), Tropical Monsoon (Am), and Savanna (Aw). It should be noted especially that the Tropical Monsoon (Am) type forms a transition between the Tropical Rainforest (Af) and the Savanna (Aw) types throughout most of the zone of the Tropical Moist (A) climates. It is probable that more complete information in the form of a closer net of observations over the whole tropical region would show this transition between all areas of Tropical Rainforest (Af) and Savanna (Aw) types. Such information is lacking, however, and, consequently, there are some places such as the northern edge of the Congo Basin in Africa and the inner part of the Amazon Basin in South America where Tropical Rainforest (Af) and Savanna (Aw) types are shown abutting directly upon one another.

The theoretical distribution of all climatic types is treated in Appendix B.

Dominant Controls

TEMPERATURE • The constant high temperatures experienced in areas of Tropical Moist (A) climate are primarily the result of location near the equator. It is in equatorial regions that insolation is greatest and most nearly constant throughout the year. The angle of the sun's rays and the length of the daylight period are primarily responsible for this condition. While the general effects of these two factors were discussed in CHAPTER 8, it is well to restate and amplify the essentials here.

Along the equator, the noon sun is vertically overhead twice during the year, about March 21 and September 21. Hence, the receipt of heat at the earth's surface is most intense at these two times. In consequence, the atmosphere above the equatorial surface is heated to its highest degree at these two times also. Along each of the Tropics, the noon sun is vertically overhead on only one day of the year, about June 21 at the Tropic of Cancer and about December 21 at the Tropic of Capricorn. There is only one period of greatest surface heating in each instance and hence only one period of maximum atmospheric heating.

At all places between the Tropics, the noon sun is overhead twice during the year; as the Tropics are approached, these periods come closer together until they finally merge. At *no* time during the year within this zone is the noon sun far from the overhead position. Because of this, there is no period when heating is greatly reduced. In terms of air temperatures, this means that the range between one part of the year and another is never very great. It is least along the equator; it increases in both directions away from the equator.

Equally important in the control of temperature is length of the daylight period. Along the equator, the daylight period is of equal length throughout the year (FIG. 8–4). In both directions away from the equator this length increases during one season and decreases during the other. At the Tropics, the longest daylight period is about 13⅓ hours out of the 24 and the shortest, about 10⅔ hours. Likewise at the Tropics, the period of longest day corresponds with the period of highest sun and the period of shortest day with that of lowest sun. Hence heating is essentially constant throughout the year along the equator, but it varies appreciably at the Tropics.

Between the equator and the Tropics, the period of longest day comes between the two high-sun periods that are closest together. For example, at 12° N, roughly halfway between the equator and the Tropic of Cancer, the noon sun is vertically overhead one day during the first part of May and on another day in early August; the longest day is roughly June 21. At either of the Tropics, the period of longest daylight is also the time of highest sun. Thus, at the Tropics, both controls of insolation—angle of sun's rays and length of daylight period—operate to produce greatest heating at one season and least at the opposite season. At the equator, the angle of the sun's rays varies less than at either Tropic and the length of the daylight period is constant. Hence the variation in amount of insolation through the year in the low latitudes (latitudes between the Tropics) is greatest at the Tropics and least at the equator. This means that mean annual temperature range decreases from the Tropics to the equator.

Despite this condition, the annual temperature range at the Tropics is relatively small. There is no season when insolation is so re-

10–5   THE Trade Wind coast of St. John Island, Virgin Islands. Note the heavy growth of tropical forest reaching to the cliffed shores and to the beach.

duced as to produce low air temperatures and there is, hence, no "winter" season.

In addition, position near a coast onto which winds are blowing, a windward coast, as in Hawaii or the West Indies (FIG. 10–5), for example, tends to reduce the range during the year. Conversely, position in a continental interior tends to exaggerate the range. These effects are the result of different rates of heating and cooling of land and water masses.

Since ranges are notably small within all Tropical Moist (A) climates, monotonously uniform temperatures are produced to an even greater extent at increased elevation above sea level in tropical mountains. The extreme of this condition is illustrated by Quito in Ecuador (FIG. 10–6). Quito lies within one degree of the equator, at an altitude of 9350 feet. This elevation, of course, lowers all temperatures so much that the climate is *not* of the Tropical

Moist (A) type, but it is the range in tropical mountains which is here the point in question. The warmest month at Quito is September, with an average of 54.9° F. The lowest average, shown alike by February, March, April, July, and November, is 54.5° F. The average annual range is thus only .4°, too small a fraction to be shown on the chart.

The control which altitude exercises over the average annual temperature range is of great significance to human activity in tropical plateau and mountain country throughout the world. Latitudinal position insures relatively even heat reception throughout the year, and altitudinal position insures coolness. At latitudes and altitudes comparable to those of Quito, the result is a climate often described as "perpetual spring." At still higher altitudes, but approximately the same latitudes, the result is a climate of "perpetual winter." Thus,

The Tropical Moist (A) Climates | 251

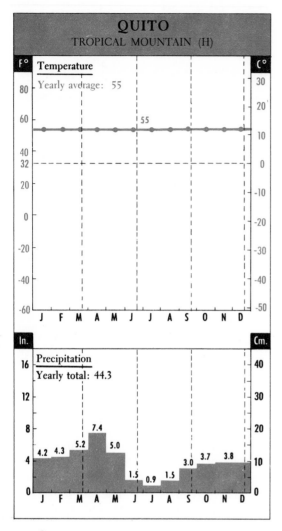

QUITO
TROPICAL MOUNTAIN (H)

Temperature
Yearly average: 55

Precipitation
Yearly total: 44.3

4.2 4.3 5.2 7.4 5.0 1.5 0.9 1.5 3.0 3.7 3.8

10–6

CLIMATIC *chart and statistics for Quito, Ecuador.*

even on the equator, it can be winter "all the time," with snow fields, small mountain glaciers, and barren rock surfaces sometimes present.

PRECIPITATION • The precipitation in all regions of Tropical Moist (A) climate is associated with a relatively small number of atmospheric conditions. These are: (1) the zone of rising air between the belts of Trade Winds; (2) onshore winds where land masses intercept the flow of the Trade Winds; (3) local convectional storms; and (4) monsoons.

Within the Doldrums, there is a zone of rising air, either thermally induced or resulting from the presence of the Intertropical Front (FIG. 9–12). Cooling accompanies the general updraft and brings about condensation of moisture with resultant heavy precipitation. Migration of the Trade Wind belts with the seasons is accompanied by a similar shift of the zone of rising air. As a consequence, the precipitation in the Doldrum belt is effective from about 10° N to about 10° S during the course of the year. At no one time, however, is this cause effective over the whole twenty-degree belt.

Since the Trades blow from an easterly direction, any east-facing coast within the regions where these winds blow provides a means of forcing air to rise and, hence, of producing rain. The seasonal migration of the Trades brings onshore winds, for part of the year at least, nearly to the margins of the low latitudes. The influence of these winds decreases away from the equator and inland from the east coasts.

In regions of such heat as those of the Tropical Moist (A) climates, local convectional storms form frequently during the warmer part of the day and produce torrential downpours accompanied by brilliant displays of lightning and heavy, almost continuous, rolls of thunder. Several of these storms usually succeed one another from shortly before noon through to evening. Each storm is more severe than the one which preceded it until, finally, with the early evening downpour, the convectional circulation is destroyed. The presence of the zone of rising air between the Trades contributes to the frequency of these storms.

The Tropical Rainforest (Af) climate occurs characteristically where the three forces so far mentioned are most strongly developed. The farther one is from the zone of convergence of the Trades, the farther one is from an east coast, and the farther one is from the zone of greatest heating in which local convection is at a maximum, the smaller is the amount of rain and the more seasonal is its distribution. Thus one passes from the Tropical Rainforest (Af) to the Savanna (Aw) climate.

Monsoons upset the simplicity of this pattern. Only where a tremendous land mass, through intense summer heating or winter cooling, forms the center of a huge indraft of moist air or a great outdraft of dry air is a monsoon typically developed. Even with the existence of monsoon circulation, the rising of air and the resultant precipitation are accomplished primarily by movement onshore at an angle to the direction of the coastline or by the presence of a considerably displaced Intertropical front. Monsoons are best developed on low latitude coasts where the Trade Wind circulation is interrupted. Such a condition exists in southern and southeastern Asia. The presence of a huge land mass north of the equator and an open ocean opposite it in the Southern Hemisphere allows the existence of a well-developed Trade Wind belt in the Southern Hemisphere, but not in the Northern. The intense heating of Asia in the period from May through September makes possible an indraft of air from over the Indian Ocean, with resultant heavy rains. During the period from November through March, the accumulation of intensely cold air over the continent not only prevents any indraft, but causes a strong movement outward, with consequent lack of rain. A similar summer indraft occurs on the Guinea coast of Africa, but the winter outdraft is far less pronounced.

There is uncertainty and irregularity of precipitation throughout all areas of Tropical Moist (A) climate, largely because of variation in intensity of the forces which cause rain. In any one year, the strength of the Trade Wind circulation may be increased or weakened beyond the average. The Intertropical front may be more or less well-developed than usual. The frequency of convectional storms may change. Monsoon winds may blow with varying strength. In regions where several of these forces act together to produce the total precipitation, the failure of any one may be accompanied by the strengthening of another; thus there is less uncertainty and less irregularity of precipitation in such places than there is where one force alone is the control. Hence it is within the marginal areas of Savanna (Aw) climate, farthest removed from the equator, from an east coast, or from a monsoon coast, that uncertainty and irregularity of precipitation are most pronounced.

THE DRY (B) CLIMATES

Characteristics

A s one proceeds from the equator toward the poles along continental west coasts, precipitation becomes markedly less in amount. Increasing dryness is reflected in the natural vegetation by the change from forest to grassland and then to desert. A zone is reached in which the climate may no longer be described as Tropical Moist (A) climate. Here, the second of the specific climatic types takes over, the Dry (B) climates.

PRECIPITATION • The outstanding features of all Dry (B) climates are the meagerness and uncertainty of precipitation. The amount of rain is nowhere equal to the potential evaporation. And even the normally small average is subject to great variation from year to year. Under such conditions, the moisture available for plant life is incapable of supporting a heavy forest vegetation. No permanent streams can rise within such areas, though large ones may cross them. Channels of intermittent streams, full-flowing for short periods after the infrequent and irregularly spaced rains, and salt lakes or mud flats, resulting from the accumulation and evaporation of moisture in shallow undrained depressions, are more characteristic. Consequently, the few usable sources of water assume importance to man far beyond that of practically all of the other features of the physical setting.

The general moisture deficiency of the Dry (B) climates cannot be expressed in terms of one specific amount of precipitation. Yearly and seasonal temperature averages affect the evaporation rate profoundly. Under some conditions of temperature, 25 inches of rain is sufficient to exceed the amount of evaporation and, thus, to produce a moist climate and its accompanying heavy vegetation. With higher temperatures, the same amount produces a dry climate with sparse vegetation. The divide between the Dry (B) climates on the one hand and all of the moist climates on the other can therefore be expressed only in terms of relationship between temperature and precipitation, not in terms of either element singly. A temperature-precipitation relationship which attempts to define the condition of dryness necessary to bring about a change in the natural vegetation from forest to grassland is taken as the limit between the Dry (B) climates and those that are moist. Actually, the limit thus defined lies *within* the grasslands, rather than at the dry edge of the forest, in most parts of the world. It is really close to the median line between the moist and the dry limits of the grassland zones of the world.

The primary division of the Dry (B) climates is into the Semiarid (BS) and the Arid (BW) types. Both types are deficient in moisture, but the Semiarid (BS) climate is wetter than the Arid (BW) type. As a consequence of this, the vegetative and soil features of the areas of these two climatic types differ markedly. There is enough soil moisture in the semiarid areas to support a continuous cover of grasses, tall on the moist margins and short on the dry margins. Within the arid areas, complete sod cover

is lacking, though the land is by no means necessarily bare of all vegetation. A sparse cover of drought-resistant grasses, bushes, and thorny plants takes the place of the continuous cover of the Semiarid (BS) areas. No parts of the world are known to be absolutely rainless though some approach that state closely. Hence, except for areas of moving sand dunes and stretches of bare rock with no cover of soil material, areas of Arid (BW) climate do have some vegetation.

Rain within areas of Arid (BW) climate comes at infrequent and irregularly spaced intervals. As a rule, there is no definite season of general rains nor is widespread rain a common occurrence. Storms are local and the effects of any single storm are not felt over any considerable area. Several months or even years may pass between successive rains. But when they do occur, they may be violent cloudbursts during which a large amount of water falls in a very short time. This form of precipitation often does extensive damage. The few stream channels fill rapidly and overflow, bringing destruction to villages and oasis gardens lying near them. And yet it is these storms which replenish the meager underground supplies of water and thus make life possible in these regions. The more gentle showers which occasionally fall barely wet the surface, and the moisture from them is soon returned to the air by evaporation. Often clouds form and rain is seen to fall from them; yet no moisture reaches the ground. High temperatures and dry air cause the evaporation of the rain during its descent. Under such conditions, the figure of average yearly rainfall fails to present a complete and true statement. It suggests meagerness only. To that must be added the concept of uncertainty and irregularity.

Precipitation in areas of Semiarid (BS) climate is not only of greater amount than in Arid (BW) areas; it is more certain, it occurs at more frequent intervals, and it is more widespread in its effects. Local convectional storms are less commonly the source of rain, and they are less violent when they occur. Ordinarily, rains come from the same sources and at the same times as those within adjacent moister regions. For example, where the Semiarid (BS) climate adjoins a moist region with winter rains, as where the Sahara grades into the lands along the southern shore of the Mediterranean Sea, the precipitation within the Semiarid (BS) climate shows pronounced winter concentration. Where, on the other hand, the Semiarid (BS) climate lies close to a moist region with summer rains, its precipitation is mainly concentrated in the summer season and the amount of rain is, of course, smaller. Because of this close causal tie, rain is more certain and affects a wider area within the Semiarid (BS) climate than within the Arid (BW) climate.

TEMPERATURE • Temperatures in Dry (B) climates represent the whole range found from the low latitudes to the equatorward margins of the high latitudes. The common feature of dryness implies no specific set of temperature values. Yet the temperatures of the Dry (B) climates have in common the element of exceptionally great range, both annual and daily, for the latitudes in which they occur.

In the middle latitudes, the range between the coolest and warmest months is usually between 40° and 50°. Summers are notably hot and winters pronouncedly cold. This condition is illustrated by the statistics and graph for Denver, Colorado [1] (FIG. 10-7A). There, January has an average temperature of 30° F. and July an average of 72° F. The average annual range is 42°. There is a definite summer season and a definite winter season.

In the low latitudes, the annual range—usually between 15° and 30°—is still very large compared to those in the Tropical Moist (A) climates or in the climates of tropical uplands or mountains. At Kayes in Mali (FIG. 10-7B), the coolest month average, shown alike by

[1] Where possible, examples of the several climatic types will be drawn from the United States even though they may not be the best possible world examples.

December and January, is 77° F. May is the warmest month with an average of 96° F. The average annual range is 19° F. Even though one season is markedly cooler than the other, no true winter can be said to exist.

It is largely on the basis of the presence or absence of a winter season that further distinctions within both the Semiarid (BS) and Arid (BW) climates are made. The lack of a cold winter season is a characteristic of Dry (B) climates within the low latitudes or on their margins; Kayes offers a good example. Within the middle latitudes, the Dry (B) climates have true winter and summer seasons, as at Denver.

Dry (B) climates with relatively low temperatures do, however, occur in two kinds of places in the low latitudes. Along low latitude west coasts, roughly between latitudes 20° and 30° in both hemispheres, oceanic influences reduce the warm season temperatures and raise those of the cold season. Not only are annual ranges thereby made smaller, but yearly averages are reduced below the figures commonly expected in low latitude locations. High elevation produces similar lowering of low latitude temperatures.

Daily temperature range is considerable in most Dry (B) climates. It is more pronounced in areas of Arid (BW) climate in continental interiors than elsewhere within the Dry (B) climates.

Low latitude Dry (B) climates have furnished the highest temperatures to be recorded on the face of the earth. Azizia, just southwest of Tripoli on the northern coast of Africa and on the margin of the low latitudes, has registered 136° F. in the shade. L. M. Nesbitt, in an account of travel across the Danakil Lowland of northeastern Ethiopia, suggests readings even higher. Maximum temperatures of over 100° F. have been recorded in every month except January at Wadi Halfa in northern Sudan, and in that month 99° F. has been attained. In the north-central Australian desert, temperature is known to have exceeded 100° F. for over sixty consecutive days.

The Dry (B) Climates | 255

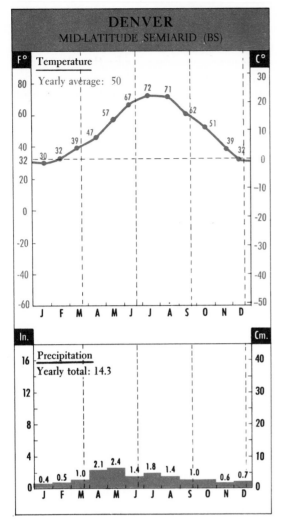

10–7 A

CLIMATIC chart and statistics for Denver, Colorado.

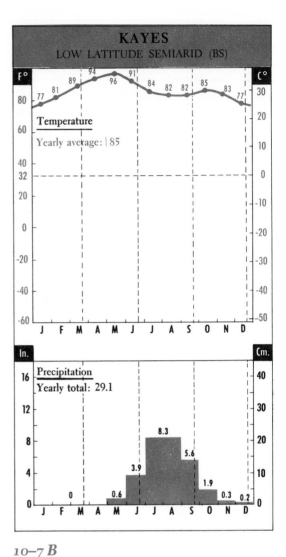

10–7 B

CLIMATIC chart and statistics for Kayes, Republic of Mali.

Despite such excessively high temperatures during the day, night readings are sometimes painfully low, often below freezing. The average daily range in areas of Arid (BW) climate in the low latitudes is usually between 25° and 30°. Extreme daily ranges are often as great as 70°; at Azizia, which holds the record, daily range has attained exactly 100°, from 126° F. to 26° F. within a 24-hour period. Ordinarily, the daily ranges are greater in the warmer part of the year than in the cooler part. But, at all times in most Dry (B) climates, the contrast between day and night is startling.

OTHER FEATURES • Two other features are outstanding in areas of Dry (B) climate. They are sunshine and wind. Both are at a maximum in low latitude Dry (B) climate, but they are significant elements in the other Dry (B) climates as well. Throughout the hotter and drier sections, skies are seldom obscured by clouds

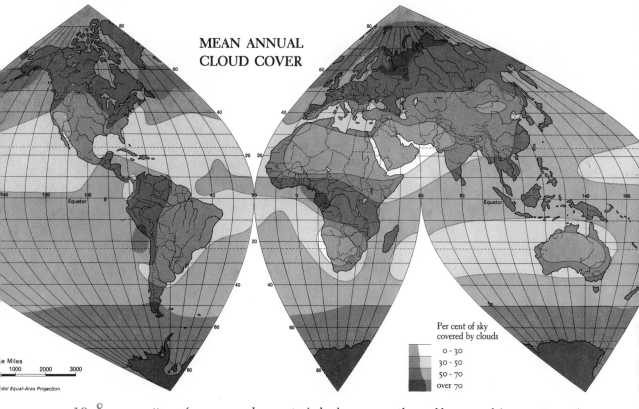

MEAN ANNUAL CLOUD COVER

Per cent of sky
covered by clouds

	0 – 30
	30 – 50
	50 – 70
	over 70

e Miles
1000   2000   3000

idal Equal-Area Projection

10–8   THE pattern of mean annual amount of cloud cover over the world, expressed in percentages of the sky ordinarily covered by clouds, denotes that most Dry (B) climates in particular are areas of low cloudiness.

(FIG. 10–8), and over 80 per cent of the possible sunlight is received at the earth's surface. Cloudiness increases to about 50 per cent in the cooler and moister sections, such as those that border the ocean or adjoin moist climates in the middle latitudes. High winds are common, especially during the daytime. As a result, the air is frequently laden with dust particles. Dust storms are often sufficiently heavy to blot out the sky. Their force is great enough, though they seldom last for long periods, to make them among the most destructive, hazardous, and uncomfortable phenomena of the Dry (B) climatic regions of the world.

Subdivisions of the Dry (B) Climates

ARID (BW) CLIMATE • The general characteristics of the Arid (BW) type as it occurs near the margins of the low latitudes are illustrated by Yuma, Arizona (FIG. 10–9A). Precipitation is insignificant in amount, and what there is, is unevenly distributed through the year. Though a yearly average of 3.3 inches is shown, the rain is uncertain and variable in amount; one year Yuma received less than one inch while in another it had over eleven inches. January is the coolest month with an average temperature of 55° F., and July the hottest with an average of 91° F. Thus the yearly range is 36°. A maximum of 120° F. has been recorded and a minimum of 22° F. There is, on the average, bright sunshine 90 per cent of the possible time. The terrifically high temperatures caused by continued blazing sun in July and August are made bearable by the dryness of the air. Relative humidity is low, averaging 55 per cent in the early morning and only 27

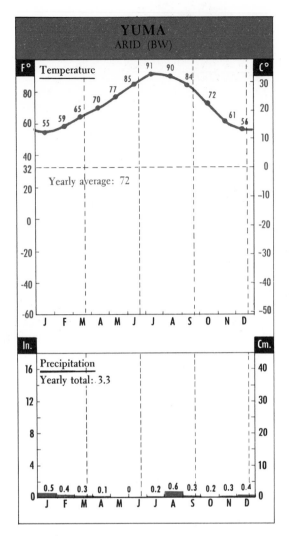

10–9 A

CLIMATIC *chart and statistics for Yuma, Arizona.*

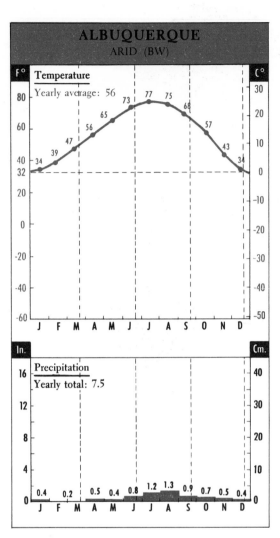

10–9 B

CLIMATIC *chart and statistics for Albuquerque, New Mexico.*

per cent in the late afternoon. Human utilization of an area with this type of climate is strictly limited to those parts which can be supplied with water in addition to that which is received as rain.

The climate of Albuquerque, New Mexico (FIG. 10–9B), is more truly representative of middle latitude Arid (BW) climate than Yuma. In contrast to Yuma, the hot season is less intense and there is a pronounced winter.

The highest monthly average temperature, that for July, is 77° F., nearly 14° less than at Yuma; the coldest monthly average, that for January, is 34° F., over 20° lower than at Yuma. The maximum in summer reaches 104° F., but the winter minimum drops to −10° F. Killing frosts may be experienced at any time from the end of October to the middle of April. Snow is not unknown as a form of winter precipitation. Bright sunshine occurs nearly as much of the time as at Yuma and the air has the same characteristic dryness. Water limits human utilization of the land as it does in all Arid (BW) climates.

SEMIARID (BS) CLIMATE • Kayes in Mali (FIG. 10–7B) has a representative low latitude Semiarid (BS) climate. A true winter season is lacking, as in the Tropical Moist (A) climates, but the range of 19° between the warmest and coolest months exceeds that which is found in the Tropical Moist (A) types. Precipitation is small in amount, yet it is much larger than that in Arid (BW) climates. Rain is distributed through the year in a manner similar to that in the Savanna (Aw) climate (FIG. 10–2B) in which drought occurs during the period of lowest temperatures. Kayes is in a region adjacent to an area of Savanna (Aw) climate and its rain is produced by the same forces. The precipitation at Kayes is, however, too small in amount to equal the potential evaporation at the temperatures there experienced. The dependence upon additional sources of moisture is less than in areas of Arid (BW) climate, yet any continued intensive cultivation of the soil demands irrigation.

Semiarid (BS) climate in the middle latitudes is characteristically represented at Denver (FIG. 10–7A). There is a marked winter season during which most of the precipitation is in the form of snow. The average annual temperature range is high, 42°. High summer temperatures are common, with 105° F. as the maximum recorded; low winter temperatures are indicated by the minimum of record, −29° F. As in the low latitudes, total precipitation is greater in amount and much more dependable than in Arid (BW) areas. While relative humidity is still low as compared with that of the moist climates, the average is much higher than that in the Arid (BW) climates. Consequently, the temperatures, especially those of winter, appear to be even more extreme than they actually are. Intensive agricultural use of land with this type of climate demands irrigation, though pastoral use and

certain phases of extensive cultivation are possible without it.

Distribution

The distribution of the Dry (B) climates throughout the world is shown on FIG. 10–10. The Dry (B) climates extend inland from the low latitude west coasts, swinging poleward as they penetrate into the hearts of the land masses. The areas of Arid (BW) climate are flanked by zones of Semiarid (BS) climate. On the equatorward side of the areas of Arid (BW) climate, the Semiarid (BS) zone provides the transition from Arid (BW) to Savanna (Aw); on the poleward side, the Semiarid (BS) zone indicates the transition from Arid (BW) climate to Moist, Mild Winter (C) or to Moist, Severe Winter (D) types.

Dominant Controls

PRECIPITATION • Distance from sources of moisture, orographic barriers, or the lack of winds moving in the right direction to transport moisture are responsible for meager rainfall in all Dry (B) climates. The total rainfall in Semiarid (BS) areas is greater than that in Arid (BW) areas because the former are nearer moisture sources or are so located that rain-bearing winds are experienced more frequently. Such precipitation as there is in areas of Arid (BW) climate results usually from local convectional storms, whereas that in areas of Semiarid (BS) climate is usually produced by causes effective in adjacent moist climatic regions. Within the low latitudes, the controls are those of the Tropical Moist (A) climates; in the middle latitudes, cyclonic storms cause the greater part of the precipitation.

TEMPERATURE • The great annual and daily ranges of temperature experienced within areas of Dry (B) climate are directly related to the dryness of the air and to the sparsity of the vegetation cover. Dry air permits a high proportion of solar energy to reach the surface

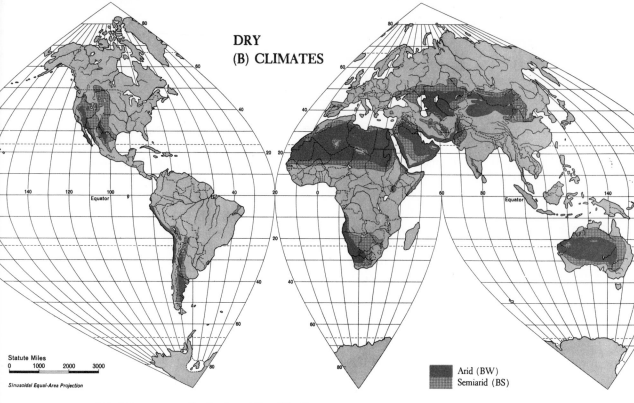

DRY
(B) CLIMATES

Arid (BW)
Semiarid (BS)

10-10 WORLD *distribution of Dry (B) climates.*

during the daylight period. Clear, cloudless skies, resulting from the relatively low moisture content of the air, allow heating to continue uninterruptedly over long hours. Little of the energy is absorbed by the sparse plant cover or used in the evaporation of water. Thus, the surface is heated to temperatures often so high as to be painful to human touch. Rapid radiation from the earth's surface produces very high air temperatures. With the setting of the sun, however, the receipt of solar energy by the earth's surface stops, although the dry air and cloudless skies allow rapid earth radiation to continue. Consequently, air temperatures drop with startling rapidity, so that the nights often seem very chilly after the glaring heat of the day. As a rule, sundown is a signal for persons to don heavier clothing.

Maximum daytime heating occurs when the noon sun is most nearly overhead. There are two periods during the year in the low latitudes

when the noon sun is directly overhead. In the areas of Dry (B) climate, these are close together. Hence only one hot season results, but that season is relatively long. Day after day, burning high sun produces the highest recorded air temperatures on the earth's surface. Though the noon sun is never at a very low angle in these latitudes, the difference in heating between the high- and low-sun seasons is more marked than in moist areas in the same latitudes. A change in surface heating is reflected quickly and almost completely because little absorption of heat by plants or little use of it in the evaporation of water takes place.

In the middle latitudes, there is no period in the year when the noon sun is directly overhead. But, in the season when the sun is highest, the daylight period is much longer than in the low latitudes (FIG. 8–4). Hence, total insolation in summer is relatively large in amount and that season is relatively hot. In winter, the sun is at a much lower angle than it ever is in the low latitudes and the daylight period is much shorter. The receipt of solar energy is thus greatly reduced. But the process of radiation is as little interrupted in the middle latitude areas of Dry (B) climate as it is in those of the low latitudes. Consequently, the low-sun season is notably cold. The range between the seasons in the middle latitudes is thus even greater than in the low latitude areas of Dry (B) climate.

Reduced temperatures and ranges are encountered in arid and semiarid areas along continental west coasts. For example, the average annual range at Lima, Peru, is only 13°, from 74° F. in February and March to 61° F. in July, August, and September. At Port Nolloth in southwest Africa, the average annual range is only 6°, from 59° F. in the warmest month to 53° F. in the coolest; and, at Cape Juby in northwest Africa, it is only 8°, from 69° F. in the warmest month to 61° F. in the coolest. In such locations, cool currents exist offshore. Air above them is cool and moisture-laden. As this cool air moves toward the warmer land, carrying fog and cloud with it, it is warmed. The fog and cloud are soon evaporated. Nevertheless, for a short distance inland, they form a moisture blanket which greatly reduces both the receipt of solar energy at the earth's surface and the rate of radiation of heat from the surface to the atmosphere. As a result, both the daily and seasonal extreme temperatures characteristic of the Dry (B) climates as a whole are rarely experienced and the ranges are thus made smaller.

1. Discuss the purpose of climatic classification.

2. Why is the ancient Greek classification of climate inadequate?

3. What does a map of climatic types actually show? How is such a map made?

4. A boundary between one kind of climate and another is represented on a climatic map by a line. Exactly what does such a line imply? If you were traveling from Chicago to New Orleans, could you tell exactly where you crossed the boundary between one type of climate and another? Discuss.

5. Why is the classification of climate based upon temperature and precipitation?

6. The Tropical Moist (A) climates are defined as having an average temperature of at least 64° F. for the coolest month of the year. Is there any specific reason for choosing this figure rather than some other?

7. Explain the lack of any considerable annual temperature range in the Tropical Moist (A) climates.

8. In what major way do the Tropical Moist (A) climates of one part of the world differ from those of another? Or are all Tropical Moist (A) climates exactly alike?

9. A climatic graph is actually a conventionalized picture of a climatic type. Tell how one may distinguish between a Tropical Rainforest (Af) and a Savanna (Aw) climate from climatic graphs alone.

10. What position does a Tropical Monsoon (Am) climate occupy with respect to a Tropical Rainforest (Af) and a Savanna (Aw) climate?

11. Explain why Tropical Moist (A) climates have constant high temperatures.

12. Why are temperatures in tropical highland areas even more monotonously uniform than those in tropical lowlands?

13. What are the major controls of precipitation in Tropical Moist (A) climates? What is their effect on the distribution of the different phases of the Tropical Moist (A) climates?

14. How does the climate of the northern Congo Basin, for example, differ from that of southwestern India? Explain some of the causes of the differences.

15. How are the outstanding features of all Dry (B) climates reflected in man's attitude toward and uses of areas with Dry (B) climates?

16. Floods are especially disastrous hazards in many areas of Dry (B) climate. Explain this apparent paradox.

17. From the description of the Dry (B) climates, it is obvious that temperatures vary considerably from place to place within areas having these climates. Why is this a matter of secondary importance, whereas in Tropical Moist (A) climates temperature is a matter of primary importance?

18. Explain the fact that there is a greater range of temperature, both diurnally and seasonally, in the Dry (B) climates generally than in the Tropical Moist (A) climates.

19. Account for the generally meager rainfall in all areas of Dry (B) climate in terms of the dominant controls of precipitation.

20. Why are temperature ranges along Arid (BW) and Semiarid (BS) continental west coasts less than in other areas with these two types of climate?

11–1

[OPPOSITE, TOP] WIND drifts snow off the edge of the Ross Ice Barrier in Antarctica. The parts of the barrier seen here vary in height from 50 to 150 feet. Continual cold is the outstanding feature of Polar (E) climates.

11 Climatic Types: The Mild Winter, the Severe Winter, and the Polar Climates

U.S. COAST GUARD

⟨[From the Tropics to the equatorward margins of the high latitudes, we have seen that the interiors of the world's land masses are occupied by great expanses of Semiarid (BS) and Arid (BW) climate. The dry continental interiors are flanked oceanward and poleward by regions of moist climates, all of which are characterized by the presence of marked temperature changes from one part of the year to another. Seasons defined by temperature change constitute the distinguishing characteristic. It should be recalled that seasons in areas of Tropical Moist (A) climates are defined largely in terms of precipitation and that temperature change is of only minor importance. In the moist *areas of the middle latitudes, temperature change is the outstanding climatic feature, precipitation providing only the secondary variations. Two major climatic categories can be distinguished: the Moist, Mild Winter (C) and the Moist, Severe Winter (D) climates.*

In the high latitudes, where the receipt of heat from the sun is small in amount during one part of the year and practically nonexistent during the other, low temperatures at all times characterize the climate. There, the last of the major climatic categories, the Polar (E) climate, is encountered.

THE MOIST, MILD WINTER (C) CLIMATES

Characteristics

THE third of the specific climatic categories is encountered as one leaves the low latitudes and enters the middle latitudes. This is the Moist, Mild Winter (C) category. These climates have certain distinguishing characteristics as do the Tropical Moist (A) and the Dry (B) climates.

TEMPERATURE • One common feature of a large group of climatic types is the presence of a definite, though mild, winter season. Temperatures during one part of the year drop below those in the Tropical Moist (A) climates previously described. The lower temperatures induce a period of rest from growth activity in the plant life. Not only does this bring about a change in the individual plant species from those characteristic of the moist tropics but it also introduces a definite seasonal rhythm in the cycle of plant life which becomes more pronounced with increased severity of the winter season.

Along the contact with the Tropical Moist (A) climates or the low latitude Dry (B) climates, the seasonal rhythm is poorly developed; many of the forest trees remain leaf-covered and green throughout the year. Near the poleward margins of the Moist, Mild Winter (C) climates, the seasonal change is marked with budding, flowering, and leafing in spring and the loss of leaves in autumn. The presence of

a winter is reflected in many other features of the physical setting. The crops which are grown, the systems of cultivation which are followed, the types of buildings in which man lives, all point toward a recognition of the seasonal rhythm.

On the tropical margins, the winter temperatures average in the high 50's, as at Hong Kong (FIG. 11–2A). There the average for the coolest month, February, is 59° F. Somewhat farther poleward, the low average is in the 40's, as at Sacramento, California (FIG. 11–2B), where the average for January is 46° F. In the continental interiors and near the poleward margins of the Moist, Mild Winter (C) climates, low monthly averages are in the 30's. Nashville, Tennessee (FIG. 11–2C), records an average of 39° F. for January. The winter is considered to become truly severe approximately where the average temperature for the coldest month is 32° F. It is this figure which is taken as the cold limit of the Moist, Mild Winter (C) climates.

The nature of the summer is fully as significant, from the point of view of human activity, as that of the winter. Near the Tropics and in the continental interiors, the summers are long and hot, frequently with averages in the high 70's or low 80's. Hong Kong has a July average of 82° F. and Nashville has one of 79° F. In coastal locations and where marine influences penetrate well into the land, the

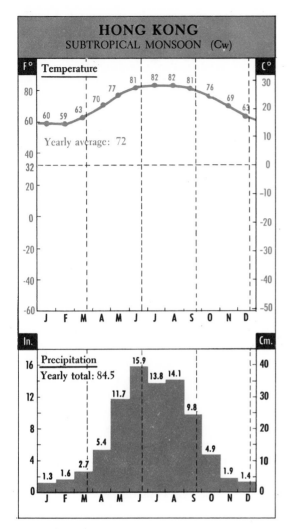

HONG KONG
SUBTROPICAL MONSOON (Cw)

Temperature
Yearly average: 72
60 59 63 70 77 81 82 82 81 76 69 63

J F M A M J J A S O N D

Precipitation
Yearly total: 84.5
1.3 1.6 2.7 5.4 11.7 15.9 13.8 14.1 9.8 4.9 1.9 1.4

J F M A M J J A S O N D

11–2 A

CLIMATIC *chart and statistics for Hong Kong.*

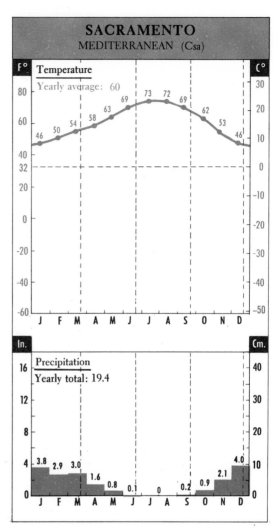

SACRAMENTO
MEDITERRANEAN (Csa)

Temperature
Yearly average: 60
46 50 54 58 63 69 73 72 69 62 53 46

J F M A M J J A S O N D

Precipitation
Yearly total: 19.4
3.8 2.9 3.0 1.6 0.8 0.1 0 0.2 0.9 2.1 4.0

J F M A M J J A S O N D

11–2 B

CLIMATIC *chart and statistics for Sacramento, California.*

summers are warm rather than hot and are somewhat shorter. San Francisco's warmest month (FIG. 11–3A) averages only 60° F. and Greenwich in England (FIG. 11–3B) records only 63° F. Some parts of west coasts in the higher middle latitudes have a very short, very cool summer. At Lerwick in the Shetland Islands (FIG. 11–3C), off the northern coast of Scotland, the warmest months are July and August with averages of only 52° F., and only three months have averages higher than 50° F.

Average annual ranges of temperature increase generally away from the Tropics and inland from windward coastal positions. At Hong Kong, the range is 23°; it is 40° at Nashville. The range at San Francisco is only 11°, but at Sacramento, only 90 miles away, it is 27°. A characteristic small range is encountered in all continental west coast areas even though they may be in relatively high latitudes. Lerwick is

The Moist, Mild Winter (C) Climates | 265

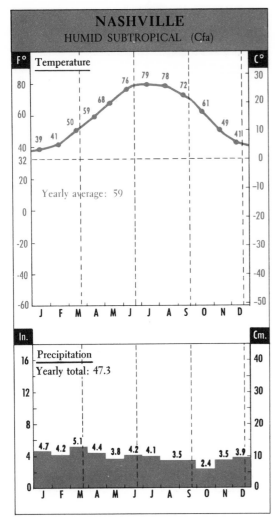

NASHVILLE
HUMID SUBTROPICAL (Cfa)

Temperature
Yearly average: 59

Precipitation
Yearly total: 47.3

11–2 C

CLIMATIC chart and statistics for Nashville, Tennessee.

(FIG. 11–2A); or it may be concentrated in the winter period, as at Sacramento (FIG. 11–2B); or it may be rather evenly distributed through the year, as at Nashville (FIG. 11–2C).

In one respect at least, an area with summer rains is like one in which the rain is spread evenly through the whole year. In both, there is usually rain in plentiful amount during the warmer part of the year when growth activity is greatest. The advantage of evenly distributed or summer rains for man's crops, and hence his food supply, is obvious. That the winter should be dry in one instance serves only to emphasize the period of plant rest induced by lower temperatures.

The condition represented by winter rain is quite different. The rain of winter is followed by summer drought fully as intense as the dryness of the Dry (B) climates. Plant growth is greatly restricted and intensive cultivation is dependent on irrigation during the growing season. Fortunately, the winters in areas where rainfall is concentrated in winter are usually mild, or even warm, so that cessation of plant growth is not characteristic, as, for example, in southern California or along the Mediterranean shores of Europe and Africa.

Precipitation varies widely in amount and in form of occurrence throughout the Moist, Mild Winter (C) climates. On a windward coast, especially if it is hilly or mountainous like that of northwestern Scotland, and on the tropical margins, as along the coast of Mississippi, Alabama, and western Florida, the amount is often excessive; 80 to 100 inches a year is not uncommon. The total is markedly less in continental interiors, as in eastern Kansas and Oklahoma, or in the lee of highlands, as in southeastern Scotland. Adjacent to areas of Semiarid (BS) climate, the rainfall in Moist, Mild Winter (C) climates may be as little as 15 inches, as at Los Angeles. But *all* Moist, Mild Winter (C) climates have average annual rainfall which exceeds average annual evaporation.

Rains in Moist, Mild Winter (C) climates

in latitude 60° N; the average annual range there is only 14°. This condition reflects strong marine controls.

PRECIPITATION • None of the Moist, Mild Winter (C) climates is deficient in moisture for the year as a whole; yet many of them show seasonal deficiencies. There are three possibilities so far as rainfall distribution through the year is concerned: the rain may be concentrated in the summer season, as at Hong Kong

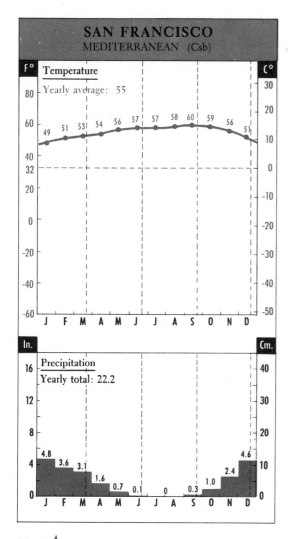

11–3 A

CLIMATIC chart and statistics for San Francisco, California.

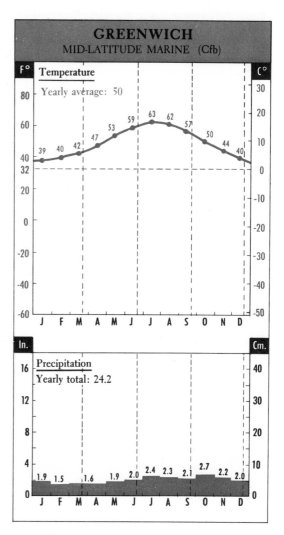

11–3 B

CLIMATIC chart and statistics for Greenwich, England.

are of both the general and the local types. The controls of precipitation vary widely but, regardless of what they are specifically, areas within this climatic zone are subject both to the kind of rain which continues gently over relatively long periods of time and to that which falls torrentially for a short period. Where the summer is rainy, thunderstorms are frequent. On the tropical margins, they are nearly as frequent as in areas of Tropical Rainforest (Af)

climate. The summer precipitation generally is of the short shower type while that of winter more commonly is lighter, but lasts through many hours or even days.

Along western coasts in the higher middle latitudes even the summer precipitation is gentle. Local convectional storms are almost unknown. Here occur some of the cloudiest and rainiest places in the world, in terms of the number of rainy days per year. Yet the amount

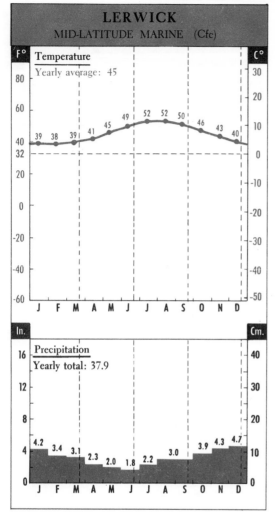

LERWICK
MID-LATITUDE MARINE (Cfc)

Temperature
Yearly average: 45

39 38 39 41 45 49 52 52 50 46 43 40

J F M A M J J A S O N D

Precipitation
Yearly total: 37.9

4.2 3.4 3.1 2.3 2.0 1.8 2.2 3.0 3.9 4.3 4.7

J F M A M J J A S O N D

11–3 C

CLIMATIC *chart and statistics for Lerwick, Scotland.*

of rain is often remarkably small. Lerwick, though recording an average yearly rainfall of only 37.9 inches, has an average of 260 rainy days per year; on the average, between seven- and eight-tenths of the skies are covered by clouds each month. Precipitation occurring under these conditions is aptly described by the expression "Scotch mist." Never is the rain really heavy enough to prevent outdoor activity, but seldom can one pass a whole day in

the open without encountering some very fine rain at least.

General rains are common in Moist, Mild Winter (C) areas where precipitation is concentrated in the winter. They may be heavy or light, and may vary in duration from a few hours to three, four, or five days. Local convectional storms are infrequent and the rain which they cause is negligible in amount.

Subdivisions of the Moist, Mild Winter (C) Climates

As has been suggested, all of the Moist, Mild Winter (C) climates have in common the facts (1) that they have more precipitation than the Dry (B) climates, and (2) that they have definite cool and warm seasons. However, differences in the occurrence of precipitation through the year and in the relative warmth of the summer are sufficient to create four distinctive types within the major category.

These four distinctive types are: (1) Humid Subtropical (Cfa) climate; (2) Mid-latitude Marine (Cfb and Cfc) climate; (3) Subtropical Monsoon (Cw) climate; and (4) Mediterranean (Cs) climate.

HUMID SUBTROPICAL (Cfa) CLIMATE • The climatic statistics and graph for Nashville (FIG. 11–2C) illustrate this type of climate. The long, hot summer—four months with average temperature over 70° F.—contrasts sharply with the winter, when the lowest monthly average is 39° F. Daily temperatures in midsummer are high, usually in the 80's or 90's, and they occasionally exceed 100° F. This heat is normally accompanied by high relative humidities so that the temperature one "feels" (*sensible temperature*) is much higher than the thermometer temperature would lead one to expect. The sensible temperature is often even more oppressive, for a short time, than that produced by the steaminess of a Tropical Rainforest (Af) climate. Relief in the form of lower temperatures and drier air may be expected at irregular intervals, however. During the winter, relative humidity is considerably reduced and temperatures often drop below freezing from November through March. However, the periods of cold are seldom long continued. Precipitation shows a maximum in spring and a minimum in late summer or autumn. Yet in contrast to areas of well-defined seasonal concentration, the rainfall is rather evenly spread through the whole year. Though the average figures show adequate moisture the year round, droughts of short duration are a common occurrence. These droughts result from the high temperatures of summer coupled with the receipt of less rain than the average figures indicate. Snow is common in winter, but it seldom remains on the ground for more than a few days at a time. The ground rarely freezes deeply and never remains frozen continuously through the season.

MID-LATITUDE MARINE (Cfb AND Cfc) CLIMATE • Though there are areas with these types of climate on the west coast of North America, better examples are to be found in northwestern Europe. Consequently, Greenwich in England (FIG. 11–3B) is chosen to represent the Mid-latitude Marine (Cfb) type. In contrast to those of the Humid Subtropical (Cfa) climate, the summers are warm rather than hot and the winters are milder. Nashville and Greenwich have the same low average temperature of 39° F. for January, yet Greenwich is 15° of latitude farther poleward than Nashville. The warmest month at Greenwich is 16° cooler than that at Nashville. In the Mid-latitude Marine (Cfb) climate, precipitation is distributed through the year in a manner similar to that in the Humid Subtropical (Cfa) climate, but rarely is it of the local convectional type. Relative humidity is higher over the year period; and there is greater cloudiness.

There is an extreme phase of the Mid-latitude Marine (Cfc) type, the essential features of which are illustrated in the statistics and graph for Lerwick, Scotland (FIG. 11–3C). The summers are so cool that agricultural use of the land is almost impossible, yet the winters

are only slightly more severe than in the Humid Subtropical (Cfa) climate. Lerwick is nearly 25° of latitude farther north than Nashville, yet its coolest winter month averages only a fraction of a degree lower. On the other hand, freezing temperatures have been recorded at Lerwick in every month except July and August. Even though the total precipitation is only 37.9 inches, that amount is excessive for, at the prevailing temperatures, evaporation is low. The land is sodden, and only at infrequent intervals does the sun break through the cloud cover to create even the impression of a dry period.

SUBTROPICAL MONSOON (Cw) CLIMATE • This type of climate is represented by Hong Kong (FIG. 11–2A), where a very hot and humid summer contrasts with a cooler and drier season. Except for the low temperatures at one season, weather conditions are similar to those in the Tropical Monsoon (Am) climate, as at Akyab (FIG. 10–2C). The winter, or cool season, dry period is seldom completely without rain, and usually enough rain falls during the summer to maintain soil moisture through the year. Since the winter is not cool enough to experience more than rare frosts, it is possible to carry on agriculture throughout the year. The average annual range, 23°, is about that which occurs on the cooler margins of the Tropical Moist (A) climates.

MEDITERRANEAN (Cs) CLIMATE • The remaining type of climate in the Moist, Mild Winter (C) category is known as the Mediterranean (Cs) climate. Among all the world's climates, it is unique in that precipitation is concentrated in winter and summers are droughty. Despite this unique feature, there are two distinct phases of Mediterranean (Cs) climates; one has long, hot summers and the other has short, warm summers.

On a continental coast fully exposed to oceanic influences, summer temperatures are reduced and winter ones increased. Relative humidity is high throughout the year. Cloudiness is characteristic and fog is a common phenomenon. Summer high temperatures seldom

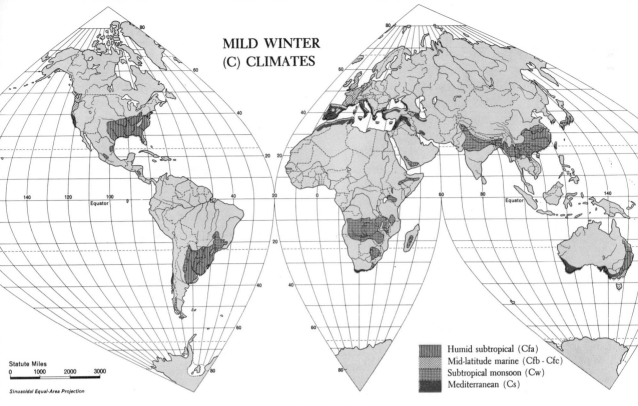

Humid subtropical (Cfa)
Mid-latitude marine (Cfb - Cfc)
Subtropical monsoon (Cw)
Mediterranean (Cs)

Statute Miles
0   1000   2000   3000

Sinusoidal Equal-Area Projection

11–4   WORLD *distribution of Mild Winter (C) climates.*

attain 100° F., and freezing days are likely to occur only during a very brief period in mid-winter and then chiefly on the poleward margins of these areas. This type is represented by San Francisco (FIG. 11–3A).

Inland, away from marine influences, summer temperatures are higher; winter ones are lower; relative humidity is lower, especially in summer; and cloud and fog are greatly reduced. This type is represented by Sacramento (FIG. 11–2B). Burningly dry, sunny days succeed one another almost without interruption through the summer. Temperatures at that season frequently approach those of the low latitude Semiarid (BS) and Arid (BW) climates, with daily maxima between 85° and 95° F. Absolute maxima are usually well over 100° F.; Sacramento, for example, has recorded 114° F. Freezing temperatures are more common than in the Mediterranean (Cs) climatic areas along coasts and may occur over a two-month period

in winter. Sacramento has recorded as many as seven nights in one year during which temperatures below 32° F. were experienced.

Distribution

Poleward from the low latitudes, the Dry (B) climates lie inland from both continental coasts, as we have seen. Between the coasts and the dry interiors, Moist, Mild Winter (C) climates are found (FIG. 11–4). West of the dry interiors, Mediterranean (Cs) types occur between, roughly, 30° and 40° of latitude in both hemispheres. They are succeeded poleward by Mid-latitude Marine (Cfb and Cfc) types which continue to approximately 60° latitude in both hemispheres. Small areas of Humid Subtropical (Cfa) climate are found in the interior adjacent to the dry margin, particularly in parts of southeastern Europe. East of the dry interiors, Humid Subtropical (Cfa) or Subtropical Monsoon (Cw) types extend poleward to about 40° latitude from areas of Tropical Rainforest (Af) and Savanna (Aw) climates.

Dominant Controls

TEMPERATURE • The presence of a winter season, with temperatures too low for Tropical Moist (A) climates, is a direct reflection of distance from the equator. In addition, distance from the equator produces increased average annual temperature range. Average annual range is controlled basically by seasonal change of insolation. Since this becomes greater as one travels away from the low latitudes, average annual ranges increase in that direction. Marine influences counteract this tendency and continental influences amplify it. Since the middle latitudes, where the Moist, Mild Winter (C) climates occur, are the zone of Prevailing Westerlies, it is along the continental west coasts that marine influences are best developed. In these latitudes, marine influences are less effective along east coasts and least effective in continental interiors.

PRECIPITATION • Numerous controls of precipitation are operative in the different types of Moist, Mild Winter (C) climates. The Prevailing Westerlies are rain-bearing onshore winds throughout the year in Mid-latitude Marine (Cfb and Cfc) areas. Cyclonic storms, following the general path of the Westerlies, add materially to the total precipitation. Areas of Mediterranean (Cs) climate likewise receive most of their rain from Westerlies and cyclonic storms, but these two controls are effective only during the winter in the latitudes where the Mediterranean (Cs) climate occurs. This is primarily a reflection of the seasonal shift of wind belts. In areas of Humid Subtropical (Cfa) climate, cyclonic storms are the major source of rain in all seasons, but to their contribution must be added that derived from local convectional storms which occur in summer. Within areas of Subtropical Monsoon (Cw) climate, major controls are the same as those in Savanna (Aw) and Tropical Monsoon (Am) climates. These are convection, movements of the Intertropical front, onshore winds in the belt of Trades, and monsoons. The slight rains of winter in Subtropical Monsoon (Cw) areas are associated with the passage of weakly developed cyclonic storms at irregular intervals.

THE MOIST, SEVERE WINTER (D) CLIMATES

Characteristics

POLEWARD from the Moist, Mild Winter (C) climates, the Moist, Severe Winter (D) types are encountered. Here again, there are distinctive characteristics for the category as a whole. Likewise, there is some variety within the category.

TEMPERATURE • Colder, longer, and more continuous winters and greater range from season to season distinguish the Moist, Severe Winter (D) from the Moist, Mild Winter (C) climates. On the equatorward margins of the Moist, Severe Winter (D) climates, the coldest month average is 32° F. Poleward from that and toward the continental interiors, winters become more and more severe. The extreme is reached in northeastern Siberia where continental influences are strongest and marine influences are totally lacking. The coldest winters in the world, excepting those in Antarctica, occur there. Verkhoyansk (FIG. 11-5A) has an average of −59° F. for January; Sredne Kolymsk (FIG. 11-5B), of −41° F. On winter nights, temperatures well below those figures are regularly experienced. An absolute minimum has been reported at Oimekon in that same general area −108° F.!

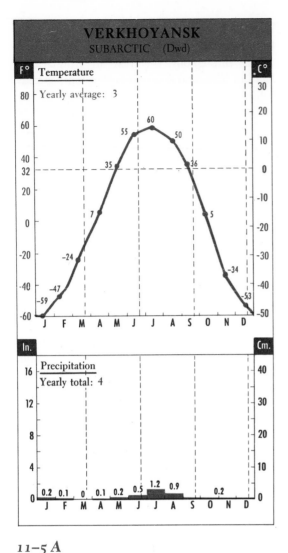

11–5 A

CLIMATIC chart and statistics for Verkhoyansk, northeastern Siberia.

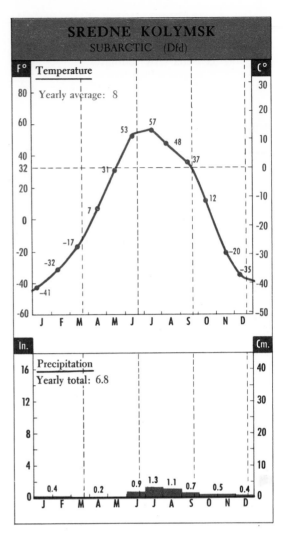

11–5 B

CLIMATIC chart and statistics for Sredne Kolymsk, northeastern Siberia.

Extreme continental position in high latitudes is necessary to the production of such low temperatures. In the Southern Hemisphere there are no large land masses in these latitudes; consequently, the Moist, Severe Winter (D) climates occur only in the Northern Hemisphere.

Not only are the winters cold; the season of low temperatures is long and continuous. Frosts are not uncommon features of the more continental of the Moist, Mild Winter (C) climates, but in the Moist, Severe Winter (D) climates they are never lacking. The ground freezes to great depth and remains effectively frozen for several months. In the most extreme areas, the subsoil is always frozen; only the topsoil ever thaws completely. The winter thus places a marked restriction on plant growth and the period during which agriculture is possible is sharply defined. The length

TABLE *11*

Effect of Latitude and Location with Respect to Coast on Average Summer Temperatures

A. DECREASE OF AVERAGE TEMPERATURES NORTHWARD IN D CLIMATIC REGIONS

PLACE	APPROXIMATE LATITUDE (N)	AVERAGE TEMPERATURE JULY
Keokuk, Iowa	40°	76.1°
Cedar Rapids, Iowa	42°	75.6°
Charles City, Iowa	44°	73.2°
St. Paul, Minnesota	45°	72.2°
Bemidji, Minnesota	48°	68.9°
Winnipeg, Manitoba	50°	66°

B. DECREASE OF AVERAGE SUMMER TEMPERATURES FROM INTERIOR TOWARD COAST IN D CLIMATIC REGIONS

PLACE	APPROXIMATE LATITUDE (N)	APPROXIMATE DISTANCE FROM OCEAN IN MILES	AVERAGE TEMPERATURE JULY
La Crosse, Wisconsin	43–44°	1050	72.8°
Mt. Pleasant, Michigan	43–44°	730	71.0°
Rutland, Vermont	43–44°	130	69.0°
Plymouth, New Hampshire	43–44°	100	68.1°
Portland, Maine	43–44°	0	67.8°

and continuity of the winters are made more pronounced by the suddenness of the transition to and from summer. The expression "spring comes with a bang" is literally true. True, also, is the corollary expression "winter comes overnight." Both spring and autumn are short. Further emphasis is provided by the long daylight hours of summer and the correspondingly long hours of darkness in winter (FIG. 8–4).

Just as in the Moist, Mild Winter (C) climates, there is great variation in the character of the summers. Long, hot summers characterize the southern margin in the continental interiors. Averages in the 70's are usual and not infrequently during the summer 100° F. is exceeded for a short period. More frequent daytime fluctuations, regularly lower night temperatures, and lower relative humidity make these high summer temperatures less oppressive than in the Moist, Mild Winter (C) climates. Summers become cooler rapidly in a northward direction (TABLE 11A) and toward coasts (TABLE 11B). One passes from the areas with

The Moist, Severe Winter (D) Climates | 273

long, hot summers to those with short, warm summers and, finally, in the northern part of the Moist, Severe Winter (D) climates, to those with very short, cool summers. The coolness and shortness of the summer in the higher latitudes are partially compensated by the longer daylight hours during that season. Close to the Arctic Circle and within it, midsummer is a time of no real darkness and the growing season is fully as long in hours as in regions much farther south (FIG. 8–4).

The average annual ranges within the Moist, Severe Winter (D) climates are the greatest in the world. Verkhoyansk, previously mentioned, has a warm month average of 60° F. and a cold month average of −59° F. Its range is thus 119°! This is, of course, the extreme. In coastal locations and along the southern margins, the range is between 40° and 50°. It increases northward and toward continental interiors. For example, the average annual range at Keokuk, Iowa, is 54°; at Winnipeg, it is 70°; that at Portland, Maine, is 46° while that at La Crosse, Wisconsin, is 57°. The ranges, greater than those of the Moist, Mild Winter (C) climates, result largely from increased severity of the winters and not from increased summer heat.

PRECIPITATION • Precipitation varies greatly in amount and in distribution through the year in the Moist, Severe Winter (D) climates, as it does in the Moist, Mild Winter (C) climates. The amount is largest in coastal areas, as at Portland, Maine (FIG. 11–6A), where as much as 40 to 50 inches may be expected. It decreases toward the continental interiors where, along the southern margins, the amount is commonly between 25 and 35 inches, as at Chicago, Illinois (FIG. 11–7A). The amount likewise decreases northward to an extreme of less than 5 inches, as at Verkhoyansk. Such a small amount recalls the precipitation of the Dry (B) climates, where the rain is uncertain in occurrence and irregular in amount. In the Moist, Severe Winter (D) climates, there is little variation from year to year either in period

or amount. That so small an amount should suffice to create a moist climate is a measure of the effectiveness of moisture in areas where temperatures are relatively low.

Throughout most of the Moist, Severe Winter (D) climates, the snows of winter and the rains of summer are rather evenly distributed. However, in northeastern Asia snowfall is meager and most of the precipitation is received as summer rain. In terms of effectiveness for man's use, the presence of adequate moisture during the season of greatest heat is of major importance. Hence, whether the precipitation is evenly distributed through the year or concentrated in summer, the end results are very similar. There are regions in which the precipitation is concentrated in winter, but these are so small and so scattered that they may be neglected in a general study of world patterns.

Winter precipitation is almost entirely in the form of snow. On all except the southern margins of the Moist, Severe Winter (D) climates, snow accumulates to form a lasting blanket through the winter; even on those margins, it may remain for several weeks at a time. The thickness of the blanket decreases away from the coasts and toward the poleward margins, not only because of the decrease in amount of precipitation, but also because of the nature of the snow crystals. Very fine, dry, tightly packed snow results from the extreme low temperatures and the relatively dry air of the continental interiors; heavy, moist, loosely packed flakes characterize snowfall in coastal regions.

Subdivisions of the Moist, Severe Winter (D) Climates

From the point of view of significance to man, there are three subdivisions of the Moist, Severe Winter (D) climates. Distinction is made primarily on the basis of the relative warmth of the summer season. The three types are: (1) Humid Continental climate with hot

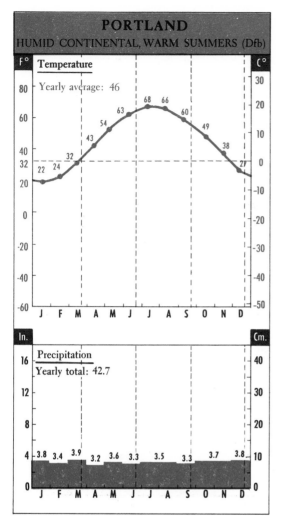

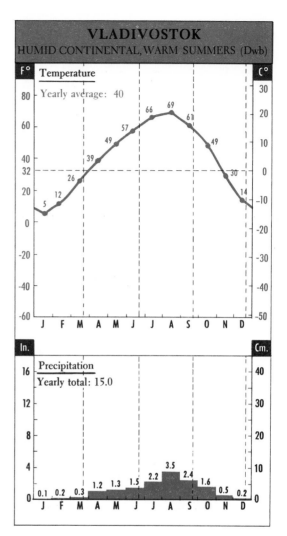

11–6 A

CLIMATIC chart and statistics for Portland, Maine.

11–6 B

CLIMATIC chart and statistics for Vladivostok, eastern Siberia.

summers (Dfa and Dwa); (2) Humid Continental climate with warm summers (Dfb and Dwb); and (3) Subarctic climate (Dfc, Dwc, Dfd, and Dwd).

HUMID CONTINENTAL CLIMATE WITH HOT SUMMERS (Dfa AND Dwa) • Within areas of this type of climate, there is variation in the distribution of precipitation through the year. In some places, no part of the year is dry; in others, there is drought during the win-

ter season. However, the summer, or growing season, is moist in both.

Chicago (FIG. 11–7A) and Mukden in Manchuria (FIG. 11–7B) represent these phases. The essential difference between them is in the distribution of precipitation through the year. At Chicago, no season is markedly drier than another though there is somewhat more precipitation in the summer months than there is in winter. At Mukden, there is notable con-

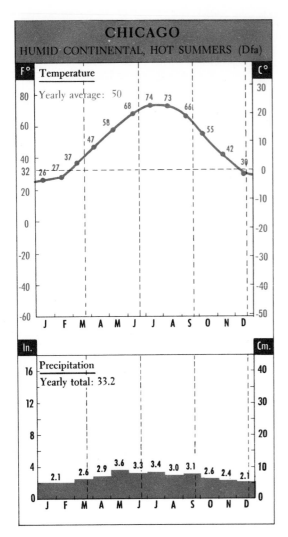

11–7 **A**

CLIMATIC chart and statistics for Chicago, Illinois.

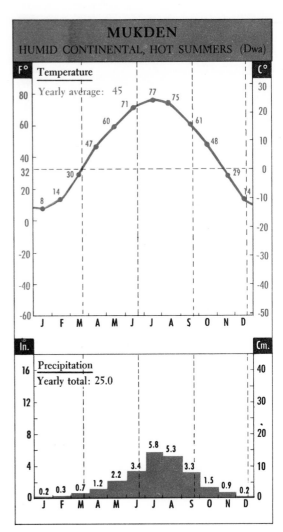

11–7 **B**

CLIMATIC chart and statistics for Mukden, Manchuria.

trast between the seasons. The three midwinter months receive a total of less than one inch while the three summer months receive 14.5 inches, 58 per cent of the total for the year. In addition, the contrast between the seasons at Mukden is marked by high relative humidity in summer and low relative humidity in winter. There is little change in relative humidity between the seasons in Chicago. Clear, cold winter days succeed one another

with few interruptions at Mukden, while spells of biting, damp cold, often windy and snowy, alternate with spells of relatively mild, drizzling rains in Chicago winters. The summers are much more nearly alike. Both places are subject to prolonged periods of sticky heat with frequent, sudden downpours of rain alternating with cool, dry periods of clear weather. In both places the summers are long as well as hot.

HUMID CONTINENTAL CLIMATE WITH WARM SUMMERS (Dfb AND Dwb) • Here, as in the Humid Continental climate with hot summers (Dfa and Dwa) just described, two phases may be recognized, one in which precipitation is spread evenly through the year and one in which there is winter drought. But this distinction is one of detail; the character of the summer is the significant feature.

Portland, Maine (FIG. 11–6A), and Vladivostok on the Sea of Japan coast of Siberia (FIG. 11–6B) illustrate the temperature and precipitation features of this type of climate. Compared to the hot summer type of climate just described, the summers in this type are only warm and are generally short. Where two months average over 70° F. at Chicago, no month averages as high as 70° F. in Portland, Maine; at Mukden, three months average over 70° F., but none averages as high as 70° F. at Vladivostok. Along with less hot and shorter summers, the winters are somewhat more severe and longer at Portland and Vladivostok than at Chicago and Mukden.

The remarkably even distribution of precipitation through the year and its large amount at Portland are indicators of coastal position. The less intense summer concentration at Vladivostok, in comparison with Mukden, is likewise a measure of coastal position. At both Portland and Vladivostok, the day-to-day fluctuation of weather is less pronounced than at Chicago and Mukden.

SUBARCTIC CLIMATE (Dfc, Dfd, Dwc, AND Dwd) • Longer and more severe winters, shorter and cooler summers, practical elimination of spring and autumn, and decreased amount of precipitation—these are the features which set the Subarctic climate off from the Humid Continental types. Dawson in Canada (FIG. 11–8A) and Okhotsk in eastern Siberia (FIG. 11–8B) are respectively good representatives of the different phases of Subarctic climate. At both places, average temperatures are below freezing for over half the year; yet summer temperatures often reach 80° F. Frosts may

occur in nearly every month. Thus the growing season is short and uncertain. Only the long sunlight hours of the short summer offer any inducement to the pursuit of agriculture.

Where continentality is extreme, as in northeastern Siberia, a phase of the Subarctic climate develops the most severe winters (Dfd and Dwd) on the earth. Sredne Kolymsk (FIG. 11–5B) and Verkhoyansk (FIG. 11–5A) illustrate this phase. Summers are essentially the same as those in other regions of Subarctic (Dfc and Dwc) climate. Maximum daily temperatures through the long days of that season often reach 80° F., but the possibility of frost is never absent. Winter air is very dry and clear through the long hours of darkness at that season. This dryness, accompanied by very little, if any, wind helps to make the low temperatures less severe in their effects on man and wild animal life than they would be otherwise. Rarely during the winter does the maximum daily temperature rise even to 0° F.

Distribution

Poleward of the Dry (B) and the Moist, Mild Winter (C) climates in the Northern Hemisphere and spreading from west to east coasts, the Moist, Severe Winter (D) climates are more extensive than other types (FIG. 11–9). They are entirely lacking in the Southern Hemisphere for reasons previously explained. The two great areas are in North America and Eurasia. On the southern edge, both west and east of the dry interior, are the areas of Humid Continental climate with hot summers (Dfa and Dwa). These give way northward to Humid Continental climate with warm summers (Dfb and Dwb), and to the Subarctic (Dfc, Dwc, Dfd, and Dwd) type.

Dominant Controls

TEMPERATURE • The great difference between summer and winter temperatures is primarily the result of location in high latitudes.

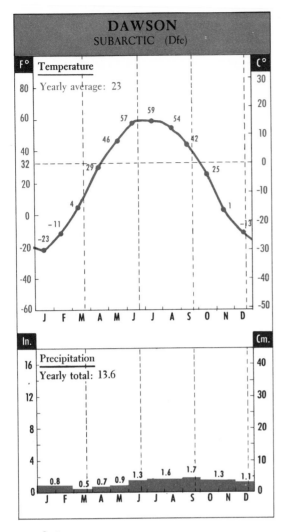

DAWSON
SUBARCTIC (Dfc)

Temperature
Yearly average: 23

Precipitation
Yearly total: 13.6

11–8 A

CLIMATIC *chart and statistics for Dawson, Yukon Territory, Canada.*

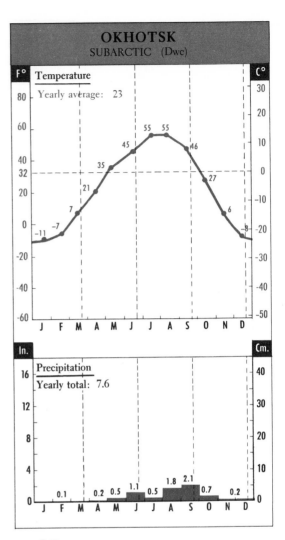

OKHOTSK
SUBARCTIC (Dwc)

Temperature
Yearly average: 23

Precipitation
Yearly total: 7.6

11–8 B

CLIMATIC *chart and statistics for Okhotsk, eastern Siberia.*

The summer sun, though never vertically overhead, is above the horizon for many hours of the day. Surface heating is small per unit of time as compared with areas farther equatorward, but it continues over a longer time in a single day. Total heating is therefore considerable. In addition, there is only a short time during each summer day when radiation from the earth continues without the receipt of

some solar energy. At the opposite time of year, the sun is at a lower angle than during the summer. It is above the horizon for only a few hours a day through most of the Moist, Severe Winter (D) climatic zone (FIG. 8–4) and actually below the horizon for many days in those areas within the Arctic Circle. Hence receipt of solar energy is very small at that season, but earth radiation continues uninter-

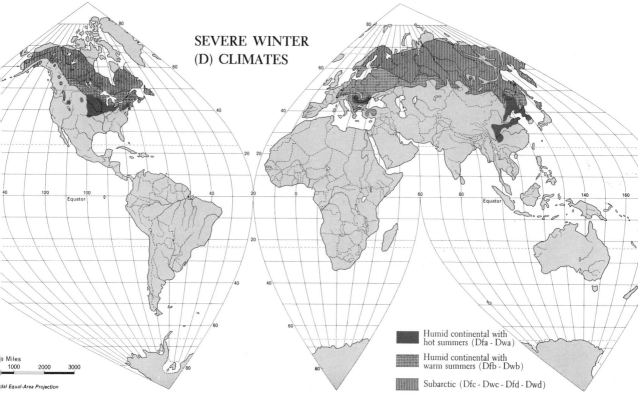

SEVERE WINTER
(D) CLIMATES

Humid continental with
hot summers (Dfa - Dwa)

Humid continental with
warm summers (Dfb - Dwb)

Subarctic (Dfc - Dwc - Dfd - Dwd)

Miles
1000   2000   3000

dal Equal-Area Projection

11–9   WORLD *distribution of Severe Winter (D) climates.*

ruptedly. Thus air temperatures become very low. The absence of any considerable amount of water vapor in the air, especially in the continental interiors, intensifies both the summer warmth and the winter cold. Marine and continental influences likewise cause variation in the degree of heat and cold.

PRECIPITATION • Precipitation in summer results both from the passage of cyclonic storms and from local convectional storms, while precipitation in winter is almost exclusively from cyclonic storms. The characteristic small amount is mainly the result of great distance from moisture sources.

The pronounced dryness of winter in north-

eastern Asia results from the intense cooling of that continent in winter. A tremendous mass of cold, dry air forms over the continent and prevents the movement of cyclonic storms across it. In summer, the mass of cold air does not exist; in fact, it is replaced by relatively warm air. A wind movement inland from off the cooler fringing oceans results. This is the means by which moisture is moved onto the continent, there to become the source of precipitation either from cyclonic storms or from local convectional systems. Along the coasts and for some distance inland, the rain at this season is remarkably like that in areas of Subtropical Monsoon (Cw) climate.

THE POLAR (E) CLIMATES

Subdivisions of the Polar (E) Climates

THE Polar (E) climates are at the opposite extreme from the Tropical Moist (A) climates; the latter have no winters and the former have no summers. An average temperature for the *coolest* month is specified as the limit of the Tropical Moist (A) climates; an average for the *warmest* month is set for the Polar (E) climates. This average is 50° F. Where no month has an average temperature of 50° F. or over, the climate is of the Polar (E) type.

There are two phases of the Polar (E) climates. Where the average for the warmest month rises above freezing, but does not ex-

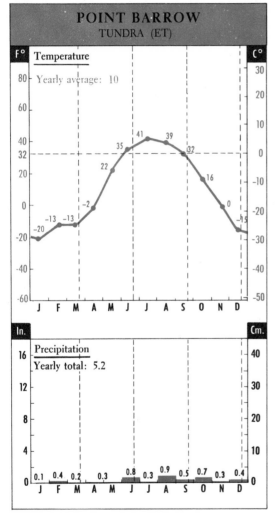

11–10 A

CLIMATIC *chart and statistics for Point Barrow, Alaska.*

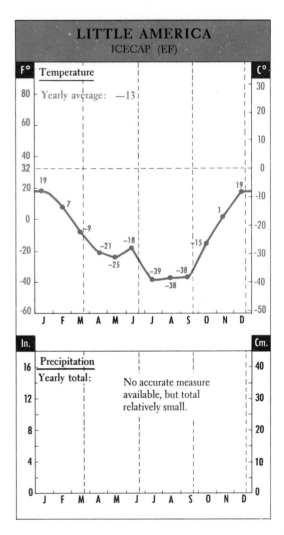

11–10 B

CLIMATIC *chart and statistics for Little America, Antarctica.*

ceed 50° F., the climate is of the Tundra (ET) type; it is of the Icecap (EF) type where even the warmest month averages below 32° F.

TUNDRA (ET) CLIMATE • Poleward from the areas of Moist, Severe Winter (D) climate in the Northern Hemisphere and from areas of Moist, Mild Winter (C) climate in the Southern Hemisphere, there is a zone in which there is no true summer, but in which temperatures do rise above freezing during part of the year at least. Severe frosts occur even during this warmer period and temperatures are too low to permit agriculture. A cushion of mosses, lichens, flowering herbs, and coarse grasses, hard frozen through most of the year but waterlogged and spongy during a few short months, covers the surface. Trees are lacking or exist as stunted caricatures of the same species in warmer climates. This is the tundra. Toward the poles, the plant cover becomes discontinuous and spotty; in the opposite direction, it gives way first to thickets of bushes and stunted trees and then to the forests of the Moist, Severe Winter (D) climates. The warmer season is hardly a summer. Yet it is warm enough to allow some plant activity. Temperatures rise into the high 60's. Then, since the boggy ground supplies excessive moisture for evaporation, the air becomes sticky and oppressive. Myriads of insects, bred in the waterlogged vegetation mat, add to the discomfort of man and beast alike. Animals like the reindeer and caribou pasture on the vegetation made available to them during this warm season. Upon these animals a scant human population, like that along the Arctic fringe of Eurasia, is based. Point Barrow in Alaska (FIG. 11–10A) indicates the temperature and precipitation features of the Tundra (ET) type of climate.

ICECAP (EF) CLIMATE • In areas of Icecap (EF) climate (FIG. 11–11), monthly average temperatures never rise above freezing. Snow and ice cover the surface throughout the year. Even though the sun remains above the horizon continuously for four to six months of the year, it circles above the horizon so low in the sky that little heating results. A steep slope facing the sun for a few hours may warm sufficiently to cause slight melting of snow and ice. In exceptional instances, the temperature may rise into the 70's for a few minutes, only to drop back again below freezing as the sun swings round and leaves the slope in shadow. An equally long period at the opposite season during which the sun is below the horizon brings continued hours of darkness and unrelieved cold. Records of temperature over long periods are not available, but those taken by polar exploring expeditions suggest the general conditions. Little America, the Antarctic base of the Byrd expeditions and one of the bases of which American operations in Antarctica during the International Geophysical Year (1957–58) made some use, offers an example (FIG. 11–10B). Only temperature observations are available. Precipitation is entirely in the form of snow. Blowing and drifting of snow have been insurmountable handicaps to accurate measurement (FIG. 11–1). Observations made have been even more spotty than temperature observations. They indicate only that the amount is small, possibly equivalent to as much as 5 or 10 inches of water.

MOUNTAIN (H) CLIMATES

WITHIN any mountain area, climate is determined largely by altitude and exposure. Increased altitude lowers temperature and exposure to winds determines the rainiiness or dryness of any specific slope. Consequently, frequent changes of climatic type are the rule. In other words, the distribution of climatic types is spotty. No single type is char-

11–11   IN Antarctica, even during the warmest part of the year (January), snow, ice, and cloud suggest the nature of an Icecap (EF) climate.

acteristic of any extensive mountain area. There is no distinctive Mountain (H) type as there is a Tropical Rainforest (Af), an Arid (BW), a Subarctic (Dfc, Dfd, Dwc, Dwd), or any of the other types already discussed.

Generally, increase of altitude lowers temperatures just as does increase of distance from the equator. There is this difference, however—decreased average annual range accompanies increased altitude. Consequently, seasons are less marked in mountains than they are in adjacent lowlands. Temperatures are monotonously uniform at high altitudes, especially if the highland rises from a region of very slight average annual range. This is indicated by the graph and statistics for Quito (FIG. 10–6), previously referred to in the discussion of the Tropical Moist (A) climates.

Temperature zones can be distinguished in all mountain areas. The greatest number occur in tropical mountains. These highlands rise from the hot, steamy lowlands of Tropical Moist (A) climate and are often high enough to extend into zones where temperatures are always below freezing. Farther from the equator, say on a mountain rising from a lowland with Moist, Severe Winter (D) climate, continuously low temperatures are encountered at a much lower elevation.

One important difference between tropical highlands and those in other parts of the world, from the point of view of human use, should be stated. In the tropics, the highlands stand above areas of excessive heat. Consequently, their middle elevations provide temperatures more desirable for human habitation than the lowlands. Outside the tropics, the lowlands have a cool or cold season which places limits on human activity. Any increase of altitude increases the intensity and length of the cool season and hence imposes even further limitations.

Up to certain levels, which vary with the local controls, total precipitation tends to be greater in mountains than in adjacent lowlands. Above those levels, the total decreases. The zone of maximum rains is usually between 4000 and 8000 feet above sea level. There is thus created a zoning of mountain climates where mountains lie across the path of rain-bearing winds. But this zoning is not always the dominant feature. Within any highland,

the slopes facing into the wind are moist while those in the lee are dry. Very sharp changes from moist to dry climates may hence be expected.

Coupling together the elements of vertical zoning of temperature, vertical zoning of precipitation, and precipitation spottiness resulting from varied exposure, it becomes evident that no one particular climatic type dominates in all highlands or even in a very large area of one highland. Highland climate is intricately detailed. The term "Mountain (H) climate" does not imply uniformity; it implies variety and spottiness of distribution of too detailed a nature for generalization on a world scale.

SUMMARY

Excluding the mountain areas of the world, there are fourteen climatic types arranged in five categories. These main categories with the types which each includes are:

A. Tropical Moist climates
   1. Tropical Rainforest (Af) climate
   2. Tropical Monsoon (Am) climate
   3. Savanna (Aw) climate
B. Dry climates
   1. Arid (BW) climate
   2. Semiarid (BS) climate
C. Moist, Mild Winter climates
   1. Humid Subtropical (Cfa) climate
   2. Mid-latitude Marine (Cfb and Cfc) climate
   3. Subtropical Monsoon (Cw) climate
   4. Mediterranean (Cs) climate
D. Moist, Severe Winter climates
   1. Humid Continental climate with hot summers (Dfa and Dwa)
   2. Humid Continental climate with warm summers (Dfb and Dwb)
   3. Subarctic climate (Dfc, Dfd, Dwc, Dwd)
E. Polar climates
   1. Tundra (ET) climate
   2. Icecap (EF) climate

· REVIEW QUESTIONS ·

1. What characteristic most easily distinguishes the Moist, Mild Winter (C) and the Moist, Severe Winter (D) climates from the Tropical Moist (A) climates? Account for the existence of this characteristic.
2. Suggest some of the ways in which the presence of a winter season is significant from a human point of view.
3. Account for the seasonal deficiency of moisture in certain of the Moist, Mild Winter (C) climates.
4. Enumerate some of the principal differences between the climate of Los Angeles and that of New Orleans. Give a reasoned explanation of the causes of the differences.
5. What part of North America has a climate basically similar to that of the British Isles? To that of Barcelona, Spain? To that of Tokyo, Japan?
6. Why is there no Subtropical Monsoon (Cw) climate in the southeastern United States while there is an area with that type of climate in southeastern Asia?
7. Explain the absence of Moist, Severe Winter (D) climates from the Southern Hemisphere.
8. In the Moist, Severe Winter (D) climates, spring and autumn are very short seasons. Why is this so?
9. Give a reasonable explanation of the fact that summer temperatures in areas of Moist, Severe Winter (D) climates often exceed 100° F. whereas in areas of Tropical Moist (A) climates that temperature is seldom attained.
10. From the point of view of significance to

man, what are the three subdivisions of the Moist, Severe Winter (D) climates? Exactly what is it that gives significance to each subdivision?

11. Is there any part of South America in which the climate is similar to that in Chicago? If so, where, specifically? If not, why not?

12. Why is it that, in northern Canada in winter, temperatures have never been recorded that are as low as those that have been recorded in Asia? In what part of Asia do the lowest temperatures occur?

13. Where in North America is the climate similar to that in Vladivostok? To that in Leningrad? To that in Hokkaido? Suggest the main reasons for the similarities.

14. The yearly amount of precipitation in Verkhoyansk is very small. Why is the climate there *not* classified as the Dry (B) type?

15. Why is precipitation a relatively insignificant factor in Polar (E) climates?

16. What is the meaning of "spotty distribution" as that phrase is used to describe Mountain (H) climates? Explain the expression "vertical zoning" as applied to Mountain (H) climates.

12 Soils: Their Formation and Distribution

U.S. DEPARTMENT OF AGRICULTURE

❡Very few people have not recognized in a casual way the rich brown coloring of one newly plowed field, the shiny blackness of another, or the yellow or red stickiness of a third. But this common observation is usually passed over, especially by city dwellers, as of minor importance. Lakes, seas, oceans, and streams are so conspicuous as to force themselves upon our attention; so, too, are landforms. Climate, though not visible, is rendered conspicuous through the other senses. Soils are not like this. Indeed, they are so lacking in prominence that they are often forgotten as constituting one of the great essentials of life. Without some covering of soil, plants could not exist; man would have no plant or animal products from the land. Even the seas and oceans would have little to offer, for it is water coursing over the land and carrying soil particles to the water bodies that supplies much basic food *to marine life. Though their functions are indirect in a sense, soils are just as fundamental to human life as are air and water.*

Variations in soil quality from place to place provide differences in habitability just as do variations in climate and surface form. The way in which man uses or misuses the soil frequently determines the relative success of settlement and the sustained productivity of one area as compared with another. No world survey should omit at least a brief consideration of soil as a vital element in the human habitat.

SOIL CHARACTERISTICS

ALL too frequently, soil is considered to be simply a collection of weathered rock material at the surface of the earth, or as "so much dirt." It is far more than this. Even the most finely divided rock is not soil. *Soil* is a mixture of mineral and organic matter with air and water. It may cover the earth's surface to a depth of only a few inches or it may be several feet deep. In a few places, as on rocky mountain crests, soil is lacking altogether. Sometimes the mineral element dominates; in other soils, organic matter, both living and dead, constitutes the bulk. Regardless of the proportions, both are present, and with them air and water.

The soil is constantly evolving. Time, parent material, slope, climate, vegetation, and bacteria all contribute to this evolutionary process. So do man and other animals, both large and small. Every conceivable gradation from weathered rock—not soil by itself—to the most complexly altered covering can be observed in detailed study. Yet from a world point of view, certain great groups of similar soils can be distinguished. Within each one of these groups, all of the soils have certain character-

istics in common. These reflect dominantly the controls of climate and natural vegetation. It is upon the nature and distribution of these types that attention is here focused.

Soil Profile

By far the larger part of the earth's soils are developed from weathered rock. As noted previously, when rock is exposed at the surface, it is subjected to both weathering and erosion, which create a mantle of unconsolidated material, known as *regolith*. Into the spaces between the individual particles in the regolith, water and air penetrate; plant roots secure a foothold; and life forms, represented by small burrowing animals, ants, earthworms, and bacteria, become established. The evolution of soil begins when organic forms start their existence in the upper part of the regolith.

The major obvious result of the soil-forming processes is the development of definite layers within the regolith. These layers are called *horizons*. Each of them is characterized by certain physical and chemical peculiarities and, within each, certain of the processes which bring about the evolution of regolith to soil are dominant. A cross section through all of the layers is called a *soil profile*.

The uppermost layer is called the *A-horizon* (FIG. 12–2). This is the zone from which ma-

---

12–1

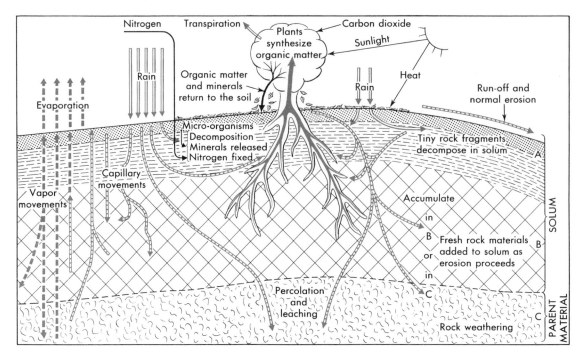

SCHEMATIC *diagram of the principal dynamic processes in a soil, much simplified. The letters A, B, and C indicate the soil horizons described in the text.*

terials are being removed either in solution or in suspension. It is often referred to as the "zone of robbery." In addition, it is considered to include organic debris which is either freshly accumulated upon the surface or partially decomposed. A walk through any wooded area will reveal the sort of material actually lying on the soil, but generally considered to be included in the A-horizon. The fallen leaves in a deciduous woodland form a brown matting, loose and rustling if dry, sticky and soggy if wet. When these leaves are kicked or scuffed up, blackened forms of older leaves are uncovered and, below them, a black mass in which the original structure has been obliterated. Beneath that is the part of the soil which is mainly mineral fragments. Similarly, the A-horizon of a pine forest has a matting of brown needles often many inches thick and below, a thin band of black, decayed and partially decayed, older needles. The black material is called *humus*. Upon the chemical re-

action and amount of the humus depend many of the specific qualities of the underlying soil. It is important to note that humus is *partially* decayed organic matter; if decay is complete, there is no humus, but only a residual mineral ash.

Below the A-horizon, there is a more compact zone in which much of the material removed from the upper layer is deposited. This layer, known as the *B-horizon*, is a "zone of accumulation." Together with the A-horizon, it constitutes the soil proper.

The third layer, known as the *C-horizon*, is the weathered parent material from which the soil is derived. Within it, there are sometimes found accumulations of chemical compounds, like white calcium carbonate or bluish-gray ferrous iron, which indicate peculiarities of soil drainage. Below the C-horizon is rock material, either consolidated or unconsolidated, which is unaltered by the soil-forming processes. To this layer, the name *D-horizon* is sometimes given. Weathering proceeds downward into it, and thus produces the regolith from which the overlying A- and B-horizons are developed.

The boundaries between soil horizons may be sharp or indistinct; they may be smooth or irregular. Not all of the horizons are present in all soils. In some places, as on a slope without vegetation, surface erosion may remove the A-horizon altogether. In other places, the B-horizon may extend downward practically to the unweathered rock so that no C-horizon exists.

Soil Color

Each horizon or part of a horizon has certain features of color, texture, and structure peculiar to itself. Perhaps the most easily observed of these features is color. In itself, color is not a complete index to soil nature. Yet it is usually a clue to the differences between one type and another.

In part, color indicates organic content. Decomposed organic matter has a blackish coloring. Where there is a large amount, the soil is black or very dark brown. As organic content decreases, the color changes through the darker browns to lighter ones. The contribution of organic coloring decreases to the point of grayness in soils where the content is low.

Chemical change in the mineral parts of the soil is responsible for other colors. Iron contributes either a reddish or a yellowish color under certain conditions. Occasionally it produces a bluish-gray mottling. Many other chemical salts are white.

The precise color of any one horizon depends upon the detailed actions of the soil-forming processes. The whole range from black to white can be obtained by differing mixtures of each color contributor. Usually, the upper part of the A-horizon is the darkest part of the soil. Downward through the A-horizon, color lightens. Ordinarily it becomes deeper again in the B-horizon, though it is seldom as deep there as in the upper part of the A-horizon.

Soil Texture

Soil particles show a wide variety of sizes which in turn produce a wide variety of textures. When the individual particles are larger than a grain of corn, they are not considered to be true soil particles. Rather they are gravelly or stony fragments included in the soil. Below that size, several categories are recognized. The major ones are sand, silt, and clay. Arbitrary limits have been set in terms of the diameter of the particles. In sand, the individual grains have a diameter between .05 millimeter and 1 millimeter; in silt, between .002 millimeter and .05 millimeter; and in clay, below .002 millimeter.

No soil exists in which all of the grains have the same size. Hence, certain classes have been established based upon relative proportion of grains of each size. Sand is the coarsest and clay the finest. Between the two, in increasing order of fineness, are loamy sand, sandy loam, loam, silt loam, silty clay loam, clay loam, and silty clay. These in turn are modified by descriptive adjectives so that a wide variety of gradations are recognized. There are, for example, very fine sandy loams or stony sandy loams.

Texture has important effects upon the ability of the soil to retain moisture and to make the necessary foods available for plants. Fine-grained particles expose more surface than do coarse-grained ones. Hence, hygroscopic and capillary water perform their functions more actively in silty or clayey soils than they do in sandy ones. Thus larger feeding surfaces for plant roots are provided in fine soils and smaller ones in coarse soils.

Within most well-developed soils, the texture of the A-horizon is generally coarser than that of the B-horizon. This condition is brought about largely by the removal of the smallest soil particles from the A-horizon by gravitational water, which deposits them in the B-horizon.

Soil Structure

Individual soil particles may group themselves in the soil in various ways. To these arrangements, the term *structure* is applied. Within each horizon in any one soil, a particular structure is characteristic. The particles may stick together in thin horizontal plates. The structure is then said to be *platy*. They may combine into more or less rounded forms of varying size. Then the structure is said to be *granular*. Many other specific arrangements have been observed. Occasionally there is no grouping of particles. Then the soil is said to have a simple structure, either *single grain*, when the particles are large like sand, or *massive*, when the particles are fine like clay.

While texture is more or less fixed for any one horizon, structure may vary from time to time depending, for example, upon the moisture content. A simple example is provided by the collection of silt in a mud puddle. During a rain and for such time afterward as water is present, a thin, fine-grained deposit lines the bottom of the puddle. After the water has drained away or has been evaporated, the silt dries out and cracks appear. Careful examination will show that the silt particles are then arranged in thin scales or plates. The change of structure in the silt of a mud puddle under differing moisture conditions is a miniature of the same process in soil. On a large scale, this same variety of change may be seen in any granular soil which has been excessively plowed and cultivated. After a time, such a soil loses its granular structure. Then, when water is applied to it in large amounts, it becomes a "soupy mud," only to dry out into hard crusts or clods.

AGENTS AND PROCESSES OF SOIL FORMATION

Soil-forming Agents

THE evolution of soil is brought about by four main agents: water, air, plants, and animals. Each of these performs certain functions, and the resulting soil reflects their combined action. Soil in one place differs from that in another because the contribution of each agent varies.

WATER IN THE SOIL · Three things may happen to water which falls upon the earth. It may run off the surface and be conveyed by streams to lakes or oceans. It may be evaporated and returned to the atmosphere as water vapor. Or it may sink into the ground and become hygroscopic, capillary, and gravitational water (see p. 89). While the effect of hygroscopic water is negligible, capillary and gravitational water are vital agents in soil formation.

Capillary water acts as the major source of plant moisture. Its amount depends upon the number and size of the spaces between soil particles as well as upon the total amount of water available to the soil. In finely divided soils, it is abundant; in coarse ones, it may be almost lacking. As the surface dries out, capillary water from the lower horizons may move upward if the soil spaces are small enough. In this manner, moisture necessary to plants is made available in periods of protracted drought. Where the movement toward the surface is pronounced and long-continued, it often causes a concentration of chemical salts, some of which may be injurious to the plant life. In this way, capillary water is an agent of soil evolution.

Gravitational water produces the most striking results within the soil. It is the major agent of color, texture, and structure changes in both the A- and B-horizons. It is thus responsible for easily observed differences between the parts of any soil profile.

Two of the major changes produced by gravitational water are physical. As the water moves downward through the A-horizon, it tends to pick up minute soil particles (the clay and silt particles). These exceedingly fine bits of matter are carried downward out of the A-horizon as the water moves through it. The process of removal of the fine particles from the upper horizon is called *eluviation*. The result of this process is a coarsening of the texture of the A-horizon, particularly in its lower part. Structure is generally altered and the spaces between the particles are increased in size. Consequently, less water is retained as capillary water, for capillary water exists only in fine, hairlike spaces. Thus the A-horizon becomes a less suitable medium for plant roots.

As the gravitational water moves downward toward the water table, its ability to carry the load of fine particles becomes less, just as a river's ability to carry alluvium becomes less as it nears or enters the body of water into which it is flowing. Eventually, the fine particles are deposited in the spaces of the B-horizon. The texture and structure of the B-horizon are thereby altered. The layer becomes more compact. Hygroscopic and capillary water are both increased in amount. The action, in combination with certain chemical changes, may be carried on to such a degree that a very stiff, impervious layer, called *hardpan*, is formed. This retards soil evolution and harms plant and animal life locally.

The third of the major functions performed by gravitational water is chemical rather than physical. As water moves downward through the A-horizon, it tends to dissolve the more soluble of the chemical elements. This process is called *leaching*, and it, also, may change both the texture and the structure of the soil. Very definitely, it changes the chemical composition, and thus it materially alters the value of the A-horizon as a source of plant food.

The exact nature of the chemical change varies with the reaction of the water. If the water is mixed with large amounts of carbon dioxide from the air or if it seeps through a heavy layer of humus, it becomes a weak organic acid. Chemical reactions between this acid water and the soil particles differ from those produced by "purer" water. However, leaching always tends to increase soil acidity.

Various chemical changes frequently affect the soil color. When the action is such as to leave the iron compounds in the A-horizon, a reddish or yellowish color results. When the iron is removed, a grayish or whitish color prevails. When the water is strongly affected by the humus through which it passes, it often imparts blackish or brownish coloring to the A-horizon.

Elements which are leached from the A-horizon are usually concentrated in the B-horizon. Thus the passage of water through the soil effects changes in both horizons.

AIR IN THE SOIL • The presence of some air in the soil is essential for plants and for soil animals. Life processes cannot go on without an adequate supply of oxygen, and though some of the plants and a few of the animals can secure it in ways other than directly from the air, most of them are unable to do so. Their survival depends essentially upon air which is present in the spaces between soil particles, spaces which are not permanently filled with water. In addition, when the soil air is charged with water vapor or with carbon dioxide given off by the plant or animal life within it, it is capable of bringing about a certain amount of chemical change by solution. The air is thus a direct agent of soil change.

In most soils, there are times when little air is present. This is true particularly during and after heavy precipitation. Then gravitational water occupies practically all of the openings, but it soon drains away and is replaced by air.

ORGANIC MATTER IN THE SOIL • Both plants and animals live in the soil and are agents of its evolution. When plant roots establish themselves, they draw water and absorb as food many of the chemical elements in the soil. Under the influence of sunlight and carbon dioxide from the air, the items drawn from the soil are converted into various new compounds, known as *organic* compounds. These are the direct foods on which the plants live and from which they develop their structures. The plants in turn provide food for animals. When the plants and animals die, both organic and mineral substances are returned to the soil either at the surface, as in the accumulation of leaves, twigs, branches, trunks, and animal remains in a forest, or in the form of dead root fibers and animals within the soil itself. The processes of decay convert the organic matter to humus. At the same time, many of the mineral elements in the decaying structures are released to the soil.

Small animals, like the earthworm, feed upon humus and carry it downward into the soil. Large numbers of bacteria feed upon it, often converting it to other forms, and mix it with the mineral parts of the soil. Fungi, plants without green color, also feed upon it and in turn produce other organic compounds. The bodies of all of these plants and animals alike provide a further source of organic matter when they die. Certain of the bacteria have the ability to take nitrogen directly from the air and transform it so that it can be used by plant roots. The presence of nitrogen-fixing bacteria in large numbers insures high soil fertility.

The mixing process and the downward movement of altered organic compounds is furthered by the action of water. Some of the compounds are extremely soluble and are hence rapidly leached away; others are quite insoluble and remain to impart black coloring to the soil.

Organic matter, either living or dead, makes for greater soil fertility and for ease of soil cultivation; normally, the more humus, the greater the friability, or "workability," of the soil. In general, where soils are well drained, high humus content implies high fertility and low humus content implies low fertility.

Principal Soil-forming Processes

Soil is formed from regolith as a result of the combined activities of the agents so far suggested. No one of them is alone responsible. It is obvious that the combinations are not everywhere the same. In some places, water is plentiful and its functions can be carried on continuously, as in areas of Tropical Rainforest (Af) climate. In other places, water is infrequently available, as in areas of Arid (BW) climate. Accumulation of organic matter is rapid in some regions—in the middle latitude grasslands, for instance. In other regions, like the deserts, it is slow. Earthworms are important soil "cultivators" in some regions, but are absent in others. Despite the infinite variety of possible combinations, the evolution of soils may be summarized in terms of three general processes: *laterization*, *podsolization*, and *calcification*. One process alone or any of them in combination may be involved in the evolution of any one soil. The world-wide soil types, or major soil groups, depend upon the balance among these processes which exists over different parts of the earth.

LATERIZATION • The laterization process is one in which leaching and eluviation are very highly developed. It occurs only where there are large supplies of moisture at temperatures which allow soil formation to continue throughout the year. Because it is continuous, soils in which laterization is the dominant process are deeper than others. The whole profile occasionally exceeds 25 feet in depth. Under the most extreme conditions, as represented in areas of Tropical Rainforest (Af) climate, bacterial life is plentiful and prevents large accumulations of humus in the upper part of the A-horizon. Organic matter is rapidly converted into a form which is quickly and easily leached away. Most of the soluble minerals are removed also. Leaching is so strongly developed that even much of the silica is removed. Only iron and aluminum oxides remain in the A-horizon. Eluviation is likewise at a maximum; the A-horizon becomes extremely coarse textured and porous while the B-horizon becomes compact and clayey. One prominent indicator of the process is color; the iron oxides give reddish or yellowish colors to the soil.

PODSOLIZATION • The podsolization (from the Russian *podsol*, alkaline ashes) process is the summation of the effects of soil agents under quite different conditions from those which produce laterization. Acid organic matter collects at the surface and decomposes very slowly. Bacterial life is meager and soil animals are few in number so that there is no intensive conversion or mixing of organic elements and the mineral parts of the soil. The A-horizon is leached of its iron and aluminum compounds and what remains is dominantly silica. It is, thus, gray or even whitish. The B-horizon is compacted by the deposit of leached and eluviated materials from above. The process occurs in humid areas with a pronounced cool

season and consequently does not continue uninterrupted throughout the year. Soils developed by it are generally very shallow, with an average depth of only 14 or 15 inches.

CALCIFICATION • The process of calcification is best developed under grass rather than forest cover. Grass feeds on large amounts of calcium brought by the roots from the lower parts of the soil. When the grass dies, calcium is returned to the upper soil layers. Grass roots and leaves provide heavy mats of organic matter. Bacterial life is plentiful. Water is not sufficient in amount to cause heavy leaching or eluviation. In contrast to soils in which laterization and podsolization dominate, those in which calcification is the most important process are not acid in their reaction.

A summary of the more prominent effects of each of these three processes on both the A- and B-horizons is given in condensed form in TABLE 12.

CONTROLS OF THE SOIL-FORMING PROCESSES

THE end product in the evolution of any one soil is determined by which of the three processes—laterization, podsolization, or calcification—dominates and by the rate at which the process operates. Five controls, in turn, determine the dominant process and its rate. These controls are (1) climate, (2) vegetation, (3) parent material, (4) slope or lay of the land, and (5) time. The first two are worldwide in their effects. The third and fourth are of extreme importance locally. The fifth control is important in all soil evolution, whether world-wide or local.

Control by Climate

Because water and air are such significant agents in the soil-forming processes, climate exerts the most important single influence on soil development. A large amount of precipita-

tion usually means a large amount of soil water. The continued presence of moisture in the soil depends largely upon the distribution of precipitation through the year. Temperature is also very significant, for the effectiveness of water as a soil agent depends upon it.

In a Tropical Rainforest (Af) climate, with constant high precipitation evenly distributed throughout the year and with regular high temperatures, there is a large amount of water available for both leaching and eluviation. Not only is the amount large, but it can continue its functions throughout the whole year, for there is no period when temperatures are low enough to freeze the water, thus reducing its activity. In addition, air and water temperatures are relatively high, and solution proceeds more rapidly at high temperatures than at low ones. In sharp contrast to such conditions are those under an Arid (BW) climate. Water is

TABLE 12

Summary of More Prominent Effects of Soil Processes

EFFECTS ON A-HORIZON

LATERIZATION	PODSOLIZATION	CALCIFICATION
1. Most chemical elements except iron and aluminum removed.	1. Most chemical elements except silica removed.	1. Only the most soluble chemical elements removed.
2. Fine particles removed producing coarse texture.	2. Fine particles removed producing coarse texture.	2. Only very finest particles removed leaving texture moderately fine.
3. Almost no humus accumulated on surface or mixed through horizon.	3. Moderately large amount of humus accumulated on surface, but little mixed through horizon.	3. Large amount of humus accumulated on surface and well mixed through horizon.
4. Considerable depth developed.	4. Only shallow depth developed.	4. Moderate depth developed.

EFFECTS ON B-HORIZON

LATERIZATION	PODSOLIZATION	CALCIFICATION
1. Elements leached from A-horizon concentrated.	1. Elements leached from A-horizon concentrated.	1. Calcium and magnesium concentrated in form of carbonate nodules.
2. Particles eluviated from A-horizon concentrated producing heavy clay texture.	2. Particles eluviated from A-horizon concentrated producing clayey texture.	2. Texture little changed by particles eluviated from A-horizon.
3. No humus mixed through horizon.	3. Little humus mixed through horizon.	3. Humus well mixed through horizon.
4. Considerable depth developed.	4. Little depth developed.	4. Little depth developed.

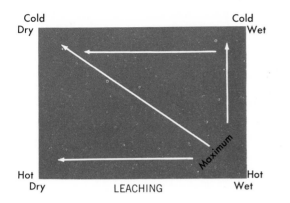

Cold Dry · Cold Wet · Hot Dry · LEACHING · Hot Wet · Maximum

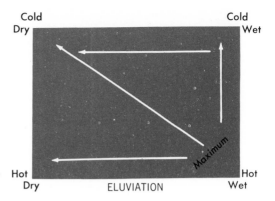

Cold Dry · Cold Wet · Hot Dry · ELUVIATION · Hot Wet · Maximum

12–3 SCHEMATIC *representation of the relations of the leaching and eluviation processes to climate. The effectiveness of each process decreases in the directions shown by the arrows. The corners of the rectangles represent climatic extremes.*

extremely small in amount and it comes at irregular intervals. Hardly any of it can sink far into the ground before evaporation has dried out the surface. Then capillary activity allows what has sunk in to rise again toward the surface. Leaching and eluviation under such a climate are at a minimum. Similarly, in a Polar (E) climate, water is seldom present in large amounts in a liquid state. When water is present in the form of ice, the processes which it carries on under warmer temperatures cannot take place.

Some of the relationships between climate and the processes carried on by water are shown in FIG. 12–3. The arrows point in the direction of decreased effectiveness of water as a soil agent.

Control by Vegetation

Control by vegetation is exerted largely through its influence on the supply of organic matter. The largest amount of humus is accumulated under grass cover and the next largest under forests. Transfer of this humus to the soil is dependent mostly upon living organisms. As previously pointed out, some climates favor plentiful soil life while others discourage it. Similarly, some types of vegetation produce

organic material which can be converted readily while others do not.

In tropical areas which are forested, the production of dead organic matter is enormous and continuous, but the climate is such that bacterial life is plentiful. Bacteria decompose plant products rapidly, reducing them to a form in which living plants can use them. Hence, there is no considerable humus accumulation on the soil nor any great permanent incorporation of organic compounds in the soil.

In forests in the higher middle latitudes, the cool, moist climate fosters accumulation of a thick layer of dead organic matter on the surface, but the formation of humus is very slow. It develops in a form which is easily leached out of the A-horizon. Climate, along with acid reaction of the A-horizon, discourages the presence of many earth animals. Hence, organic matter is not made easily available to plant roots in a form which they can use. Despite this, much of it is actually carried down into the B-horizon.

A definite relationship exists between climate and vegetation on the one hand and the dominating processes in the soil on the other. Areas of Tropical Rainforest (Af) climate with its accompanying type of forest are areas where laterization is at its height; areas of Humid

Controls of the Soil-forming Processes | 295

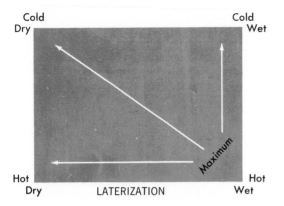

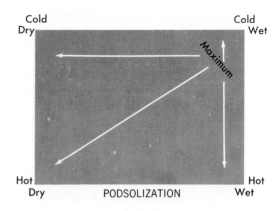

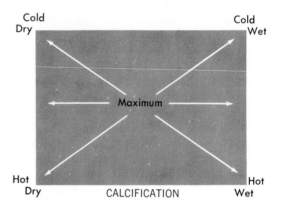

Continental (Df) climate with its accompanying type of forest are areas where podsolization is paramount; and in regions along the wet margins of Semiarid (BS) climate with associated grassy cover are areas where calcification dominates. These relationships are summarized in part in FIG. 12–4.

Control by Parent Material

As one travels through any small area, it is easy to see differences between soils, especially when fields are being plowed. Some soils may be yellowish and sandy, blowing with every wind; some may be sticky, red clay; some may be yellowish-brown and rich looking. Often these differences can be traced to differences in underlying rock, the *parent material* from which the soils are derived.

Parent material obviously contributes to the nature of the soil. Unless the parent material contains certain chemical elements, the soil must of necessity lack them. If the products of weathering are fine-grained, then the soil also can be expected to be fine-grained. Parent material provides the specific combination of chemical elements in the regolith and greatly influences its texture. Those traits are passed on to the soil.

Differences of this sort induced by parent material may be of tremendous significance locally and regionally. They provide the finer, more detailed, patterns. But they are of little

12–4

SCHEMATIC *representation of the relations of the soil-forming processes to climate. The effectiveness of each process decreases in the directions shown by the arrows. The corners of the rectangles represent climatic extremes.*

service in a study on a world scale. From a world point of view, the controls of climate and vegetation combine to establish certain major climax types toward which all soils are developing. The controls of climate and vegetation thus mask that of parent material when the world is the object of view rather than a locality or a region.

Control by Slope

Slope induces local and regional variation just as does underlying rock. On steep slopes, runoff is rapid and large in amount. Not only does it have effective force as an agent of erosion; it diminishes the water available to sink into the ground and carry on the soil-forming processes. Frequently, slope lands are so badly eroded that an A-horizon is lacking altogether. In extreme cases, the whole profile may be lost and the slope may be soil-less, clothed in parent material or in coarse rock fragments.

Slope likewise may induce poor drainage. Undrained depressions may exist where the water table is so close to the surface as to prevent the downward percolation of water and thus to eliminate air from the soil spaces. The normal processes of leaching and eluviation cannot go on under this condition. Soil evolution is stopped.

Over wide areas of gently sloped surface, the effect of the lay of the land is minimized; the other controls operate more strongly. Gentle slopes decrease both the rate and amount of run-off, thus reducing erosion and making more water available as an agent of soil formation.

Control by Time

Time is the prime requisite in the production of all soil. On a world scale, differences of parent material and of slope can be overcome, given sufficient time. Under each climate and vegetation cover, a major variety of soil will develop. Just how long a time is necessary cannot be stated with any meaning in terms of human life. Observations are plentiful to indicate the basic importance of this control, however. On the steppes of European Russia, deep black soils occur clear across the zone of grass which follows the wet margin of the Semiarid (BS) climate. Under these soils lie crystalline rocks in some places and sedimentaries in others. Some of the surface was covered with glacial debris and some was not. But the soil cover shows similarity throughout. A long enough time has elapsed so that the controls of climate and vegetation have left their unmistakable imprint.

SOIL CLASSIFICATION

As in the study of climate and landforms, it is necessary to recognize certain groupings of soils in order to compare one part of the earth with another. Major categories are erected upon the basis of soil traits which reflect the controls of climate and vegetation. These controls are operative over large areas and traits due to them, therefore, provide the most obvious means of world comparison.

The major categories are really the *mature* types toward which all soils under the same climatic and vegetational controls are developing. They are the end products which may be expected of the action of soil-forming processes through long periods of time.

Because the controls are operative over great areas or zones of well-drained and gently sloped land, the major categories are called *zonal* soils. Within the extent of any one zonal soil, local controls of relief, parent material, or detailed differences of climate and vegetation all may produce variations. Some of the variations occur in areas of more than one zonal soil; these variations are therefore called *intrazonal*. For other soils there has not been enough time to produce characteristics determined either by climate or by vegetation. Soils in which this is true are called *azonal*.

As was true in studying the controls of the soil-forming processes, attention must be directed either to the world-wide pattern or to the local or regional pattern. It is the zonal soils which provide the usable world pattern. Though intrazonal and azonal soils are matters of great significance locally and regionally, they are of little service in a study on a world scale. Therefore, attention is here directed to the zonal soils alone.

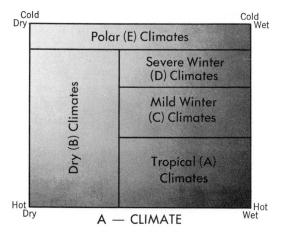

A — CLIMATE

Diagram corners: Cold Dry (top left), Cold Wet (top right), Hot Dry (bottom left), Hot Wet (bottom right).

Polar (E) Climates
Severe Winter (D) Climates
Mild Winter (C) Climates
Dry (B) Climates
Tropical (A) Climates

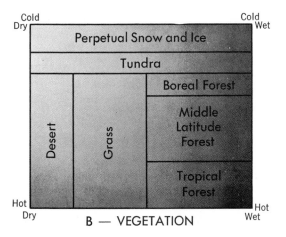

B — VEGETATION

Diagram corners: Cold Dry (top left), Cold Wet (top right), Hot Dry (bottom left), Hot Wet (bottom right).

Perpetual Snow and Ice
Tundra
Boreal Forest
Middle Latitude Forest
Desert
Grass
Tropical Forest

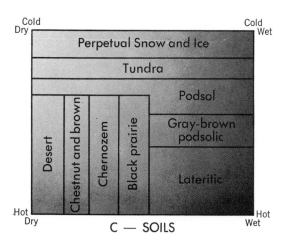

C — SOILS

Diagram corners: Cold Dry (top left), Cold Wet (top right), Hot Dry (bottom left), Hot Wet (bottom right).

Perpetual Snow and Ice
Tundra
Podsol
Gray-brown podsolic
Desert
Chestnut and brown
Chernozem
Black prairie
Lateritic

12–5

SCHEMATIC *representation of the distribution of climatic types, natural vegetation associations, and zonal soils. The corners of the rectangles represent climatic extremes. Comparison suggests the interrelationship of these three elements of the physical setting. (After Blumenstock and Thornthwaite, "Climate and the World Pattern," in* Climate and Man, *U.S. Department of Agriculture, 1941)*

Zonal Soils

The great zonal soils, often called the *great soil groups*, of the world have both internal and external features reflecting the combined controls of climate and vegetation. Where they are well developed, they occur over many kinds of parent material. Their profiles are the result of long-time action by soil-forming processes which operate over wide areas. Five principal types are recognized. Where the process of laterization is dominant, the resultant soils are known as *lateritic soils*. At the opposite extreme within forested and humid areas, podsolization is the principal process and the soils are called *podsols*. Where calcification is the prime process, the resultant soils are called *chernozems* (from the Russian *chernozem*, black earth). In arid regions where all soil-forming processes proceed at a very slow rate, the soils are spoken of as *desert soils*. Where continued cold persists and all processes are slowed, *tundra soils* are found. Between these extreme forms, there are many gradations, certain of which are sufficiently pronounced to warrant recognition as distinct zonal soils. Thus, as one passes from areas of lateritic soils to areas of podsols, laterization becomes less and less significant and podsolization more and more so. One zonal soil is recognized in this transition, the *gray-brown podsolic soils*. Lateritic soils, gray-brown podsolic soils, and podsols are all formed in forested regions.

As one proceeds from regions with these types toward areas of chernozems, one passes through a zone in which the dark brown or black coloring under grass cover indicates a kind of balance between the three processes of laterization, podsolization, and calcification. Under such conditions, *black prairie soils* develop.

On the dry side of the chernozems, decreased effectiveness of the soil-forming processes is evidenced by increased shallowness of profile and lightening of soil color. Calcification occurs throughout areas of grass and desert vegetation, but it is less intense in the drier areas. Between the chernozems and the desert soils, one final zonal type is recognized, the *chestnut and brown soils*.

A check list of the zonal soils follows:

1. Lateritic soils
2. Gray-brown podsolic soils
3. Podsols
4. Black prairie soils
5. Chernozems
6. Chestnut and brown soils
7. Desert soils
8. Tundra soils

In summary, it should be reiterated that zonal soils are the fundamental types, the *mature soils*, toward which all types are developing. The close relationships which exist between climate, natural vegetation, and soils are represented schematically in FIG. 12–5.

Other Categories of Classification

In detailed soil study, further division is made within each of the zonal types. Of great local importance is the soil *series*. A soil series is a group of soils having profiles similar in their major characteristics and all developed over the same kind of parent material. The series is broken down into *types*, determined

---

TABLE *13*

Classification of One Specific Soil

GROUP—gray-brown podsolic
SERIES—Hillsdale
TYPE—sandy loam
PHASE—gravelly

Soil is referred to as a *Hillsdale sandy loam, gravelly phase.* This is recognized as being within the gray-brown podsolic zonal soil group.

---

largely by the texture of the A-horizon. The types are further differentiated into *phases* which represent features of significance in soil use, such as slope, stoniness, and the like. TABLE 13 illustrates the foregoing classification for a specific soil.

While all of these categories are of major significance in detailed examination, they do not clarify the world picture. We speak of broadleaf deciduous forest, as will be indicated in the following chapter, just as we speak of gray-brown podsolic soil; we do not list the many kinds of trees which make up the forest, nor should we try to consider the many series, types, and phases which make up the gray-brown podsolic soils. Our attention must be focused upon the same degree of detail in all the features of the physical setting, recognizing, at the same time, the generalizations necessarily implied.

NATURE AND DISTRIBUTION OF ZONAL SOILS

Each zonal soil is really a group or family of soils, some of which have developed mature profiles and others of which are immature. The following descriptions of the characteristics of each zonal soil apply to the mature profile. It is very important to realize that mature soils are rare in many areas, such as Kentucky and Tennessee. On the other hand, it must be remembered that all soils with immature profiles are evolving, under the controls of climate and vegetation, toward one or the other of the mature forms.

Lowland Soils

LATERITIC SOILS • Reddish and yellowish color and considerable depth are among the earmarks of all lateritic soils. The profiles of all of them show only a thin covering, if any, of organic matter (FIG. 12–6A). In the most completely laterized forms, the A-horizon is reddish, coarse textured, and very porous, while the B-horizon is deeper red in color and relatively fine-textured. A depth of 8 to 10 feet is not uncommon. In areas where there is some evidence that podsolization is active, red and yellow lateritic soils take the place of the extreme forms. In the former type, the thin surface layer of organic matter is underlain by yellowish-brown highly leached material. In the B-horizon, the color becomes a deep red. In the latter type, the A-horizon is grayish-yellow and highly leached. It grades into a yellowish, clayey B-horizon.

Throughout all areas of lateritic soil, the intensity of leaching and the small accumulation of humus tend to produce soils which are relatively infertile from the point of view of both mineral and organic plant foods. Continuous heavy cropping is impossible without heavy fertilization. Then, too, the porosity of many lateritic soils makes irrigation a necessity in areas of protracted seasonal drought.

The great zone of lateritic soils is the forested region of the tropics and the lower middle latitudes. In the Americas, these soils extend from the Amazon Basin southward into southeastern Brazil and northward through Middle America into the southeastern United States (PLATE v). Central Africa, the southeast coastlands of that continent, and the lowland portion of nearby Madagascar form a second large region. Southeastern Asia and the southwest Pacific Islands constitute the third great region. The soils of the Mediterranean fringe of Europe and of the southern peninsulas of Australia are so generally similar that they too are included in the lateritic soil zone.

GRAY-BROWN PODSOLIC SOILS • Poleward from the regions of lateritic soils and still within forested regions, the soils show marked features of podsolization. The surface accumulation of humus is still relatively thin, though thicker than in the lateritic soils (FIG. 12–6B). Below the humus, a grayish-brown, rather heavily leached A-horizon gives way to a dark brown, fine-textured B-horizon. The whole profile is shallower than that of the lateritic soils, usually reaching a depth of about four feet. Leaching is less in these soils than in those of the tropics and subtropics, and more organic matter is incorporated in them. Consequently, the gray-brown podsolic soils are of medium fertility and are much more retentive of moisture than the lateritic soils.

The great areas of gray-brown podsolic soils are three in number (PLATE v). The northeastern United States is the single important area in the Americas. In Europe, a wedge stretches inland from the Atlantic coast to the heart of European Russia. In Asia, interior and northern China, Korea, and northern Honshu in Japan have similar soils. It should be noted that all of these are areas of relatively high population density and that they are important agricultural regions. That agriculture still remains prominent in all of them is in

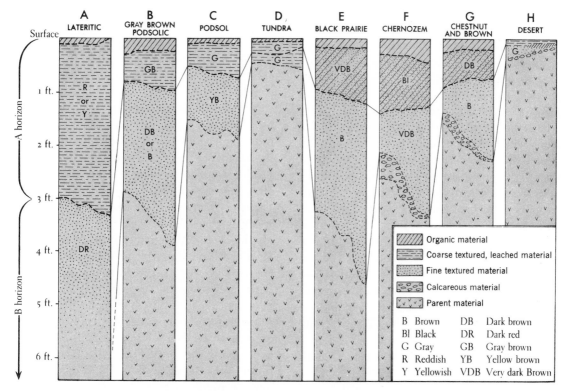

A LATERITIC · B GRAY BROWN PODSOLIC · C PODSOL · D TUNDRA · E BLACK PRAIRIE · F CHERNOZEM · G CHESTNUT AND BROWN · H DESERT

Surface

A horizon

1 ft.
2 ft.
3 ft.

B horizon

4 ft.
5 ft.
6 ft.

Organic material
Coarse textured, leached material
Fine textured material
Calcareous material
Parent material

B	Brown	DB	Dark brown
Bl	Black	DR	Dark red
G	Gray	GB	Gray brown
R	Reddish	YB	Yellow brown
Y	Yellowish	VDB	Very dark Brown

12–6   SCHEMATIC comparative profiles of the eight zonal soils. The scale at the left applies to all eight profiles. The lines between profiles connect the bottoms of the respective A-horizons and the bottoms of the respective B-horizons. Note that individual horizons vary in depth; the change from A-horizon to B-horizon, or from B to C, does not necessarily occur at exactly the same depth everywhere in any one soil.

large part a reflection of careful human management of the soil.

PODSOLS · These soils develop mainly under coniferous forest in relatively cool climates. A thin layer of humus lies upon a coarse-grained, whitish or gray, heavily leached horizon (FIG. 12–6C). This in turn breaks sharply to a brownish layer which is very compact. The whole profile is very shallow, usually less than two feet in total depth. The natural fertility of podsols is low.

These soils dominate in the northern forested lands of North America and Eurasia (PLATE V). In North America they extend uninterruptedly from central Alaska eastward past the northern Great Lakes to the Atlantic coast, where they extend from eastern Maine to southern Labrador. In Europe the podsols begin on the wetter and cooler sides of the British Isles. They pick up, after a short break, in southern Norway, Sweden, Finland, and the northern U.S.S.R. to spread in an increasingly wide belt across northern Europe and Asia to the Pacific shores.

TUNDRA SOILS · Poleward from the zone of podsols (PLATE V) and also in many high mountain areas, the surface is covered by a mat of dark brown, partially decayed vegetation (FIG. 12–6D). Under this, in more favorable locations, grayish horizons are observable, from a few inches to a foot or so in thickness. Under these layers, there is usually a permanently frozen mass. Actually, very little evidence is present to indicate that the more common soil-forming processes have acted upon the parent material. There is considerable mixing of mineral and organic materials through the alternate actions of freezing and thawing. Where the soil has sufficient depth, where the growing season is long enough, and where the soil dries sufficiently to allow cultivation of even the most meager sort, natural fertility often surpasses that of the podsols.

BLACK PRAIRIE SOILS • Under a tall grass cover in a region of humid climate, a soil of high fertility develops. A thick mat of grass roots gives way to a very dark brown horizon (FIG. 12–6E). This grades through lighter browns to a light-colored parent material. The whole profile varies from three to five feet in depth. The high percentage of available organic matter and the relatively slight leaching leave ample plant food.

One of the most important areas of black prairie soils occurs in the United States (PLATE v). There it forms a belt along the dry margins of the lateritic soils, the gray-brown podsolic soils, and the podsols. Through southeastern Europe and in isolated spots through central Asia, these soils occupy similar positions with respect to the other types. Other areas include a strip through Paraguay, northern Argentina, northern Uruguay, and southeastern Brazil in South America and two prominent patches in the Sudan region of Africa.

CHERNOZEMS • These soils are found on the dry margins of black prairie soils. They show a thick mat of grass roots at the surface, grading downward into a black A-horizon (FIG. 12–6F). With depth, the color shades through the browns to a lighter colored parent material. At a depth of from two to four feet, there is a layer of whitish nodules which are accumulations of calcium. Chernozem is only slightly leached, has a high organic content, and large amounts of available calcium. Consequently, its natural fertility is high. However, it is not well suited to the production of plants which demand large supplies of water for it occurs on the margins of the humid climates. Nevertheless, the chernozem belts have become the great surplus wheat-producing regions of the world.

In the Americas, there are two chernozem belts (PLATE v). One stretches from the Peace river country of Canada southeastward through the Dakotas to central Texas. The other forms a northward-jutting wedge from the Pampas of Argentina and southern Uruguay. In Eurasia, the chernozem belt extends from southern European Russia past the southern end of the Ural Mountains into southwestern Siberia. Surrounding the lateritic soils in Africa are narrow zones of soils so nearly like chernozems, even though they have a reddish cast, as to be called by the same name.

CHESTNUT AND BROWN SOILS • On the dry side of the chernozems, the soils are lighter in color and the layer of white nodules is closer to the surface (FIG. 12–6G). A thin mat of grass roots is underlain by slightly leached horizons which grade through lighter and lighter brown down to the calcium layer. In the chestnut soils, this layer may be as deep as three feet below the surface; in the brown soils, it may be as shallow as one foot.

The outstanding areas of chestnut and brown soils are those in the United States just east of the Rocky Mountains (PLATE v), in Argentina just east of the Andes Mountains, and in Australia, forming the fringes of that continent's desert heart. In the Soviet Union, chestnut and brown soils form a border for the chernozems from the Caspian shores to Lake Balkhash. In Africa, the greater part of the Sudan region and the wet margin of the Kalahari have soils of this type.

DESERT SOILS • Where desert soils exist, they are very shallow. Seldom do they measure more than a few inches from the top to the bottom of the profile (FIG. 12–6H). Grayish and only slightly altered parent material is closely underlain by a zone of calcium nodules. Because of the slight degree of leaching, desert soils are often of quite high fertility when water is made available to them.

The distribution of desert soils corresponds closely to that of Arid (BW) climates (PLATE v).

Upland Soils

Because of the significance of slope in their development, the soils of mountain regions show less distinctly the controls of climate and vegetation. In some mountain areas, soils do attain some of the characteristics of the zonal types, but distribution is spotty just as it is with mountain climate and mountain vegetation. Consequently, no attempt has been made to indicate the detailed variations on a world scale. The outline of the world pattern of mountain soils (PLATE v) is the same as that of mountain climate (PLATE IV), mountain surface (FIG. 7–2), and mountain vegetation (PLATE VI).

MAN AND SOILS

THE discussion of soils so far has stressed what may be called the "natural" agents and processes of soil formation and the resultant nature and distribution of zonal soils. Nevertheless, it must not be forgotten that, in many parts of the world, man has altered and continues to alter the environment in which soils develop. Among other things, he has changed the rate at which natural processes operate; some of them are speeded, others are retarded, and still others are made completely inactive. He has likewise affected the agents of soil formation: water has been increased or decreased in amount, humus has been destroyed or added, and soil life has been altered. Such actions have not destroyed the general world pattern of zonal soils, but locally they have made profound changes.

In detail, no single human act produces the same result in all soils; each soil reacts to man's efforts in its own way. Yet, certain common practices have definite general results in all soil evolution.

Some Changes in Soil Environment Induced by Man

VEGETATION REMOVAL • When man begins to cultivate land, his first action is to remove the cover of natural vegetation, or as much of it as he can. Many primitive peoples, like those of the Amazon forest, burn off the smaller plants and girdle the larger and taller ones so that they die. Other more advanced peoples cut down the forest and remove the stumps. Pastoral peoples are also indirectly responsible for vegetation removal through the feeding habits of their animals. Up to a point, this removal may not be serious. On the other hand, when too many animals are pastured in a given area or when they crop the grass too closely in their feeding as sheep often do, bare surface is exposed. Gradually, the original vegetation is either completely destroyed or is in part replaced by other types.

Whether it is in forest or grassland, destruction of vegetation removes one of the natural controls of soil formation. It also removes a major soil constituent, humus. The balance of the whole soil environment is upset. With that comes a change in soil life and a change in erodibility of the soil itself.

CULTIVATION • When soil is brought under cultivation, both its texture and its structure are modified. Digging and plowing may bring the B-horizon to the surface and bury the A-horizon beneath it. Constant working, as with a hoe or cultivator, alters soil structure by breaking up the grouping of soil particles at the surface. In consequence, natural processes of soil formation are materially altered. For example, a mixture of coarse particles from an A-horizon with fine particles from a B-horizon decreases the size of spaces between individual particles near the soil surface. The effect of this is to retard the downward movement of gravitational water and, at the same time, increase the supply of capillary water. Both leaching and eluviation are thereby reduced.

Beyond mechanical changes which accompany cultivation, there are those which result from the growing of a new cover. The new plants may have a different root structure as, for example, that of a grain crop compared with a forest. This means different feeding habits; grains derive most of their food from the soil proper, whereas trees obtain a large share of theirs from parent material. Also, the absence of roots following extensive clearing, as of a forest, alters the environment for soil life. Then, too, when the crops are harvested, the greater part of the plant cover is removed. Thus, the chemical elements on which the crop feeds are permanently removed and, unless they are artificially replaced, the soil is impoverished.

Again, continued cultivation of the soil makes it easily susceptible to increased surface erosion by both running water and wind. When vegetation is heavy and the upper surface of the soil is not broken, individual particles are not easily removed. Runoff of rain water is reduced by plant cover and downward percolation is increased. Without plant cover, runoff is large in amount and the power of erosion is therefore great. Plants also protect the surface from the sweep of wind. A cultivated surface with fine soil particles laid bare facilitates removal by both water and wind.

MANAGEMENT • When man uses soil to produce the plants which he desires, he may follow certain practices which are calculated to make the soil more suitable for the plants he wishes to grow; this is called *soil management*. For example, an area may be cleared for the purpose of cultivation. After it is cleared,

it may be discovered that the soil, for one reason or another, is too moist for the desired use. Drainage must be improved, either by ditching or by some other means. In another locality, soil may be so coarse as to have excessive drainage. Then, some procedure must be adopted which will make up for the lack of moisture. In many areas where moisture is deficient either climatically or *edaphically* (i.e., for reasons pertaining to the soil), irrigation must be instituted before the soil can be made to produce. Whatever man does by management alters the action of the soil environment.

Some Problems Arising from Man's Use of the Soil

SOIL IMPROVEMENT • There is a distinction between soil fertility and soil productivity. Fertility implies the presence of the chemical elements necessary for specific plant growth in adequate amounts, properly balanced with the other elements, and readily available to the plant roots. A soil which is extremely fertile for potatoes may be quite infertile for wheat, since the potato needs certain chemicals in relatively large amounts while wheat needs others. Productivity, on the other hand, implies not only the proper constitution of the soil, but its proper management as well. By management, man can alter productivity materially and rapidly. He can therefore improve it from the point of view of his own use. He can supply more water to it or remove excess water from it; he can change structure by tillage; he can rotate crops so that certain soil minerals are replenished and proper balance insured; and he can add to the humus content by growing cover crops and plowing them under. Similarly, he can change the rate of surface erosion by planting certain crops to hold the soil in place. All of these practices come under the head of management. By good management, man can improve soil locally.

SOIL EXHAUSTION • All too commonly, man has brought about the destruction of soil

12–7   PERMANENT *pasture which shows severe gullying and sheet erosion in south-central New York. Snow lies in the gullies.*

either by exhausting its fertility or subjecting it to accelerated forces of surface erosion. Soil exhaustion, or loss of fertility, does not occur rapidly when natural forces are unhampered. Admittedly, heavy leaching and eluviation remove chemical elements from the A-horizon and change the texture and structure of the soil. But there is constant return of chemical elements from soil organisms and from the plants which clothe the surface. Growing plants take chemicals directly from the soil. When these plants die or lose leaves and branches, the chemicals are, in large part, returned to the top of the soil. From there, they are eventually reincorporated into the soil proper by the action of water and soil organisms. In the same way, the soil organisms themselves are part of the cycle.

When man clears land and plants a certain crop on it, he is indirectly removing part of the soil. In growing, the crops use certain chemicals just as the natural vegetation did. But at harvest, there is nearly complete removal of the plant cover; plant remains are not left to be reincorporated in the soil. If the process is repeated time after time, and if no procedure is established to replenish the elements lost, the soil becomes exhausted so far as those elements are concerned. Even if the weathering of the underlying rock releases a new supply, the natural replenishment rate is slow. From man's point of view, this results in smaller and smaller crop yields until, eventually, it is uneconomic to continue planting and harvest. In the past, the solution has frequently been land abandonment rather than corrective management, and a resource is lost.

SOIL EROSION • Abandonment of exhausted soil leaves an opening for accelerated erosion, especially if the soil is an upland one. With-

12–8 GULLYING *in these Georgia fields has created a miniature canyon cutting even into bedrock.*

out man's intervention, there normally is erosion of all upland soils and deposition of soil material in lowland areas. Youthful streams cutting into an interfluve wear away soil and carry it downstream perhaps to be deposited on the flood plain of an old valley or in a delta. But this normal process is slow. Among other things, it is partially restrained by vegetation cover. If man uses land until the soil is exhausted and then abandons it, if he manages it poorly, or if he simply removes the vegetation as in lumbering operations and abandons it, the work of running water and of wind is greatly speeded. Rills or sheet erosion developing on bare sloping fields during every rainstorm wash away a large part of the A-horizon (FIG. 12–7). Repetition soon creates gullies through which much of the B-horizon

is removed. In some instances, these gullies cut down through the C-horizon to underlying rock (FIG. 12–8). The soil is thus lost through "man-induced" erosion.

No process that man yet knows can speed up creation of new soil from rock. The relatively slow process of weathering followed by the alteration of the regolith by water, air, and living organisms produce soil only through very long periods of time. Once destroyed by man, this great resource is, for all practical purposes, irretrievably lost. By good management, flexibly applied for each soil, man can do much to conserve soil and to increase and sustain its productivity (FIG. 12–1). Yet, in so doing, he does not break the broad pattern created by the zonal soils, the great soil groups of the world.

Soils: Their Formation and Distribution

· REVIEW QUESTIONS ·

1. In your own words, describe the significance of soil to man.
2. Explain how horizons are developed in soil.
3. Suggest some reasons why the boundaries between soil horizons are sometimes sharp and sometimes indistinct.
4. Is color a good clue to major soil differences? Has soil color anything to do with soil fertility? Explain.
5. Account for the fact that soil particles vary in size. Just how does this create different soil textures?
6. If you were a farmer, would it make any difference to you whether the soil in a particular field was massive or granular? In what way?
7. It is common for both farmers and home gardeners to speak of hardpan. Do they use the term correctly? Is it possible to tell whether a soil is likely to have a hardpan before it is plowed or dug? Under what conditions might a hardpan be expected to be present?
8. Why is air essential in the soil? What would result if all air were excluded from all soils?
9. Suggest some ways in which organic matter is important as a soil component.
10. Is there any way in which leaching can be

stopped? Would a soil benefit, from the point of view of fertility, if leaching did not occur?

11. Choose one of the zonal soil types and analyze the part played in its development by each of the controls of the soil-forming processes.

12. Can all of the material at the surface of the earth be called mature soil? Illustrate your answer by reference to specific examples.

13. Are the majority of the world's soils zonal, intrazonal, or azonal? Explain your answer fully.

14. Why is it necessary, or even desirable, to recognize further division within the zonal soils?

15. What zonal soil is found in the Amazon Basin? In central Iowa? Give the major reasons for its existence in each area.

16. It is sometimes said, "Soil erosion might be a blessing in disguise for some areas in the rainy tropics." Is there any basis of fact for this statement? Propose a line of reasoning to support this contention.

17. Is it true that use of the soil by man always means its impairment or destruction?

18. If you were a farmer in the United States, in which of the zonal soil areas would you choose to have your farm? Discuss.

19. Of what significance is it that soil exhaustion be checked? That soil erosion be checked?

20. Soil erosion in the United States alone actually costs the people of the country billions of dollars per year. Suggest some of the ways, direct or indirect, in which these losses occur. Is the problem as severe in all parts of the world? Discuss a few remedies.

13–1

[OPPOSITE, TOP] ELK *at the edge of the forest in the Grand Teton National Park, Wyoming.*

13 Natural Vegetation and Animal Life

PHILIP GENDREAU

⟨ OUTSTANDING *variety in the human habitat is created by differences of vegetation cover from place to place. A forest landscape is distinctive, whether the land is flat or gently rolling, whether it is hilly or even mountainous. Lands with grassy cover look and are different from similar surfaces that are forested or barren. Woodland which is green throughout the year contrasts vividly with an area in which the trees lose their leaves during one season. From such easily observed characteristics comes some realization of the greater or lesser habitat value to man of one area as compared with another. For example, the forests of the Amazon Basin look and are different from those of Mediterranean Europe. When the Portuguese and Spanish encountered the Amazon forest during their exploration and colonization of*

South America, they found it to be a barrier which, to them, proved insurmountable. It was nothing like the forests they knew and used to their advantage in the Iberian Peninsula. For them, the Amazon forest had no habitat value.

Animal life, too, presents a further measure of habitat value. On the East African Plateau, the big game country, wild animals are an ever-present hazard both to human life and to property. Similarly, in Panama the yellow-fever mosquito created an inhospitable and dangerous habitat for man. Not until this insect pest was destroyed was it possible to construct the canal which links the Pacific with the Atlantic. Conversely, use of the northern forested area of Canada or of northeastern European Russia depends in large part upon the relatively dense population of fur-bearing animals.

Native vegetation cover and animal life were originally the direct bases for all human existence. They supplied the essentials of food and clothing. Both have been profoundly altered by human use of the land, particularly where men have congregated in large numbers. Certain plants provide food, others supply raw materials for commerce and industry, and some simply beautify the setting in which men live. Others have been removed. In densely populated regions, the selected few that have been retained or introduced from other areas may be only a pitiful reminder of a once luxuriant variety. Similarly, animals have been tamed to provide food, raw materials, labor, and even companionship. Others have been killed off, greatly reduced in numbers, or forced to migrate to areas less desired by man.

Where man's inroads have not been extensive, plants and animals stand as visible and direct indicators of the physical equipment of an area for human living. This is more obvious in the instance of vegetation, for plants are immobile. Their whole nature is determined by the combination of elements of the setting in the specific place in which they grow. Temperature and moisture, qualities of soil, and even details of surface all restrict the type of vegetation, so that actually the plant cover is the observable result of the combination of all.

Yet, in the broadest sense, climate exerts the principal influence on natural vegetation. Over large areas, the particular kind of plants is determined largely by temperature and moisture, both of which are primarily elements of climate. In more restricted areas, the nature of the soil may be an effective control. While a climate may be suitable for one characteristic plant cover, the soil may be so porous or so infertile as to prevent the growth of the expected types and to allow the growth of others in their stead. For example, a Semiarid (BS) climate has, in general, enough precipitation to support a continuous cover of grasses, though not enough for trees. Yet there are many *areas of Semiarid (BS) climate where the soil is so porous that it retains too little of the moisture which falls upon it to support even grass. In such places, desert plants take over. The vegetation is thus edaphically rather than climatically determined.*

Animals are less accurate indicators of the physical equipment of an area, for most of them can move about beyond the confines of any one small region for the food and water necessary to them. Animals therefore provide only an approximate measure of the quality of the setting. Our primary concern, then, is the world distribution of natural vegetation. This offers not only the most obvious clue to essential differences among habitats, but also a gauge of their desirability for human living.

MAJOR CATEGORIES OF VEGETATION AND ANIMAL LIFE

Plant Associations

FROM a world-wide viewpoint, there are three main plant associations. These are *forest*, *grassland*, and *desert* (FIGS. 13–1, 13–2, and 13–4). The number of specific plants which make up any one of these associations is almost infinite. However, it is on the dominant type of vegetation rather than on individual plants that attention must be focused when the world pattern is the subject of study. To be sure, trees are the dominant plants in a forest association, but there are many woody shrubs, grasses, and other ground-covering forms included in the association. Grassland is characterized, as the name implies, by grasses and other nonwoody plants, but it includes numbers of shrubs and even some trees. Similarly, desert associations often include many of the grasses, shrubs, and occasionally a few trees; the latter are the exception rather than the rule.

Vegetation cover in some areas appears to be neither forest, grassland, nor desert. It consists mainly of a thicketlike growth of low, woody plants, like the *chaparral* of California. Detailed studies would, of course, recognize in this type of cover a distinct association, *scrub* or *shrub*. But on a world scale, the common practice is to include this kind of vegetation within the forest association and to refer to it as *scrub forest*.

FOREST CHARACTERISTICS • The larger plants which make up the forest association demand more moisture than those of either grassland or desert. Water must be present in the soil in large enough amounts to satisfy the needs of the trees. This necessitates relatively large amounts of precipitation. Likewise, water must be present in the soil in a liquid state, rather than frozen, so that the plant roots may make use of it.

Plant growth generally ceases when air temperature drops below 42° F. Where temperatures that low or lower persist throughout most of the year, forest is usually lacking, either because the amount of precipitation common in areas of continued low temperature is too small for tree growth, or because the growth period (above 42° F.) is too short.

Variations in moisture and temperature are reflected in certain outstanding differences among trees. Some trees retain most of their foliage at all times. They do drop leaves, but

13–2   TYPICAL steppe, with its short-grass vegetation on the high plains of Kansas. The circular depression in the foreground is a buffalo wallow. Note the wheel tracks stretching straight across the surface toward the buildings in the background.

only one by one and never all at the same time. Such trees are known as *evergreens*. In contrast to these, there are other trees that lose all of their leaves at one season and acquire new ones at another season. Trees which show this seasonal rhythm are known as *deciduous* trees.

Where temperatures are always high and precipitation is heavy throughout the year, trees are evergreen, like the live oak and the red bay in the Gulf Coast region of the United States. Where there is a deficiency of moisture for an appreciable part of the year, either through lack of precipitation or through lowering of temperature so that the moisture is ice-locked and hence not available to the plant roots, a period of rest from growth is introduced into the annual cycle. Under these conditions, trees may be deciduous, like the maples, elms, and hickories of the northeastern United States.

Though the existence of a period of rest from growth may induce the deciduous habit just described, plant structures may be such as to make possible the retention of foliage

despite periodic lack of moisture. Reaction to dryness is often indicated by leaf form. A tree may be either *needleleaf*, like the pine, having leaves that are very narrow in proportion to their length, or *broadleaf*, like the maple, having leaves that are relatively wide in proportion to their length. Most needleleaf trees lose and add leaves regardless of the season, but they do not lose all of their leaves at any one time; that is, they are evergreens. Broadleaf trees may be either evergreen or deciduous.

The more common needleleaf trees develop their fruit in the form of woody cones. They are, therefore, commonly referred to as *conifers* or *coniferous trees*.

On the basis of the characteristics described above, four main kinds of trees may be distinguished. These are: broadleaf evergreen, broadleaf deciduous, needleleaf evergreen, and needleleaf deciduous. There are whole forests dominated by each of the first three types. For example, the forests in areas of Tropical Rainforest (Af) climate are made up predominantly of broadleaf evergreen trees; those in areas of

Humid Continental climate with hot summers (Dfa and Dwa), of broadleaf deciduous trees; and those in areas of Subarctic (Dfc and Dfd) climate, of needleleaf evergreens. Trees of the fourth type, needleleaf deciduous, do not commonly occur as a distinct forest type. Needleleaf deciduous trees, like the larch, occur rather as individuals within forests dominated by other kinds of trees.

GRASSLAND CHARACTERISTICS • Grassland (FIGS. 13–2, 13–3) has typically a smooth cover of vegetation only occasionally interrupted by isolated trees. In some places, low woody plants are intermixed with the grass, but nowhere are they so numerous as to dominate. The grasses vary in height from a few inches to several feet, depending largely upon the climate and soil. Most of the individual plants are *perennials;* that is, they continue their growth from year to year. A few of them are *annuals* that complete their life cycle during a single growth season, but leave seeds which reproduce the cycle the next season.

Grass needs less moisture than trees do; hence it forms the normal vegetation in drier parts of the world. But as dryness increases, as along the boundary between the Semiarid (BS) and Arid (BW) climates, grassland gives way to desert vegetation.

DESERT CHARACTERISTICS • In contrast to forests and grasslands, the vegetation of the deserts, both the deserts of dryness (FIG. 13–4) and those of continued cold, is relatively light or almost entirely lacking. There is no continuous cover like that formed by the grasses, and no close crowding of plants as in most forests. Yet the desert, except for the icy wastes of the Arctic and Antarctic, is seldom without some vegetation. Very little of the world's land area is completely barren. An absolutely bare, sandy waste—the popular concept of a desert—is infrequently encountered. To be sure, there are some areas where sand and rock seem to exist without any plant cover, but close examination normally reveals the presence of at least a few specially adapted plants. Individual plants are

13–3

A MAN-MADE prairie. Second-year stand of a grass similar to the original prairie cover, near Mankato, Kansas.

widely scattered and many of them are dormant throughout the greater part of the year, but, following one of the irregular rains which characterize desert regions, the barrenness is soon dispelled. Plants in profusion burst into active life, hurrying to complete the growth cycle while moisture is available.

All the plants in the desert association are *xerophytic;* that is, they are plants that are structurally adapted to a limited supply of water. Both *perennials* whose growth period may be short or even intermittent and *annuals* that are able to complete their cycle quickly are included. Particularly striking are the many *succulents,* or watery-tissued forms, like the cactus, capable of storing moisture for long periods of dryness.

Included within the desert association are the *tundras* (FIG. 13–5) which fringe the poleward edges of the forest association. Tundra is the name applied to the particular group of plants like mosses, lichens, sedges, some grasses and bushes, and even stunted trees that exist where continued low temperatures produce extremely adverse conditions of growth. It should be noted that the word tundra is often used

Major Categories of Vegetation and Animal Life | 313

13-4

DESERT *vegetation in the American southwest.*

to mean the area where this kind of vegetation is found as well as the vegetation association itself. During most of the year, water is present only in the form of ice and is hence not available to the plants. During the very short period of temperatures high enough to allow plant growth, there is usually an excess of water resulting primarily from poor drainage and low evaporation. Slopes are commonly very gentle in tundra regions, and this hinders rapid surface drainage; temperatures are rarely high enough for a sufficiently long period to bring about thawing of the subsoil, so that underground drainage is impeded. Excessive water about the plant roots retards the growth processes with much the same result as too little water. Though for different reasons from those applicable in the dry deserts, most of the individual plants which make up the tundra vegetation, or *cold desert*, are xerophytic. It is

mainly for this reason that tundra is classed as part of the desert association.

Natural Vegetation Types

The major plant associations are composed of distinctive *types*, or minor associations, indicated in TABLE 14. Each type will be characterized and its distribution outlined later in this chapter.

Within mountainous regions, there is usually a combination of several of the vegetation types listed in TABLE 14. The expression *mountain vegetation* is used to convey this idea despite the fact that the combination changes from one mountain area to another. In a sense, mountain vegetation forms an added type.

Native Animal Types

As has been previously suggested, any attempt at fixing exactly the distribution of native animal life is seriously handicapped by the mobility of the animal population. Though animals are usually limited to certain rather broad ranges within which they find the necessities of life, most of them do not remain fixed

URBAN C. NELSON, U.S. FISH AND WILDLIFE SERVICE

13-5

TUNDRA *on the Colville river delta in northern Alaska. Note the flowering plants (marsh marigold) which fringe the small pond in the foreground while ice still covers the larger pond in the background.*

TABLE 14

Natural Vegetation Types

I. FOREST ASSOCIATION
  A. Tropical forests
    1. Tropical rainforest or selva
    2. Tropical semideciduous or monsoon forest
    3. Tropical scrub or thorn forest
  B. Middle and high latitude forests
    1. Mediterranean scrub forest
    2. Broadleaf and mixed broadleaf-coniferous forest
    3. Coniferous forest

II. GRASSLAND ASSOCIATION
  A. Tropical grassland or savanna
  B. Middle latitude grasslands
    1. Steppe
    2. Prairie

III. DESERT ASSOCIATION
  A. Desert shrub and barren desert
  B. Tundra

in any one small region. Their distribution can be suggested only roughly as a sort of adjunct to that of natural vegetation.

Most animals can be divided broadly into two main groups: the *herbivores* and the *carnivores*. Herbivores, or herbivorous animals, are those that secure their food directly from plants. Ground animals of small size like the rabbit, larger ones like the deer, and tree-living (*arboreal*) forms like the monkey are herbivores. It is obvious that they must live where the plants upon which they depend for food grow. A monkey would find it difficult to live in a grassland just as a horse would in a desert. Often, also, animal distribution is limited directly by climate. While the monkey is an arboreal animal, he would be unable to withstand the rigors of a Subarctic (Dfc) climate even though that climate normally is a forest-producing one. In a general way, there is a certain degree of correspondence of the pattern of animal distribution to that of vegetation types. For example, the giraffe, as a native animal, is seldom found outside tropical grasslands, or *savannas*. This is not to say that the giraffe is common in *all* savannas.

The flesh-eating animals, or carnivores, like lions, tigers, and wolves, depend upon herbivores for their food supply. Consequently, the distribution of carnivores mirrors not only that of the herbivores, but, indirectly, that of the natural vegetation types.

Many animals are *omnivorous*; that is, they eat both plants and other animals. Frequently, the struggle for adequate food makes them omnivores; when there is a plentiful food supply, they are entirely herbivorous or entirely carnivorous. Many of our domestic animals are omnivorous, but, in their original wild state, this was true only under great stress. The dog may prefer meat; he belongs to the same general group as the wolf. Yet more often than not, the dog is fed items which are made from plant products; seldom does he have an entire meat diet.

Birds, insects, and reptiles all add their bit to the various habitats of the world's land surface; so do fish and other water-living forms to the earth's waters. Only loosely is there a correlation between their distribution and that of certain vegetation types for, like other animals, they are mobile. The migration of many of the northern forest animals poleward onto the tundra during the summer and back again to the forest during the winter is paralleled by the seasonal migration of many birds. The appearance of the robin in New England in early spring gives indication that the long winter is over, just as a high, southward flight of geese in perfect V formation on a snappy, clear fall morning presages the coming of winter. The furious buzz of the June bug against the screen is an indicator of early summer just as is the stinging attack of the mosquito or the irritation engendered by the ubiquitous housefly. In climates without great seasonal change, the presence of many of these animals is a permanent part of the physical scene; where seasonal change is noticeable, the animals come and go.

VEGETATION TYPES AND THEIR DISTRIBUTION

Tropical Forests

ONE of the heaviest forest covers to be found anywhere in the world exists in the regions of Tropical Rainforest (Af) climate. Constant heavy precipitation and constantly high temperatures, the two characteristics of the Tropical Rainforest (Af) climate, provide the condition for a vast "natural greenhouse" in which the forest is evergreen and broadleaf. As one proceeds away from the regions of Tropical Rainforest (Af) climate through Tropical Monsoon (Am) and Savanna (Aw) zones, the optimum conditions for forest development vanish. Increased prominence of the dry season over the rainy season soon removes the possibility of broadleaf evergreen forest. Smaller and smaller amounts of precipitation compel a thinning of the forest and a decrease in the size of the individual plants until finally a limit is reached beyond which it is too dry for trees. Even in sufficiently wet areas, the existence of definite cool and hot seasons beyond the margins of the Tropical Moist (A) climates brings about a change in species which make up the forest so that the whole aspect is altered. In such areas, the tropical forest is supplanted by a middle latitude forest.

Three major forest types may be recognized in tropical regions. Transition from one to another is gradual and often the types are intermingled along wide zones rather than cut off sharply. Nevertheless, marked distinctions set them apart from one another. The three specific types of tropical forest are *tropical rainforest*, *tropical semideciduous forest*, and *tropical scrub forest*. These are often called *selva*, *monsoon forest*, and *thorn forest*, respectively. In addition to the major types, there are three associated secondary ones. These are *mangrove*, *jungle*, and *galeria forest*. Each of the three major types will be treated separately while the secondary types, usually occurring in such small areas as to be impossible to illustrate on maps of the scale used in this book, will be treated only in terms of their specific relationship to the others (FIG. 13–6).

TROPICAL RAINFOREST OR SELVA • Selva is the most luxuriant of the various tropical forest types. From the air, it resembles a rolling green sea. Tall trees crowd so closely together that their crowns form a dense irregular canopy through which very little sunlight penetrates to the ground. On close examination, the crowns are seen to be arranged in layers or stories. The lowest lies at about 75 feet above the ground, the second at about 100 feet. Above that second story extend the upper trunks, branches, and foliage of the forest giants rising to 125 feet or more. Except where the forest has been removed, the canopy of leaves is unbroken. As a result, the interior of the forest is dark and the air in it is still and moist. Trunks rise straight and branchless to the crowns, which are always green, for water is continuously available to the tree roots. So plentiful is the moisture supply that the trees are usually shallow-rooted, and depend largely on buttresslike ridges at the base of the trunks for their support. The trees are broadleaf evergreens; though a tremendous number of species is included, rarely are there sizable stands of any one species. Where the forest is undisturbed by man, it is unusual to find more than

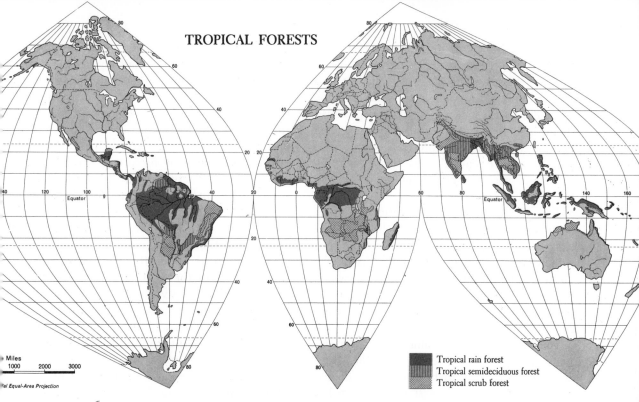

Miles
1000   2000   3000

al Equal-Area Projection

Tropical rain forest
Tropical semideciduous forest
Tropical scrub forest

13–6   THE *tropical forests of the world occur in most of the northern two-thirds of South America, the southern half of Africa, and South and Southeast Asia and neighboring archipelagoes.*

three or more individuals of any one species in an acre of forest.

Though the forest is evergreen, there is constant loss of leaves from each tree throughout the year. On the tree, there is equally constant leaf replacement. Thus, a steady supply of dead and decaying matter falls to the forest floor and it might be expected that litter would accumulate in large amounts. However, the rapidity of decay under such hot, moist conditions as prevail within the forest, and the activities of insects like termites and wood beetles, are so great as to remove most of the material almost as it falls. Consequently, the floor of the selva is remarkably clean. In addition, the absence of sunlight prevents the growth of much underbrush. Movement through the forest is, therefore, little restricted.

Characteristic also of the selva is the unusually large number of *epiphytes* and *parasites.*

Epiphytes grow on other plants, but do not secure their food from them; parasites grow on and do secure their food directly from other plants. In great profusion, both sorts hang ropelike from the tree crowns or jut out from the trunks. Many of them, such as the orchids, which are epiphytes, are brilliantly flowering. Together with the density of the trees, they convey the impression of superabundant plant life. This kind of forest is often incorrectly called jungle.

Jungle is dense undergrowth or second growth in tropical forest areas. It occurs only where sunlight can penetrate to the forest floor. In most selva, the shading of the forest floor is so complete that only removal of the tree crowns will admit the sunlight necessary for heavy ground-plant growth. This occurs characteristically in three kinds of places.

Where man clears the forest or where light-

Vegetation Types and Their Distribution | 317

ning strikes and burns it, dormant plant seeds are quick to germinate and the struggle toward the sun begins. Thousands of plants in a tangled thicket vie with each other for the space left by the fallen giants which preceded them. This is ordinarily *dry jungle,* so called because the plants rise from relatively dry and firm ground. Eventually, the faster growing and larger specimens crowd out the others and the spot of jungle disappears.

The second characteristic location of jungle is on steeply sloping land where the sun's rays can penetrate between the tree trunks and thus come to the forest floor. This is also dry jungle, but it is often more permanent than that which springs up in clearings, for the trunks of the trees provide less shade than do interlocked crowns.

The third location of jungle is in the wet spots of the tropical forests: along the banks of streams too wide to be completely shaded by the crowns of the forest giants on either side, on the flood plains of mature and old-age rivers, on shelving lake shores, or near the seaward edges of low coastal plains. This is the *wet jungle.* The dense tangle of vegetation rises directly from shallow water or from deep mud. It is difficult to tell where the land begins and the water leaves off. Myriads of insects and many reptiles make the wet jungle a place to be avoided. Wet jungle is much more permanent than dry jungle, for the places in which it occurs are usually too moist for most of the tree species found in the selva.

It is the wet jungle which gave rise to the idea of jungle as the usual vegetation type in equatorial regions. As early explorers penetrated the land along great rivers, their way lay between jungle-fringed banks. Seldom did this jungle stretch back from the river for more than a few hundred yards, but to most explorers attempting to find a route away from the stream, the dense vegetation seemed to continue without end. From this came the inference that jungle persisted throughout in these latitudes. Actually, once the jungle fringe

is breached and the forest attained, undergrowth usually becomes relatively light.

Another of the secondary types, *mangrove,* is found where tropical forest comes down to the sea or to a tidal inlet. Mangrove is sometimes spoken of as a kind of wet jungle. It becomes established on very shelving, muddy coasts where there is no strong current and only moderate fluctuations in the level of the sea between high and low tide. At low tide, tripodlike prop roots rise out of the mud flats, the roots of one individual mangrove interlocked with those of the next to form a close-knit wall. Well above the place where the roots rise out of the mud, and just above the level of high tide, heavily leafed branches bush out. At high tide, the fringe of green may stand a considerable distance out from the shore. The roots are then entirely covered by water. So thick is the barrier formed by mangrove that sediments brought from the land by the rivers are held close to the shore. A mangrove fringe thus acts as a "land builder" along shelving tropical shores.

Where rivers cut deeply into the land, selva is often confined to valley sides or levees, and lighter forest dominates the interstream spaces. If the band of selva along either bank is narrow, quite distinct from the lighter forest of the lands back from the river, and if the tree crowns meet over the stream, the impression is created of a green tunnel through which the river flows. This type of forest is known as a *galeria* forest. Most commonly it occurs where the river flood plains make moisture available to the trees despite a climatic dry season. In other words, the long fingers of tropical forest which reach into tropical grassland are the ones to which the term galeria is most commonly applied. It is equally applicable, though not so easily noticeable, where narrow bands of selva penetrate into regions clothed with tropical semideciduous or tropical scrub forests.

Animal life in the selva is primarily arboreal, or tree-dwelling. Ground animals are few and of small size, for food is difficult to secure on the floor of the forest. There, only myriads of insects add their constant hum to the gloomy, dripping wetness. High above in the crowns of the trees, brilliantly colored birds, monkeys and other similar animals, insects, and reptiles seeking sunshine make up for the quiet of the forest depths. Most of the tree animals are herbivorous, but there are a few small carnivores. Colorful and profuse as this tree life is, it offers relatively little to man as an added resource of the forest.

Selva constitutes one of the most extensive types of forest remaining in the world. Destruction and alteration of it have been great in a few localities, such as Java and India, but elsewhere little of the selva has been entirely removed. Where clearings have been made, regrowth is rapid unless measures are taken to restrict it. Rubber, cacao, cabinet woods like mahogany and ebony, many gums and resins, and both edible and commercial nuts are all derived from trees native to the selva. (In addition to their use as food, nuts sometimes are the basic raw material in the manufacture of soap and fertilizer.) Many tropical fruits have local use and some, like the banana, are significant items of world trade. But throughout the selva, there is one great handicap to intensive utilization. The trees of any one species are widely scattered and, unless some device like the creation of an artificial forest similar to those of the Malayan rubber plantations is resorted to, small-scale forest industries cannot operate efficiently or without great cost. In lumbering, for instance, selective logging rather than "over-all" logging must be practiced. Distance from world markets and from large supplies of labor adds materially to the difficulties of exploitation. It is generally suggested by foresters and lumbermen that, with large-scale operations, it is possible to assemble many different kinds of wood instead of carrying on selective logging and thus to exploit tropical forests economically. Despite this suggestion, selva products, except for a few items

like Brazil nuts or chicle, an important ingredient of chewing gum, remain luxury goods.

The largest areas of continuous selva occur in South America and in equatorial Africa. Less extensive areas of this type of forest are to be found in Middle America, southeastern Asia, and the East Indies.

There is close correspondence between the distribution of selva and Tropical Rainforest (Af) climate, as can be seen from a comparison of PLATES IV and VI. Nevertheless, the correspondence is not complete. In Liberia, for example, the vegetation is selva, but the climate is Tropical Monsoon (Am). Here, even though there is a period of less rain, soil moisture is never insufficient to satisfy the needs of the forest. Minor discrepancies of this sort result from many causes; prominent among them are edaphic factors (factors concerning the soil), lack of numerous long-time climatic observations, and lack of exact information regarding the detailed distribution of vegetation types. Despite such minor discrepancies, the similarity of climate and vegetation patterns on a world scale is pronounced. This applies not only to the selva and Tropical Rainforest (Af) climate, but to all of the natural vegetation types and the climates in which they characteristically occur.

TROPICAL SEMIDECIDUOUS OR MONSOON FOREST • Beyond the limits of Tropical Rainforest (Af) and the wetter portions of Tropical Monsoon (Am) climate, increased severity of the dry season enforces more and more strongly a period of rest in plant growth. The forest becomes lighter, the individual trees more widely spaced, and the low undergrowth heavier. Pure stands of one species are common, like the teak forests of Burma. The forest is semideciduous; the dry season prevents most of the trees from being evergreen. Some of the trees do retain their foliage, but by far the greater part of the forest is dry and brown throughout the nearly rainless period. Many of the species common to the selva are found in this monsoon forest, but a large number of them that are evergreen in the selva are deciduous in the monsoon forest.

Jungle is more truly typical in monsoon forest than in selva because of the wider spacing of the big trees. As a result, passage throughout this forest is much more difficult than it is through the selva. Only here and there, particularly on low river flood plains or on low-lying coastal strips, is there a sufficient number of broadleaf evergreens so that sunlight is cut off from the forest floor and jungle is thereby eliminated. Mangrove is a characteristic coastal fringe, and narrow stringers of galeria point out the river courses across low-lying plains.

Areas of monsoon forest are generally more easily cleared by primitive groups because of the smaller size of the ground plants. Consequently, there are fewer and less extensive areas of it remaining. Commercial operations to recover forest products are easier than they are in the selva, for the more frequent stands of one individual species make possible economic utilization of the resource. Among the trees of this forest which are of great commercial significance is teak, which is particularly desirable because of its strength and durability.

Tropical semideciduous forest is generally found in areas of Tropical Monsoon (Am) climate and in the wetter parts of areas of Savanna (Aw) climate. Its greatest extent is on the continent of Asia (FIG. 13–6), where it stretches, with some interruption from other vegetation types, from the Western Ghats of India to the northeast coast of Australia. Other areas of tropical semideciduous forest occur in Africa, South America, Middle America, and the West Indies.

TROPICAL SCRUB OR THORN FOREST · As the annual rainfall decreases and the dry season becomes longer within areas of Tropical Moist (A) climate, not only does the forest change to a lighter, entirely deciduous type, but it even acquires characteristics which are definitely xerophytic. Low-growing trees with thick bark, smaller leaves, and thorns replace those of the semideciduous forest or selva (FIG.

13–7). Undergrowth increases in density and many thorny plants replace soft-tissued ones. The forest looks almost like scrubby second growth. In some places, it is so scattered and grasses take over so much of the space between trees and bushes that the name forest hardly seems applicable. In other places, a dense tangle of gigantic brambles with many low trees jutting above it seems to be fully as luxuriant as the selva during the wet season; during the dry season, the leafless, thorn-covered branches intertwine to form a brown, impenetrable wall.

Along river flood plains galeria forest makes a break here and there in the scrubbiness of the cover, much of which may justly be called jungle, though of a dry sort. Mangrove only infrequently forms a characteristic green fringe in areas where thorn forest comes to the sea.

In both the tropical semideciduous and the tropical scrub forests, ground animals are numerous. Many large herbivores, like the elephant in Asia and Africa or the giraffe in Africa, live on the margins of these forests where they give way to tropical grasslands. The larger carnivorous forms like the lion and the tiger make the lighter woodland fringes their usual home, migrating with the movements of the herbivores out onto the grasslands and back into the forests. Arboreal animals, birds, insects, and reptiles are even more numerous than in the heaviest selva. The forest-grassland margin in the tropics supports the world's densest remaining native animal population. This is especially true where human beings are few, as in central Africa, but even in the heavily peopled regions of Asia, destruction of life and property by animals is so common as to provide a serious handicap to the maintenance of human settlement.

The areas of tropical scrub forest (FIG. 13–6) lie adjacent to the other types of tropical forest in Africa, Asia, Australia, and South America. The tropical scrub forest is actually a transition belt between the denser forests and the grasslands.

13–7   THESE two views from Brazil suggest the variety to be found in the tropical scrub forest. Right: A wet phase, known as the campo cerrado, north of São Patricio in the State of Goiás. Left: A dry phase, known as caatinga, west of Campina Grande in the State of Paraíba.

Tropical Grassland or Savanna

Within areas of Savanna (Aw) climate, the total amount of precipitation decreases as one moves poleward toward the dry lands and as one moves from east coasts toward the interior. Decrease in total annual precipitation means less and less moisture for the support of tree cover. At the same time, there is an increase in the length of the dry season which likewise produces conditions unsuited to tree growth. First, as we have seen in the discussion of the tropical forests, the trees acquire the deciduous habit; then they become of smaller stature and are more and more widely scattered. As trees cease to be the dominating forms, first bushes and then grasses take over. Eventually, the land is characterized by grass cover rather than by forests. These are the tropical grasslands, or *savannas*, and they extend generally from areas of drier Savanna (Aw) climate well into the regions of Semiarid (BS) climate. Along their drier margins, these grasslands are sometimes spoken of as *tropical steppes* (FIG. 13–8).

The grasses of the savannas generally are coarse and rank-growing. Most of the plants grow singly, though some grow in clumps or tufts. In either instance, there is considerable bare ground between the plants; no turf or sod is formed. At the beginning of the rainy

13–8

TYPICAL dry-margin savanna near Kimberley, Republic of South Africa.

Vegetation Types and Their Distribution | 321

13–9   THE savanna of eastern Colombia seen from the foothills of the Andes. Note the galeria forest along the stream courses.

season, young blades of a dull green color, looking something like oats, shoot up rapidly. As the plants mature, the blades become stiff and sharp-edged; eventually they attain a height of from two to twelve feet. With the coming of the dry season, the grasses dry out to a dusty brownish color and slump to the ground.

It is almost impossible to set any precise limit to the wet edge of the savanna, for the forest dies out irregularly and spottily. Where· savanna abuts upon selva, there are grass-covered openings within the forest on one side of the boundary and clumps of selva trees scattered irregularly through the grass on the other side. When clumps of trees are dotted through grassy plains, the cover is called *park grassland*. Where savanna joins tropical semi-deciduous or scrub forest, a scattering of grassy

openings within the forest gives way to a dotting of low trees and bushes through the grass, and the cover is known as *scattered tree savanna* (FIG. 13–9). Another common type, especially in Africa, finds the continuity of the grass broken by the occurrence of flat-topped acacia trees; this is called either *acacia–tall grass savanna* or *acacia–desert grass savanna*, depending upon the luxuriance of the grass mantle growing between the trees. In some places, the land is covered by grasses uninterrupted by either trees or shrubs and the grasses may be higher than a man on horseback. All gradations from what is almost a forest through to the surface which has no continuous cover are included under the broad heading of savanna or tropical grassland, just so long as grass is the dominant plant form. It is a vegetation type which reflects limited available water

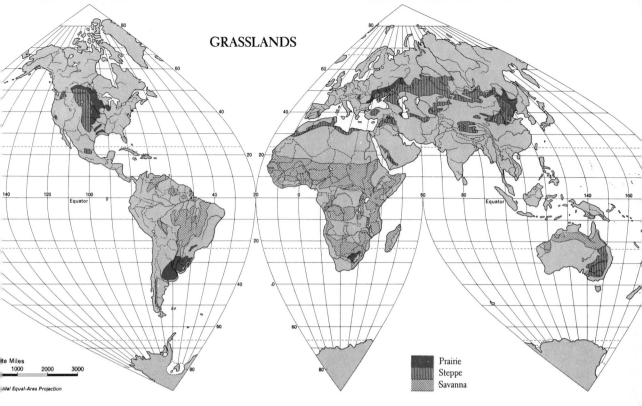

GRASSLANDS

Prairie
Steppe
Savanna

ite Miles
1000   2000   3000

idal Equal-Area Projection

13–10   THE grasslands of the world cover large portions of all the continents except Europe and Antarctica.

supply combined with constantly high temperatures throughout the year.

Because the savannas provide easily accessible food for many herbivorous animals, both from the grass and from the foliage of the low trees, they generally have a large native animal population. Numerous herbivores obviously attract a large population of carnivores, insects, and reptiles. Grass and brush offer optimum conditions for insect life, especially during the steamy dampness of the rainy season. Termites, mosquitoes, and other insects like the tsetse fly, carrier of the dreaded sleeping sickness, abound. Large numbers of reptiles and birds find ample food in the form of insects and small ground animals.

The animal population of the savannas benefits and increases also because of the absence of great numbers of humans. The difficulties, for primitive peoples, of clearing the land of its heavy cover of grass, of overcoming

insects or the danger of destruction by carnivorous animals, of adapting to seasonal water deficiency or seasonal flood destruction—all these make the savannas less desirable as human habitats than many other regions of the world. Thus these difficulties help to preserve native animal life.

There are tropical grasslands in Africa, South America, and Australia (FIG. 13–10), where they abut upon or are enclosed by some type of tropical forest (PLATE VI). On their dry sides, the savannas give way to desert.

Though the vegetation map of the world (PLATE VI) shows a sharp boundary between the tropical forests and the tropical grasslands, there are actually many fingers of galeria forest reaching out into the grasslands along the rivers. Similarly, many small clumps of forest trees interrupt the grassland. But both the galeria forests and the clumps are too small to be shown on maps of this scale.

Vegetation Types and Their Distribution | 323

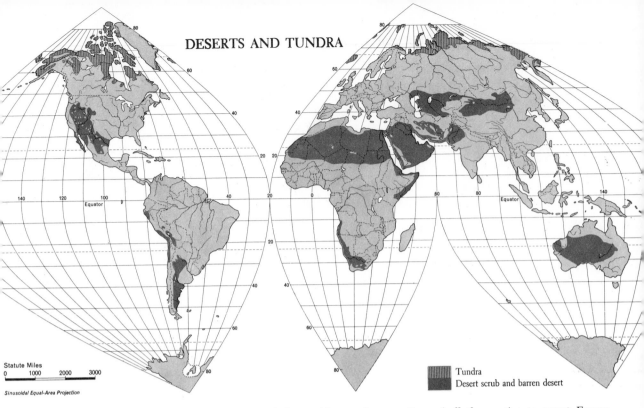

Statute Miles
0   1000   2000   3000

Sinusoidal Equal-Area Projection

Tundra
Desert scrub and barren desert

13–11   THE *deserts and tundras of the world cover large portions of all the continents except Europe and Antarctica.*

Desert Shrub and Barren Desert

Only xerophytes can find sufficient moisture to form a permanent, even though thin and scattered, vegetation in the drier parts of the low latitudes and on into the drier middle latitude areas, the areas of Arid (BW) climate. Some places are even so dry as to prevent the precarious foothold of stunted bushes and bunch grass; in those places, sand and rock wastes, seemingly interminable, stretch without a vestige of plant cover. Actually, little of the surface is absolutely barren, but only along occasional watercourses or close-grouped about the infrequent springs is the vegetation even temporarily heavy. Over most of the land small patches of short grass or isolated bushes gain a foothold. Most of the time they are brown and lifeless, but when water becomes available, a

bright green coloring makes sharp contrast with the soft browns and yellows or the brilliant reds of the rock and sand. Desert vegetation begins where dominant grass cover ends; both on the equatorward and on the poleward sides, grass borders the desert.

Most of the world's deserts extend from tropical west coasts inland and poleward. In all of them, the plants are xerophytic and sparse. The greatest of all deserts is the Sahara, which has its beginning on the west coast of Africa (FIG. 13–11) and stretches 3500 miles across the northern part of the continent. Throughout its whole length, it is seldom less than 1000 miles wide. From the Red Sea, desert continues, with occasional interruptions, into the heart of Asia. Other less extensive deserts exist in Africa, Australia, South America, and North America.

Middle Latitude Grasslands

Except where it comes to the sea, desert vegetation normally gives way to grass. As along other vegetation boundaries, the change is a gradual one. As one passes to wetter and wetter regions, grass becomes more and more luxuriant until it, in turn, gives way to forest. Through the zone in which grass is dominant, two distinct types, *steppe* and *prairie*, are recognized: *steppe* is a short-grass cover in which individual plants usually form a continuous mat some four to eight inches in height, and *prairie* is a tall-grass cover, also continuous, but with a height of from one and a half to two feet on the average. The boundary between the two corresponds roughly to that between the Semiarid (BS) climates and the humid types like Humid Subtropical (Cfa) and Humid Continental (Dfa). Most of the steppe lies in areas of Semiarid (BS) climate, and most of the prairie on the drier margins of the humid types, as in the Great Plains of the United States.

STEPPE • The term *steppe* as here used is applied to short-grass areas within the middle latitudes (FIG. 13–2). Sometimes, the expression *tropical steppe* is used to describe the drier margins of the savanna. These are, to be sure, characterized by relatively short grass, yet there are frequently included many scattered xerophytic shrubs and even a few spindly, stunted trees. In this way, the tropical steppe differs radically from the middle latitude short-grass areas. In the latter, the matlike carpet of grassy plants extends mile after mile without noticeable interruption by trees or shrubs except near some wet spot or along a stream.

Like savanna, steppe once provided a suitable habitat for herbivorous animals, though, since the cover was less heavy, fewer individuals could be supported by it. Carnivorous animals too were originally present, but they were fewer than in savanna. Lower temperatures and a smaller animal population supported a reduced insect and reptile life; for this reason, the steppes were even more habitable for some animals than were the savannas. Floods and droughts were less severe because rainy and dry seasons were less pronounced than in areas of Savanna (Aw) climate or in areas of Semiarid (BS) climate adjacent to Savanna (Aw). But, because of this very desirability, man could and did make greater inroads upon the steppes. Native animals like the American buffalo were killed off or driven out, and much of the land was brought under the plow. Except in the African and possibly the Australian steppes, man, with the plants and animals he has domesticated, now dominates.

The distribution of steppes over the world is shown in FIG. 13–10. It should be noted that steppes fringe the edges of the deserts in the middle latitudes (PLATE VI).

PRAIRIE • Most of the world's prairie has been destroyed either by being plowed up in the advance of agriculture from wetter lands, as in the westward spread of settlement in the United States, or by being invaded by domesticated plants, as in the Argentine Pampas.

Prairie is a distinct type of middle latitude vegetation (FIG. 13–3). Its most extensive development was found in the Americas (FIG. 13–10) before the coming of the white man. Spreading out from the face of the southern Canadian Rocky Mountains, it formed a crescent which extended eastward to Winnipeg and crossed into the United States in North Dakota and western Minnesota. It widened southward to include central Illinois and a small portion of Indiana, and then narrowed to pinch out in central Texas. Outlying bits fringed the Gulf Coast of Texas and Louisiana. In South America, the Argentine Pampas, and the Argentine Mesopotamia, the whole of Uruguay, and the southernmost part of Brazil formed the world's second largest prairie region. In Africa, a small triangle of prairie occurred in eastern Orange Free State and Basutoland, where it occupied an unusual position as a transition from steppe to savanna (PLATE VI). Its occurrence there resulted primarily from lower temperatures induced by the considerable elevation of this portion of the South African Plateau. In Europe, the Hungarian Plain, the Walachian Plain, Bessarabia, and a wedge-shaped strip through south-central Russia to the southern end of the Ural Mountains were comparable prairie regions. The only extensive area in Asia was that of the Manchurian Plain. Elsewhere on that continent, the transition from steppe to forest was so rapid or so poorly marked that no true prairie regions can be said to have existed.

Middle and High Latitude Forests

Outward from the desert interiors of the continents, one passes through a definite sequence of vegetation types from desert to grassland to forest. Within the tropics, where the temperatures are constantly high, the sequence is determined almost solely by the availability of water. In the middle and high latitudes, the sequence still depends on the availability of water, but it is further modified by marked seasonal fluctuation of temperature. All of the climates of the middle latitudes aside from the Arid (BW), the Semiarid (BS), and the drier margins of the Moist, Mild Winter (C) and Moist, Severe Winter (D) types have ample available moisture to provide for a forest cover. There is considerable variety in the forest cover, however, due to contrasts in seasonal distribution of precipitation or in severity of the winter. There are three principal forest types in the middle and high latitudes: *Mediterranean scrub forest, broadleaf and mixed broadleaf-coniferous forest,* and *coniferous forest* (FIG. 13–12).

MEDITERRANEAN SCRUB FOREST • The Mediterranean forest is dominantly broadleaf and evergreen despite the fact that it occurs in areas of pronounced seasonal drought. Mediterranean (Cs) climates have sufficient precipitation to support a forest, but very little of this precipitation comes during the period of highest temperatures, the season when plant growth

would ordinarily be expected to be most active. In the tropics, where a dry season prevails, the trees are adapted to the dry season by their deciduous character. In the Mediterranean forest, the plants are not commonly deciduous; they are adapted to drought in a variety of other ways. They are markedly xerophytic. Trees are generally low with gnarled, thick-barked trunks. The root systems spread wide laterally and reach deep into the ground. The leaves are small, thick, and waxy. Evergreen oaks, particularly cork oak, olive, and chestnut are common trees. A mild seasonal rhythm makes the plants look gray or brown, almost blending with the color of the soil from which they grow, during the height of the summer. With the fall comes the sprouting of new leaves and through the winter the greenness prevails, reaching its peak with the flowering of early spring. This is gradually succeeded by fading and apparent lifelessness during the summer. Yet at no time are the plants completely dormant. Then, too, the trees are widely spaced and between them grows a ground cover of stunted trees and low bushes, densely packed in wetter areas and very sparsely sprinkled over the land in the drier regions. This low brush growth is called *maquis* in the European areas and *chaparral* in the California region. There are many sections where maquis takes over entirely and grows so thick as to form an almost hopelessly tangled barrier fit only for the pasturage of a few goats. Grass is not common despite the relatively large spaces between the trees and bushes. Only in the Californian areas of this type of vegetation is there any considerable amount of grass intermixed. Sprinkled through the dominant broadleaf evergreen woodland are many conifers like the Bishop pine and the Monterey cypress of California and the maritime pine in Europe.

Most Mediterranean forest regions have been so long settled that the vegetation has been markedly altered by man. The greater part of what remains is the scrub form, maquis or chaparral, rather than true forest. It is possible

13–12 Upper left: *A pathway through mature Mediterranean forest near Bussaco, Portugal.* Upper right: *Mid-latitude mixed hardwood forest in Indiana.* Lower left: *Characteristic virgin Douglas fir forest in British Columbia.* Lower right: *A stand of loblolly pine in a southern pine forest in South Carolina.*

that these forms do not represent the original cover, but rather a second growth which developed following the destruction of the forest. Whatever changes have been wrought, the Mediterranean forest is unique in that it is still basically a broadleaf evergreen type in an area of seasonal drought.

The distribution of Mediterranean forest is shown in FIG. 13–13. Of all the major vegetation types, this forest is the least extensive.

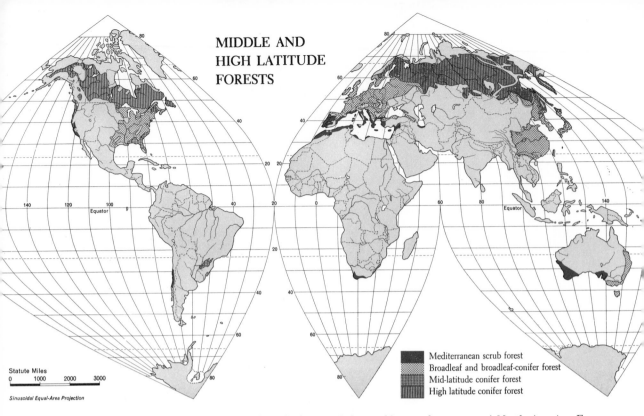

MIDDLE AND
HIGH LATITUDE
FORESTS

Mediterranean scrub forest
Broadleaf and broadleaf-conifer forest
Mid-latitude conifer forest
High latitude conifer forest

Statute Miles
0   1000   2000   3000

Sinusoidal Equal-Area Projection

13-13 THE *middle and high latitude forests of the world cover large areas of North America, Europe, and Asia, but only small portions of South America, Africa, and Australia.*

BROADLEAF AND MIXED BROADLEAF-CO-
NIFEROUS FOREST • Where the tropical forests come to the margins of the low latitudes
east of the dry continental interiors (PLATES
IV and VI), they are succeeded poleward either
by broadleafs of a somewhat different type or
by a forest of conifers. Climatically, these areas
have sufficient moisture for tree growth and
the winters are not cold enough to enforce a
rest period. The forest is normally broadleaf
evergreen. The individual trees belong to different species than those of the selva; they are
less closely crowded, and the forest undergrowth is usually more dense. Epiphytes and
parasites are common. The whole forest looks
like a miniature selva.

Where poor sandy soils occur, conifers replace the broadleaf evergreens. In swampy
lowland areas, a dense forest dominated by
cypress trees, which frequently push their

rounded heads to a height of 100 feet from
a buttress-rooted base, is common (FIG. 13–14).
Within these swamps, a dense tangle of low
bushes and trees, interlocked with epiphytes
and parasites, creates a gloom and dankness
reminiscent of the wet jungle.

Where the winter season is more severe,
as in the higher middle latitudes, the forest
changes to one of broadleaf deciduous trees
with scattered conifers (FIG. 13–12). Seasonal
rhythm becomes well established with budding, flowering, and leafing in spring, a full
greenness in summer, and the brilliant change
of leaf color with the coming of the first frost.
Then the bare branches of the broadleafs,
contrasting sharply with the dark green of the
conifers, form the distinctive winter scene.
Many of the broadleaf species, the oaks for
example, are the same as those which occur
as evergreen trees farther equatorward, but in

328 | *Natural Vegetation and Animal Life*

this middle latitude forest, the profusion of secondary plants is missing. Undergrowth is usually heavy, but is largely composed of small specimens of the trees which dominate the forest. The accumulation of litter on the forest floor from the seasonal dropping of leaves and the occasional fall of branches and trunks is great. It is not rapidly destroyed for, under the climatic conditions which exist, the rate of decay is slow. Hence, much of it remains to furnish soil-enriching material.

In this woodland, pure stands of broadleafs like maple, oak, and hickory cover areas of better soil, while similar stands of conifers like pine, fir, spruce, and hemlock are to be found on poorer soils. Here and there, grassy openings break the continuity of the forest. Edaphically dry localities produce a low bushy cover in which plants like heather form a woody mantle. To these areas the name *heath* is given. Edaphically wet sites are clothed in a similar low vegetation in which many of the ground mosses combine with heather and similar plants to form the *moors* or *moorlands* (FIG. 13–15). *Meadows* of tall grass and *canebrakes*,

13–14

TYPICAL *cypress swamp on Weeks Island, Louisiana.*

thickets of large jointed-stemmed grasses, edge the rivers where wide flood plains have developed.

Of all the forest types in the world, this mixed broadleaf-coniferous type has suffered the most destruction by man. A broadleaf,

13–15   A MOOR *in the northwest highlands of Scotland, near Loch Shin. As in this instance, much of the world's moorlands provides pasture for sheep.*

Vegetation Types and Their Distribution | 329

deciduous woodland once covered much of the British Isles; today, less than five per cent of it remains or has been replanted. In the eastern and central United States, less than one-tenth of the original forest has been preserved. In China, only vestiges give evidence of the luxuriant forest that once must have spread over the whole land. After the supply of broadleafs was exhausted, scattered conifers provided a convenient source of softwoods. They, too, have largely been removed. The plentiful game and fur-bearing animals that formerly inhabited these regions disappeared with the forest. Indiscriminate killing threatened to exterminate many species and nearly succeeded in doing so before hunting regulations were imposed. Other species migrated to the forests farther poleward.

Last to be attacked of the middle and higher middle latitude forests were the coniferous forests of the southeastern United States (FIG. 13–13) and the equatorward edge of the northern coniferous forests like those of the northwestern United States (FIG. 13–1) or of Sweden and Finland. This is less through man's design than through the distance of the forests from densely settled regions which demand their products.

Ruthless destruction has left a host of problems for man to solve. One of the greatest of these is soil erosion. Forest removal makes little, if any, change in precipitation; yet more moisture is available as an agent of erosion. Less moisture filters into bare soil than into forest-covered soil; runoff is thus increased by forest removal. Gullying and sheet erosion produce surfaces unfit for cultivation where remedial measures are either not taken or, too often, are taken only too late. A large proportion of the rainfall flows over the surface of the ground to the streams, carrying with it an increased load of sediment. Formerly ample stream channels can no longer handle flood loads, and control works are necessary to preserve the valley lands from destruction. This is only a suggestion—all that can here be made

—of the significance of widespread forest removal.

The world distribution of broadleaf and mixed broadleaf-coniferous forest areas is shown in FIG. 13–13. The main Northern Hemisphere areas correspond roughly to regions of high population density. It is within these areas that forest removal has been greatest.

CONIFEROUS FOREST • Mixed forest continues poleward approximately to the boundary between Humid Continental climate with warm summers (Dfb) and the Subarctic (Dfc) climate (PLATES IV and VI). There, a coniferous forest takes over. This high latitude forest is ordinarily called the *boreal forest* or *taiga* (FIG. 14–3). In these latitudes, increased coolness and shortness of the growing season provide a climatic environment in which few of the broadleafs thrive. Some of them like birch, poplar, alder, and willow are numerous, but the great bulk of the trees are needleleafs. Needleleaf trees like pine, cedar, spruce, hemlock, and fir do not grow more satisfactorily in this setting because it is ideal for them; rather they dominate because the broadleafs are less well adapted and therefore provide less competition. The forest is tall, dark green, and close-packed along its equatorward margin, but it becomes more and more stunted and scattered as its poleward edge is approached. Frequently, there are extensive swampy interruptions in which tamarack, cedar, and spruce dominate, or in which excess of water produces a quaking bog of low-growing, leathery-leafed bushes, mosses, and grasses which form a spongy mattress between stunted trees. This is the northern *muskeg* (FIG. 13–16). In some sections, such as Siberia, the amount of precipitation is so slight as to rule out forest as a complete cover. In such places, steppelike grass often extends over wide areas between thin, scattered patches of conifers. Also, in regions of pronounced glacial scour, like the Laurentian Upland, extensive and numerous outcrops of bedrock as well as many glacial ponds and marshes make the northern forest a very patchy affair. Where the

13–16

MUSKEG *in the northern coniferous forest of Canada. Stunted and misshapen trees, many of them dead, rise out of a waterlogged mat of grassy and bushy vegetation, filling in what was originally a pond.*

original cover has been removed, broadleaf deciduous trees are most numerous in the second growth. Low, thin-trunked saplings rising from a thicket of stunted brush form an almost useless covering which the conifers replace very slowly.

In addition to the taiga, there is one dominantly coniferous forest which should be noted. It is found on the margins of the low latitudes in the southeastern United States (FIG. 13–13). It differs markedly from the taiga, for it is a sparse woodland of pine almost unmixed with broadleafs. Tall, thin trunks rise unbranching to light, spreading crowns from a sparsely covered forest floor. Undergrowth is light; only here and there in small areas of good soil is there a heavy tangle of deciduous bushes to interrupt a scanty ground cover of grass.

The native animal life of the boreal forests is probably more abundant than that of any middle latitude forest. Streams, lakes, and ponds support a varied fish life represented by such species as bass, pike, pickerel, muskellunge, and trout. In the forest itself are many animals both large and small. Common exam-

ples, found in the Canadian taiga, are moose, caribou, deer, bear, wolf, fox, beaver, mink, marten, muskrat, weasel, and rabbit. In addition, there are many birds such as loons, geese, ducks, partridge, owls, song sparrows, and chickadees. Some of the wild life is migratory; caribou move into the protecting forest in winter and northward onto the tundra in summer; ducks and geese spend their winters in warmer climates far to the south, returning to the northern forest in summer. However, most of the animals remain in the taiga the year round.

Any mention of native animals should include insects, particularly flies and mosquitoes. Though short-lived because of the long season of cold, they constitute a scourge to man and beast alike during the short summers. They do not carry diseases like their counterparts in warmer lands—one need have no fear of malaria or yellow fever—but their bites and stings are a severe trial. It has been said that the great drawback to life in the taiga is not the short summer nor the long bitter cold winter, but the flies and mosquitoes.

Wild animal life is a major resource of the boreal forest except in scattered farming and mining localities. From the forest have come, and still do come, many prime pelts to the great fur markets of Europe and North America. As a wood resource, the boreal forest is less valuable than is commonly supposed. Its patchy and broken distribution and the small size of most of the trees mean that the total board-footage is comparatively small. Only on the warmer margin, where trees are larger and more easily accessible, does the forest furnish much lumber. As a pulpwood resource, however, the boreal forest offers much greater possibility.

Extensive coniferous forest is limited to Northern Hemisphere areas (FIG. 13–13). Taiga occurs only in regions of Moist, Severe Winter (D) climate, and it will be remembered that such climates are developed only in the Northern Hemisphere. The southern coniferous forest of the United States is essentially edaphi-

Vegetation Types and Their Distribution | 331

cally determined. It has no true counterpart in the southern continents, though the Paraná pine forest of southeastern Brazil occupies a climatically similar location.

Tundra

North of the boreal forests, tundra forms the final fringe (FIG. 13–11). Since the tundra is of such little significance to man, no distinction of variety is made on the vegetation map. Near the forest margin, it is heavier than elsewhere and is actually intermingled with stunted forest specimens, some so small as almost to belie the fact that they are trees. Trunks about the size of an ordinary lead pencil, with other features in proportion, represent many years of exceedingly slow growth. Farther from the forest margin, woody plants and bushes are absent, and the grasses, mosses, lichens, and sedges form an even mat over the whole surface. Still farther poleward, the cover is reduced to isolated patches of these plants with much bare ground between. Finally, all signs of vegetation disappear and bare rock or ice forms the surface. The transition is in many ways similar to that which is encountered in crossing from the forest through grassland into desert.

The great areas of tundra are on the Arctic fringe of North America and Eurasia; from there long fingers stretch southward along highland zones. In the Antarctic, tundra is almost entirely lacking, for the icecap extends over almost the whole of Antarctica.

Mountain Vegetation

In the mountains, pronounced vertical zoning of vegetation corresponds to the vertical zoning of mountain climates. The sequence of types approximates the sequence from the equator to the poles. In a middle latitude mountain region, the lower slopes are clothed with deciduous broadleafs, followed in succession by zones of coniferous forest, a tundra-like cover known as *alpine meadow*, bare rock, and even, near the high peaks, a zone of permanent snow. In tropical mountains like Mount Ruwenzori in east-central Africa, the sequence includes tropical forest, broadleaf evergreen forest similar to that of the middle latitudes, broadleaf deciduous forest, coniferous forest, alpine meadow, and finally no vegetation. The particular zoning depends first upon the type found at the base of the mountain. The number of zones in the sequence decreases as one gets away from the equator.

But this zoning is not always present with diagrammatic simplicity. It will be remembered that in mountain climates, details of position and exposure result in a spotty distribution of climatic types. Similar spottiness is reflected in the details of vegetation. Because of local dryness, the expected pattern of forest zones may be broken by the occurrence of a grassland or a desert vegetation type, or a broadleaf forest may be interrupted by a needleleaf variety. While the general sequence can be stated, local departures from it frequently are so great as to appear to upset the whole pattern. For that reason, the collective expression, mountain vegetation, provides a category which includes all of the types previously discussed. No attempt is made to indicate on the world map the detailed distribution from place to place. The outline of regions of mountain vegetation (PLATE VI) is the same as that which appears on the climatic map and on the surface map.

Natural Vegetation and Animal Life

• REVIEW QUESTIONS •

1. Give some examples, drawn from different parts of the world, to indicate the significance of natural vegetation in man's habitat.

2. In what ways does native animal life contribute to or hinder human use of an area?

3. Natural vegetation may generally be considered as visible evidence of the climate of an area. Why? What causes major departures from this generalization?

4. What are some of the basic differences between evergreen and deciduous trees? Between needleleaf and broadleaf trees? Give examples of each type.

5. Why are tundras included under the heading of deserts? Explain.

6. Explain the difference between a major plant association and a natural vegetation type.

7. Why is it that the word "jungle" is so often erroneously used to mean almost any type of tropical forest?

8. Suggest a reason, from the point of view of human activity, for recognizing the kinds of places where jungle is likely to occur.

9. The statement is made: "The forest-grassland margin in the tropics supports the world's densest remaining native animal population." Why should this be so? Discuss fully.

10. If the savannas have as many trees as their descriptions imply, why are they called grasslands?

11. Why is the area in northern South America which is known as the Llanos of the Orinoco not one of the world's greatest cattle countries?

12. Much of the world's prairie and steppe is today surplus grain-producing land. Present a reasoned discussion why this should be.

13. The mid-latitude forests of the world have suffered heavy destruction in Europe, North America, and Asia. Suggest some of the reasons for this.

14. Do the mid-latitude forests offer the same problems to human activity as do the tropical forests? Explain fully.

15. Explain the vertical zoning of vegetation in mountain areas. Give examples from your own experience if possible.

14 Regions in Physical Geography

NATIONAL FILM BOARD, CANAD

BECAUSE *this introduction to geography is organized on a "systematic" rather than a "regional" basis, the preceding chapters have dealt singly with the physical elements of geography. There have been separate discussions of water features, landforms, climates, soils, and natural vegetation and wild animal life* (TABLE 1). *Mineral resources have been omitted from this survey purposely, for their principal significance arises from man's utilization of them. In the physical or natural setting, mineral resources are no different from other rocks. However, when man extracts minerals from the ground, they become effective contributors to the cultural or human setting. Treatment of them thus has been delayed and included under the cultural elements.*

Relationships among the physical factors have certainly not been ignored in the foregoing discussions, but comparatively little has been done to "treat together the things that actually are together." There remains the need to present the physical picture as a whole—the need to understand the significance of the various physical elements as they intermesh to constitute the reality of the physical geographic regions of the continents.

The chief advantage of the regional treatment is that it "leaves together" elements and conditions which actually occur together. It provides a workable understanding of areas as they exist in physical complexes comprised of several elements. In addition, it enables the student of physical geography to compare and contrast the many different kinds of areas which together make up the world's physical geography—a scene of much variety and appreciable change through time. Of course, the systematic study of the physical elements, one by one, is absolutely fundamental. There is the basic and initial need for the study of climate as such, landforms as such, and so on through all the physical elements. But all this, to possess full geographic reality, must be rounded out by a study of "wholes," in which the elements are seen in their true relations to one another and not simply as single elements. By way of a very rough analogy, physical geography may be compared to an automobile engine. To comprehend the engine one must take it apart. He must learn the appearance and nature, as well as the function, of each part. But, if he stops there, he has no real knowledge or appreciation of the engine. At that stage, the engine is no more than a helter-skelter collection of parts strewn on the garage floor. It has to be put together and operated as a real engine before one can appreciate it as a functioning complex. Moreover, it must be taken apart and put together again before it can be compared with other types of automobile engines. In similar fashion, the data of physical geography may well be examined, element by element, and then studied in combination within an area, whether the area be one of the major or lesser components of the world physical scene. By so doing we begin to comprehend the many physical scenes which constitute man's habitat and which man both adapts to and modifies.

A region is any part of the earth's surface which is recognized and delimited for a particular purpose. There are many types of regions, large and small, geographic and nongeographic. Any region, regardless of its type, possesses some unifying element or combination of elements. A state, such as Illinois, is one kind of region—a political region. Its area and shape are determined by the position of the political boundary and its basic unity is an outgrowth of the state constitution and the state laws. A country, such as France, is another

14—1 [OPPOSITE, TOP] WINTER in the Northern Forest Lands of Quebec Province in Canada.

example of a political region. The trading area around a city is another kind of region—an economic region. The part of Europe occupied by the Magyars is an ethnic region. The territory under the Tennessee Valley Authority is a planning region. But what is a physical geographic region?

PHYSICAL GEOGRAPHIC REGIONS

THE physical geography of any area is made up of a number of physical or natural elements. A physical geographic region is an area in which there is some conspicuous unity in the expression of these elements. The essential unity may rest primarily upon landforms, soils, a combination of climate and vegetation, or other natural elements or combinations thereof. The physical regionality of the Black Hills is based upon landforms, which distinguish the Black Hills from the surrounding Great Plains and the regional subdivisions within the Black Hills from one another. Basic to the regionality of the Sahara is climate. Supporting the broad concept of regional integrity of such an area as the Tropical Rainforest Lands of the Amazon Basin is a combination of climate, major landform, and natural vegetation, plus directly associated conditions of drainage and mature soils. This does not mean that the Amazon Basin is exactly the same throughout. It does not mean that the distributional patterns of the unifying elements coincide exactly in all parts or on all margins of the area. But it does mean that there is either coincidence or strong correspondence of the "key" patterns within the Amazon Basin, and it does mean that there exists an extensive physical core within which natural conditions are more alike than different, a physical core which field studies show to be recognizably distinct from those of surrounding areas.

The dominance of one or more natural elements in establishing the essential unity of a given physical geographic region must not be misinterpreted. There are several elements in such a region; each must be recognized and the significance of their mutual relationships must be appreciated. For example, the Sierra Nevada of California is a physical geographic region; yet to say that it is such a region because of landform conditions is only a "starter." Many more items must be considered. Among these are the type of mountains present, the difference between the glaciated and unglaciated portions, the vertical zonation of vegetation and of climate, the seasonal changes, and the difference between the windward and leeward sides. Understanding of the entire "physical complex" is necessary if the fundamental geography of the Sierra is to be comprehended.

Physical geographic regions, or physical complexes, are of different sizes, as witness the Sahara and the Lake St. John Lowland. Large ones usually are divisible into several subregions and even the smallest normally possesses at least two subregions. In the Lake St. John Lowland, for example, the geographer must recognize a minimum of two subregions (see CHAPTER 1). One is the part of the lowland in which clay soils predominate; the other is the part covered by extremely sandy soils interrupted here and there by swamp soils. These are intraregional differences, yet both subregions are part and parcel of a physical unit whose "oneness" rests primarily on landforms.

Major Physical Geographic Regions

As used here, the term "major physical geographic regions" refers to those of great area—

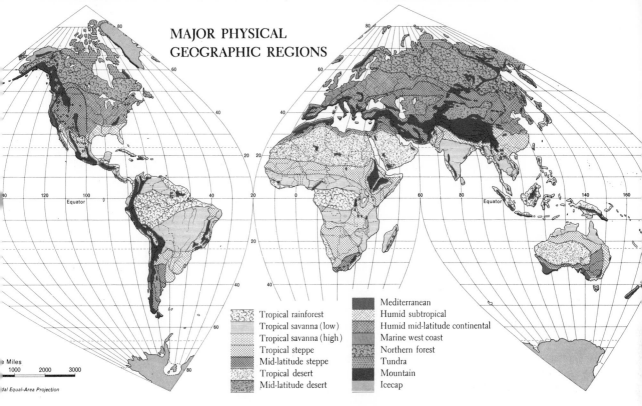

MAJOR PHYSICAL GEOGRAPHIC REGIONS

Tropical rainforest
Tropical savanna (low)
Tropical savanna (high)
Tropical steppe
Mid-latitude steppe
Tropical desert
Mid-latitude desert

Mediterranean
Humid subtropical
Humid mid-latitude continental
Marine west coast
Northern forest
Tundra
Mountain
Icecap

Miles
1000   2000   3000

dal Equal-Area Projection

14–2   THIS *generalized map of major physical geographic regions represents one way of recognizing the larger component complexes which together comprise the basic physical divisions of the world (see text discussion). These major physical geographic regions are known as "lands."*

those of continental rather than local scale. Examples are the Tropical Rainforest Lands, the Mediterranean Lands, and the Tundra Lands (FIG. 14–2). Because on such a scale more conditions are related, directly or indirectly, to climate than any other single geographic element, these regions are basically climatic. Yet they are more than climatic regions, for within them there is a similarity or unity in other physical conditions, such as vegetation and soils. In order to be more specific, and to illustrate the degree to which the idea of major physical geographic regions possesses utility, it may be helpful to discuss one such region as an example.

THE NORTHERN FOREST LANDS: AN EXAMPLE • The Northern Forest Lands, limited as the name indicates to the Northern Hemisphere (FIG. 14–2), have their greatest extent

in Eurasia, where they sweep from the eastern edge of the Norwegian mountains to the mountains of eastern Siberia and beyond, in places, to the shore of the Pacific. To the north they are barely cut off from the Arctic Ocean by the Tundra Lands. To the south they merge with the Humid Mid-latitude Continental Lands on both the east and west. In the continental interiors they give way to the Dry Lands.

In North America, the Northern Forest Lands occupy the greater portion of Canada and part of interior Alaska. The major extent is from the eastern foot of the Canadian Rockies to southern Labrador and Newfoundland. As in Eurasia, they are located between the Tundra Lands on the poleward margin and either Dry Lands or Humid Mid-latitude Continental Lands on the equatorward margin, as

14–3   AIR view of a portion of the Northern Forest Lands in Canada. Note the many lakes and ponds and the dominance of forest cover.

well as merging upward along parts of their margins with the Mountain Lands.

The most readily visible feature of the Northern Forest Lands is the vegetation which gives them their name (FIG. 14–3). It is mainly a coniferous forest in which spruce, balsam fir, and cedar are dominant trees, although there is a considerable admixture, even solid stands, of such trees as poplar, birch, alder, and willow. Along the equatorward margin, where the growing season is longer, there are some pines and a more frequent occurrence of broadleaf deciduous trees, including maples, oaks, and wild cherry. The farther north one goes, the smaller the trees and the fewer the tree species. Hardiest of all are the spruce, birch, and willow. However, where they finally interfinger with or, in some places, invade the Tundra, they can hardly be called trees; the spruces become mere bushes and the birches and willows are little more than matted, vinelike masses which hug the ground. Most of the Northern Forest is broken and patchy, espe-

cially in the parts which have been subjected to pronounced scouring action by continental glaciers. Such parts often are comprised more of exposed bedrock, lakes, and ponds than they are of forest. Present, too, are numerous relatively open swamps, including muskegs, in which there are only a few trees rising above a low cover of bushes, mosses, and cranberry vines (FIG. 13–16). As has been previously indicated, richness and variety characterize the native animal life.

The climate of the Northern Forest Lands is one of long, cold, snowy winters and short, cool, rainy summers. It is the Subarctic type of climate (chiefly Dfc and Dwc, but with occurrences of Dfd and Dwd—see PLATE IV). Precipitation is greatest along the warmer margins and very scant on the colder margins. However, the precipitation is all very effective, because temperatures are sufficiently low during nearly all of the year to preclude rapid evaporation. Essentially, there are two seasons: summer and winter. What might be called autumn and spring are very short periods of rapid change either from summer to winter or from winter to summer. During the long winter season the streams and lakes are covered with thick ice and drifted snow and the forest itself is snow-mantled, even though the mantle is very thin on the tundra margin. When summer arrives for its short stay, the snow melts away, the ice on the lakes turns gray and mushy and finally disappears, and the ice on the streams pushes and grinds its way along in the "break-up" of winter.

While natural vegetation and climate constitute the unifying combination of the full sweep of the Northern Forest Lands, considerable variety is supplied within these lands by local, or comparatively local, differences in landforms, drainage, and soils. Large portions of the Northern Forest Lands were "worked over" by continental glaciers, especially in North America (compare FIGS. 6–33 and 14–2). In such portions, the landforms are those typical of glacial scour (*roches moutonnées*, scour basins, glacial troughs, etc.) or of glacial deposition (morainal ridges, ground moraine, eskers, etc.). Directly associated with them is the typical glacially deranged drainage with its characteristic ponds, lakes, swamps, and wandering streams. Associated, too, are distinctive soil conditions. In the areas of glacial scour there is no more than a thin and patchy veneer of soil, soil-less bedrock being very prominent on the higher parts, such as *roches moutonnées*. In the lower parts are several local types of immature soil, the type depending largely on the kind of glacial debris dropped in a given place or on soil drainage, for poor drainage has caused swamp or bog soils in many areas.

Conditions of drainage, landforms, and soil are more nearly "normal" in the unglaciated portions of the Northern Forest Lands. Here are found the ordinary patterns of stream drainage, dominantly dendritic, with ponds and lakes generally absent. However, swamps may be large and numerous in some of the lower parts of the unglaciated areas. This is chiefly because streams become ice-dammed during the "breakup" and water rises and spreads over adjacent territory. Because this happens each year, and because the summers are not sufficiently long or dry, the flooded areas do not have a chance to dry out before the cold season arrives. The minor landforms of the unglaciated sections, mainly valleys and interfluves, are much like those developed in other humid regions. Youthful, mature, and old valleys are to be found, and the same is true of interfluves. In the parts which are nearly level, and at the same time well drained, occur the mature soils known as podsols. These reflect primarily the climate and the natural vegetation and the lack of disturbance by glaciation. Podsols have developed in some of the glaciated portions, particularly on well-drained sands, but are less extensive than in the unglaciated sections.

Although necessarily short and incomplete, the foregoing discussion of the Northern Forest Lands provides insight into the nature of one large physical geographic region. Also, it illustrates the practical utility of the concept of such regional distinction—of keeping together certain mutually extensive conditions that are together in reality. If all such large regions are recognized and studied, one by one, and then compared and contrasted with one another, it becomes possible to acquire at least a general knowledge and appreciation of the world's physical geography. It is one way of grasping "in complex" the outstanding physical elements of the earth's surface. It is suggested that the reader try it out for himself on one or more of the earth's major physical geographic regions. For example, FIG. 14–2 shows the world distribution of those areas which collectively are referred to as the Hot Desert Lands. These lands, like the Northern Forest Lands, possess a certain broad unity encompassing a good deal of variety within their borders. Careful perusal of pertinent sections of the foregoing chapters will reinforce the understanding, and will also provide data for recognition of variety within the Hot Desert Lands.

Lesser Physical Geographic Regions

Following the discussion of major physical geographic regions, it is useful to change the scale of inquiry and consider those which are smaller. These lesser regions, like the larger ones, contain the same physical elements and possess some unifying condition or combination of conditions. If all of them are studied, the world can be "filled in" as far as its physical geography is concerned, much as one completes a puzzle by recognizing the pieces and fitting them together properly. Examples of lesser physical geographic regions are the North China Plain, the Central Valley of California, the Po Basin in Italy, and the Nashville Basin in Tennessee. In most instances, the unity of lesser physical geographic regions rests on landforms (as in the Nashville Basin), but it may be based on other physical conditions, such as drainage (as in the Great Swamp of western Siberia), or soil conditions (as in the Black Belt of Alabama). This situation is somewhat in contrast to that in larger physical geographic regions, where the unity is associated with conditions of climate or a combination of climate and natural vegetation. Following is a brief discussion of the Central Valley of California, one of the lesser physical geographic regions of North America.

THE CENTRAL VALLEY OF CALIFORNIA: AN EXAMPLE • The Central Valley, or Great Valley, of California is an elongated plain about 400 miles long and 50 miles wide, lying between the high Sierra Nevada on the east and the much lower Coast Ranges on the west (FIG. 14–4). It is a structural, rather than erosional, depression which is slowly being filled with large amounts of stream-borne materials from the Sierra and lesser amounts of similar materials from the Coast Ranges. When viewed from the Sierran foothills, or

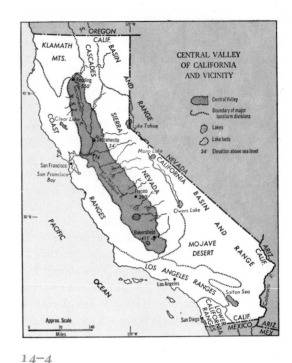

14–4

CALIFORNIA's *Central Valley is an alluvium-floored plain. Except for the narrow outlet to San Francisco Bay, it is encompassed by hills and mountains.*

the abruptly descending edge of the Coast Ranges, the Central Valley seems as flat as a table top. Even when examined from numerous points within the Valley itself, the surface still appears nearly level, for most of the slopes are long and gentle and local interruptions within the nearly level surface are minor.

Alluvial fans constitute the land surface of nearly all of the Central Valley. Large ones built out from the Sierra Nevada commonly reach more than halfway across the Valley and join with one another laterally to form a continuous piedmont alluvial plain. Smaller fans from the Coast Ranges likewise reach into the Valley. Some of them join with one another to produce locally continuous alluvial piedmonts, but others exist as separate fans. The invasion of the Valley by fans from the east and west and at both ends indicates the presence of completely surrounding hills and mountains. Only at the narrow break through the Coast Ranges to San Francisco Bay is there a low way into or out of the Central Valley. Thus, the regional boundary of the Valley is a definite and continuous line separating the "valley-fill" from the adjacent hills and mountains.

Were it not for the gap leading to San Francisco Bay, the Central Valley would be a huge lake. Streams from the high mountains to the east pour rainwater and meltwater from snow and ice into the plain below. Chief among these streams are the Sacramento river and the San Joaquin river. They meet in tangled, marshy channels just east of San Francisco Bay and then flow westward into the Bay. Smaller streams from the Coast Ranges also flow into the Valley, but nearly all of them are intermittent and their waters are quickly lost into the coarse alluvial fill of the fans. The portion of the Valley south of the "elbow" of the San Joaquin is an area of interior drainage. Even the larger streams from the Sierra soon sink into the ground and the smaller ones barely issue from the mountains. Here and there are exceedingly level lake beds which are covered with very shallow water in particularly rainy years. If there were to be, as there has been in the past, a series of very rainy years, these low spots would become relatively permanent lakes and their waters would rise until a stream flow making junction with the San Joaquin would be established.

As can be inferred from these drainage conditions, the climate of the Central Valley becomes progressively drier from north to south. At the northern end the average annual precipitation is about 30 inches; at Sacramento it is about 19 inches; at the midpoint of the Valley it is about 10 inches; and at the southern end it is about 5 inches. Technically, the northern half of the Central Valley has a Csa climate (interior phase of the Mediterranean type of climate) and the southern half, BS with patches of BW (Dry climates, partly

Semiarid and partly Arid). Throughout the Valley, summers are hot and dry and winters are cool and rainy (with more rain being received in the northern portion). Frosts are common during the winter, but the Valley as a whole has an average frost-free season of at least seven months.

The soils of the Central Valley are mainly alluvial fan soils. Because of this, there is great variety in local soil types. Some are sandy, some gravelly and bouldery, some clayey, some loamy, and so on. In general, soils are coarser near the heads of the alluvial fans and finer on the lower margins of the fans. Because the growth of alluvial fans still continues, soils are distinctly immature. The comparative meagerness of precipitation and the generally porous nature of the alluvial materials results in soils which are essentially "droughty" in nature. There are, to be sure, some wet or even waterlogged soils, but they occur only along the flood plains of the lower Sacramento and San Joaquin rivers, or at the low "delta" section where the two streams join, or in the lowest spots of the areas of interior drainage south of the San Joaquin. In these same low spots there are areas of saline soils.

Recent, porous alluvial soils and either meager or deficient rainfall resulted in a grassland vegetation, with lines of trees along the permanent streams. The original grass, now largely replaced by non-native grasses, was dominantly patchy and broken and was of the type usually referred to as Pacific bunch grassland. Marsh grass occurs in the river bottoms of the permanent streams and coarse reeds (tules) grow in other wet places, particularly in the lowest spots in the section marked by interior drainage. Some parts are without natural vegetation, especially the lake bed surfaces in the south and the occasional "blow areas" where sand dunes are present.

In summary, the Central Valley of California is one example of a lesser physical geographic region. Its unity is based first and foremost on the fact that it is a continuous alluvial

14–5 PART *of the southern end of the Central Valley, near Bakersfield, California, showing a portion of the valley floor and Sierra Nevada foothills.*

plain which is completely walled in by hills and mountains (FIG. 14–5). Other aspects of its over-all or general uniformity are to be seen in its young alluvial soils and grass vegetation and its condition of relative dryness. It is a physical complex which contrasts sharply with the surrounding regions.

The foregoing treatment of the Central Valley is obviously sketchy and incomplete, but it will serve to illustrate the concept of *lesser* physical geographic regions as opposed to *major* physical geographic regions of the world.

• CHAPTER OUTLINE •

Regions in Physical Geography

PHYSICAL GEOGRAPHIC REGIONS
  Major Physical Geographic Regions
    THE NORTHERN FOREST LANDS: AN EXAMPLE

Lesser Physical Geographic Regions
  THE CENTRAL VALLEY OF CALIFORNIA: AN
    EXAMPLE

1. What is a region?
2. Give some examples of different kinds of regions.
3. What is a physical geographic region?
4. As used in this chapter, what is the distinction between "major physical geographic region" and "lesser physical geographic region"?
5. Discuss the general nature of the physical geography of the Northern Forest Lands.
6. Discuss the general nature of the physical geography of the Central Valley of California.
7. Using the world maps in the front of this book and other maps and data in the several chapters, describe the outstanding characteristics of the physical geography of the Tundra Lands (FIG. 14–2).

III

ELEMENTS OF THE CULTURAL SETTING

15 World Population

UNITED NATIONS

AMERICAN AIRLINE

⟮ THE *first and quite certainly the foremost of the many cultural elements of geography is man himself. How many people are there in the world? How are they distributed over the face of the earth? How closely are they crowded together, or how widely are they separated from one another? These are questions the answers to which provide much of the basis for understanding (1) the changes which man has wrought in the physical environment and (2) the limitations which the physical environment has placed upon man.*

The whole of human history has been concerned with learning how to live in the variety of physical environments encountered over the face of the earth and how to live with the constantly increasing numbers of human beings and their works. Man's first efforts, like those of any other animal, were primarily to secure food and protection directly from the physical environment. Slowly in the beginning, but with ever-increasing tempo, man came to alter what he found, or to discover new ways of using it to make his existence easier. He learned to tame animals and plants in order to provide for himself a more dependable food supply. He learned to use animal and plant products for clothing to protect himself against heat, cold, and moisture. He learned to build houses rather than to seek caves and trees for shelter. And, as he learned how to use the physical setting better, his numbers increased.

Eventually, a stage was reached at which it was easier for some individuals or groups to move to new areas rather than to try, with their existing culture, to increase the facilities for living together. Repeated through centuries, this pressure toward migration brought about a spread of human beings over most parts of the earth's surface. All sorts of physical environments were encountered, but relatively few of them offered entirely satisfactory habitats. Some proved quite uninhabitable until cultural evolution made possible new ways of living; some still remain unable to support more than a temporary population.

The most favorable areas, considering the stage of man's cultural development, became the nuclei toward which all mankind was drawn. They form the great centers of population today—clear-cut, densely populated regions as opposed to vast sparsely settled or uninhabited areas. Uneven spread of human beings over the world is a geographic reality the details of which may be found in the facts of population numbers, distribution, and density.

POPULATION NUMBERS

Present World Population

THE exact number of human beings in the world is not known, but reasonable estimates are available. The total figure at any one time cannot be known for several reasons. Among these, two may be suggested: first, there is continual loss through death and continual addition through birth, both of these changes proceeding at rates which are variable in time and from place to place; second, the

15–1

[OPPOSITE, TOP] EXTREMES of settlement types. Left: A village in Somalia. Right: The view northeast over midtown New York.

methods of demographic accounting (census taking, vital record keeping, etc.) are neither uniform nor completely reliable throughout the whole world. Even were these methods to be made uniform and completely reliable, there would be little value in knowing precisely how many people there were in the whole world at any one instant of time. The total is so large that a few millions may be neglected without altering the general view of man in his habitat.

Sound estimate indicates that there were approximately 2,902,000,000 human beings spread very unevenly over the whole world by mid-1959 (TABLE 15). Several countries have completed censuses since 1959, but most of the countries of the world have not. Hence, it is necessary to turn to uniform estimates for

TABLE *15*

Approximate World Population, 1959

CONTINENT OR OTHER AREA	TOTAL POPULATION	PER CENT OF WORLD POPULATION
Asia (excluding U.S.S.R.)	1,612,000,000	55.5
Europe (excluding U.S.S.R.)	421,000,000	14.5
North and Middle America	260,000,000	9.0
Africa	247,000,000	8.5
Union of Soviet Socialist Republics	211,000,000	7.3
South America	136,000,000	4.7
Australia and Oceania	15,000,000	0.5
Antarctica	0	0.0
Total	2,902,000,000	100.0

SOURCE: Generalized from Tables 1 and 2 in *United Nations Demographic Yearbook, 1960*.

valid comparison. The most recent of these, and those most generally accepted, are contained in the *United Nations Demographic Yearbook*, 1960 (published in 1961). These estimates are for mid-1959. Asia was the home of by far the largest number, roughly 56 per cent of the total. Into little Europe were crowded just over one-seventh of all the people in the world. At the opposite extreme, Antarctica had no permanent population and Australia, nearly as large as Europe, supported less than one-third of one per cent of the world total.

In terms of political units, over half the world's population lived in four countries: China, India, the Union of Soviet Socialist Republics, and the United States of America. China alone, with 669,000,000, accounted for over 23% and India, with 402,000,000, nearly 14%. Though the U.S.S.R. and the United States followed next in order of total number, they were far below China and India. The U.S.S.R. had a population of 211,000,000 and

the United States, of 178,000,000. These four political units were the giant countries in terms of population numbers. Though the actual figures are changing constantly, the relative position of the countries, both as compared with each other and with other countries, has not changed materially over the past decade.

Population Growth

Throughout human history, world population has continued to grow. The rate of growth was slow at first, but it has increased rapidly during the past few centuries. With the very simple hunting-fishing-collecting economy practiced by early man, any given area could support few individuals. As agriculture and the domestication of animals were invented, the ability of certain areas to support larger groups became evident. In addition, these cultural inventions made possible permanent habitation of new areas. Further inventions and the improvement of those already existing brought

TABLE *16*

Estimated Total World Population and Population Increases by Periods

YEAR	ESTIMATED WORLD POPULATION	INCREASE PER FIFTY-YEAR PERIOD	PERCENTAGE INCREASE
1650	545,000,000		
1700			
1750	728,000,000	(91,500,000) [1]	14.2
1800	906,000,000	178,000,000	24.4
1850	1,171,000,000	265,000,000	29.2
1900	1,608,000,000	437,000,000	37.3
1950	2,495,000,000 [2]	887,000,000	55.2

[1] Average of fifty-year periods for century.
[2] United Nations estimate.

SOURCE: After estimates cited in A. M. Carr-Saunders, *World Population*. Oxford: Clarendon, 1936. Estimate for 1950 from *U.N. Demographic Yearbook*, 1960.

with them increases of population. Yet, though certain small areas came to have very large populations, most of the world remained empty or sparsely occupied until the stage of cultural evolution known as the Industrial Age was reached.

The Industrial Age had its beginning in northwestern Europe, and it was there that rapid population increase first occurred. The effects of industrialism were rapidly diffused throughout large sections of the world. Movement of large groups of people from one part of the world to another, such as the large-scale colonization of the Americas by Europeans, became feasible for the first time. Advances in medical science changed the balance between births and deaths. Technological advances made possible the use of different kinds of physical environment and allowed the accumulation of surpluses. What was lacking in

one place could be secured from another as facilities for movement over the earth were developed. Dependence upon any one small area for the support of a given group of people was greatly modified or, in some instances, altogether eliminated. In a sense, nearly the whole earth came to be the habitat of the peoples provided with adequate means of transportation.

Some notion of the increase in actual numbers may be gained from TABLE 16. No reasonable estimates can be made of world population for periods before 1650 even though such estimates may be available for specific small areas. Actually, of course, the figures since that date are themselves not precise, but they are sufficiently accurate to give some concept of the tremendous spurt in population growth which has accompanied the spread of industrialism over the world. Not only has the total increased steadily; it has increased at a faster and faster rate.

GROWTH CATEGORIES • While world population shows few signs of having reached a peak number, its growth is not uniform in all regions and among all groups of people. Basically, the number of people in any area depends on the balance between birth and death rates. These rates change with a great variety of causes, but essentially with some major new discovery whereby man's base of operations and existence is in some way expanded. For example, the changes resulting from industrialization have combined to reduce mortality rates through improving the conditions of life. At first, birth rates increased materially, but shortly they began to decline. Causes of this decline are extremely complex and difficult to assess properly. Yet, one specific factor can be noted; under the industrial mode of life children were no longer the great economic advantage they had been in previous rural living. The end result is that, with the impact of industrialism, there is at first a remarkable increase in population, which is followed in time by the slowing of the rate of increase so that the total numbers grow either very slowly or remain more or less constant. Actual decline of total numbers may eventually occur.

On the basis of birth and death rates alone, four major categories of population growth may be recognized. These are: (1) high birth rates and high death rates, producing slow total increase; (2) high birth rates and falling death rates, producing rapid total increase; (3) falling birth rates and falling death rates, producing slow total increase; and (4) low birth rates and low death rates, producing very slow increase or relative stability.

An increase in population measured simply as a percentage is not a full indicator of growth. Rather there must be consideration of the *trends* in both birth and death rates. Many factors, especially economic ones, may alter the trend of these rates within short periods of time. The United States provides an example.

For some considerable time, the death rate has been consistently low; during the first quarter of this century, the birth rate likewise remained little changed. The birth rate declined during the 1920's and the 1930's, a period of severe economic stress; with it, the rate of growth of the total population decreased. During the 1940's and the 1950's, the death rate remained essentially what it was earlier, but the birth rate increased; hence, the rate of growth of the total population increased markedly. Where low death rates prevail, changes of rate of growth are essentially a function of minor shifts in birth rate.

WORLD PATTERN OF GROWTH • It was previously noted that large increases in population occurred first in northwestern Europe. The 100 million people in Europe in the middle of the seventeenth century had become four times that number by the middle of this century. The increase began in the late seventeenth century and attained its greatest rate in the late nineteenth century. After slowing perceptibly in the first part of the twentieth century, gains have again become evident. However, it is chiefly in the eastern and southeastern parts of the continent that moderately rapid growth can still be expected.

Throughout the rest of the world, the areas to which the features of the Industrial Age were transmitted earliest have shown a tendency toward stabilization, and even decline, in population numbers. This is notably true in North America, Australia, and New Zealand. On the other hand, the large populations of southern and eastern Asia, of northern South America and Middle America, and of northern and southern Africa have evidently just reached the stage in which western Europe found itself when its population increase was greatest. Central Africa and the Malagasy Republic remain as areas of both high birth and high death rates. It must be remembered, however, that the complex causes of rate changes may alter the world pattern within relatively short periods of time.

POPULATION DISTRIBUTION

THE distribution of population over the earth is extremely uneven. Antarctica and a few isolated islands scattered through the world's oceans are entirely free of permanent human habitation. At the opposite extreme, in areas like Java, many millions of people live in close proximity to one another. This unevenness creates one of the most significant cultural patterns: the pattern of population. One of the best ways to show the pattern of population distribution over the world is by the use of a *dot map*.

Dot Maps

When numerical data are available for any given area and when it is desired to show the arrangement of the data on a map so that the pattern will be easily visible, the dot map is a most useful device. Each dot that appears on the map represents a certain number of units, such as 500 people or 10,000 acres of land. Dots are placed on a base map so that each one represents the center of the area in which the specified number of units is found. Obviously, dots are closest together where the units are most numerous in actuality and farthest apart where the units are least numerous in actuality. In some areas, dots may merge, while in others they may be widely separated or lacking entirely. The variations in their relative distances create variations in shading on the map and by that means convey the notion of pattern distribution. FIGURE 15–2 is a dot map of world population.

On the scale on which FIG. 15–2 is constructed, the main purpose is to show where there are large numbers of people and where there are few. One cannot use the map for detailed comparison between small areas, principally because of the difficulty of making an actual count of the number of dots in one area as compared with another. Where there are large numbers of people, the dots form a solid shading; at the other extreme, a single dot often serves for hundreds of square miles. Nevertheless, this map does make easily visible the nuclear areas about which the world's population is oriented.

Main Features of World Population Distribution

Four parts of the world stand out as centers of large population clusters (FIG. 15–2): eastern Asia, southern Asia, western Europe, and central eastern North America. In all four, many of the dots are so close together as to be indistinguishable as separate dots. From these centers, the dots thin out to become widely scattered or absent altogether.

In great contrast to the main four, many areas are nearly or completely empty of dots. This is true of Antarctica, the greater part of Australia, the central and northern portions of Asia, the northern fringe of Europe, the Saharan portion of Africa, the northern portion of North America, and the interior of South America. The cold lands of the world, the great deserts, and the tropical heart of South America are conspicuously empty.

Between the areas of great concentration and those of great emptiness, population spreads thinly over the land, creating fringe zones of moderate numbers. Here and there, as in the Nile valley or on the island of Java, large numbers of people occupy relatively small and isolated areas which give way without transition to practically empty lands or to the sea.

In general, the pattern shown on FIG. 15–2 cannot be expected to undergo radical changes in the future. Many of the forces which determine the distribution of population are fixed. For example, in northern China, there is a great extent of plain limited to the north, west, and south by more rugged lands and to the east by the sea. Across this surface flows

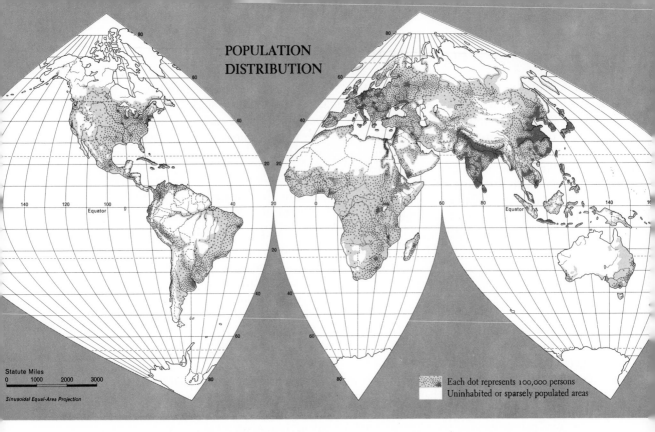

POPULATION
DISTRIBUTION

Statute Miles
0   1000   2000   3000

Sinusoidal Equal-Area Projection

Each dot represents 100,000 persons
Uninhabited or sparsely populated areas

15–2   THE *distribution of population over the earth is extremely uneven, with four widely separated regions bearing extremely heavy concentrations: eastern Asia, southern Asia, western Europe, and east-central North America.*

a great river in a course which has shifted frequently. The climate of the area (PLATE IV) is Semiarid (BS) and Humid Continental with long summers (Dwa), thus placing it on the margin of the region of normal humid agriculture. As yet, human beings cannot alter the climate. Though many efforts have been made, control over the shifting course of the river has not yet become adequate. The character of the land as a plain cannot be changed. Hence, the physical base upon which the people depend is essentially a constant. True, the people themselves can alter their method of living. Instead of remaining farmers, they may become industrialists. Communication lines may be amplified so that the area will be less dependent upon its own resources and become less of a subsistence area. Nevertheless,

these changes will not occur rapidly and they will not destroy the existence of a nucleus in the world population pattern. The details of arrangement within this area may change and its outlines may expand or contract, but there appears to be no force which will eradicate it throughout the life of many generations.

Continental Patterns of Population Distribution

ASIA • A glance at the dot map of world population distribution (FIG. 15–2) reveals two great areas of concentration in Asia: the eastern fringes of the continent and India. Within each of these general areas, variations of intensity are observable.

The eastern Asiatic zone begins with the

three southern islands of the Japanese group. From that location, the belt of large numbers of people moves across to the inner, or western, coastal zone of Korea and on through southern Manchuria. It is practically continuous as far as China, but within China several centers of large population stand out. The North China Plain, the basins along the Yangtze river, the lower valley of the Si river, and the coastal region between the mouths of the Yangtze and the Si are all areas supporting tremendous numbers of human beings. Parts of two large islands off the Chinese coast belong also to this great population concentration: western Taiwan and northern Hainan.

At the southern frontier of China, the great concentration of population ends. From there to India, only small clusters, separated from one another by stretches of nearly empty land, can be noted. On the islands southeast of the mainland, population is likewise scattered except in Java, southwestern Celebes, and the northwestern Philippines.

Again on the mainland, the great populations of India and Pakistan stand out with a sharpness equal to those in eastern Asia. The zone of large numbers follows the Ganges river from its delta well westward to the headstreams of the Indus river. Likewise, the east coast of the Indian peninsula throughout its whole length and the west coast northward to just beyond Bombay are peopled by large numbers. Southwestern Ceylon may be considered a further extension of this major population concentration.

Except for the areas mentioned, the great expanse of the Asiatic continent is comparatively empty of human beings. A delicate trace of peopling appears north of the Aral Sea and extends eastward along the Chinese frontier. Small and poorly defined clusters are attached to the upper portions of the rivers emptying into the Aral Sea. A very thin scattering marks the western and northern Chinese boundaries and the margins of Afghanistan.

One clear relationship is evident in both the eastern and southern regions of concentration: the great populations live on the plains areas (compare FIGS. 15–2 and 7–11). Most of the peoples of Asia are rural and their livelihood depends upon intensive cultivation of flat and well-watered or irrigable alluvial lands. In many places, the break from intensively occupied land to unoccupied land is line-sharp; often it is so clear that a map of population distribution might equally well be a map of plains (FIG. 5–2).

Large concentrations in Asia are, as a rule, not the expression of large cities with their attendant masses of population both within the city itself and in its suburbs; they are rather the result of an even spread of agricultural villages over the land. Even in the spottily occupied lands of the southeast, attachment to the alluvial plains is marked. In Burma, the delta and the middle valley of the Irrawaddy are the foci; in Thailand, the lower valley of the Chao Phraya stands out; in South Vietnam, the delta of the Mekong and the small coastal plains on the South China Sea form the centers of concentration. Again, in Java, the large populations live on the plains, but on that island there are also volcanic soils of exceptional fertility which play an important part in detailed population distribution.

The narrow wedge of population in Asiatic U.S.S.R. is of quite different nature. It corresponds closely to the eastward extension of the great Black Soil (chernozem) Belt which starts in southern European U.S.S.R. (PLATE V). An added factor making for concentration of people is the presence of the Trans-Siberian Railway linking a chain of growing urban centers and offering transportation facilities to urban and rural dwellers alike.

The empty and nearly empty spaces in Asia (FIG. 15–2) remain so largely because they are physically ill suited to agriculture. In the north, the lands are too cold; there also many of the plains areas, as the lower Ob valley, are too poorly drained. Central Asia is too mountainous, too dry, or, because of elevation, too cold. Southwestern Asia is too dry; and southeastern Asia, too rugged. Into all of these regions, the great masses of Asia's peoples have not spread. Despite changes in technology, it is doubtful if these vacuums of Asia will ever be settled by the tremendous numbers of people, ever increasing, which clog the lowlands of the continent's eastern and southern fringes.

EUROPE • The most striking feature of the distribution of population in Europe (FIG. 15–2) is the concentration which appears about the southern end of the North Sea. In the British Isles, London forms the main center. Outward from it, an essentially even spread over the English Lowland continues northward along the east coast into central Scotland and westward to the Welsh Uplands. On the European mainland, a heavily populated coastal zone extends from the mouth of the Seine in France to the mouth of the Elbe in Germany. From this coastal strip, the zone of greatest numbers reaches inland, sending one arm southeastward along the southern margin of the Plain of North Europe into the Ukraine (compare FIGS. 15–2 and 7–11) and another southward along the Rhine river into Switzerland.

In addition there are a number of separate population centers. One of the largest focuses on Moscow. Another is the solidly filled lowland of the Po river in northern Italy. The western coast of Italy in the vicinities of Naples and Genoa form added nuclei, as do Barcelona in Spain and Oporto in Portugal. Similarly, coastal Sicily is densely peopled.

Population spreads relatively evenly over most of the rest of the continent, thinning out to nearly empty land north of the 60th parallel (roughly north of the latitude of Stockholm) and near the Caspian Sea. In Europe there is not the sharp transition between heavily populated areas and empty areas that there is in Asia. Furthermore, in the areas where the dots are thinly scattered (FIG. 15–2), there appear

well-defined nuclei which give the pattern a spotted look, as in the European U.S.S.R. This results principally from the fact that Europe is much more highly industrialized than is Asia. Cities, often quite widely separated, form points of attachment for larger numbers of people, while agricultural population is much more thinly spread over the land between the cities.

There is a certain correspondence between the areas with large numbers of people and the areas of plains (compare FIGS. 15–2 and 7–11), but the relationship is not so clearly illustrated in Europe as it is in Asia. To be sure, one can make out the pattern of the most rugged mountain ranges, as for example the Alps, the Carpathians, and the Apennines. Yet the hilly zone stretching from eastern France to southern Poland is in many places peopled by as large numbers as the Plain of North Europe and by even larger numbers than much of the plains land of Russia. Evidently other factors than surface play important roles in the distribution of population over Europe.

Since the population is more completely industrialized than in Asia, it is more closely tied to the basic sources of industrial power—coal, especially—and to routes which make possible the easy movement of people and goods. Many of Europe's population nuclei are the coal fields which dot that continent, as for example, the Ruhr field of west Germany or the Midlands area of Great Britain. Likewise, the main lines of transportation which, like the Rhine river, give easy access to the continental interior from the fringing seas, form axes of settlement. This is not to say that the plains are avoided; rather, the other types of surface are used by large numbers of people to whom flatness of land and alluvial soils are not of major concern.

Climate, too, plays a significant part in ordering the distribution of population. The cold northern edge of the continent with Subarctic (Dfc) and Tundra (ET) climates is virtually empty of people as is also the area of Arid

(BW) climate adjacent to the Caspian Sea. Much of the interior of the Iberian Peninsula is empty too, because of climatic conditions adverse to agriculture.

Over the whole continent, the relationship of the distribution of people to the land is much more complex than it is in Asia. No one element in the physical setting can alone be held responsible. The complex culture of the West is better able to contend with adverse features of the physical setting; the ability of the land to support population under that culture is very different from the ability of the land to support population under Oriental culture.

NORTH AMERICA • The third main area of population concentration lies in eastern North America. Consideration of the population dot map (FIG. 15–2) makes it evident that this concentration is less clear-cut than that of either Asia or Europe. The greatest numbers of people live within the triangle whose points are Boston, Washington, and Chicago. Outward from this core triangle, dots spread relatively closely and evenly southward to the Gulf Coast. Westward, close spacing comes to an end almost along the 100th meridian (western Kansas). Beyond that line, there are a few small clusters, but only three of them, all lying close to the Pacific coast in the Puget Sound–Willamette Valley lowland, the San Francisco embayment, and the Los Angeles area, represent considerable numbers of people.

The tendency toward a spotted, or nucleated, pattern is even more noticeable than in Europe, primarily because of the even greater urbanization of North America. The foci are cities rather than intensively used agricultural lands. The great river plain of the Mississippi, while not empty, is settled by far fewer human beings than the river plain of the Yangtze in China (FIG. 15–2). Yet the relatively low density of rural areas is not a reflection of the lack of significance of agriculture; it results rather from differing methods of land use and also from differences in the length of time the land

has been occupied by agricultural people. In China, in fact in all areas occupied by Oriental peoples, human muscle supplies the power upon which agricultural production depends; in the United States, perhaps more than in any other area of Western culture, machines provide the power in agriculture as in all other phases of economic activity. Fewer people are engaged in direct agricultural labor and hence any specific area of agricultural land is peopled by smaller numbers.

Strikingly empty are the North American lands of Subarctic (Dfc) and Tundra (ET) climate (compare FIG. 15–2 and PLATE IV). The sharp break between nearly empty and moderately full lands in the interior of the United States lies close to the location of the boundary between the Semiarid (BS) climates and the humid ones. The mountain, hill, and plateau regions of the West likewise stand out as "empty" lands. The reasons for the distribution pattern in North America are complex, perhaps even more complex than in Europe, but, nevertheless, evidences of the significance of the physical setting are unmistakable.

OTHER CONTINENTS • Among the other continents, Africa supports the largest number of people. Particularly striking are the large numbers in the lower valley of the Nile (FIG. 15–2). There, on a well-watered river plain like a trench cutting across barren desert, millions of agricultural people make their home. This ribbon of heavily peopled land is comparable on a small scale with the great river plains of Asia, but it is quite unlike any other area of large numbers on the African continent.

Such other well-populated areas as there are in Africa are widely scattered and discontinuous. In the northwest, the Atlas lands form one notable zone. Here, plains are limited in area and isolated from one another, forcing settlement of hilly and mountainous terrain. Along its southern margin, this belt is limited by Arid (BW) climate.

A faint sprinkling of dots over the great western bulge of the continent shows three

15-3

JOHANNESBURG, *Republic of South Africa, as seen from the summit of one of the gold mine dumps.*

main nuclei of population, all of them in Nigeria. In the north is Kano, the ancient city which is a southern gateway to trans-Saharan routes. The other two nuclei are in southern Nigeria on either side of the lower course of the Niger.

Two other foci are to be seen in central eastern Africa; one on the highlands of Ruanda-Urundi at the northern end of Lake Tanganyika, and the other in Uganda northeast of Lake Victoria. The final African center lies on the South African Plateau near Johannesburg (FIG. 15-3). The location of these three centers is not determined by the presence of plains. The centers in Ruanda-Urundi and in Uganda are clusters of native peoples carrying on an agricultural economy. Their concentra-

tion is in part due to purely political action. The land was restricted by the governing European powers in the past to native ownership and occupancy, in a delayed attempt to correct earlier seizure of native lands. The Johannesburg nucleus is primarily an indication of the mineral wealth of the nearby Rand.

The population of South America (FIG. 15-2) is clearly arranged in clusters about the fringes of the continent. Each cluster is isolated from its neighbors by empty or virtually empty land. In the Pacific coastal regions, the main clusters are almost all away from the sea. Within the low latitudes, they occupy the comparatively cool highland basins; beyond the Tropic, in central Chile, they occupy the longitudinal valley between the coast range and the sea. In eastern South America, there is closer attachment to the sea; only in southeastern Brazil, near São Paulo and inland from Rio de Janeiro, are uplands the site of settlement. The huge empty interior of South America is tropical forest and grassland never occupied by any large number of native peoples and quite undesirable for colonization by people of European origin. South of the fortieth parallel or about the latitude of Bahía Blanca in Argentina, dryness, coldness, and ruggedness are the qualities which preclude intensive settlement.

Australia is the most nearly empty of all the continents on which a permanent population exists. Four focal cities (Brisbane, Sydney, Melbourne, and Adelaide) can be noted along the southeastern coastal stretch (FIG. 15-2), but there are no "filled-up" areas. Only a few dots indicate the presence of the scanty population of the rest of the continent.

POPULATION DENSITY

THE dot map of population distribution (FIG. 15-2) portrays the spread of people over the earth and gives some notion of the relative numbers living in one area as opposed

to another. Yet in the more crowded regions it gives little idea of *the number of persons per unit of area.* It does not answer the question, how do the main centers of eastern Asia compare with those of Europe in terms of close packing? In other words, it gives no quantitative knowledge of intensity of population. One of the devices which amplifies the understanding derived from the dot map is the map of population density (PLATE VII).

Meaning of Population Density

ARITHMETIC DENSITY • The most common expression of population density is a statement of the number of people living in a unit area, ordinarily the number of persons per square mile of land. This is known as *arithmetic density*, or *man-land ratio*. When one says population density, it is arithmetic density that is meant unless another type of density is specifically mentioned. Arithmetic density is usually expressed as a figure which is obtained by dividing the number of people in a given territory by the number of square miles included within the territory. For example, there are approximately 11,780 square miles of land in Belgium; the population, in 1959, was approximately 9,104,000. We may say then that the arithmetic population density of Belgium was 773 per square mile. This figure of density includes all types of land within the unit and makes no distinction between isolated small population groups or individuals on the one hand and concentrated large groupings on the other. It can therefore give only a broad suggestion of the real intensity of population. This is particularly true when the base units of land are relatively large; the smaller the land unit used, the more nearly accurate is the impression derived.

Despite this handicap, the idea of arithmetic density may be used to good advantage to amplify the idea of population pattern. As has been stated, the world population is approximately 2,902,000,000 and the world's total land area is about 57,300,000 square miles. The average density for the world is, then, 51 per square mile. Yet it is perfectly obvious from our study of the dot map of world population distribution (FIG. 15–2) that the arrangement over the earth is far from uniform. Actually, densities range from zero persons per square mile in Antarctica to over 100,000 per square mile in some of the world's larger cities. If, however, the land surface of the earth is considered in small enough units and the density for each of the small units is plotted on a map, there emerges a revealing pattern of population densities (PLATE VII).

OTHER TYPES OF DENSITY • The idea of population density may be treated in many ways other than the simple statement of man-land ratio. In detailed studies of small areas, these other measures of density are usually of greater significance than the commonly used arithmetic density. In the attempt to understand the problems of underpopulation or overpopulation, of the ability of the land to support population, or of land use, it is frequently desirable to know how many people there are in any given area per unit of arable land (land fit for cultivation). The figure expressing this relationship is known as the *physiological density*. Similarly, another frequently used figure is that of *agricultural density*, or the number of agriculturally occupied people per unit of arable land. *Rural density* is the number of people carrying on rural activities and living in rural settlements within a unit area; *urban density* represents the number of people carrying on urban activities and living in urban centers within a unit area. The major difficulty involved in the use of any of these types of density for world comparisons is the inadequacy of data. While there are sufficiently accurate figures available for area and population in relatively small units, at least for the parts of the world where the greater numbers of the world's people live, there is far from adequate information on arable land and on the economic activity of individuals. It is therefore more desirable to use arithmetic density for world comparisons, but it is absolutely essential to remember the shortcomings of the results.

Density Maps

Maps of population density are frequently used instead of dot maps to indicate the distribution of people over the land. Actually, a greater contribution is made when they are used in conjunction with dot maps. Since the dots on most dot maps are placed approximately where the population actually lives, the detailed pattern of distribution which results is a relatively accurate one; however, there is nothing about a dot map that expresses quantitatively the number of people per unit of land. On the other hand, the density map does show how many people live on a given unit of land, but does not show just where within the unit these people live. Together, the maps show both the "where" and the "how closely packed."

World Population Densities

The world map of densities (PLATE VII) re-emphasizes the broad pattern expressed by the dot map of population distribution (FIG. 15–2), but does so in quantitative terms. By a comparison of the two maps just referred to, this point can be illustrated. One of the areas where large numbers of people are concentrated is the North China Plain. On the dot map, it is clear that the number is large and that the area occupied has a distinct shape; on the density map, the shape of the intensively occupied area is less exact, but one can see that, while the density is over 250 per square mile for the whole region, there is one strip along the inner edge of the plain where the density rises to over 500 per square mile.

Very high densities in dominantly rural areas are characteristic of the Asiatic population concentrations. There, intensive use of the relatively small amounts of level alluvial land supports almost unbelievable densities. Rural density exceeds 1280 per square mile, more than two per acre, on many of the small plains of the Japanese islands. In the Canton area of

South China, average densities over 4000 per square mile are reported.

Similarly, great densities are to be found in the dominantly rural valley of the lower Nile.

In other areas, high densities result mainly from the spatial frequency of large cities, as, for example, in the Rhine–Ruhr area of Germany or the London and Lancashire districts of England. Some of the large cities of the world have extraordinary densities where, for example, the crowding has become so great as to force a vertical layering of population in closely packed apartment districts. And all of the cities of the Western world have huge temporary densities at least during the busy, daytime hours. In centers like New York, with its great office buildings and stores, its skyscrapers so characteristically American, the daytime population density may temporarily exceed a million per square mile.

AREAS OF ESPECIALLY HIGH DENSITY • Outstanding in the eastern Asiatic area of dense population are the areas with densities over 500 per square mile (PLATE VII). In the Japanese islands, the plain upon which Tokyo stands is the northeastern end of such an area. A zone extends southwestward to include all of the small plains which border the Inland Sea between the islands of Honshu, Kyushu, and Shikoku. In China, as has been noted, the inner central portion of the North China Plain has densities well over 500 as do also a small portion of the Szechwan Basin of the upper Yangtze, the lower portion of the Yangtze Plain and the river's delta, the small plains which fringe the southeast coast, and the Canton region in the delta of the Si. The southern portion of Taiwan and some parts of Java are likewise extremely densely peopled. In the Indian peninsula, the lower and middle valley of the Ganges and small portions of both the southeastern and southwestern coastal lowlands support well over 500 persons per square mile.

The European nucleus shows fewer and

less extensive sections of very high density, while those of North America are still more limited. In the British Isles, the Central Lowland of Scotland, the Newcastle, Lancashire, Cardiff, and London areas reach slightly above the figure of 500. On the mainland of Europe, the Flanders Plain, the Rhine Delta, the middle Rhine–Ruhr area, and the Dresden section of Germany are the only sizable regions which reach the 500 figure. In North America, only the coastal zone between Boston and Philadelphia attains such density.

The only other area of very high density is the valley of the Nile in its Egyptian portion. There, the degree to which people are crowded together becomes all the more noticeable because of the nearly empty lands on either side of the valley.

AREAS OF ESPECIALLY LOW DENSITY • At the opposite extreme in the density scale lies Antarctica with a density, so far as permanent population is concerned, of zero per square mile. The same applies to inner Greenland. Much larger areas show densities below two per square mile. The great belt of land with Arid (BW) climate reaching from the Atlantic coast of northern Africa through Arabia and northeastward into western Manchuria is, for the most part, very scantily populated. From northern China, this thinly peopled zone spreads further northward to include all of northern and eastern Siberia and westward over the Arctic fringe of Europe. Throughout this whole zone, climate is an effective deterrent to the support of great population densities. Likewise, isolation or difficulty of access, an expression of the location factor, plays its part in keeping the density low.

The same influences are significant in producing the areas of low density through many other parts of the world. In southwest Africa and over the larger part of Australia, Arid (BW) climate prevails; and population densities are very low. In the Patagonian portion of South America and in the Great Basin and Rio Grande areas of North America, similar conditions prevail. Subarctic (Dfc) and Tundra (ET) climates coupled with isolation produce the thinly peopled expanse of Alaska, Canada, and Labrador. The presence of rugged high mountains suggests the dominant reason for low densities in many parts of Alaska, western Canada, and the central western United States as it does also for some of the Andean sections of southern South America.

Other prominent areas with a density less than two per square mile are to be found in the northern interior of South America and in western and northern New Guinea. Here again, difficulty of access and climate are the main reasons.

Limitations on Population Density

From the preceding brief examination of the areas of extreme population density, it is evident that the limitations imposed on density are not derived from the elements of the physical setting alone. The quality of the physical base is, to be sure, a significant part of the story, but it is not the whole story. Density really depends primarily upon how people make a living, that is, upon occupations; occupations are strongly dependent in turn upon the nature of the physical setting. Yet actually, it is nowhere too hot, too cold, too dry, or too wet for man to live; rather, it is everywhere basically a question of whether man knows how to and can *make a living* in an area or not.

Consider western and northern New Guinea. A review of the climate, landforms, native vegetation, and soils is sufficient to convince anyone that the physical setting is not radically different from that of the Ganges Delta. Yet, New Guinea supports fewer than two persons per square mile while the Ganges Delta supports over 500. Again, many parts of the Amazon Basin are similar to southern Nigeria physically; yet, southern Nigeria is inhabited by from 50 to 100 persons per square mile while little of the Amazon Basin can show a density as high as 25 per square mile. The lower valley of the Yangtze in China has densities far over 500 per square mile; density in the lower Mississippi valley in the United States, a broadly similar physical area, drops below 25 per square mile.

Sufficient examples have been given to show that elements other than physical must be effective limitations on population density. If the physical base does not provide the answer alone, then we must turn to the cultural scene. How do the ways of living and of making a living of the inhabitants of New Guinea differ from those of the people of the Ganges Delta? Are the people who live in southern Nigeria the same in their way of life as those who inhabit the Amazon Basin? Do the people of central China use the land in the same manner as those who occupy the lower Mississippi valley?

When we examine these questions we must seek the relevant social, economic, and political facts. Such facts are often more significant in the explanation of the irregular scattering of population over the world and of the varying population intensities than are the features of the physical setting. The relevance and significance of social, economic, and political facts are pointed up by the facts of settlement, which are discussed in the next chapter.

• CHAPTER OUTLINE •

World Population

POPULATION NUMBERS
  Present World Population
  Population Growth
   GROWTH CATEGORIES
   WORLD PATTERN OF GROWTH

POPULATION DISTRIBUTION
  Dot Maps
  Main Features of World Population Distribution
  Continental Patterns of Population Distribution
   ASIA

EUROPE
NORTH AMERICA
OTHER CONTINENTS

POPULATION DENSITY
  Meaning of Population Density
   ARITHMETIC DENSITY
   OTHER TYPES OF DENSITY
  Density Maps
  World Population Densities
   AREAS OF ESPECIALLY HIGH DENSITY
   AREAS OF ESPECIALLY LOW DENSITY
  Limitations on Population Density

• REVIEW QUESTIONS •

1. Has there been any change, throughout the period of human history, in the limitations imposed upon man by the physical environment?
2. Why have certain physical environments proved uninhabitable while others have been eminently satisfactory human habitats?

3. Is there any close relationship between the area of a country and the size of that country's population? Is there any close relationship between the physical nature of the country and the size of its population?
4. Outline the broad features of world population growth.

5. What are the four major population growth categories? How do they differ from one another?
6. Why is the rate of population growth not uniform over the whole world?
7. Describe the main features of world population distribution. Offer some reasons for the "blank spots" on the world population map.
8. What are the outstanding features of population distribution in Asia? What relationships between population distribution and physical features of the land are outstandingly evident?
9. Why does the population pattern of Europe have a "spotted look" while that of Asia does not?
10. Why is arithmetic density of population so common a basis for the construction of world population maps?
11. For what purpose would a world map of agricultural population density be especially useful? Why?
12. Is there any reason to believe that population density is causally related to the character of the physical setting? Discuss.
13. What consideration is basic to the study of limitations of population density, from a geographic point of view?
14. Give some examples of social, economic, and political facts which must be considered in any well-founded attempt to understand population distribution over the world.

16 Settlement Types and Contrasts

⟨ THE *relationships between people and land are not fully expressed by descriptive statements of numbers, distribution, and density of population. These facts alone tell only part of the story of how people of one area are grouped as compared with those of another area. Only the fuller knowledge of population arrangement provides specific information about man-land relationships. This arrangement is termed* settlement; *the details of arrangement of population on the land for any one area are spoken of as that area's* settlement pattern.

Settlement pattern is the result of the interplay of many elements, both cultural and physical. Of all of these elements, the ways in which man makes his living, his economies, have perhaps the most significant role to play. To an important degree, the economy reflects the physical nature of the land and

the cultural attainments of the people who occupy it. If we are to under-
stand differences in settlement over the face of the earth, we must consider
the broad classes of economy. Each class represents one kind of solution to
the problem of mastery of the human habitat.

RELATIONSHIP OF SETTLEMENT
TO OTHER CULTURAL ELEMENTS

Economies

HUNTING-FISHING-COLLECTING • The simplest of all economies is the *hunting-fishing-collecting* economy. In this type of economy, the populace is almost completely absorbed in securing food, shelter, and clothing from the area in which it lives. Adjustments are made to the character of the physical setting with little attempt to change that setting. It is obvious that such an economy places strict limits upon the size of the human group which is supported in any given area. At best, the occupying of an area is temporary. Mobility is essential; the human group has no fixed place of abode. While temporary marks may be left upon the landscape, those marks are sooner or later either obscured or obliterated.

The hunting-fishing-collecting economy is strictly dominant in only a few areas of the world today. These areas are on the fringes of the heavily peopled parts of the human habitat. In the East Indies and on the poleward margins of the Americas and Eurasia, small groups still live primitively by hunting, fishing, or collecting, or by the combination of all three. A few small groups in the Amazon and

African forests and the Bushmen of the Kalahari in South Africa still follow this primitive way of living.

PASTORALISM • With the domestication of animals came a way of making a living which differed from the hunting-fishing-collecting economy—*pastoralism* (FIG. 16–2). Man's problem became one of watching over animals, seeing that there was food and water for them, and protecting them from wild animals. Pastoralism offered support for larger human groups, but it still demanded mobility. Thus it acted as a determinant of a particular kind of settlement pattern.

AGRICULTURE • Still another economy, *agriculture*, developed when man domesticated plants. Here for the first time came the possibility of permanent attachment to the land. When sedentary, as opposed to migratory, agriculture developed, man truly "settled down." It was no longer necessary for him to hunt for food or to move continually in search of pasturage for animals. Agriculture enabled man to select a place of habitation and to live either in groups or in isolation, that is, in either a clustered or a scattered settlement pattern.

MANUFACTURING • Finally, man developed *manufacturing*, the most complex of his economies. This way of making a living requires not only direct production from the earth, but alteration or combination of agricultural and mineral products. Since it demanded living in groups usually fixed in certain small parts of the earth, this economy produced spectacular effects upon the arrangement of population

16–1

[OPPOSITE, TOP] IN *the extensive loess region of northern China, agglomerated rural settlement is the rule. Note the intensive use of level land and the terracing of steep slopes to increase the amount of level land in this densely peopled area.*

16–2   PASTORALISM *demands mobility, especially where pasture is scanty. A herd of goats in Big Bend National Park, Texas.*

over the land. Here the physical setting has a prominent place, for the availability of raw materials is equally significant with the availability of manpower.

EXPLOITATION • As adjuncts to the manufacturing economy, two other economies have arisen. The need for accumulation of materials brought into being an amplification of the simple hunting-fishing-collecting economy. The increased use of metals in manufacturing necessitated the securing of materials directly from the earth's crust by mining. The forests were used to supply wood and other plant materials by modern forest operations like lumbering or gathering of fruits, gums, saps, and the like. The sea provided still further raw materials. All of these ways of making a living, in so far as they are carried on without thought of replacement of the resource, may be spoken of as *exploitation*.

COMMERCE • Manufacturing implies division of labor and exchange of products. When the individuals involved are directly concerned not with the making or altering of products for human use, but with bringing together raw materials or transporting and distributing manufactured products, they are engaged in *commerce*.

Both exploitation and commerce are limiting elements in settlement pattern. Mining involves the concentration of human beings where there are ore deposits. Exploitation of the forest may require either large numbers concentrated at one site or very small groups scattered through the forest. Use of the sea requires ports on the sea's edge. And commerce demands ties to certain sites at route ends and crossings.

VARIETY WITHIN ECONOMIES • There is an almost infinite variety in the practice of any one economy by different peoples; in addition, variety is introduced into any economy with the passage of time. Consider, for example, agriculture. Agricultural methods differ noticeably from one group to another even though the physical settings occupied by the two groups may be quite similar. Likewise, there is change in the agricultural methods of any one human group through time. Both of these facts affect settlement pattern materially. The wheat agriculture of the Great Plains of the United States differs in many ways from that of the Russian steppes, to suggest only one example of difference between human groups. And the mid-nineteenth century grain agriculture of New England has been supplanted by dairying and specialty cultivation today, to suggest the changes within the same cultural group through time.

Variations of the magnitude just cited are important matters in detailed study. Yet they cannot be fitted into a survey on a world scale. It is rather to the broad classes of economy enumerated above and to their outstanding role in the development of settlement pattern that attention is here directed.

Other Cultural Factors

In addition to the broad economies which are listed above, one must take into account the cultural heritage of the individual group if one is to understand the settlement pattern of any area. Different segments of the human race have acquired, throughout their histories, certain ways of doing things, certain attitudes, certain ways of thinking. All of these cultural ways are made observable in the forms of individual buildings, settlements, fields, modes of transport, and other cultural impedimenta. No two groups develop the same culture; each has its own way of fitting into the physical setting and of making use of the elements of that setting.

Many of the features of settlement are brought about simply because people of one culture are more or less able to make use of a given physical setting than people of another culture. In many instances, such features as political organization, language, and religion have profound effects upon group habits, reactions to other groups, and, ultimately, upon the way in which people occupy land. The political organization of a group provides the areal framework for the legal or jurisdictional systems by which groups of people carry on the business of making a living. So far has this cultural element been associated with human living that little of the world's land area remains upon which the pattern of political control is not impressed. Lines on the map show how far the control of one political group extends. Nearly the whole of the earth is divided among the many sovereign states. The political map of the world (PLATE II) is the map which is perhaps most commonly thought of as providing a key to essential differences from one part of the human habitat to another.

Language differences (FIG. 16–3) create still another pattern which has a place in the detailed understanding of how people use the land. Language is the principal means by which ideas are transmitted; often language differences are the principal reasons for failure in the transmission of ideas. Thus, they play a vital part in the convergence or divergence of human group relations, and in similarities or differences throughout the human habitat.

The role of religion is much more difficult to assess. There exist no truly adequate measures by which an accurate map presentation of the world pattern of religions may be shown in detail. Further, adherence is no measure of effective living within any given religious creed. Yet differences in religion provide still another pattern (FIG. 16–4) which is effective to a degree. It underlies the moral codes of human groups. In such a role, it makes a contribution to total culture and thus conditions the man-land relationships. Linguistic and religious differences are noted here for Europe because the patterns there are relatively simple ones.

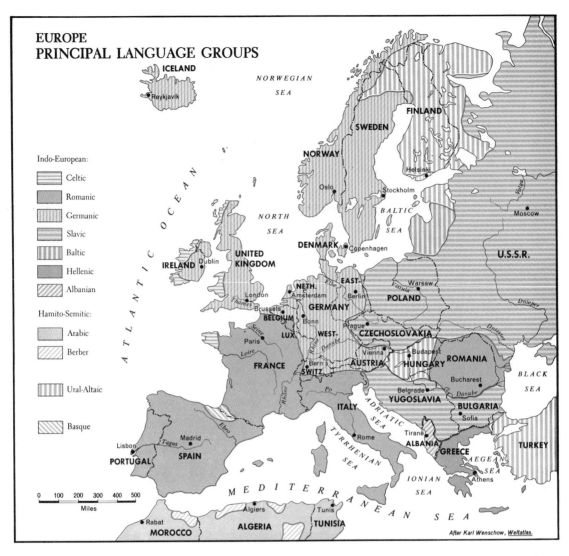

EUROPE
PRINCIPAL LANGUAGE GROUPS

Indo-European:

Celtic

Romanic

Germanic

Slavic

Baltic

Hellenic

Albanian

Hamito-Semitic:

Arabic

Berber

Ural-Altaic

Basque

After Karl Wenschow, *Weltatlas.*

16-3   LANGUAGE *groups indicate cultural associations. In Europe and adjacent areas, they help to explain many of the cultural differences from place to place.*

While each group has developed its own cultural hue and there are therefore a great number of culture groups in the world, two great cultures stand out clearly in the world today—the culture of western Europe and the Americas, known collectively as *Western* or *Occidental* culture or civilization, and the culture of eastern and southern Asia, known as *Oriental.* Western culture is distinguished basically by its dependence upon the use of machines powered by chemical and electrical energy; Oriental culture, by the use of human power.

Largely through its use of machine power, Western culture has spread from its original European base throughout most of the world. First, it moved by colonization to the Americas and then through trade to Africa and the

EUROPE
DOMINANT RELIGIOUS AFFILIATION

Legend:
- Protestant (Christian)
- Roman Catholic (Christian)
- Orthodox (Christian)
- Moslem

ICELAND
Reykjavík

NORWEGIAN SEA

SWEDEN
FINLAND
NORWAY
Oslo
Helsinki
Stockholm
BALTIC SEA
Moscow
U.S.S.R.
Volga

NORTH SEA

DENMARK
Copenhagen

UNITED KINGDOM
IRELAND
Dublin
London
Thames

NETH.
Amsterdam
Elbe
EAST-GERMANY
Berlin
Warsaw
Vistula
POLAND

BELGIUM
Brussels
Bonn
WEST-GERMANY
Prague
CZECHOSLOVAKIA
Dnieper

LUX.
Paris
Seine
Loire
Rhine
Danube
Vienna
AUSTRIA
Budapest
HUNGARY
ROMANIA
Dniester

FRANCE
SWITZ.
Bern
Po
Belgrade
Danube
Bucharest
BLACK SEA

ITALY
ADRIATIC SEA
YUGOSLAVIA
BULGARIA
Sofia

PORTUGAL
Lisbon
Madrid
Tagus
SPAIN
Ebro
Rome
Tirane
ALBANIA
GREECE
TURKEY
AEGEAN SEA
Athens
IONIAN SEA

TYRRHENIAN SEA

M E D I T E R R A N E A N   S E A

0 100 200 300 400 500
Miles

Algiers
Tunis
Rabat
MOROCCO
ALGERIA
TUNISIA

Modified from Karl Wenschow, *Weltatlas.*

16–4   DOMINANT *religious affiliations suggest the basis for world variety.*

East. Advantages both in numbers of people and in equipment made possible an early disruption of the culture groups which the Europeans found in North America and a somewhat slower one in South America. The effects on native cultures in Africa occurred less rapidly and were less complete largely because there was less attempt at actual colonization; the possibilities of trade were of prime importance and the effects of contact were largely observable only in the slow disintegration of the African ways of living rather than in a wholesale destruction of them.

Last of all, and well after industrialization had become the keynote of Western culture, the active spread to the centers of Oriental culture took place. Here also, Western influences have altered and continue to alter the native culture; yet there is a profound difference from what has happened elsewhere.

In the Orient, the numbers of people are far greater than in any other area to which Western ways have been transferred. The West has had to superimpose itself on an already complex culture. Orientals began to take over enough salient features of what the Westerner offered to give a semblance of complete absorption. This is illustrated by the industrialization in Japan from the late 1860's to the 1940's and its revival in China and Japan since 1947, as well as by the expanding industrialization of India.

Slowly the industrial or machine way of life spread to other Oriental culture areas, to India, China, and even to parts of the East Indies. But Western ways have been imposed upon a base and not substituted for it. Western culture in the Orient is like a layer of paint upon a wooden house. Though eastern and southern Asia have felt the contact of the West, the underlying Oriental culture still remains.

Through the past three decades, cultural change has been particularly apparent within the U.S.S.R. It cannot yet be stated whether the change has brought about a real amalgam of Western and Oriental cultures or is simply a phase in the evolution of Western culture. On the surface, like a veneer, Western cultural forms, represented chiefly by dependence upon use of machines, are certainly evident. Beneath the surface, the use of human power still prevails. Yet one distinguishing characteristic labels the Soviet development as somewhat different from both the standard Western and the standard Oriental cultures; that is the complete elimination of private ownership and the substitution for it of state ownership. The individual human being is, for the Soviet group, no longer the unit; rather, the whole population operates collectively for the state.

Whether the development within the U.S.S.R. is viewed as an amalgam of the two dominant world cultures or as an evolutionary phase of one of them, the way of life which it represents has spread rapidly from the former European Russia over a significantly large portion of the Eurasian land mass. On the west, it comes into direct contact with typical Western culture, and has actually superseded it in part of the contact zone; on the east, it is spreading actively through a large segment of Oriental culture, apparently more thoroughly than typical Western culture did before it. There is certainly indication that a third culture, the *Soviet* culture, may be attaining the world significance of the Western and Oriental cultures.

Because its ideology is directly concerned with the place of the individual in the scheme of the state, Soviet culture must inevitably have effects upon the way in which the individual makes a living and, through this, upon settlement. These effects may be found to differ greatly from those of Western and Oriental cultures; at present, however, it is not clear exactly what the differences are.

In the more isolated parts of the world like the interior forests of the Amazon Basin or the nearly unknown interiors of Borneo and New Guinea, for example, native cultures still bear little of the imprint of the two dominant world cultures. But native cultures play less and less significant roles throughout the world. Their effect in shaping settlement patterns is confined to small areas and to small populations. They exist really as curious fragments from the past.

Consider, for example, the change which has come in the life of the Eskimo. Prior to contact with European peoples, the Eskimo was a primitive hunter and fisher. His very life depended upon his skill in securing the necessities for survival by seeking out the animal life over long distances and with crude implements. When Europeans came, the Eskimo was provided with firearms which made hunting easier for a time, until the kill exceeded the rate of reproduction. This meant first of all a change from essentially mobile to sedentary settlement. Where formerly a family group, or perhaps two or three such groups, might select dwelling sites at one place, remaining so long as the supply of food within hunting distance was sufficient, there came to be larger settlements near the points where contact with the Europeans could most easily be made. The balance between the ability of the land and sea to support and the way of living of the group was destroyed. It became impossible for the Eskimo to exist in his former habitat; he became a charge of the European peoples since he had adopted some features of their culture.

The economy of a people and the accompanying cultural heritage have the greatest potency in lending individual character to settlement in any one area. A physical setting may impose limits more or less broad upon utilization by human beings; but, for every economy, there are as many settlement possibilities as there are culture groups. Realizing this, one can recognize that the study of the cultural elements must not be a detailed catalogue; rather, it must be an analysis of those features which are areally and humanly of major significance.

MAJOR CONTRASTS IN SETTLEMENT

Mobile versus Sedentary Population

I N SOME parts of the world, human beings, in making their living, move from one place to another without fixed abode. These people are *nomads*, like many of the tribal groups of inner Asia. Their whole living depends upon herds of animals such as sheep and goats. Most commonly, nomads inhabit desert margins where rainfall is irregular in occurrence and uncertain in amount. The animals must have pasturage, and this means a constant search for areas of plentiful grass. Nomads must be ready to move when word of rainfall in any accessible area reaches them, for rainfall means new pasture. Though nomads live in groups, their dwellings are purely temporary and are easily moved from one location to another.

Similar to the nomads of the desert margins are those of the Arctic tundra: for example, the Lapps of northern Scandinavia. These small groups depend for their whole existence upon the reindeer; their arrangement upon the land is a shifting one between the summer pasturage in the tundra and winter shelter within the margins of the northern coniferous forest, or taiga.

In other areas, such as some of the tropical forests, some tribal groups depend entirely upon what they can secure from hunting and fishing, or by collecting the edible plant products of the forest. For a period, they attach themselves to specific locations, building crude dwellings as centers of activity (FIG. 16–5), but the time comes quickly when the local sources of supply are exhausted and the group must move to a new area. The population is a mobile one, although perhaps not as mobile as the

ARCHBOLD EXPEDITION, AMNH

16–5

A DESERTED *native encampment on the floodplain of the Idenburg river in north-eastern Netherlands New Guinea. Crude settlements of this sort form temporary centers for the small, mobile populations of the tropical forests.*

nomadic groups that depend upon animal pasturage.

The Eskimos of the Arctic fringelands are another example of a mobile population, shifting their place of attachment to the land with the demands of their fishing-hunting-collecting way of making a living. They are less mobile than the forest tribes or the nomads, for certain locations are known by them to offer better bases for hunting, fishing, and collecting than others, and to these bases they frequently return. Yet the imprint they make upon the land is slight.

Unlike mobile populations, most of the world's people are tied to specific places on the surface of the earth. This *sedentary* or fixed population provides relatively long-lasting patterns and forms which can readily be observed and compared. A knowledge of these essential elements is basic to an understanding of the cultural phase of the human habitat.

Disseminated versus Agglomerated Population

Among sedentary populations, the character of settlement varies widely. At one extreme is the isolated dwelling which houses a single individual or family (FIG. 16–6). At the opposite extreme, dwellings may be so closely massed as to leave no part of the local surface uncovered, or at least only a small plot surrounding or next to each of the individual dwellings. In some of the world's large cities, population closeness is measured not in terms of the area occupied, but actually in terms of vertical as well as horizontal arrangement. Apartments crowd one small group on top of another. People are literally "piled up."

When individual dwellings are scattered over the land, the population pattern is said to be *disseminated*. When dwellings are packed close together, the settlement pattern is spoken of as *agglomerated*. As the derivation of the word implies, disseminated population is population "scattered abroad," population which

is strewn like seed over the land. Similarly, agglomerated population is population "collected into a mass."

It must be clearly stated that the two terms, disseminated and agglomerated, are used relatively. Study on a world scale precludes considering each individual human being. It is necessary to use a coarser base, which can reasonably be the dwelling. On such a scale, complete dissemination is understood to mean a scattering of single dwellings, with their associated buildings, over a given area, so arranged that there is no suggestion of grouping or clustering. Complete agglomeration, on the other hand, implies close massing of dwellings and other buildings with no isolated dwellings between clusters.

Dissemination may characterize population arrangement in either sparsely or densely settled lands. No minimum or maximum distance between buildings can be stated to serve as the line between dissemination and agglomeration. It is simply the scattered or clustered nature of the pattern which the descriptive term indicates. Also possible is the mixed or combination pattern in which agglomerations are spotted throughout a general background of disseminated settlement.

Man is, after all, a gregarious animal; he tends to live in groups rather than alone. There is ample evidence to show that man existed first as a tribal animal wandering about in search of food. When agriculture was invented, the tribal groups settled down. Thus early sedentary population assumed an agglomerated pattern. In many parts of the world, this agglomerated pattern has persisted right down to the present. Dissemination came relatively late in the human time scale. Though it characterizes relatively few parts of the world, those parts are extensive.

Rural versus Urban Population

The distinction between rural and urban, like the distinction between disseminated and

16–6   ISOLATED *farmstead in the wheatlands near Dimmitt, Texas.*

agglomerated in the description of settlement pattern, is a relative one. There is no immediately evident sharp line which divides rural folk from urban. A *rural* population means one predominantly engaged in primary production of the basic necessities of life directly from the land itself. An *urban* population means one which has no direct interest in the production of the materials of food, shelter, or clothing from the land itself. Urban folk are engaged in transporting, manufacturing, buying, and selling the materials for their food, shelter, clothing, and general comfort; or in educating the people, managing the affairs of state, or merely "living in town."

Obviously, rural population is more likely to be arranged in a disseminated pattern than urban population. Yet rural folk need not necessarily be scattered over the land. In fact, agglomerated rural population is more common and more numerous, for the world as a whole, than is disseminated. Urban population is almost entirely agglomerated. It is estimated that fully three-quarters of the world's population lives in agglomerations of one type or another.

Despite the huge size of many centers like London, New York, or Tokyo, the actual total of urban population is far less than the total of rural population. Urban settlement characterizes the Western world, specifically Europe and the areas colonized by peoples of European origin. On the other hand, the rural agglomeration is most typically Oriental.

Major Contrasts in Settlement | 371

EVEN today, in this Machine Age, dependence upon primary production from the land is fundamental to our whole existence. Direct use of the land is the way of living for the vast majority of human beings; most populations are rural. Their arrangement on the land is the matrix in which urban populations are set.

Agglomerated Rural Population

A rural agglomeration is a relatively closely built cluster of buildings surrounded by fields, pastures, or woodland areas. Dwellings constitute a large part of the cluster, but there are also storage sheds for farm produce and implements, and barns for housing animals. Possibly there are a church, a school, and a town hall. Practically the entire population is concerned with cultivating the surrounding land or in raising animals—in living directly from the land. To augment their living, some of the inhabitants may engage in selling some commodity. For example, someone in the settlement may offer food for sale and possibly add to that a small supply of tools or machinery. Professional people, like doctors, ministers, and teachers, may live in the agglomeration. But primarily, the life of the settlement is tied to the land and, except as the settlement may contribute its agricultural surpluses to the outside world, it is essentially self-contained. The settlement is first and foremost the dwelling place of an agricultural society.

Rural agglomerations are usually described as *hamlets* or *villages*. There is no clearly defined difference between the two except in size; hamlet is used to describe a very small rural settlement of, say, five or six, or even fewer, dwellings and their associated buildings, whereas village implies a greater number. Generally, too, village implies a greater number of people who are not directly concerned with farming, and it suggests the presence in the settlement of buildings set aside as retail stores.

The appearance and structure of the hamlet or village varies widely from one part of the world to another. There is no universal characteristic except that of function; always, the agglomeration forms the dwelling place for a group engaged in direct use of the land. Beyond that, the number, size, appearance, and arrangement of buildings corresponds to the traditions and habits of the particular group of people and to the nature of the land from which they derive their living.

For example, the typical village in many parts of southern Japan consists of a close-packed cluster of bamboo and thatch dwellings and sheds, so tightly pressed together as to allow only narrow passageways between adjacent buildings. The whole settlement occupies a bit of ground only slightly above the level of the surrounding irrigated rice fields. Seldom are there roads leading to and from the village. Narrow pathways following along the tops of the low dikes which separate the rice fields are the only connecting lines from one village to the next. Commonly, the village is encircled by a brushy hedge which stands out prominently because of the absence of trees and bushes elsewhere.

Inhabitants go out from the village early in the day to work their fields, returning again at night. A farmer's land is seldom in one continuous piece; it is likely to be in several fragments in scattered locations about the settlement. The whole life of the inhabitants, often members of only one or two large family groups, is a daily pulsing out onto the land and back into the village. The fact that the landholdings are scattered and the cultivation intensive means that the villagers must devote constant attention to their work. The village is the focal point from which a small portion of the human habitat is made to perform its function.

16–7   A TYPICAL *hilltop village in south-central France: Turenne, near the southwestern edge of the Massif Central.*

The hamlets or villages in many parts of Europe are in considerable contrast to those of the Orient. In south-central France, for example, villages like Turenne (FIG. 16–7) are common. Turenne crowns the top of a low hill, with fields spreading down the slopes and away from the settlement. Its center is roughly rectangular in shape, with a château at one end and a church at the other. Forming the sides of the rectangle are the houses of the rural inhabitants, built one against the other. There is thus enclosed a *place*, or square, with

exits on either side of the church and château. Immediately back of the houses on the hill slopes are small kitchen gardens. Farther down the slopes are larger fields and, beyond them, pastures and bits of woodland.

There is the same daily movement out from the village to the fields and back, but it does not have the regularity characteristic of the Oriental village. Agriculture is less intensive and demands less constant attention in France than in the Orient. In addition, the village is not so completely a family settlement. Finally,

Rural Settlement | 373

the European village is tied in by roads to the transportation net of the larger areas; the village in Europe is not so self-contained as is that of the Orient.

In certain other parts of Europe, as in Hungary, rural agglomerations of several thousands of people are not uncommon features. These huge villages cover considerable areas of land, with each dwelling and its associated buildings set on a small plot. But the farm buildings are definitely clustered, arranged along streets to form collected settlements set in open cultivated or pastured land.

In the eastern seaboard regions of the United States, as in New England or the South, agglomerated rural settlement was the early mode. In colonial New England, farmhouses were built close together, usually fronting on a *common*. The common was originally a pasture area near the farmhouses, owned and used collectively by all the inhabitants of the village. Where it still remains today, it has become the village park. In the South, early establishment of plantations with their needs for large labor forces and the consequent importation of slaves developed another kind of rural agglomeration in the compact slave quarters.

These few examples suggest that there is great variety in the detail of rural agglomerated settlement. The unifying characteristic is the tie of the population to the land.

Disseminated Rural Population

Isolated farmsteads form another rural pattern (FIG. 16–6). The farm dwelling with its adjacent barns and sheds forms the population unit. Fields, pastures, and other land, from all of which the family draws its living, stretch out from the central unit unbroken by other buildings. The distance between farmsteads may be slight, say one-quarter of a mile, or great, as much as several miles. There is none of the compactness of the agglomeration; nor is there the daily flow of large numbers of

people to surrounding fields. Land used intensively usually lies close to the farmstead itself. Extensively cultivated lands, pastures, and wooded areas are commonly farther away. Each farm serves as a unit in itself, not as a fragment of a larger integrated hamlet or village.

World Distribution of Rural Settlement

The farm village characterizes the greater part of the Orient. Except for a few relatively small areas like Hokkaido, the northern island of the Japanese group, isolated farmsteads are rare. Throughout the southern islands of Japan, the densely peopled plains of China, Indonesia, Malaya, India, and Pakistan, close-set compact hamlets and villages are sprinkled thickly through the intensively cultivated flatter land (FIG. 16–1).

On through the Near East, as in the lowland of the Tigris and Euphrates rivers, and into Africa, as in the valley of the Nile, the rural agglomeration persists almost exclusively. In the larger part of Africa which is occupied by native peoples, like the Guinea lands, the Congo Basin, or parts of the East African Plateau, the agglomerated pattern of rural settlement is repeated.

The hamlet or village is the characteristic settlement unit through most of southern and eastern Europe. Even into the western part of that continent, it continues as a prominent form, but with the disseminated pattern becoming more and more prominent as one proceeds northwestward. Yet even in northwestern Europe, a thin scattering of rural population fails to mask the basic agglomerated pattern.

Through South and Middle America into Mexico, agglomeration is the rule, but in North America, and especially in the United States, it is virtually absent.

In colonial days, rural settlement in what became the United States followed the European tradition, with rural agglomeration the dominant form. Tradition, of course, was undoubtedly responsible, but the need for protection in a relative wilderness also lent strength to the tradition.

After the emergence of the United States as a nation, a land survey system was established for the public lands in the interior and later extended through the West. This system provided a framework within which a disseminated rural settlement pattern could develop.

Essentially, the survey system consisted of a series of grids or checkerboard designs of lines so numbered that each square had a specific designation. An east-west line was selected as a *base line* for each grid and a north-south line crossing the base line was selected as a *principal meridian* (FIG. 16–8). Six-mile-wide strips were laid off parallel to the base line; each strip was called a *township* and was numbered north or south from the base line. They were crossed by six-mile-wide strips parallel to the principal meridian; each of these was called a *range* and was numbered east or west of the principal meridian. Thus the land was blocked off into squares six miles on a side. Each of these squares was in a certain numbered township and also in a certain numbered range; it bore a designation like "Township 2 North, Range 3 East," often abbreviated as "T2N, R3E" (FIG. 16–8). There were many other squares in the grid bearing the designation "Township 2 North" and many others bearing the designation "Range 3 East." But no other square in the same grid had the same combination. Often the exact designation was replaced by a name, as, for example, "Oxford Township."

Each of the large divisions was further laid off into 36 squares, each one a mile on a side. These were called *sections* and were numbered beginning with the northeasternmost as 1 and following the scheme shown in FIG. 16–8. Thus any single square mile could be designated exactly. For example, as shown in FIG. 16–8, T2N, R3E, Section 31 can represent only one specific square mile. Its location is known with reference to the base line and principal meridian.

If only one base line and one principal meridian had been established for the whole United States, each land description would have been unique. Actually, several base lines and several principal meridians were established as the country expanded westward (FIG. 16–8, upper part). Consequently, it is necessary to mention the specific *grid* which is referred to, as well as the range and township. For example, one would speak of "Township 2 North, Range 3 East (T2N, R3E) on the *Michigan* base line and principal meridian," or "on the *Illinois* base line and principal meridian," whatever the case might be. One of the reasons for establishing several base lines and several principal meridians lies in the fact that the numbers can thereby be kept relatively small, minimizing confusion. Still another lies in the difficulty of the mechanics of surveying an east-west line as long as the width of the United States or a north-south line stretching from Mexico to Canada.

More detailed subdivision of the land is possible, as is indicated in FIG. 16–8. At the time when land was opened for settlement under the survey plan, the area available for homesteading was set at 160 acres. This is one quarter of a square mile, or one quarter of a section. Further, the survey provided that space for a roadway was to be maintained along each side of each section.

The relatively large area of the farms and the availability, theoretically at least, of roadways helped to bring about a settlement pattern in which farmhouses and buildings were disseminated rather than agglomerated (FIG. 16–9). As settlement spread into the drier West, larger and larger acreages were allowed for homesteading, so that farms came to be spaced more widely. Mechanization of agriculture and advances in transportation have likewise tended to increase dispersion.

Where physical obstacles, like swamps, lakes, or excessively steep slopes existed, there

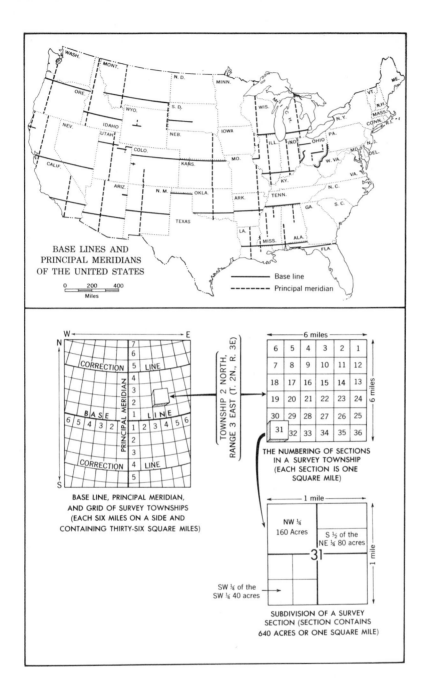

BASE LINES AND
PRINCIPAL MERIDIANS
OF THE UNITED STATES

0   200   400
Miles

―――― Base line
‑ ‑ ‑ ‑ Principal meridian

BASE LINE, PRINCIPAL MERIDIAN,
AND GRID OF SURVEY TOWNSHIPS
(EACH SIX MILES ON A SIDE AND
CONTAINING THIRTY-SIX SQUARE MILES)

TOWNSHIP 2 NORTH,
RANGE 3 EAST (T. 2N., R. 3E)

THE NUMBERING OF SECTIONS
IN A SURVEY TOWNSHIP
(EACH SECTION IS ONE
SQUARE MILE)

NW ¼
160 Acres

S ½ of the
NE ¼ 80 acres

SW ¼ of the
SW ¼ 40 acres

SUBDIVISION OF A SURVEY
SECTION (SECTION CONTAINS
640 ACRES OR ONE SQUARE MILE)

16–8

THE scheme of the rectangular land survey system of the interior and western United States.

is departure from complete regularity. Survey errors have also brought departure from true rectangularity in some areas. Yet, the arrangement of roads, fences, and fields commonly show by the regularity of direction and shape the influence of this type of land survey. And,

where it exists, farmsteads are scattered rather than clustered.

It is in lands quite recently settled by peoples of northwestern European origin, or under their influence, that the disseminated pattern is most characteristic. In addition to the

376 | *Settlement Types and Contrasts*

16–9　THE *pattern of dispersed rural settlement near Morley, Iowa, reflects the framework created by the rectangular land survey system.*

United States, Canada is an area of scattered rather than clustered rural population. So also are most of Australia and New Zealand, the areas of European colonization in South and East Africa, and some parts of South America. The "habit" of agglomeration has been lost in these areas.

URBAN SETTLEMENT

THE basic clue to the difference between a rural agglomeration and an urban agglomeration is the function or functions which the agglomeration performs. What is the purpose of the settlement? We have seen that the hamlet or village is essentially a cluster of dwellings and associated buildings which houses people most of whom are engaged in the direct use of the land. There is no great difference between one section of a rural agglomeration and another; the form and structure, or *morphology*, of a rural settlement is relatively simple. In an urban center, most of the people are engaged in other activities than the direct use of land. The settlement includes the dwellings of these people, but it also includes buildings of quite different aspect where the various economic activities are carried on. There is a marked difference between one section of an urban agglomeration and another. For example, an urban center existing on a coast and serving as a port has a definite dock and warehouse district quite distinct from, say, the residence district. Thus, the morphology of an urban settlement is more complex than that of a hamlet or village. Since it is from function that this essential difference between rural and urban agglomerations derives, it is to the study of urban functions that one must turn for the first clue to the character of urban settlement.

Urban Functions

Urban functions are of six major kinds. In the United States, the one that comes first to mind is, ordinarily, the making or adapting of goods for human use. More often than not, it is done on a large scale as *manufacturing*. It may, however, be carried on on a relatively small scale as a *craft*.

Next most common is the function of the exchange of goods, or *commerce*. There are really three facets to this function. One of these is *collection*, or the bringing together of large amounts of goods for efficiency in handling. For example, mining provides raw materials for manufacturing, but often ores or concentrates must be brought together from many small sources so as to be available in large enough amounts. So also must the products of the forests and seas be accumulated. Storage of large amounts of agricultural and manufactured goods to facilitate later exchange likewise requires the performance of the function of collection. In the exchange process, the *distribution* function must also be performed, as, for example, when materials are brought into a port in large bulk and then sent out in smaller lots. Exporting centers and supply centers carry on the same type of activity. Commerce may also involve *transfer*, as in the instance of change of method of transportation. Where river transport has to give way to overland transport, or vice versa, transfer is essential to the performance of the commercial function.

There are four other functions which are known as urban. *Administration*, as in government, is a necessary function of organized social life which must be carried on at some center of population. Similarly, the function

of *defense*, as illustrated in fortress towns or naval bases, is necessary and can be performed only in agglomerated settlements. Universities, religious centers, and art centers perform a *cultural* function. (It should be noted that *cultural* is here used in a very restricted sense.) Lastly, health and tourist centers perform the function of *recreation*.

The urban functions, then, are manufacturing, commerce, administration, defense, culture, and recreation. They stand contrasted to rural functions. When the population of any agglomeration, regardless of actual numbers, is primarily engaged in cultivating the land or in raising animals, the agglomeration is described as rural; when the population is in greater part engaged in one or more of the urban functions, the agglomeration is described as urban.

Situation and Site

SITUATION • To understand any agglomeration, it is necessary to appreciate its relation to the area in which it is located: its regional position or *situation*. This does not mean the precise location, which is indicated by latitude and longitude, but rather the relationship of the agglomeration to the region which it serves. For example, New York City is located on the coast of the northeastern United States where an embayed river mouth offers possibilities for the development of a protected harbor and where a fairly open valley system (that of the Hudson–Mohawk) affords relatively easy access to the interior of the United States (FIG. 16–10A). To illustrate further the idea of situation, it may be said that Paris lies near the center of the Paris Basin where tributary streams converge upon the Seine river to form a focus of routes (FIG. 16–10B). In this statement, the expression Paris Basin is understood to imply a plains area of northern France encompassed on the north, east, and south by nearly continuous belts of upland. The breaks in the upland rim, like the

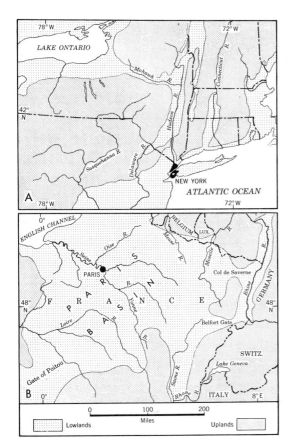

16–10

SITUATION *features of two present-day metropolises. A. New York. B. Paris.*

Gate of Poitou to the southwest and the Col de Saverne to the east, form natural land routes which center, as do the streams, upon the Paris location.

SITE • In contrast to the concept of situation, the detailed position of the agglomeration on the land is spoken of as the *site*. The site may be a hilltop, a peninsula, an island, or any other such specific bit of the surface.

The original site of New York City was the downstream end of a relatively high island near the seaward end of the estuary of the Hudson river. The present site includes not only the whole of this island, but the entire surface of other nearby small islands, the ad-

jacent end of Long Island, and the nearby shores of the mainland (FIG. 16–11A). The original site of Paris was an island in the Seine river a short distance downstream from the junction of the Seine and the Marne, where relatively high land approached close to the river's edge on both banks (FIG. 16–11B). The present site includes not only the original island, but the flood plain and valley slopes on both sides of the Seine upstream to just beyond the Marne junction and downstream for a distance of several miles.

Both situation and site change with the passage of time. Increase in population in any agglomeration brings with it expansion over a larger area, as has been suggested in the examples of New York and Paris. Loss of population may cause contraction of the site.

So far as situation is concerned, change is perhaps less obvious, but it is nevertheless real. For example, modern highways may bypass an old agricultural market town. The flow of goods is thereby diverted and the market loses its significance as a regional commercial center; its situation is changed. Or the productivity of an area might be altered by a shift from agriculture to manufacturing; new urban centers might arise to replace or compete with an older service center. The situation of the older agglomeration might thereby be radically changed.

Morphology

SIZE • Urban agglomerations cannot be reliably distinguished from rural agglomerations by size alone. An agglomeration may consist of a relatively small cluster of dwellings housing few people and covering only a few acres of land, or it may have inhabitants numbering in the millions and be so extensive as to cover hundreds of square miles. But neither the number of people nor the areal extent are sure measures of the function or the importance of the agglomeration. To be sure, rural agglomerations are usually smaller than urban ones.

Urban Settlement | 379

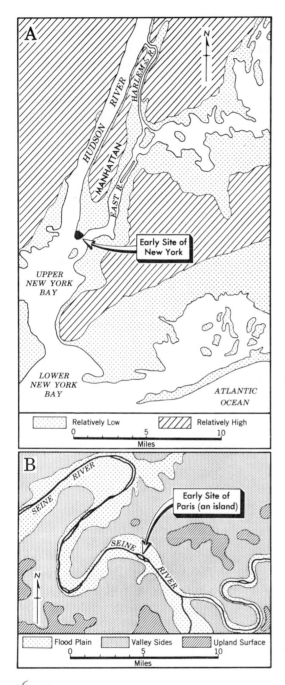

16–11

SITE *features of two present-day metropolises. A. New York. B. Paris.*

Likewise, large centers are usually of more importance than small ones. Yet a small collection of buildings at a grain-collecting center in the wheatlands of the Great Plains of the United States, and the few people who live in them, may have a regional significance far beyond that, say, of twice as large a settlement in the more heavily populated Northeast.

Size is often used arbitrarily, for convenience, as in the United States censuses in the past, to distinguish between rural and urban agglomerations. But such arbitrary distinction may lead to misunderstanding of the significance or even the nature of the settlements of any area. Only broadly, and then only as a contributing element to the whole problem, may emphasis be placed on size alone.

INTERNAL PATTERNS • The skeleton of any agglomeration is the pattern or scheme of its streets, which may be arranged either according to some geometrical plan or completely without regularity. Often the features of site conspire to favor certain lines of movement between buildings over others, and thus to determine the over-all configuration. Again, site may impose no control, so that the pattern develops entirely in accord with the desires or whims of the inhabitants.

In urban agglomerations that are old and had their origins in simple groupings of rural people, the patterns of streets may be quite irregular. The exact alignment of early houses and other buildings was not a matter of importance to the inhabitants. As the settlement grew large enough so that actual, formal streets were laid out, they had to follow as best they could the irregular lines between buildings. Many of the street patterns in lower New York (FIG. 16–12A) or the heart of Paris (FIG. 16–12B) are of this sort.

Sometimes pattern has been determined, directly or indirectly, by government decree. The urban settlements of Spanish America were laid out with a central plaza and streets parallel to its sides. Thus came a pattern of rectangular nature, with streets crossing one

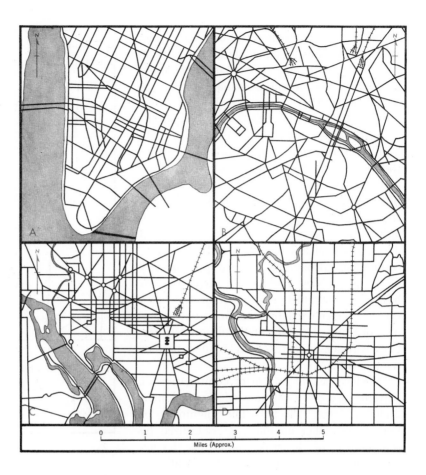

16–12

PATTERNS of principal streets in parts of four urban agglomerations. A. Lower New York. B. Central Paris. C. Central Washington. D. Central Indianapolis.

another at right angles. In the central and western United States, the rectangular land survey previously described brought original focus upon roads crossing one another at right angles. Generally, in crossroads agglomerations, additional streets developed logically along lines parallel to the roads forming the crossroads and thus at right angles to one another.

Increasing importance and size of an agglomeration create the need for speed and ease of access to its center from the periphery. Thus came the development of the radial pattern whereby streets lead from points on the periphery directly to a common center, much as the spokes of a wheel lead from the rim to the hub. Cross streets then tend to assume a weblike arrangement. The skeleton of streets

in Washington, D.C. (FIG. 16–12C), is a complex combination of radial and rectangular patterns. So is the skeleton of Indianapolis (FIG. 16–12D), although that is simpler.

Beyond these three basic patterns, irregular, rectangular, and radial, there are many others which have grown out of the vagaries of private individuals or of real estate development. These are irregular in a sense, but they are usually symmetrically so. Circular drives, curving and recurving lines, figure eights, and dead-end courts leading in from each of four sides of a large rectangular block are some of the familiar forms to be encountered in present-day growing urban agglomerations.

All of the patterns may occur in combination as well as individually, especially in large urban areas. As one proceeds uptown, the irregular pattern of lower New York (FIG. 16–12A) becomes a well-crystallized rectangular pattern, with only one notable exception, Broadway. The repeating radial patterns of Washington, D.C., are imposed upon a rectangular base (FIG. 16–12C). The radial pattern about the Place de l'Etoile in Paris links tenuously to the irregular framework farther into the old city, to the circular boulevards which belt the city, and to the great cross avenues of modern construction which tear right across the old irregular pattern (FIG. 16–12B). Similarly, where peculiarities of site restrict full development of any one pattern, local modifications are introduced. For example, the city of Syracuse, New York, has a street pattern basically rectangular, but much of the city's site is characterized by drumlins. The steepness of slope of certain of the drumlins interferes with an unrestricted rectangular pattern (FIG. 16–13).

Whatever single pattern or combination of patterns exists, the character of the agglomeration is deeply affected. The alignment of houses and other buildings is crystallized by the position of the streets and thus the agglomeration acquires a fixed quality. Additions to it or subtractions from it, both measures of growth, must in some way be articulated with the existing pattern. Despite changes of detail, the agglomeration as a whole retains a distinctive appearance, determined at bottom by its pattern of streets.

PROFILE OR CROSS SECTION • Something of the nature of any agglomeration is told by its *profile*, or sky line. In small rural settlements, the buildings are often widely spaced. Individual houses rise above low sheds, and huge barns may overshadow all. Rising near the center of the settlement may be the thin spire of a church. The whole profile of a small rural settlement is irregular and jagged, although trees often raise their rounded crowns to soften the sharpness of angular roof lines. Large urban agglomerations, especially in the United States, present quite a different profile.

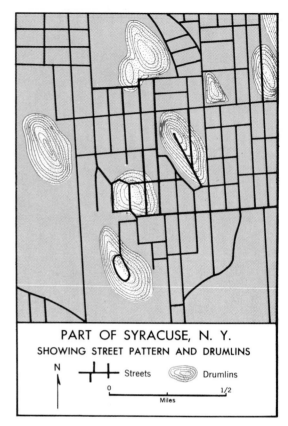

PART OF SYRACUSE, N. Y.
SHOWING STREET PATTERN AND DRUMLINS

N   Streets   Drumlins

0   1/2
Miles

16–13

PROMINENT *landforms may be responsible for irregularities in street pattern, as in the southeastern part of Syracuse, New York. There, steepness of slope on some of the drumlins which are part of the site has necessitated departures from true rectangularity.*

The outer edges may look like the profiles of rural settlements. As the center is approached, the buildings become more massive and higher, giving to the profile almost the impression of the cross section of a pyramid. The lines are straight or symmetrically rounded, man-made forms rather than natural ones.

In other parts of the world, this "piling up at the center" is less characteristic than in the United States. In Japan, for example, an urban agglomeration has a profile which, because of the absence of tall buildings, is almost indistinguishable from that of a rural settlement.

Only by great length does it suggest large size and reveal urban nature.

FUNCTIONAL AREAS • Urban agglomerations perform various functions for the groups living in them and for the area which surrounds them. While these functions may occur singly or in combination, each one involves certain types of buildings: for example, the appearance of a retail store like a grocery store, carrying on the commercial function, contrasts sharply with the appearance of a factory, which carries on the function of manufacturing. Similarly, a zone of retail stores or a shopping center within an agglomeration creates a scene quite different from the scene created by a grouping of factories. A residential zone is easily distinguished from, say, the campus of a college.

Each function presents a distinctive form, which tends to be localized within the agglomeration. An area which performs a special function is known as a *functional area*. Taken together, functional areas form a discernible pattern. They provide the remaining element of the morphology of agglomeration.

It is common, in American settlements at least, to refer to the downtown section. Usually, this means the section of the settlement which is given over to stores, public buildings, and the like. It is usually a part of the settlement definitely removed from individual residences, although large apartment buildings are often located in the downtown section. Similarly, there is generally a factory section. On the part of Americans, the concept of functional areas is thus tacitly recognized.

Within older settled parts of the Western world, distinctions between the specialized areas of any agglomeration are less clearly marked than in newer settlements. The history of the growth of any agglomeration often reveals why the various functions are performed in scattered rather than in collected zones. In European settlements, for example, residence often is maintained close to or in the same building with retail stores. The function of commerce may thus be so scattered as to leave no impression of a "downtown" section. In Oriental settlements, the same building may house a craft workshop, serve as the residence of the craft workers, and, at the same time, house persons engaged in intensive agriculture on a small plot of land nearby.

The arrangement of the functional areas results from the interplay of a wide variety of forces. At an early stage, the intersection of two highways, which may have given rise to the settlement in the first place, may be an attractive site for a store. Here people from the vicinity come to purchase needed supplies or to dispose of surplus agricultural items. In time, a second store may be established because there is good commercial opportunity. A third and many others may follow. An inn may be built near the crossroads. Gradually, there appears a nucleus within which all the buildings are used for commerce; they are occupied during the day by the people who are engaged in the performance of that function, but no one lives in them. A distinct functional area develops, a *commercial core* in this instance (FIG. 16–14A).

Sometimes factories are attracted to a commercial core by the presence of a large number of people, families of those active in commerce, which provides an available large labor supply. Wealth accumulated in commercial activity might be available for investment in industry.

However, if past growth of the commercial core has made land values too high, and the presence of residences about the commercial core makes adjacent land unavailable, factories are forced to the outskirts of the settlement. Gradually, under such conditions, there might grow up an industrial belt encircling the commercial and residential centers (FIG. 16–14B).

The growth of any agglomeration brings with it continual, far-reaching adjustments of its functional areas. If a settlement has developed a commercial core surrounded by residences which, in turn, are encompassed by a ring of

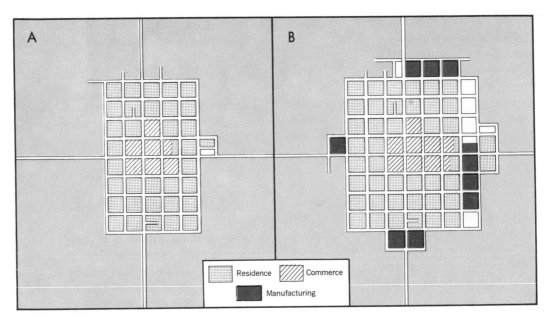

16–14   ARRANGEMENT of functional areas in hypothetical urban settlements, assuming a rectangular
street plan. A. A town with commercial core surrounded by residences. B. A small city with
commercial core, residence zone, and incipient manufacturing belt. In A, note the concentration
of commercial function near the intersection of through roads. In B, note the fringe location
of manufacturing and the close approach of the commercial core to the industrial belt along a
through route.

manufacturing plants, further growth in population requires expansion of the residence area. Often the only possibility lies in jumping beyond the manufacturing ring; soon new residence areas appear on the fringe, sometimes close to the factories for the workers, and sometimes well away from the factory belt for those who can afford to choose their own site. Here and there, small agglomerations may develop physically entirely separate from the original nucleus but economically still be part of it.

As newer residence areas spring up, there is usually a decline of the old residence belt near the center of the settlement. This decline is accompanied by outward spread of the commercial core and inward growth of the manufacturing belt. Old residences of the settlement's youth become rooming houses, gradually deteriorating and eventually being removed to make way for expansion of the other functional areas. To such zones on the fringes of the commercial core, the name *blighted area* or *slums* is frequently given in American cities.

With continued spread, distances within the agglomeration, especially between the residence districts and the commercial core, become so great that new scattered nuclei of commerce begin to appear irregularly in the outer residence districts. These are the occasional "corner stores," the "neighborhood shopping centers," so characteristic of growing American cities.

Further still, modern transportation has made it possible for urban folk to have their dwellings at considerable distances from their work. Intangibles, like the desire for space, and tangibles, like tax rates, have both contributed to the migration of urban people away from the urban nucleus. Where this movement has actually occurred, a zone of interpenetration of urban and rural settlement, the *rural-urban fringe*, has come into being.

Similarly, as the agglomeration spreads, details of site such as steepness of slope or the presence of a lake shore or a river may limit the growth of one or another of its functional areas. Congestion of traffic may necessitate cutting new streets or widening old ones. This in turn may bring about the rearrangement of functional areas, thus altering the whole character of the urban unit. Both physical and cultural elements combine to create the individuality of any urban agglomeration. Thus cities grow and change.

A conspicuously different type of growth has been evidenced in northwestern Europe since the late 1940's; most of it has been planned growth. Widespread destruction during World War II necessitated much rebuilding. In addition, marked increases in an already dominantly urban population have required expansion of living and working facilities. Rebuilding has frequently been feasible on such a large scale that the whole morphology of the urban area has been changed; even the site has, in some instances, been materially altered, as, for example, in Plymouth, England. In other instances, whole new towns have been planned and built on sites not formerly occupied by urban areas, as at Cumbernauld in Scotland.

In Great Britain with its high urban population density, the idea of the completely planned urban area, with limits placed upon its ultimate size, is strongly supported. Most of the development has so far been in terms of small urban units, but it has been announced that planning for a new city of a quarter of a million population is in progress. This is considered to be an attempt to halt the further spread of the mammoth London agglomeration. With proper planning before establishment of an urban area and with restrictions placed upon its ultimate size, all matters of situation, site, and morphology can be controlled so as to produce the most economically sound solution to the problem of increasing urbanization.

Types of Urban Agglomerations

As specified earlier, an urban agglomeration is one in which the greater part of the population is engaged in the performance of one or more of the urban functions. Geographically, the whole agglomeration is considered as the unit. Often, a continuously built-up area forming one agglomeration includes several political units. As a geographical unit of settlement, New York City, for example, spreads not only beyond the political city limits, but even across state boundaries. It is, nevertheless, all one urban agglomeration. No one can tell from the appearance of the agglomeration where one crosses a "city line." Similarly, there is no break in the geographical continuity of urban settlement in passing from the political unit of Chicago into Evanston.

Considered in this way, there are three types of urban units: town, city, and metropolis. Distinctions among these three are made first on the basis of the number of functions which each performs and secondly on the basis of morphology.

TOWN • When a single one of the urban functions dominates the life of the agglomeration, that agglomeration is known as a *town*. To be sure, in most American market towns, there are town halls or public buildings which indicate that government is carried on. There are schools and churches, visible evidences of the cultural function. Perhaps there is a printing shop where a newspaper is printed. And there may be a golf course, or a park with tennis courts, or a swimming pool. Yet the main function of the center is as a market for farm produce; its place in the region depends on commerce.

CITY • When an urban area acquires a second important function, it becomes a *city*. The acquisition of one or more additional functions materially complicates the pattern of functional areas. There is no longer simply a downtown section and the residential area; there are at least three clearly marked elements. In the example already given, if a market center should add a manufacturing zone, there would be three functional areas: the commercial core, the manufacturing zone, and the residential area.

Commonly, a successful market town in America adds the function of manufacturing. In this growth, the manufacturing plants are not like the newspaper which provides service primarily to the people of the town; rather, they are independent entities, serving a market well beyond the immediate confines of the settlement in which they are located.

Again, a market town may grow to such prominence that it is selected as the administrative center for a relatively large area, and carries on governmental functions as a county seat or a state capital.

Usually, city populations are larger than town populations. Yet, this is not imperative. The essential distinction lies in the greater structural complexity of the city. As a city adds to its functions, it tends to spread over a greater and greater area. On its outskirts, it begins to develop miniature reproductions of its own central section; thus, *suburban communities* come into being. Or a city, like Los Angeles, may spread to engulf other cities and towns and thus further add to its already great complexity.

METROPOLIS • The spread of the urban way of life coupled with population increases of tremendous size have created many huge urban areas throughout the world (TABLE 17). New York, London, and Paris are examples. Increase in size has been attended by constantly increasing complexity. Not only has each agglomeration passed the stage at which its patterns were easily comprehended and its individuality as an urban unit recognized; each has expanded so as to become a large region in its own right. Yet each performs urban functions for a greater and greater surrounding tributary area. Eventually, the tributary area has grown to include a large part of, or even the whole of, the human habitat. Such a cen-

ter carries no longer merely a local or national significance, but rather world import; it may properly be called a *metropolis*.

No specific figure of size can be used to define a metropolis. In general, that name is not applied to urban units with a population of under one million, but not all settlements of over one million may be accounted metropolises. Metropolis implies the presence of *satellite cities*, cities in their own right which have been tied into, or engulfed by the spread of, one huge urban nucleus. Really, an undefinable atmosphere of world significance coupled with large size and great morphological complexity justify the use of the term metropolis. When the agglomeration is clearly a part of the region in which it exists, when it performs urban functions dominantly for that region alone, it is not classed as a metropolis no matter how large the number of its inhabitants or what the extent of built-up area.

There are in the Orient several urban agglomerations of over one million inhabitants, complex in structure and performing many of the urban functions, and yet primarily of local significance. These are huge cities, but not metropolises. Nagoya in Japan is such a city; in contrast, say, with Tokyo, Nagoya is of relatively little note outside Japan. Similarly, Madrid has few of the metropolitan characteristics of Barcelona in Spain.

Though the term metropolis is not a rigid one, an approach to exactness may be made by study of the area economically tributary to an urban unit, that unit's *trade area*. It is easiest, of course, to delimit the trade areas of towns. Those of cities and metropolises are harder to discern. In studying a market town, for instance, one can plot easily the farm area it serves. At some distance from the town, the flow of goods and people is away from rather than toward the town, marking the commercial divides between one center's trade area and another's. By joining together the divides on all sides of a settlement, its trade area may be outlined. As an illustration, the trade areas

TABLE *17*

Metropolitan Areas of 1,000,000 or More as of January 1, 1961

	NORTH AND MIDDLE AMERICA	SOUTH AMERICA	EUROPE	U.S.S.R.	ASIA	AUSTRALIA	AFRICA
Over 10	New York		London		Tokyo–Yokohama		
5 to 10	Chicago Los Angeles	Buenos Aires	Paris	Moscow	Calcutta Osaka–Kobe Shanghai		
3 to 5	Detroit–Windsor Mexico City Philadelphia San Francisco–Oakland–San Jose	Rio de Janeiro São Paulo	Berlin Essen–Duisberg–Dortmund	Leningrad	Bombay Peiping Tientsin		Cairo
2 to 3	Boston Cleveland Montreal St. Louis Washington, D.C.	Santiago (Chile)	Birmingham Budapest Hamburg Madrid Manchester Rome Vienna		Bangkok Canton Chungking Delhi–New Delhi Hong Kong Jakarta Madras Manila Mukden Wuhan	Sydney	
1 to 2	Atlanta Baltimore Buffalo–Niagara Falls Cincinnati Dallas Havana Houston Kansas City (Mo.) Miami–Fort Lauderdale Milwaukee Minneapolis–St. Paul Pittsburgh San Diego–Tijuana Toronto	Bogotá Caracas Lima	Amsterdam Athens Barcelona Brussels Bucharest Cologne Copenhagen Düsseldorf Frankfort am Main Glasgow Katowice–Zabrze–Bytom Leeds–Bradford Lisbon Liverpool Mannheim–Ludwigshafen–Heidelberg Milan Munich Naples Newcastle upon Tyne Prague Stockholm Stuttgart Turin Warsaw	Baku Donetsk–Makeevka Gorki Kharkov Kiev Novosibirsk Tashkent	Ahmedabad Bandung Bangalore Changchun Chengtu Dairen Fushun Harbin Hyderabad Istanbul Karachi Kunming Kyoto Lahore Nagoya Nanking Pusan Saigon Seoul Sian Singapore Surabaja Taipei Taiyuan Tehran Tsingtao Yawata–Kokura–Shimonoseki	Melbourne	Alexandria Johannesburg–Germiston

SOURCE: Adapted from a list compiled by Richard L. Forstall, Rand McNally & Company. Reproduced with permission.

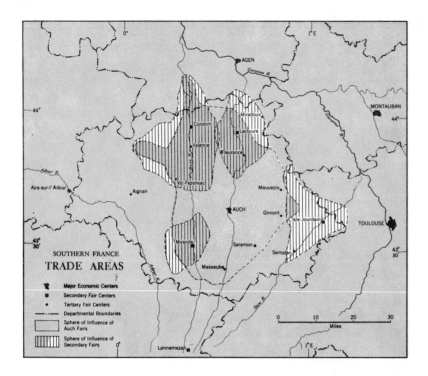

TRADE areas of a section of southwest France in which periodic fairs are still important economically. Note that the trade area of the fairs at Auch, the largest urban center in the Department of Gers, includes much of the trade areas of the fairs in secondary centers.

of a section of southern France are shown in FIG. 16–15.

Trade areas of towns may overlap slightly. In addition, those of towns combine to form those of cities. There is, thus, greater overlap in the instance of city trade areas than in those of towns. Pyramiding in this fashion, areas tributary to urban centers tend to become more extensive as the size and complexity of the centers increase. When it is apparent that the greater part of a continent and even areas across oceans on other continents lie directly within the trade area of any huge city, then that city may properly be classed as a metropolis.

Distribution of Cities

The urban form of settlement is relatively closely limited in its distribution over the world. The large city is seldom to be found in areas of low population density. In detail, there are exceptions to this generalization. For example,

Madrid, with a population of about two million, stands conspicuously in the thinly peopled expanse of the Spanish Plateau, and Rome rises abruptly out of almost empty surrounding lands. Yet, from a world view, the thinly peopled areas are nearly devoid of large urban areas.

With only a few exceptions, cities are not found in the great lowlands of the low latitudes. Bombay, Calcutta, Singapore, Jakarta, Canton, and Manila in the Asiatic sphere and Rio de Janeiro in South America stand as the major exceptions. In the low latitudes, despite the scarcity of cities, there are some of the world's greatest population densities. Thus, it can be seen that urbanization is not a necessary corollary of high population density.

Examination of the distribution of cities reveals no strict tie to climate. Though mountains usually preclude the growth of large cities, landforms are seldom major determinants in city distribution. Nor can the character of the native vegetation be demonstrated to be the outstanding control; nor can soil. Of all the physical elements of the habitat, mineral resources appear to have the greatest attractive force. Yet, for example, while cities do exist on coal fields, not all coal fields have cities on them. One is forced to conclude that world distribution of cities is not accountable for in terms of the physical setting alone, or even primarily.

What does become evident about the world distribution of cities is that they are most numerous in the middle latitudes and that, in Europe and America, they are the dominant features within these latitudes. Considering the history of urban forms, one comes to realize that urbanization has become more and more a hallmark of what we call Western civilization. As the culture of the West spread over the various continents, urban settlement spread with it. Instead of developing slowly from rural settlements, as did the cities of early

history in the lands adjacent to and on the shores of the Mediterranean Sea and the later ones of northwestern Europe, urban forms were often created anew as the lands of the world were brought within the European sphere.

The world distribution of cities, then, reflects the spread of a culture, the Western or European, more sharply than it does any other element of the human habitat. Where that culture has been brought by actual colonization, as in the United States or Australia, urban forms are even more prominent than in the region of their origin. Where Western culture has come only as a control in the form of government or commercial activity, as in India or China, urban forms have likewise appeared, but they rest as unassimilated forms on a plain of rural settlement types. It is as a measure of the spread of the culture of the West that the distribution of cities may best be understood.

· CHAPTER OUTLINE ·

Settlement Types and Contrasts

1. Why do areas of similar physical setting have different habitat values for human groups?
2. Why is mobility essential to a human group with a hunting-fishing-collecting economy?
3. In what parts of the world would one expect pastoralism to be the dominant economy? Why?
4. List as many phases of agricultural economy as you can. Give an example of an area in which each of these phases is dominant.
5. Explain just why it may be said that manufacturing, or industry, is the most complex economy.
6. Why are exploitation and commerce spoken of as "adjuncts to manufacturing economy"?
7. It is often implied that there was no evolution of economies from hunting-fishing-collecting through pastoralism and agriculture to manufacturing for all human groups. Discuss the soundness or unsoundness of this implication. Give supporting examples.
8. What is the general importance of cultural heritage in settlement pattern?
9. List some of the outstanding differences between Oriental and Western cultures. Indicate how these differences are reflected in settlement pattern.
10. Suggest why Western culture has spread over a larger portion of the earth than has Oriental culture.
11. What is the basis for considering that a new culture may be developing within the U.S.S.R.?
12. What are the major contrasts in settlement? Give specific examples of areas in which each of the major settlement types is found.
13. In what ways do the forms created in the landscape by a mobile population differ from those created by a sedentary population?
14. Is there any precise means of distinguishing definitively between a disseminated and an agglomerated population? Discuss.
15. Offer a reasoned explanatory argument in support of the statement, "Urban settlement characterizes the Western World."
16. Why is some consideration of rural settlement necessary in geographic study of the world, even in this Machine Age?
17. What is meant by the "range-and-township" land survey system?
18. What are some of the reasons for irregularities in the range-and-township type of survey?
19. What are some of the effects of the range-and-township type of survey upon settlement?
20. What is the difference between a hamlet and a village? Is the difference clear cut?
21. Can agglomerated rural settlement be associated with specific parts of the world? How can the association be explained?
22. What are the urban functions? How do these functions produce differences in the appearance of urban agglomerations as contrasted with rural agglomerations?
23. From your own observation, give examples of urban agglomerations which perform different urban functions.
24. Differentiate between situation and site. Give specific illustrations.
25. Enumerate the elements which, collectively, constitute the morphology of a population agglomeration. Which one is most significant in determining whether the agglomeration is rural or urban?
26. Describe, geographically, the population agglomeration with which you are best acquainted. Is it a hamlet, village, town, city, or metropolis? Support your statement as completely as possible.
27. List several examples of towns, cities, and metropolises. Be prepared to tell why you classify each one as you do.
28. What is the significance of a trade area for any urban agglomeration?
29. Why are there so few large urban centers in the tropics?
30. Can any single element, either cultural or physical, explain fully the settlement pattern of any area in the world? Discuss with specific illustrative examples.

[OPPOSITE, TOP] "WET-LAND," or "paddy," rice in an intensively cultivated portion of Java.

17 Agriculture and Animal Husbandry

CORSINI, STANDARD OIL CO. (N.J.)

⟨[NO ONE *knows when man first became a farmer; by the time he learned to keep even the most simple of records, there was mention of crops, agricultural practices, and ceremonies associated with planting and harvesting. Among the oldest of agricultural peoples are those of Iraq, Egypt, Iran, Afghanistan, India, and China. The very beginnings of agriculture probably occurred somewhere in southwestern Asia, at least 6000 years ago.*

The first farmers were essentially primitive gardeners, for their tools were few and crude, and they cultivated only small pieces of land. They used pointed sticks or simple wooden hoes to break the ground, planted seeds by hand, and, in the end, reaped a meager and hard-won harvest.

As time passed, more and more wild plants were tamed for use, and farming

Agriculture and Animal Husbandry | 391

tools slowly became more numerous and more efficient. Small sickles with flint cutting edges were among the earliest harvesting tools. By 1000 B.C., sickles with metal blades were in use in Egypt. A great advance over the hoe was made when crude wooden plows were invented to help break the soil. Moreover, by this time animals had been tamed and some of them were hitched to plows to help man do his work; no longer was he completely dependent on his own limited muscle power. Despite continued advance, it was not until the nineteenth century that the metal plow came into use. The steel plow, invented in 1833, has played a large part in world agriculture because it enables man to break the tough sod of the grasslands; before its introduction, it was easier to clear the forests and grub out stumps than to tear through the tangled mat of roots present in grassland soils. Thus, new inventions not only made the farmer's work progressively easier and allowed him to increase production from land already under cultivation, but also enabled agriculture to spread much more widely over the earth.

The nineteenth century was a period of great agricultural progress, just as it was a time of rapid advance in manufacturing and commerce. In fact, the connection between them was very close: new machines demanded more raw materials, many of which came from farm, ranch, or plantation; and many of the new inventions were those which facilitated farming operations and the domestic and international exchange of both raw and finished goods. The commonly used term "Industrial Revolution" actually had a twin whose name was "Agricultural Revolution." Multiple, or gang, plows, as well as mechanical seeders, reapers, binders, and threshers, were some of the new tools provided (FIG. 17–2). At first, horses and mules provided most of the power for the machines, but by the end of the century many of them were engine-powered. While all this was going on, plant scientists discovered or developed new crops, some of which were able to live in colder and drier parts of the earth than was previously considered possible. Again, the result was an increase in the amount of land under cultivation.

The foregoing account might give the impression that the world's agriculture is entirely, or almost entirely, modernized, or that it is chiefly an agriculture of machines and scientifically selected crops. Actually, the vast majority of the world's farms today are still run in old-fashioned and often primitive ways. This is especially true in Asia, where slightly more than half the people of the world live, in the poorer sections of Europe, and in extensive portions of Africa and South America. Modern agriculture is perhaps best exemplified in the United States and sections of southern Canada, although it is not limited to these areas. In the United States, continuing advances during the twentieth century have gone so far as to play a prominent part *in bringing about an actual decrease in acreage of harvested crop land without a corresponding decrease in total production.*

THE SIGNIFICANCE OF AGRICULTURE

MANY dwellers in the United States and other highly industrialized and urbanized countries seldom appreciate the fundamental importance of agriculture in their lives. Of course, farmers and ranchers realize its significance, but millions of urban residents scarcely give it a thought. They get milk from the milkman, meat from the butcher, vegetables and fruits from the grocer, and bread from the baker, or they obtain all of them in one supermarket. For them, agriculture might be an activity practiced on the moon. Only when supplies are scarce, as during a war, does production from the soil really enter their minds.

Food for Man

Probably the chief concern of at least half the people of the world at this very minute is to get enough food to stay alive. The struggle for subsistence has been the lot of the majority of mankind for centuries. It is nothing new for millions of persons to starve to death in China and India in a single year. One famine year in China is estimated to have cost the lives of ten million Chinese, and this takes no account of malnutrition and disease among those many other millions who somehow stayed alive. Europe, too, has seen its share of famine, whether caused by crop failure or the ravages of war.

Admittedly, the world has a host of problems to solve, yet outstanding experts in world affairs state that the problem of food is the greatest of all. Hence, no matter how other activities progress, agriculture must be successful at all costs. If it is not, we are faced with a largely hungry world, one in no mood or condition to solve other serious problems. It is

17–2   MODERN machinery in the wheat fields near Vernon, Texas. A small combine is harvesting and a large gang disc plow is turning over the stubble and the topsoil.

17–3   BEEF *cattle being fattened in a Corn Belt feed-lot. These cattle were brought from western range lands to be fattened for market.*

often said that hunger encourages endeavor, but the truth is that hunger first creates unrest, then desperation, and later complete apathy.

Food for Animals

Food for animals and food for man are not entirely separate. It is true that many domestic animals are not destined to become human food, but great numbers of them are raised specifically for this purpose. Regardless of their use, animals have to be fed, and usually man has to provide their food in the form of hay, corn, oats, or some other crop. Several of the world's major crop regions have become animal regions as well. This is particularly true where population is not so great as to preclude the use of the land for the production of animal foods, to be consumed indirectly by man in the form of meat and animal fats. One good example of a crop region which has become an animal region is the United States Corn Belt. It is not only a corn belt, but a hog belt, a beef belt, and a major area of mut-

ton and poultry production (FIG. 17–3). Denmark offers another example. There almost all of the agricultural land produces food for dairy cattle, hogs, and chickens. The result has been an astonishingly large production and export of bacon, eggs, and butter.

Raw Materials for Factories

We may appreciate the importance of crops for human food and livestock food, but rarely do we connect them properly with industry. In several countries the processing and manufacturing of foodstuffs constitutes a major industry. As will be pointed out in the chapter on industrialization, the processing and manufacture of foodstuffs holds first place among United States industries. In addition, many other industries depend on farms, ranches, and plantations for raw materials. Common examples are the cotton textile, woolen, silk, leather, rope and twine, and rubber industries. Less well-known industries consume large amounts of crops in order to produce soaps, cosmetics, paints and varnishes, industrial alcohols, starches, sugars, and even medicines. Each year more industries become dependent, or partly dependent, on products obtained from the soil. One example of an industrial crop, out of many that might be selected, is soybeans. One manufacturer once seriously stated that he could make an entire automobile, except the engine block, from soybeans.

The statement is not so far-fetched as it sounds. It is perfectly possible to make such products as artificial rubber, synthetic cloth, paint and varnish, glass, and many other materials from soybeans. The chemical "breakdown" of soybeans continues and the end of possible uses has not been reached, whether for industrial purposes or for the purposes of providing both animal and human food.

LIMITING FACTORS: PHYSICAL

AGRICULTURE is not practiced in all parts of the world and, no matter how much it continues to spread, there will always be areas in which crops cannot be grown (except at excessive costs) and few, if any, livestock can be raised. FIGURE 17-4 provides a generalized world view of the regions in which crops and livestock are produced; it also emphasizes those areas which are essentially noncrop, non-livestock-producing. The extent of agriculture is determined by a number of limiting factors which operate in complex and interdependent fashion. Some of these factors are physical and some are cultural. The chief physical factors are climate, landforms, soils, drainage, native vegetation, and, to some extent, wild animal life.

Climate

Granting the presence of land, the most fundamental limitation on the extent of agriculture is climate. Climate not only affects the spread of agriculture as a whole, but limits, often drastically, the distribution of individual crops. In Canada, for example, the northern limit of agriculture is determined by temperature, reflected in the length of the frost-free season. In the Ecuadorean Andes, agriculture is also limited by the temperature factor, except that the limit there is an upward, instead of a poleward, limit. The Sahara, ex-

cept for oasis production, is devoid of crops not because of temperature conditions, but because of insufficient rainfall. In those parts of the world with a Mediterranean (Cs) climate there are some sections—sections where irrigation is not practiced—in which crops can be produced during the cool, mild, and rainy winters, but not during the hot, dry summers. Again, moisture is the controlling factor, but in this instance it operates to control agriculture in a time, rather than a space, sense.

Climate sets definite limits to the cultivation of many crops. The coconut palm thrives in the tropics and invades the milder portions of the subtropics in a few places, but it cannot grow elsewhere. Essentially the same is true of bananas. Citrus fruits grow in the tropics and subtropics, but the highest quality fruit is obtained in the milder portions of the subtropics, particularly in those sections that have the Mediterranean (Cs) or the Humid Subtropical (Cfa) climate. Some varieties of wheat can be grown successfully in areas with as little as 10 inches of annual precipitation, other varieties require 20, or more, inches. Such examples could be multiplied many times.

Landforms

The lay of the land constitutes another major factor in the determination of agricultural distributions. The bulk of the world's agricul-

AGRICULTURAL AND NONAGRICULTURAL REGIONS

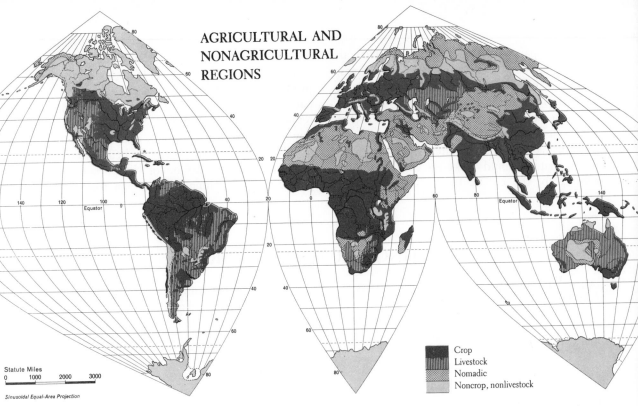

Crop
Livestock
Nomadic
Noncrop, nonlivestock

Statute Miles
0   1000   2000   3000

Sinusoidal Equal-Area Projection

17–4   THE *agricultural regions of the world are represented by* (1) *crop producing regions mainly asso-ciated with humid, long growing season conditions,* (2) *livestock producing regions mainly asso-ciated with grassland and mountain conditions, and* (3) *nomadic herding regions mainly associ-ated with desert, tundra, and mountain conditions. The noncrop, nonlivestock regions are mainly associated with extremely arid or cold conditions.*

ture is carried on in plains or undissected pla-teaus. Wherever surfaces are too rough, as in mountainous areas, cultivation of the land is seriously handicapped or precluded alto-gether. Even in hilly regions and in too greatly dissected plains and plateaus, agriculture is restricted, not only because of the physical difficulties of tilling the land, but because of high costs of production. Only where level land is scarce does agriculture ignore in any im-portant way the usual relationships between crops and landform conditions. In such in-stances, the land surface often is man-modi-fied, as by the construction of terraces, or else crops which do not demand level land, such as certain tree, bush, or grass crops, are chosen.

Besides affecting the extent of agriculture in a general way, landforms sometimes determine the distribution of crops within localized areas. For example, there are many coastal and near-coastal valleys and basins in California where the general physical conditions are satisfactory for citrus fruit production, but groves are found only in certain parts of these valleys and basins. With occasional exceptions, the reason for the exact location is a landform reason; the groves lie on the middle and upper portions of alluvial fans where the surface has sufficient tilt to insure air drainage to the point where frost damage is prevented or greatly minimized (FIG. 17–5). Thus, landforms, like climate, often play a large role in deciding where agriculture does or does not exist.

There is always danger of implying that the relationship between landforms and agriculture is iron-clad and immutable. Such an implication is not intended. It has been emphasized, rather, that landforms play an important part in the distribution of agriculture and that, in many instances, they set surprisingly rigid limits, even within comparatively small areas.

Soils

Another important factor in shaping the pattern of world agriculture, both in general and in detail, is soil. Soil, of course, is not divorced from climate and landforms, nor from other conditions such as drainage and natural vegetation. Yet soils, in their own right, play a significant part in helping to determine "what crops grow where." There is, for example, the correlation between certain varieties of wheat and the distribution of chernozem soils. This is seen in the spring wheat belts of the United States, Canada, and the Soviet Union. The correlation between the black prairie soil and high corn yields in Iowa is easily recognized; again, it "takes more than soil," but soil is definitely one of the major factors. The "terra rossa" soils of São Paulo State, Brazil, have had much to do with the leadership of that area in world coffee production. Light, coarse-textured soils have enabled Maine's Aroostook County to become a leading producer of high-grade white potatoes. The dark muck soils of sections of the glacial deposition region of southern Michigan favor the growing of commercial celery.

In a negative sense, the soil-less or nearly soil-less condition of many parts of the world has prevented the growth of any crops whatever. Many valley bottoms, otherwise suitable for crops, are so completely floored with boulders and large gravels that they cannot be used for agriculture. In many irrigated areas bedrock, unmantled by soil, interrupts the crop pattern. In the agricultural region of southern Sweden, for example, many of the "bald spots" represent the outcropping of soil-less, glaciated bedrock.

Because of recent and rapid advances in soil science and land-use practices, it is difficult

17–5

CITRUS fruit groves, chiefly orange, on an alluvial fan piedmont near Los Angeles, California.

to know how far to generalize regarding soil fertility. We often say, "This soil is fertile." What we should say is, "This soil is fertile, or productive, for white potatoes"; "This soil is fertile for Red Fife and other similar varieties of wheat"; or, "This soil, if supplied with phosphates and nitrates, will be fertile for oranges." In many sections devoted to intensive, commercial crops, the soil is no more than a material in which to bed the plants and to hold them as they grow. For example, parts of the Coachella valley of southern California specialize in early ripening Thompson seedless grapes. Most of the grapes grow in what was recently little more than drifted dune sand. The dunes were leveled and vineyards planted; the desert-dry sands were irrigated and large amounts of fertilizer added. The grapes feed and thrive on artificially supplied water and artificially supplied foods; the soil is literally no more than a satisfactory "plant holder."

Limiting Factors: Physical | 397

Another aspect of soils is "tear-down," as opposed to "build-up." Many soils have been worn out by a combination of perennial cropping and nonfertilization; still others have been allowed to erode to the point of extinction or to the point where they can no longer be cultivated (FIG. 12–8). Such despoiling obviously affects the world pattern of agriculture, as well as the distribution of particular crops; worse, it affects the ability of the world to feed itself and provide essential raw materials.

Drainage

There are many sections of the earth where drainage conditions are such as to preclude agriculture. Most of these are the swampy or marshy lands. Some of them are small, such as "wet spots" in river flood plains, but others are comparatively large, such as the coastal marshes of the Atlantic and Gulf Coastal Plains, the delta of the Mississippi, or the extensive wet lands found in regions of glacial scour and deposition.

Other sections, even though not swampy or marshy, are too greatly subject to damaging floods for regular cropping. Many parts of the dry lands that might be irrigated are not used because of the menace of flash floods. However, in irrigated dry lands and humid lands alike, man often takes the gamble—and suffers periodic devastations as a result. One of the major physical problems in the United States is to develop the control of surface waters, whether in individual farm fields or in entire drainage basins, to the point where crops and agricultural resources are not damaged or destroyed.

Native Vegetation

Even native vegetation has an effect on the world's agricultural pattern. As noted earlier, the grasslands greatly discouraged cultivation until the comparatively recent invention of the steel plow opened up many new areas,

such as the prairie and steppe of the United States, for a new extension of agriculture.

All of man's crops have been derived from native plants. The original location of individual native plants determined, until very recent centuries, where crops adapted from them grew. White potatoes, native to the highlands of Peru, required centuries to spread in the New World, and they were unknown in the Old World until the sixteenth century. There potatoes soon became very important in the agricultural economy of several countries, including Germany and Ireland. The so-called Irish potato actually is a historically recent immigrant to Ireland. Other wild plants which became crops in the New World and then traveled to the Old are tobacco, maize, cacao, and rubber. From the Old World to the New came wheat, sugar cane, cotton, coffee, tea, oranges, and several other crops.

Animals and Disease

Animals (including insects) and diseases of plants affect agricultural production and the distribution of many crops. The rabbit, intro-

17–6

A CORNFIELD *ruined by locusts.*

duced into Australia by man, has become an agricultural scourge. In some areas, deer or other large herbivores consume low-growing crops and kill orchard trees by eating the bark. Moles do great damage to crop roots. Certain birds, such as the crow, consume untold amounts of grain. Locusts can sweep an entire countryside clean of all portions of crops which grow above the ground (FIG. 17–6). Fungus diseases do great damage to crops in all parts of the world. Such damage may be critical. Ecuador, for example, dropped from leadership in world cacao production to the point where she now furnishes only a minor part of the supply. While the trouble was partly economic, the main reason was cacao fungus. Insects,

such as the Japanese beetle or the cotton boll weevil, can decrease crop yields critically. On the positive side, insects, by insuring pollination, help the production of many crops. Some insects, by their presence or absence, determine whether certain crops can be grown at all. When the Smyrna fig was introduced to California, the trees thrived but bore no fruit. The problem was a puzzling one: climate, soil, and other physical conditions were satisfactory, but still, no fruit. The answer was discovered to be the fig wasp; it was not native to California and it was needed to insure pollination. As soon as the wasp was introduced, the problem was solved and California fig production became successful.

LIMITING FACTORS: CULTURAL

THE major cultural controls affecting agriculture are cultural inheritance, plant selection and breeding, money and labor, transportation and markets, laws and other regulations, and the competition of other activities.

Cultural Inheritance

The manner of living and making a living, which is to a large extent handed down from generation to generation, exerts strong control over the distribution of agriculture as a whole and over the distribution of individual crops. To be sure, some cultures have developed in parts of the world where an agricultural economy is not possible. This is true, for instance, of Eskimo culture. However, there are other cultures which, as far as physical conditions are concerned, could have become agricultural, but did not. In the South Sea Islands some groups found it so easy to obtain their food from the sea and from wild plants that they had no inclination to till the soil. Indians living in parts of Canada, where at least some agriculture could have been practiced and has in

fact been introduced by the white man, chose to live by hunting and fishing, even though the living they made in that way was usually a precarious one.

But there were many peoples who did learn to tame wild plants and till the soil. As they moved, they carried seeds and their agricultural practices with them. Thus, they extended agriculture as a way of living and insured a wider and wider distribution of particular crops. Rice production spread from small beginnings somewhere in southeastern Asia until, today, it is found in all parts of that continent which are physically suited to it. Cultural groups outside of Asia learned of rise production and adopted it during and following the Age of Discovery. Many other crops, such as maize, wheat, and sweet potatoes, spread in a similar way. Some crops became so typical of certain cultures that they named those cultures: we speak of the "rice culture" of the Orient, and the "corn (maize) culture" of Mexico. In a similar fashion, particular agricultural practices have attached their names to certain cultures, as the "milpa culture" of the Amazonian Indians, the "peasant culture" of Poland, or the "plantation culture" of the Malay Peninsula.

Plant Selection and Breeding

During nearly all the time that man has practiced agriculture, the selection and breeding of plants usually have been matters of trial and error or of accident. The most recent period has seen great change. In many, though far from all, parts of the agricultural world, plant selection and breeding have been placed on a scientific basis. In addition, plant scientists roam the world seeking new plants and plant varieties which can be adapted to other than their native areas. The combination has resulted, for example, in wheats more resistant to drought, adapted to shorter growing seasons, or less subject to mildew and other diseases. New varieties of potatoes have been developed for particular climatic and soil conditions, as well as for resistance to disease. All such achievements affect world agriculture, either by extending it to new areas or by making it more successful in areas where it is already established.

Money and Labor

To bring land under cultivation and insure production from it, money, or capital, is usually necessary. In some instances, the amount of capital needed is small; in others, very large. The establishment of a farm in the equator-ward portion of Canada's northern forest region requires comparatively little capital. The farm is small, land costs are relatively low, and many of the materials needed for fences, barns, homes, and fuel can be obtained from the forest itself. In addition, hunting and fishing help to supply food for the farm family and wild hays can be cut to help feed farm animals. Quite in contrast, a large amount of capital is needed to set up a wheat ranch in North Dakota. Land is high in price, and large

acreage is necessary for successful commercial production. Several kinds of expensive machinery are needed, fertilizers must be purchased, and wages must be paid. Also, reserve funds must be available to survive crop failures resulting from drought, storm, abnormally heavy precipitation, plant diseases, and occasional locust plagues—let alone times of low prices for wheat.

Even more capital is needed to start a tropical plantation (FIG. 17–7), especially in a new area. Land must be purchased, or leased; vegetation must be cleared away and then fought continually to prevent its return. Planting and cultivation costs are high, and fertilizer must be purchased. Added to all this, several years must elapse before there is any return on the

17–7

HARVESTING in a plantation of young banana trees in the Guayas Lowland of Ecuador. Note the position in which the fruit grows on the trees.

investment. For example, from seven to nine years are necessary to bring a rubber plantation into production; during those years, expenditures are heavy and income from other crops which are grown until the rubber trees come into production is moderate.

Some parts of the earth are so constituted that only huge investments can make them productive; government assistance as well as private capital may be necessary. This is particularly true of desert and steppe areas, which require elaborate systems of reservoirs, main canals, lateral canals, small ditches, and flood-control works, as well as ability to meet the water costs which continue after irrigation systems are completed (FIG. 17–8). If the agricultural use is dependent on ground water, rather than reservoirs, etc., then drilling, pumping, and maintenance costs are involved. Heavy capital outlays are also necessary to bring swamp or marsh lands into agricultural use. Expensive drainage ditches must be dug and maintained, drain pipes must be laid in the fields and, very often, pumping must be carried on. Thus, in one fashion or another, money plays a vital part in shaping the world pattern of agriculture.

Some crops and some systems of agriculture have high labor requirements, others low ones. But labor is always involved. It is closely related to money because labor must be paid for, except where the family alone can furnish all the labor needed. On the Canadian farm mentioned above, cash outlay for labor is practically nil; so is it in the rice areas of South China. But on the Dakota wheat ranch, despite wide use of machinery, labor costs are appreciable. On the tropical plantation they are still higher; even if individual wages are low, the number of laborers required is so great that the total cost is high.

The problem of labor is not necessarily solved by money. Some regions are partly or completely deficient in the supply of labor, and either laborers cannot be found elsewhere or, if found, they will not go to the areas where

R. M. GLENDINNING

17–8

THE first trickle of water moves in a section of the Coachella branch of the All-American Canal, near the Salton Sea, in southern California.

they are needed. One of the major problems in producing rubber in the Amazon Basin is lack of labor within the area and the unwillingness of laborers from other regions to go there. On the other hand, in industrialized nations, particularly the United States, life in the cities has proved so attractive that manpower has been drained away from the farms without any compensating flow from the cities, thus creating a different kind of labor problem.

Transportation and Markets

The problems of handling, moving, and selling agricultural products are so great and so varied that their detailed consideration would fill volumes. Hence, the treatment here must run the risk of brevity and the dangers inherent in generalization.

If products are consumed locally transportation is easy. Most of the rice of China is eaten within a few feet or rods from where it grows. Most of Ireland's potatoes are consumed on the farms which produce them.

Limiting Factors: Cultural | 401

But with surplus production transportation becomes the paramount problem. Sugar cane must move quickly from the fields to the plants which squeeze the juice from it; otherwise the cane spoils. After the juice is obtained and processed into raw, unrefined sugar, the sugar must travel rapidly to refineries usually located at some distance from the plantations. Bananas, in Middle America, must be picked green and moved quickly to the ports for loading into ships. Specially constructed refrigerated ships then carry them to distant ports. The ship's holds must be kept at a certain temperature and proper ship speeds must be maintained; otherwise the bananas arrive in port too ripe for the handling they receive first in the wholesale houses and then in widely scattered retail establishments. California oranges must be picked at just the right degree of ripeness, hauled by truck from the groves to the packing houses, where they are culled, given a protective coating, wrapped, and boxed, and then sent in refrigerator cars to eastern markets. Without such facilities, including the refrigerator cars, a major part of California's agricultural business would be impossible. The problem of transport is particularly critical for all perishable products, whether sugar cane and bananas or oranges and truck crops. Where the proper type of transportation is not available, certain kinds of production cannot be carried on, no matter how favorable all the other factors may be.

A product such as wheat, if properly handled, is practically nonperishable; yet even wheat demands a great deal of handling and some special transport equipment and facilities. It must be hauled from the thresher to a collection point on the farm, then to the nearest railroad, where it is stored in grain elevators. From the grain elevator (FIG. 17–9), it must move in railroad cars to the milling centers or to ports where it is loaded into ships for export. For example, Canadian wheat from southern Manitoba travels by rail to Fort William on Lake Superior, then by lake boat to some port, such as Kingston on Lake Ontario, or Montreal on the St. Lawrence river, and then across the Atlantic to the large wheat-receiving port of Liverpool.

In addition to transportation, there is the problem of prices and the market. Obviously, there is no point in producing goods for sale and moving those goods expensively over long distances, unless there is someone to buy them in sufficient quantities and at a sufficiently high price. Price, an extremely variable thing, is the final determinant of farm production. Man could produce bananas in Greenland under artificial conditions if he could sell them for a sufficiently high price. The American Southwest could supply huge quantities of vegetable rubber, from such a plant as guayule, if the selling price were high enough. When prices are high, even distant and inefficient areas may be able to move and sell goods at a profit. When prices are exceptionally low, even regions favored by optimum physical conditions and nearness to market may be unable to sell their goods at a profit. Thus, certain regions may produce wheat in some years and not in others; other areas produce sugar beets during certain periods and no sugar beets at other times.

Laws and Other Regulations

Under totalitarian government, the agriculture of a nation may be regimented to the point where physical controls lose much of their normal importance and where such cultural controls as cost of transportation, availability of labor, and size and character of market cease completely to have effect. Agricultural activities are of a sort and in such a location as dictated by the government. They may pay for themselves, or not. Thus, wheat may be grown in a region usually given over to corn, or cotton may be grown on land that is usually reserved for tobacco. Or, agriculture, regardless of individual crops, may be carried on in regions better adapted to grazing or

17–9 TYPICAL *arrangement of railroad yard and grain elevators in Kansas City, Missouri, for the handling and storing of wheat.*

forestry. Such procedures are often the result of an attempt on the part of a government to insure self-sufficiency, regardless of cost. Sometimes they result from the desire of a government to insure amounts of a given crop sufficient to be sold in large quantities to other nations, in exchange for materials lacking or available in only small amounts in the homeland. Such drastic controls affect the agriculture of only a few nations, but some of these nations are large—large enough to be major forces in world agriculture. Notable among them is the Soviet Union.

Control of agriculture within national boundaries is not limited to totalitarian states. At times of overproduction even democratic countries may establish direct or indirect controls. Farmers may be paid not to plant par-

ticular crops and be denied certain privileges if they do not cooperate in the government's program. In other instances, a collapsed market may be artificially supported by government price-setting or by government buying in large amounts. Both of these procedures have been used at times in the United States. When the world coffee market dropped to a very low level, the coffee producers of Brazil went broke by the thousands. The Brazilian government bought huge amounts of coffee in attempts to keep up the price. Much of it was stored in warehouses, but thousands of bags were dumped into the sea or burned in locomotives in place of coal.

Agriculture may face other types of controls. In some parts of the United States, for example, agriculture is now prohibited. Some of

Limiting Factors: Cultural | 403

these are sections which are not well suited to agriculture and where it has proved too expensive to maintain roads, schools, and other services. Such prohibitions are determined by local governments and are based on local zoning ordinances. Other parts of the United States, some of which are very large, are set apart as national forests and national parks. Within them, private uses of the land, including agriculture, are stringently regulated or prohibited. Sometimes state laws affect agriculture or a particular crop both within and outside the state. California, for instance, has a law which prevents the importation of avocados, so that avocado growers of other states cannot compete in California markets. Most regulations of this sort, however, represent attempts to prevent the spread of plant diseases. In other instances, the importation of certain crops is not prohibited, but the crops have to undergo rigid inspection before they are allowed entrance. This does not prevent imports, but it does set up barriers which are costly and time-consuming, however necessary some of them may be.

Agricultural products which cross international boundaries are often faced with stringent regulations as to quality, nature of packing, possibility of disease, and so on. Sometimes for political reasons the importation of a crop is prohibited from certain areas, but allowed from others. Sometimes the rules seek to prevent the dumping of cheap products on the market. Again, many of these rules represent an attempt to insure clean, high-grade, disease-free products.

In addition, tariff laws affect the movement of farm products. The tariff may be set so high as effectively to prevent imports, or just high enough to protect domestic farmers from the competition of products which can be more cheaply produced elsewhere. The United States tariff on foreign sugar is not high enough to prevent imports, but it is high enough to enable domestic raisers of cane and especially beet sugar to meet the outside competition.

What this one law accomplishes can be appreciated when one realizes that without it there probably would be no commercial cane or beet sugar raised in the entire United States.

Many other illustrations might be given to show how laws, regulations, or agreements affect agriculture in various ways. Those already given are sufficient to indicate that the nature and distribution of agriculture are related to many factors besides climate, soils, capital, labor, transportation, and markets.

Competition from Other Activities

There are many parts of the world which are admirably suited to the production and sale of crops, but where crops are not grown. Usually, this is because the land is more valuable for other uses. In the Los Angeles metropolitan area, for instance, many thriving and profitable walnut and orange groves, as well as truck gardens, have been displaced by homes, apartments, streets and sidewalks, factories, or lumberyards. As profitable as agriculture was on these lands, it could not compete with the values established by urban land use. An interesting result is the encouragement of agriculture in areas farther removed from the metropolitan region. Much the same thing has occurred in the Detroit area and other large city regions. As the cities have grown, and as they have acquired satellite towns and cities, land in farms has become land in city blocks and in factory districts.

In a different area of California, east of Sacramento, another use of the land likewise has resulted in displacement of agriculture. Here, in several districts, huge gold dredges have chewed up many farms and left only debris-piled wastelands behind them. In many parts of Texas and Oklahoma, ranches have given way to forests of oil derricks. Parts of New England have seen farmlands become resort and recreational areas. Other sections of the country have seen mine buildings and mining dumps take the place of farm buildings and fields. Many mountain and hill valleys and basins, formerly devoted to agriculture, have been incorporated as parts of national forests and national parks. Thus, in one manner or another, competing uses have curtailed or displaced agriculture.

TYPES OF AGRICULTURE

AGRICULTURE is not "just farming"; agricultural products and practices differ greatly from one region to another. The differences reflect many physical and cultural factors, ranging from location, climate, and soil to density of population, stage of economic development, general cultural background, and governmental controls. Thus, the agriculture of the United States Corn Belt is different from that of the Cotton Belt, and both differ markedly from that of the Amazon Basin or the Ganges Plain of India. Differences also occur within relatively small areas. There is great contrast, for example, between truck farming and dairy farming in southern Michigan, or between subsistence farming and plantation farming in a local section of the Philippines.

Subsistence Agriculture

PRIMITIVE • Subsistence agriculture characterizes those farming areas which consume all, or nearly all, of the products locally grown, as opposed to commercialized farming regions whose products mainly are sold and consumed "off the farm." Subsistence agriculture is of two general types: primitive and nonprimitive.

Primitive subsistence agriculture may be either migratory (shifting) or sedentary. The migratory kind, known variously as milpa, fang, ladang, chena, or caingan, is limited largely to the rainy tropics and their immediate borderlands. It is practiced where there is a great deal of room and few persons.

There are many reasons for the migratory nature of this kind of farming. Chief among them are the poor soils and the rankly growing vegetation of the humid tropics. It is easier to move than to attempt to fertilize the soils or combat the encroaching vegetation. It is easier, likewise, to let nature restore the soil and, after this has been accomplished, to return to the use of the same plots of ground, perhaps many years later. Lesser reasons for migrating range from epidemics and insect pests to wild animal depredations and the desire to build new homes and villages rather than repair old ones.

Migratory agriculture, or shifting cultivation, as might be expected of farming that is on the move, is simple (FIG. 17-10). Spots of better soil are chosen near the villages and the trees are either girdled or fire-killed so that they shed their leaves and allow sunlight to reach the ground. The ground around the dead trees is loosened with a sharp stick or a simple hoe or spade and the crops are planted. As the crops grow, a weedy jungle of new plants grows along with them. The natives may or may not weed the small fields. Typical crops are maize, yams, manioc, peanuts, beans, peas, bananas, and sugar cane. After the crops are harvested and the jungle has taken over again, the field may be cleared by using machetes and fire. If the soil is worn out, the field is abandoned without clearing the brush; if not, the field may be used for two or three years. In any event, it is soon abandoned and a new field is chosen. When all the better spots of a local district are used up, the entire village may move to another district where the process is repeated. Thus this type of agriculture is migratory in two senses: it moves from one place to another within a local area and, if there is room, then moves to another area.

17–10 A NEWLY cleared garden in the tropical forest of northwestern New Guinea where migratory agriculture is practiced.

The sedentary kind of primitive subsistence agriculture normally occurs in areas where population is relatively dense or where climate and soil are more conducive to permanent use of the same fields. It, too, is found mainly in the tropics, but is more characteristic of hills, plateaus, and mountain basins than of the hot, wet lowlands (FIG. 17–11). Tools and tillage practices are simple and the crops are much the same as in migratory agriculture, except where production is carried on at elevations so great that crops like yams, bananas, and sugar cane cannot be grown and are replaced by others, such as white potatoes and other tubers. Typical regions for sedentary subsistence farming are the equatorial Andes, the Middle American Highlands, western Ethiopia, and parts of the South African Plateau.

NONPRIMITIVE • The impression is often given that all subsistence agriculture is primitive and that it is limited to the tropics. This is not true. There are many sorts of subsistence agriculture which are far from primitive, in the sense in which the word is normally used, and they are found in the subtropics, middle latitudes, and high latitudes, as well as within the tropics. They cannot all be discussed here, but some representative examples will be given.

Along the southern margin of the northern forests in Canada, Sweden, the Soviet Union, and other areas are numerous farms which are primarily subsistence farms. Some of them are essentially "pioneer" farms, but many of them have been too well and too long established to be called pioneer undertakings. Although farm equipment and land-use practices are comparatively simple, they can hardly be termed primitive. Farms with plows, hayrakes, harrows, and permanent fences, as well as draft animals, sheep, cattle, and poultry, are not primitive, however simple they may appear.

The use of new and especially adapted crops, such as particular varieties of white potatoes, as well as the latest information from agricultural experiment stations, renders the term further inapplicable. Neither can the long-established and comparatively involved agriculture of such peoples as the Hopi Indians of Arizona be called primitive in any strict sense. Also, near most of the cities of the United States are large numbers of subsistence farms. Although small, they are usually very modern in appearance and farming practices. To be sure, some of them sell a few products, but not on a scale that would warrant their being called commercial farms. Many of them are run by persons who have tired of city life and have set up a family farm economy that allows them to subsist almost entirely from the land.

To take an entirely different sort of example, most of the rice farms of the Orient cannot be termed primitive, even though they represent the ultimate in subsistence agriculture (FIG. 17–1). These farms, if one may call them such, illustrate agricultural practices which are known to be at least 4000 years old and are probably much older. Every bit of land that can be used is used to the utmost. Each farm family has on the average only two or two and one-half acres of land to supply it with practically all the essentials of life, as well as to pay taxes. There is little land and there are many mouths to feed. The land is worked and reworked. All possible fertilizer, including the waste products of the human body, is carefully collected and placed on the land. Rice is the king crop chiefly, though not entirely, because it will yield more food per acre than any other crop. The result is that these Oriental rice farms represent the height of intensive agriculture, even more than do the densely populated farming lands of Europe, whether in Poland or Belgium. Obviously such permanent and highly specialized agriculture is not primitive, despite its ancient character and the absence of modern machinery or even of draft animals.

17–11

PRIMITIVE agriculture of the sedentary type, in the highlands of Colombia, near Bogotá.

Commercial Agriculture

PLANTATION • Commercial agriculture, like subsistence agriculture, includes many different varieties. For purposes of simplicity, it may be divided into commercial plantation agriculture and commercial farming. The latter includes ranching, fruit growing, and truck gardening.

Plantation production is limited chiefly to the tropics (FIG. 17–7). It supplies the demand of mid-latitude consumers for such products as bananas, cane sugar, cacao, copra, coffee, tea, rubber, and many others. It is based on foreign capital, scientific knowledge, and, usually, cheap labor. Not so many years ago the terms "plantation agriculture" and "foreign plantation agriculture" were synonymous. Today, it is necessary to distinguish between them. This is the result of the accumulation,

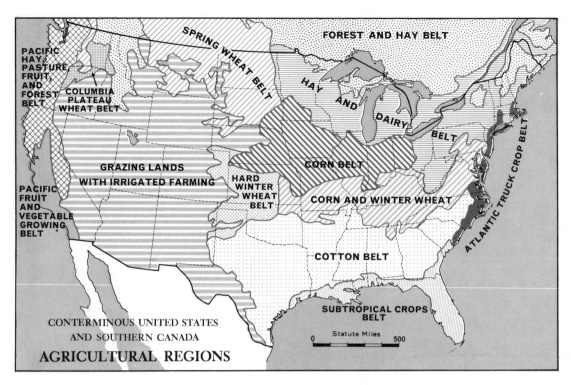

17–12   THE combination of large area and wide variety in physical conditions has allowed man to develop extensive and varied agricultural regions in the United States and Canada.

on the part of some natives, of sufficient experience and capital to allow them to engage in plantation production of their own. One example of this is rubber production in the Malay Peninsula and the adjacent islands of Indonesia. Foreign plantations produce by far the greater amount of rubber, and a better grade of rubber, but native plantation production is improving and it is offering more competition each year. The major obstacle to native plantation production has been lack of sufficient capital to buy or lease the land, clear and plant the land, fight the weeds and diseases, properly prepare and transport the products, and, far from least, to wait a number of years before the plantation is making returns on the investment. Plantation production is a large undertaking and a considerable gamble. Even if the physical and other difficulties are solved, a plantation may come into production only to find that the market for its product has collapsed and the crops cannot be sold for enough even to meet running expenses, let alone interest on investment.

COMMERCIAL FARMING • Commercial agriculture is very widespread in the subtropics, the mid-latitudes, and parts of the high latitudes. It is represented by such areas as the cotton regions of India and Pakistan, the citrus districts of Florida and California, the truck-farming areas and the Corn Belt of the United States (FIG. 17–12), the Spring Wheat Belt of the United States and Canada, and the dairy region of northwestern Europe. Some varieties of commercial farming, notably truck farming and citrus production, make intensive use of the land and use large amounts of fertilizer. Others, the Spring Wheat Belt of the United States and Canada for example, make very extensive use of the land and little use of fertilizers. Much heavy machinery is used to cultivate and harvest the crops, and land units are very large. Increased production is normally obtained by cultivating more land rather than by using the land already under cultivation more intensively.

MAJOR CROPS

THE world's agriculture, whether commercial or subsistence, is based on an extremely large number of crops. Out of all the crops which man raises to feed himself and his animals, there are some which are so important as to be called key crops. The following discussion is devoted to them.

Rice

This crop is the world's chief food. No one knows the exact number of rice eaters in the world, but it is certainly at least half of the earth's three billion inhabitants. Most of them live in the densely populated lands of the Orient, although there is a slowly increasing use of rice among the peoples of Africa and Latin America. The great bulk of the world's rice is consumed as rough, unpolished rice. This is fortunate, because the highly polished rice, such as one usually finds in the markets of the United States, has been processed to the point where most of the minerals and vitamins contained in the coatings have been removed. A diet based on polished rice is greatly deficient; one based on rough rice is less deficient than has commonly been supposed. If it were not, most of Asia's millions would not be able to exist.

The major part of the world's rice is grown in the tropical and subtropical monsoon lands of south and east Asia and Indonesia (FIG. 17–13). While several types of rice are grown, most of the varieties are cultivated in flooded fields called "paddies" (FIG. 17–1). This accounts for the designation of "wetland" or "paddy" rice, as opposed to "dry rice" which is grown in the same manner as wheat or other "dry" grains. As the world's chief subsistence crop, nearly all rice is consumed within local producing areas. Only a few areas are able to produce a surplus. No matter how much rice the major regions grow, even two crops a year in climatically favored sections, there is barely enough, or, in some sections and in particular years, not enough. The chief surplus regions of the world are in Burma and Thailand. From these regions, the rice moves mainly to India, China, and Japan. That these regions are able to produce more than they need not only reflects excellent physical conditions for rice production, but also the fact that they are not as densely populated as the other rice lands of the Orient. In all the Oriental rice regions, surplus or not, the way of life is so closely entwined with rice, including preparation of the land, planting of the shoots, harvesting, and threshing, that the entire culture of the people is commonly referred to as a "rice culture."

Maize

As either a subsistence or a commercial crop, maize has wide geographical range. From its original homeland in the high slopes and basins of the northern Andes and the Middle American Highlands, it has spread over much of the Americas and, since the days of Columbus, to many other sections of the world. Today, it is cultivated from the equator to the margins of the northern forests and from sea level to altitudes, in the tropics, as high as eight or nine thousand feet. Moreover, maize is raised in the regions of heaviest rainfall and, under irrigation, in the driest deserts. There are many

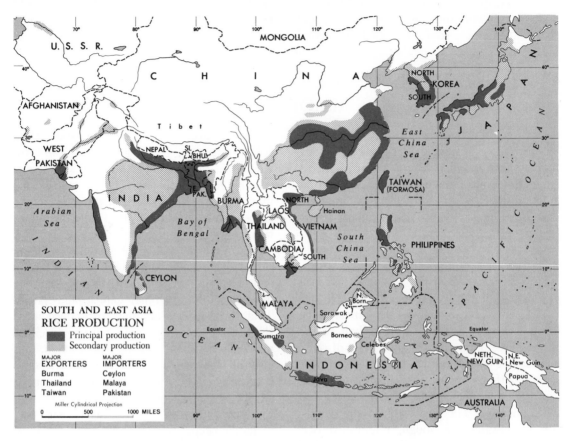

17–13 MOST major rice-producing areas of the world are in south and east Asia and Indonesia, with China producing about 43%, and India about 17% of the world total. Also most of the world trade in rice focuses on the area of south and east Asia.

varieties and new ones are developed from time to time. Each variety represents some adaptation to length of growing season, amount and distribution of rainfall, resistance to disease, or some other critical physical element.

Maize has a versatility which makes it one of the most important of all crops. It will grow and yield at least a small crop under even adverse conditions of soil and climate. Under favorable conditions, it produces heavy yields. After it is grown, it can be easily stored for either short or long periods; thus the yields of bountiful years can be used as "food in the bank" for lean years. Moreover, it is a nu-

tritious food for both man and his livestock. As a human food it is prepared and consumed in many forms, ranging from corn-on-the-cob, parched corn, stewed corn, and corn meal, to hominy and special breakfast foods. From it also are made cornstarch, corn syrup, corn oil, and industrial alcohol, as well as whiskey. The leaves, stalks, and kernels furnish fodder for animals, and the cobs furnish corncob pipes.

Maize has played a significant role in the history of the United States. It has been said that the westward movement of our people was based on "corn and jerky." To a measurable extent this is true. The explorers and

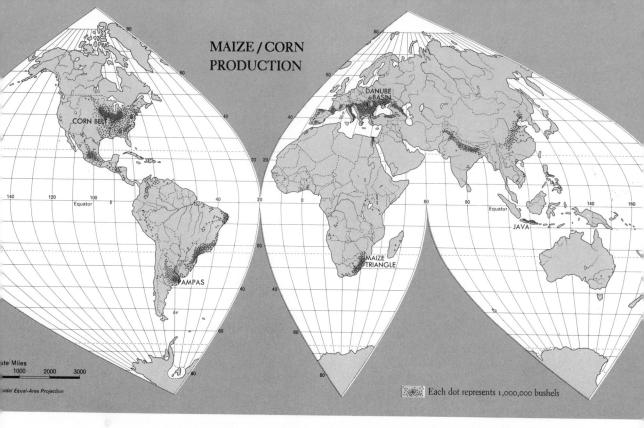

MAIZE / CORN PRODUCTION

CORN BELT

PAMPAS

DANUBE BASIN

MAIZE TRIANGLE

JAVA

ute Miles
1000   2000   3000

pidal Equal-Area Projection

Each dot represents 1,000,000 bushels

17–14 PRINCIPAL maize/corn-producing regions are found in Africa, Europe, Asia, and the Americas, with United States production accounting for over half of the total world production. Maize/corn production is primarily associated with either the Humid Continental or the Humid Subtropical climates.

scouts carried dried corn and jerky, or dried meat, in leather pouches. These foods, plus water, enabled them to travel freely for long distances. The settlers, pushing west with their animals, wagons, and meager household furnishings, carried maize with them, and it was the initial crop to be planted on their wilderness farms. Usually it was first planted in small hills scattered among girdled trees. Maize, as a first-season crop, gave them food for themselves and their livestock. Augmented by fish and game, it provided them with a toehold while the farms were being soundly established.

The major maize-producing regions are not located just anywhere that maize will grow. They are in the regions of most favorable climate and richest soils, although there are

several areas well suited to maize where population is so dense that other crops of still higher yield, such as rice or potatoes, take precedence. The chief commercial regions occur in association with either the Humid Continental climate with hot summers (Dfa, Dwa) or the Humid Subtropical (Cfa) climate (FIG. 17–14). The best maize soils are the black prairie, brown forest, or recent alluvial soils. When maize can compete economically with wheat, it yields heavily on chernozems. With proper soil management practices, commercial yields also are obtained from the yellow forest soils.

The Corn Belt of the United States (FIG. 17–12) leads the world. It has no close rival, either in size or yields. Although most of the

Major Crops | 411

maize is used at home for animal feed, there is considerable export to western Europe. From 85 to 90 per cent of the maize is used to feed and fatten livestock, chiefly hogs and cattle. By contrast, the Argentine maize region, producing far less, normally exports most of its crop to western Europe. The Argentine has considerable good cornland, but fewer people and, more significantly, fewer animals to feed.

The United States Corn Belt, an area as large as France, extends from central Ohio to western Kansas and from the latitude of the Ohio valley to that of the southern Great Lakes region. On the north it merges with the Hay and Dairy Belt, on the south with the Corn and Winter Wheat Belt, and on the west with the Winter Wheat Belt and part of the Spring Wheat Belt. To the east it is limited by the Appalachian Uplands. In general, the northern and western boundaries are climatic and the southern and eastern reflect soil and landform conditions. The northern limit is essentially the isotherm of 70° F. average for the three summer months. The western limit, near the 102nd meridian, is approximately the 8-inch summer season rainfall line. South and east of these two lines occurs the hot, "muggy and showery" weather which is so excellent for maize and so difficult for human beings. The eastern limit marks the beginning of the higher, rougher, and more poorly soiled Appalachian country; the southern, the rougher, more dissected lands of the Corn and Winter Wheat Belt. Here, too, soils are poorer, as one progresses from the glacial soils on the north to the nonglacial and often thin and stony soils in the south. Maize yields are higher in the western two-thirds of the Corn Belt, where the soils are mainly those of the prairie and prairie margin. These rich, dark soils from Illinois to Iowa and Kansas are truly "the land where the tall corn grows."

The remaining major maize regions of the world lie in the northeastern part of the Argentine Pampas, the Walachian Plain of Romania and part of the U.S.S.R., the Hungarian Plain, and the portion of China where the Yangtze river and the Hwang Ho most closely approach each other (FIG. 17–14). Lesser, but still important, regions are in the southeastern United States, the Mexican Plateau, southeastern Brazil, southern Europe, southeastern Africa, and parts of India and Indonesia. Beyond these are countless minor spots, such as a rainforest farm in Brazil, a maize patch in the high Andes, or a farm in the forest of northern Minnesota.

Wheat

The world's many varieties of wheat are descended from a cereal, or kernel-producing, grass which originally grew wild somewhere in southwestern Asia. Following its domestication, it spread slowly to several different sections of Asia, Europe, and northern Africa. Kernels of wheat have been found in the wrappings of mummies from the tombs of ancient Egypt. Since 1500 A.D. it has been introduced to the Americas, South Africa, Australia, and New Zealand. Today, the kinds of wheat are very numerous; many of them are strains recently developed by plant scientists for regions of short growing season or low rainfall. Other new varieties resistant to wheat diseases have also been created.

Most of the world's wheat is grown in the mid-latitudes; lesser amounts are produced in the subtropics and the equatorward portion of the high latitudes. Wheat rarely is grown in the tropics, except in a few tropical highlands and a few small sections of irrigated lands in the tropical deserts (FIG. 17–15). It does better than competing crops on the dry margins in the mid-latitudes, and for this reason the major commercial wheat regions tend to correlate with the cooler Semiarid (BS) and the dry-margin portions of the Moist, Mild Winter (C) and Moist, Severe Winter (D) climates. Large amounts, although not enough to meet requirements, are grown under distinctly humid conditions in western Europe, where the cli-

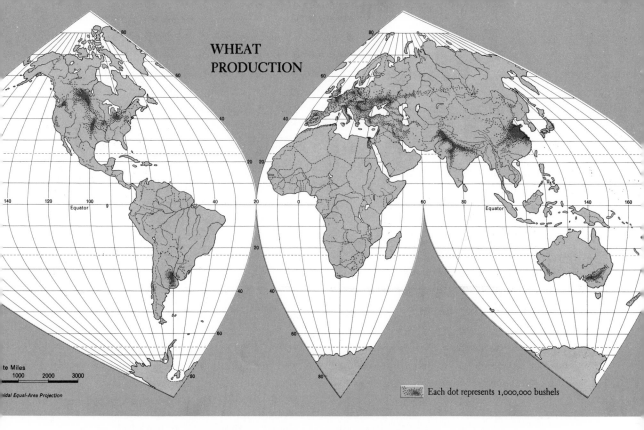

WHEAT
PRODUCTION

Each dot represents 1,000,000 bushels

te Miles
1000   2000   3000

nidal Equal-Area Projection

17–15   PRINCIPAL *wheat-producing regions occur extensively in the mid-latitude areas of the Northern Hemisphere, with the largest areas of production in the semiarid lands or the drier margins of humid lands.*

mate is Mid-latitude Marine (Cfb). Per-acre yields there actually are higher than in the wheat belts of the United States and Canada; this is so by reason not only of climate, but also of intensive agricultural practices. The commercial, surplus-producing regions of today correlate chiefly with the dark grassland soils: black prairie and chernozem. The latter is said to be the best wheat soil that the earth has to offer, and it accounts for much of the agricultural wealth of such nations as the United States, Canada, U.S.S.R., and Argentina.

The varieties of wheat may be grouped in two categories: spring wheat and winter wheat. Winter wheat is planted in the fall, grows during the winter and spring, and is harvested in late spring or early summer. Obviously, the winter wheats can be grown only in those regions which have a mild or a not-too-long-and-

severe winter. Spring wheat, grown farther poleward, is planted in the spring, grows during the summer, and is harvested in the fall. Bushel for bushel, most of the world's wheat is winter wheat, although many of the highest-grade commercial wheats are spring wheats. Because of the wide range of harvest times for winter and spring varieties, wheat, even in a given hemisphere, comes onto the market over a number of months. In the United States, for example, winter wheats grown farthest south are harvested as early as May and spring wheats grown farthest north are harvested as late as September. Thus, the United States wheat harvest lasts from May to September. Argentine wheat, grown in the Southern Hemisphere where the seasons, as compared to the Northern Hemisphere, are reversed, is harvested from early December to early February. The combination of spring and winter wheats and the two-hemisphere production results in at least some wheat coming onto the world market in every month of the year.

Another useful twofold classification of wheat that should be noted is hard wheat and soft wheat. There are many varieties of each, of which some are spring wheats and some are winter wheats. In general, there are more soft wheats in the winter wheat regions and more hard wheats in the spring wheat areas; probably because of climatic requirements more than anything else, because the hard wheats need drier climates and the soft wheats need more humid climates. In comparison to soft wheats, the hard wheats have less starch and more protein, and make "stronger" dough.

Unlike corn, wheat's major use is as food for humans, although small quantities are fed to livestock, particularly poultry. Most wheat eventually becomes bread, although appreciable quantities are used for macaroni, spaghetti, pastries, and special foods, such as breakfast foods, meat substitutes, and imitation coffee. Particularly in the United States, wheat flours are very highly refined; so much so that it has been found wise to add vitamins and minerals to replace losses incident to high refinement. In many countries, whole wheat flour, producing a coarser, darker bread, is most common. Such bread may be less attractive, but it is much more nutritious. Actually, even though we in the United States are hardly able to realize it, only a small proportion of the world's inhabitants can afford bread or other products made from wheat. Wheat is not the common grain for many millions in the Orient, nor for many who live in Africa and Latin America. Even in northern Europe, with all its wheat, the major bread is a coarse, dark, and heavy rye bread.

The chief wheat-producing nations are the United States, Canada, and Argentina in the Western Hemisphere, and the U.S.S.R., India, Pakistan, China, and many others in the Eastern Hemisphere (FIG. 17–15). In recent years,

the U.S.S.R. has taken the lead in world wheat production away from the United States. The bulk of the wheat of the U.S.S.R. is grown in the southern part of the Russian Plain, in a large triangular area which has its base on the northern shore of the Black Sea and its apex approximately at the southern end of the Urals.

The United States wheat belts are four in number. One of them shares part of the land of the Corn Belt and of the Corn and Winter Wheat Belt (FIG. 17–12). Production is greatest in the area between the Mississippi and Lake Erie, usually called the Soft Winter Wheat Belt. Just to the west, lying principally in Kansas and Oklahoma, is the Hard Winter Wheat Belt. To the north, chiefly in the Dakotas and southwestern Minnesota, is the Spring Wheat Belt. The fourth region lies in the Northwest, in the portion of the Columbia Basin east of the Cascades, mainly in southeastern Washington and northeastern Oregon. This region is ordinarily referred to as the Columbia Plateau Wheat Belt. Most of Canada's wheat is produced in the Spring Wheat Belt of the Prairie Provinces, chiefly in southern Manitoba, Saskatchewan, and Alberta. Argentina's main region is the famous Wheat Crescent which arcs around the western margin of the Pampas. Australian wheat is grown mainly in the Murray–Darling Basin, inland from Adelaide. Another region lies in the southwest, in the area between Perth and Albany. The wheat of India is concentrated in the northwestern part of the country, notably in Punjab. China's wheat region occurs in the North China Plain and immediately adjacent territory. Unlike the other wheat regions noted above, China's, despite heavy production, is not a surplus region.

The major wheat-exporting nations are the United States, Canada, Australia, and Argentina. The United States and Canada combined supply about 70 per cent of world wheat exports, with the United States often furnishing nearly twice as much as Canada. It will be noted that the major sellers of wheat are those countries which have extensive areas of "wheat soils" and "wheat climates" (in which other crops have, so far, not competed too greatly with wheat), as well as relatively sparse populations.

The heaviest flow of export wheat goes from the United States and Canada to the British Isles and western Europe. Other major flows are from Australia and Argentina to the same West European destination.

Other Grains

Rice, corn, and wheat are the key grain crops of the world. However, there are several other important grains; locally, any one of them may be of first importance. Chief among them are rye, oats, and barley.

Rye production is largely concentrated in Europe. It can be successfully carried on in areas where soil is too poor and climate too cold and damp for wheat. It is the source of the "black bread" which is basic in the diet of most eastern Europe's peoples. Oats, consumed by both animals and humans, are apt to be king in regions of poor soil and cool, very damp climate, even though they are also grown in greater quantity in more favorable areas. The chief oats areas are in northern Europe, the northern United States, and southern Canada. Barley has the greatest climatic tolerance of any of the important grains. It is raised, in varying amounts, all the way from the tropical deserts into the northern forests, but the heaviest production occurs in northern Europe, central China, Korea, Japan, and the north-central United States. It is an important hay and grain crop for animals and an important human food; some varieties are used for the making of malt. International trade in rye, oats, and barley is small; this is especially true of rye and oats.

Vegetables

The production of vegetables is so widespread and a part of so many different agricultural systems that it is difficult to be specific about it. Vegetables appear in the "migratory" fields of the Amazon Basin and the Congo Basin, in small plots on tropical plantations, on the dikes which separate paddy fields in the rice lands, on the typical Corn Belt farm, in the forest-bordered farm of Canada or northern New England, and in many other areas. Some are even raised in underground greenhouses in a few places in the tundras of the Soviet Union.

Truly commercial production of vegetables occurs mainly in the vicinity of large cities, chiefly those of the United States and Europe. Some of this production, particularly in the United States, occurs in areas appreciably removed from the cities, but tied in very closely by means of rapid transportation, allowing fresh vegetables to be placed quickly on city markets. In addition, there are many vegetable farms, whether near or far from urban areas, whose products are locally canned, quick-frozen, or otherwise processed before being sent to market. It is interesting to note that truck farms near large cities represent a very intensive use of the land, comparable to that in the densely populated areas of the Orient. Where climate allows, more than one crop is produced each year, the land is highly tilled, and large amounts of fertilizer are used. Even where the climate is humid, irrigation is often used to prevent crop failure because of a dry spell and to force the growth of the vegetables. Normally one thinks of irrigation as part of wet-land rice culture or associated with the growth of crops in arid or semiarid regions, but it is a significant part of commercial vegetable growing in humid lands as well.

In the United States, vegetables grown only for home consumption are found chiefly to the east of the 20-inch rainfall line (FIG. 17–16). They are most concentrated in the area which extends from the northern part of the Cotton Belt to the southern Great Lakes and from the Mississippi to the Atlantic seaboard. In the Northwest, there are local concentrations in the Puget Sound and Willamette valley lowlands.

Vegetables raised to sell occupy much less land than those raised for home use. Most of the commercial vegetable districts are located within or on the edge of the most densely populated part of the United States (FIG. 17–16). Others are located in the South and in the valleys and basins of California. These southern areas, with their subtropical climates, are able to place vegetables on the northeastern

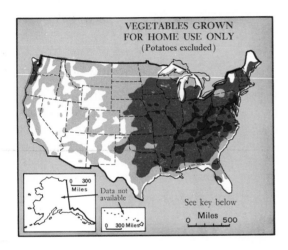

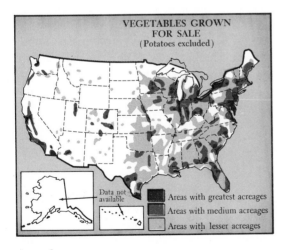

17–16

THE general pattern of vegetable production in the conterminous United States.

markets long before locally grown ones are available. They enjoy a lucrative off-season business. This is particularly true of the California truck districts, many of which can supply fresh vegetables all winter long.

Fruits

TROPICAL FRUITS • Within the tropical regions, with their continuous growing season, a wide variety of fruits is produced. Most of them, whether wild or cultivated, are found in the tropical humid regions, but others occur in oasis agriculture in tropical dry lands. Tropical humid fruits include coconuts, breadfruit, mangoes, oranges, and bananas. Those raised in tropical oases include dates, oranges, lemons, apricots, and grapes. With few exceptions, tropical fruits are subsistence rather than commercial products. Some coconuts are exported, but most of the commercial coconuts are shipped in the form of dried coconut meat, known as copra. Copra is an important source of vegetable oil for soaps, cosmetics, salad oils, and margarine. Copra cake is also used as a feed in regions of dairy cattle specialization. Major copra producers are Indonesia and the Philippines. The oil palm, also a tropical fruit tree, competes with coconut oil in mid-latitude markets. It bears a small, soft fruit, and oil is obtained both from the fleshy outer part and from the kernel. Chief production regions are along and near the shores of the Gulf of Guinea and in Indonesia.

Of all the tropical fruits, the banana is the one which is the most important in mid-latitude food markets. The banana long has been a major food in southern Asia, to which region it is native. More recently it has become an important food in most of the world's wet, tropical areas. However, its commercial production, almost entirely on foreign plantations, is very limited, both geographically (FIG. 17–17) and as to particular varieties. There are many varieties of bananas, some edible and some not. The major edible variety of com-

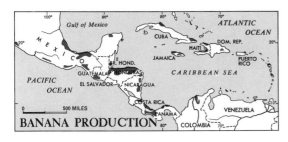

17–17 COMMERCIAL bananas are grown principally in the hot, wet, tropical lowlands of the Caribbean area. Commercial olives are grown principally in the coastal Mediterranean areas.

mercial bananas is the large yellow kind, the only variety commonly found in mid-latitude markets. It is grown almost entirely in hot, wet lowlands of the New World, particularly on the shores of the Caribbean. Middle America and the West Indian islands produce more than half of all commercial bananas (FIG. 17–17). Most of the plantations are American-owned and -operated, and nearly half of all commercial bananas are sold in the United States. The remainder are sold in the British Isles, France, and Germany.

SUBTROPICAL FRUITS • The subtropical regions, both humid and dry, are areas of many fruits. In addition to fruits of their own, they have become the home of fruits introduced from the tropics and the mid-latitudes. Because the subtropics have a winter season, however mild it may be, certain mid-latitude fruits, used to winters, can grow there. The long, hot summers, coupled with no more than mild winters, allow certain tropical fruits to grow. Common subtropical fruits are oranges, grapefruit, lemons, peaches, apricots, plums (including prune plums), olives, figs, and grapes. One hears a great deal, for example, of Spanish olives, Georgia peaches, Florida grapefruit, and California oranges and grapes. Most of the commercial subtropical fruits are produced in the United States and along the Mediterranean shores of Europe, Asia Minor, and northern Africa. Lesser amounts are grown in the subtropics of the Southern Hemisphere, as in middle Chile, the

La Plata region of Argentina, southeastern Australia, and southern Africa. The subtropical portion of Asia, with its many millions of mouths to feed, cannot afford to use very much land and energy to grow fruits. From the large number of commercial subtropical fruits, the citrus fruits, olives, and grapes have been singled out for separate discussion here.

Of the many kinds of citrus fruits, oranges, grapefruit, and lemons are most important commercially (FIG. 17–18). The orange, native to southeastern Asia, was introduced to the Mediterranean region during the fifteenth century. From there it was carried, a bit later, to the New World, still later, to Australia and South Africa. Although many varieties grow in the wet tropics, it is the specially developed varieties of the subtropics which are in most demand on world markets. In fact, the best varieties are grown as far poleward as the orange tree can survive. In such locations, the groves often have to be protected from winter frosts by means of such devices as heaters, smudge pots, or wind-circulating machines. Were it not for man's assistance, the orange would have a slightly smaller latitudinal range than it now has.

The major producing regions are in the Mediterranean countries, Brazil, and Florida and California in the United States (FIG. 17–18). Southern China is a heavy producer, but not for export. It may come as a surprise that Spain supplies over one-third of all export oranges though its total production is far be-

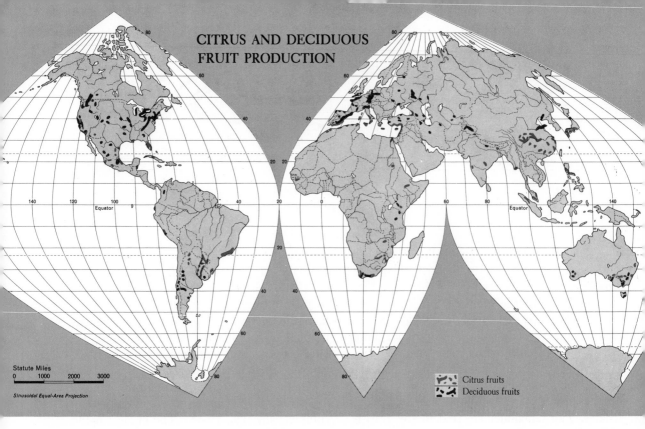

CITRUS AND DECIDUOUS FRUIT PRODUCTION

Statute Miles
0   1000   2000   3000

Sinusoidal Equal-Area Projection

Citrus fruits
Deciduous fruits

17–18   COMMERCIAL *fruit is produced in every continent except Antarctica. Citrus fruit is grown mainly in regions of Mediterranean or Humid Subtropical climates. Deciduous fruit is grown principally in the mid-latitude areas of the Northern Hemisphere.*

low that of the United States. Spanish and other Mediterranean Basin oranges travel to markets in western and northwestern Europe. United States oranges are principally consumed at home, although attempts are being made to increase the export of California oranges. California oranges, especially the navels, are able to stand long shipments because of their thick and relatively tough skins. However, production costs, including irrigation, are much higher than in such countries as Spain, Italy, and Algeria.

Moreover, the rapid expansion of urban and suburban areas in southern California has caused wholesale destruction of orange groves in recent years.

Commercial orange production is highly localized within the United States. The major

districts are located in central Florida, in the piedmont basins and valleys of southern California, on the flanks of the San Joaquin valley of California, and in the extreme southern part of Texas. Aided by irrigation, California is able to market oranges the year around; peak harvests for navel oranges occur in the winter and for Valencias in the summer. Florida's orange groves, unirrigated, produce only a winter crop, although total production is now well ahead of that of California. Most of the districts of the world which produce oranges also grow grapefruit and lemons. In the United States, the chief grapefruit districts are in Florida, southern Texas, and California. Also, there are important areas of "desert grapefruit," particularly in the Coachella–Imperial Valley of California and the Salt River valley of Arizona. United States lemons are grown mainly in the California citrus areas. The United States leads in world production with Italy second, and Spain and Greece far behind.

Olives are typical of the parts of the subtropics with a Mediterranean (Cs) climate. Unlike citrus fruits, they are not adapted to the Humid Subtropical (Cfa) climate. The chief production regions occur on the shores of the Mediterranean (FIG. 17-17). Although some olives are consumed in pickled form, both green and ripe, their main use is for oil. Olive oil has many uses, from anointing oil, soaps, and cosmetics to salad and cooking oils. It is most important as a food oil, particularly in those countries which do not produce large amounts of animal fats for table and kitchen use. Spain and Italy, the largest producers, vie with one another for first place in world olive production (FIG. 17-19).

Grapes, like olives, are admirably suited to the portions of the subtropics with Mediterranean (Cs) climate. Some species of grapes are grown in mid-latitude regions, but most of the commercial grapes are Mediterranean both in origin and in present cultivation areas. There are three main kinds of grapes: table, raisin, and wine. Some varieties can be used for all three purposes, but, as a rule, particular varieties are grown for a single purpose. Again, the main production regions fringe the shores of the Mediterranean Sea. Other important districts occur in California, Argentina, and Chile. There is considerable specialization by individual districts. In California, for example, the small valleys north of San Francisco Bay specialize in wine grapes, the Sacramento area in table grapes, and the Fresno district in raisin grapes. The Fresno district is the leading raisin producer of the world. Similar specialization occurs elsewhere in California, as well as in the other grape regions.

MID-LATITUDE FRUITS • Most of us are best acquainted with apples, cherries, peaches, pears, plums, Concord grapes, and the wide variety of other fruits which are produced

17-19

OLIVE *groves near Córdoba in southern Spain.*

mainly outside of the tropics and subtropics. Fruits are grown to some extent in all mid-latitude regions, including mid-latitude dry lands where irrigation water is available. Apples, represented by many varieties, are most widespread and can be grown farther poleward than the others. Those apples grown for commercial purposes, rather than home consumption, come from particular, specialized districts. In the United States, for instance, famous apple districts include the Yakima (FIG. 17-20) and Wenatchee valleys of Washington, the Lake Ontario shore of New York State, and southern New England. The portion of Wisconsin which lies between Lake Michigan and Green Bay is a famous cherry district. The Hood river valley of Oregon specializes in pears; the northern Chesapeake Bay region in peaches. Concord grapes, which are particularly susceptible to frost dam-

Major Crops | 419

Sugar Cane and Sugar Beets

The tropics and the mid-latitudes together provide the world with its sugar. Practically all the cane sugar is produced in the tropics, with minor amounts in the mildest portion of the subtropics, and all the beet sugar is produced in mid-latitude regions, both humid and dry (FIG. 17–21). Those sugar beets grown in the dry lands are raised under either irrigation or dry-farming practices, depending on the degree of local moisture deficiency. Pound for pound, more of the world's sugar is derived from sugar cane, although beet sugar has made tremendous gains in the past half century.

Sugar cane is native to southeastern Asia. It has spread widely to most parts of the humid tropics and to some irrigated sections of the tropical deserts. Its occurrence in a few subtropical locations, such as southern Louisiana, represents its most poleward extension. Sugar cane produces the richest juice in those parts of the tropics where a season of plentiful rain is followed by a season of abundant sunshine and less rain. Thus, despite wide tropical distribution, the major commercial cane regions are found in association with the Savanna (Aw) type of climate and with the warmest margins of the Humid Subtropical (Cfa) climate. While India ranks high in production of sugar cane and cane sugar, it is a noncommercial producing area. As noted previously in connection with such commodities as rice and maize in China and wheat in western Europe, large production does not necessarily mean a surplus, especially where there are many mouths to be fed. The most important cane regions in the Northern Hemisphere are in the West Indies, Mexico, the Philippines, Taiwan, Hawaii, southeast China, and India. Cuba (FIG. 17–22) has been the main large exporter of cane sugar, normally exporting more than all other exporters combined. The cane areas in the Southern Hemisphere are mainly in southeastern Brazil, eastern Australia, South Africa, Argentina, Indonesia, and Peru.

17–20

APPLE orchards cover many square miles in the Wenatchee and Yakima valleys of Washington.

age, are produced chiefly along the southeastern shore of Lake Michigan and the southern shore of Lake Erie. Those two sections are so located in relation to water and prevailing wind direction that frost damage is kept at a minimum. As the land warms up in the spring, the cool winds from the lake surfaces keep the air over the land from warming too rapidly; this prevents early blossoming of the grapevines and keeps the blossoms from being "nipped" by spring frosts. Otherwise, the first warm spell would cause the grapes to blossom, and spring frosts, occurring after the first warm weather, would damage or totally destroy the crop.

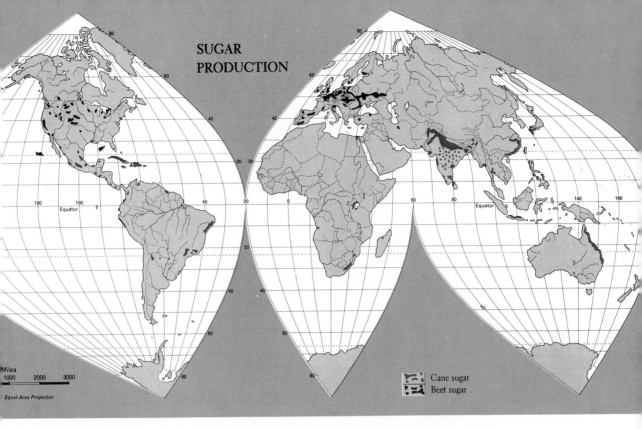

SUGAR PRODUCTION

Miles
1000 2000 3000

Equal-Area Projection

Cane sugar
Beet sugar

17-21   BEET sugar production occurs principally in mid-latitude areas of Europe and the United States. Cane sugar production is limited principally in the humid tropics and subtropics. Though India produces more cane, Cuba is the world's largest producer of cane sugar.

The heaviest movements of cane sugar are primarily to the United States and secondarily to the British Isles. Continental Europe has developed beet sugar production to such a degree that it imports only comparatively small amounts of cane sugar.

The world's sugar beets are grown mainly in few areas (FIG. 17-21). The heaviest production is found in a belt extending from the central part of the southern Russian Plain westward through Poland and East and West Germany into northern France, and southward into the Po Lowland of Italy. The U.S.S.R. leads in production, followed by West Germany, Italy, and France. The only other major sugar beet areas are in the United States, chiefly in the western Great Plains, the Salt Lake area, California, and Michigan. Califor-

nia is by far the leading state. Beet sugar is more expensive to produce than cane sugar and it provides less sugar per acre. However, its "waste" products, the tops and pulp, help to feed domestic animals. Unlike cane sugar, the international flow of beet sugar is geographically restricted; it is limited to the countries of western and central Europe, and even there it is not of great volume. Little of it moves far from the districts where it is produced, or into international markets.

Coffee, Tea, and Cacao

Some of the world's agricultural products are used wholly or in part for beverage purposes. Corn is used to make Bourbon whiskey, barley malt to make Scotch whiskey and beer,

Major Crops | 421

17–22 CUTTING *and hauling sugar cane on a Cuban plantation. Judging by the number of short and tall tree stumps still present in the crop area, this is new cane land.*

rice to make rice wine, and so on. Chief among the nonalcoholic beverages are those made from coffee, tea, and cacao. All three are in sufficient demand to place them among the key agricultural commodities.

Coffee was first domesticated in the uplands of Ethiopia and was introduced to Arabia during either the fourteenth or fifteenth century. From Arabia it spread to India and the East Indies. Java became a major producer and this gave rise to the expression "a cup of Java." Coffee production in the New World, in Middle America, South America, and the West Indies, was greatly encouraged by the inroads of fungus disease in East Indian coffee plantations. The major commercial varieties thrive best in humid tropical uplands which possess rich soils. The largest of these areas occurs in the southern part of the Brazilian Highlands, in the state of São Paulo (FIG.

17–23). There the combination of a tropical upland climate and rich "terra rossa" soil has made possible the world's major coffee region. Thanks chiefly to the São Paulo region, Brazil produces fully as much coffee as all the other coffee regions of the world combined, and it has no close rival in coffee exports. Santos, the major outlet, leads all coffee-exporting ports of the world. Other important centers of coffee production occur in the plateaus and foothills of Colombia and Middle America, the central African plateaus, southern India, and in the foothills of Java and Sumatra in Indonesia. Colombia ranks second in world coffee production and export. The United States imports over half of all export coffee; the other major importer is France, with the other countries of western Europe taking smaller amounts.

The world's principal tea regions lie in southern and eastern Asia and in Indonesia

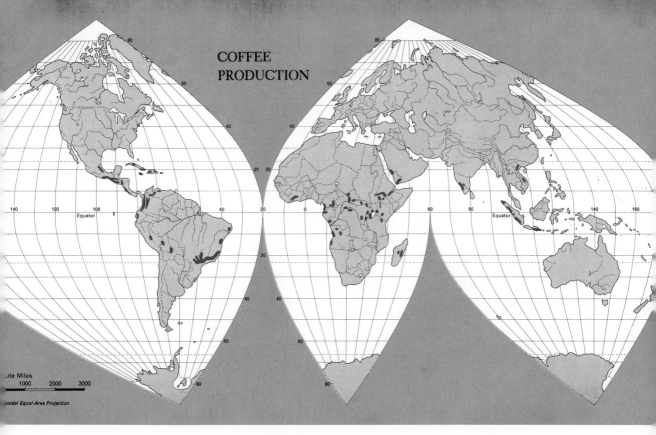

COFFEE
PRODUCTION

17-23   COFFEE *production is principally associated with tropical mountain and hill slope conditions. Brazil produces more than half of the world's total production, and Latin America as a whole accounts for 80% of the total annual crop.*

(FIG. 17-24). Tea is mainly a "hillside" crop because it cannot be allowed to occupy land that is useful for rice or other essential Oriental foods (FIG. 17-25). Most of the plantations occur in areas of Subtropical Monsoon (Cw) or Humid Subtropical (Cfa) climate and, in lesser numbers, in areas of Tropical Moist (A) climates. The leading tea producers and exporters are India and Ceylon. Together these two produce 60 per cent of the world total and furnish three-fourths of the tea exports. More than half of the exports go to the British Isles. About one-tenth go to the United States and lesser amounts chiefly to Canada, Australia, and the U.S.S.R. The Englishman's tea, whether consumed in the homeland or in the Commonwealth, supports most of the commercial tea business of the Orient.

Cacao is the source of chocolate and cocoa. It differs from tea and coffee in that it is used widely in candies, frostings, cosmetics, and some kinds of soap, as well as as a beverage. Cacao is native to tropical America, but most commercial production is now in tropical Africa (FIG. 17-24). The chief exporter is Ghana, which, with Nigeria and the Ivory Coast, furnishes about 53 per cent of the world supply. In the Americas, Brazil and the Caribbean region supply about 28 per cent. Ecuadorian production, once of major importance, is now quite small. Cacao demands a "hothouse" climate; this limits it to the tropical rainforest areas or, at best, to the hottest and wettest margins of the savannas. The big importers are the United States and western Europe, with the United States importing about as

Major Crops | 423

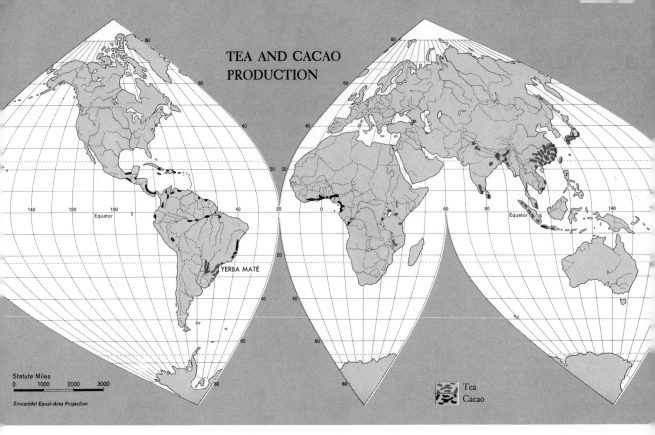

TEA AND CACAO PRODUCTION

YERBA MATÉ

Statute Miles
0   1000   2000   3000

Sinusoidal Equal-Area Projection

Tea
Cacao

17–24 TEA *is principally a product of tropical and subtropical hill slopes of Asia's eastern and southern countries. India is now the world's leading producer, followed by Ceylon and mainland China. Cacao is a crop of the hot wet tropics, principally in Africa and, to a lesser extent, South America.*

much as all the nations of western Europe combined.

Cotton

Since about 1800, the world has witnessed a tremendous increase in cotton production. Before that time cotton cloth was very expensive; it was essentially the rich man's cloth. Some kinds of cotton were so costly that only royalty could afford them. An instance of this is corduroy, which means literally "the cloth of the king"; today, we think of it not as the king's cloth, but as the cloth of the workman, the hunter, and the fisherman. The great change was brought about by a series of inventions. Eli Whitney's cotton gin, invented in 1793, enabled the cotton fibers to be plucked

more rapidly from the cotton seeds, to which they stubbornly adhere. It became possible for a single machine to "gin" more cotton in a day than a man could in a month. Other inventions, made during the later 1700's, made it possible for machine spinning and weaving of cotton to displace slow and tedious hand operations.

With cotton in great demand as the "people's cloth," production spread and increased, and several regions of the earth became known chiefly for the cultivation of the cotton plant. Today, there are more pounds of cotton produced than pounds of all other natural commercial fibers combined. Most of the commercial cotton is grown in Humid Subtropical (Cfa) climates, although important amounts are produced in Savanna (Aw) climates, as in

17–25   TEA *harvesting on a Ceylonese plantation.*

the Deccan of India, in Subtropical Monsoon (Cw) climates, as in China, and in certain Arid (BW) climates under irrigation, as in Egypt and Soviet Turkestan (FIG. 17–26). The greater bulk of the world production is short-staple cotton (varieties of cotton with fibers less than one and one-eighth inches in length); considerably lesser amounts are long-staple. The latter fibers are not only longer, but much silkier; they are used for the more expensive types of cotton cloth and for cordage in the manufacture of automobile tires. One very famous variety is Egyptian long-staple.

The major cotton region of the world is the United States Cotton Belt (FIG. 17–12). Despite increasing competition from other regions, such as the São Paulo area of Brazil, the Cotton Belt still produces about one-third

of the world's cotton (FIG. 17–27). The combination of relatively cheap and abundant land, cheap labor, and a Humid Subtropical (Cfa) climate enabled the Cotton Belt to become the paramount commercial region. The United States furnishes close to half of the world exports, followed, in order, by Egypt, Pakistan, Brazil, and Mexico. China is the only major producer which is not an exporter; despite her huge production, she must import cotton. United States export cotton goes mainly to England and secondarily to continental Europe and Japan. Pakistan's export cotton goes mainly to England and secondarily to Japan and China. Significant in world cotton production is the increase in Soviet Turkestan. The U.S.S.R. now ranks third in world cotton production. It is far behind the United

Major Crops | 425

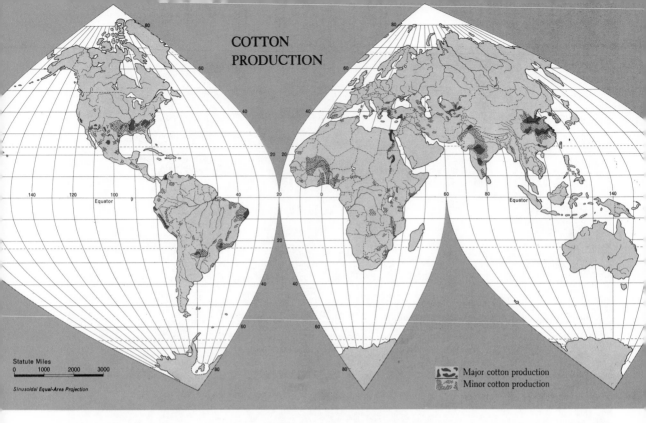

COTTON
PRODUCTION

Statute Miles
0   1000   2000   3000

Sinusoidal Equal-Area Projection

▨ Major cotton production
▨ Minor cotton production

17–26   THE world's cotton production is closely associated with the Humid Subtropical (Cfa), the Savanna (Aw), and the Subtropical Monsoon (Cw) climates, particularly in the United States and Asia. The United States alone produces about 30% of the world's total, while south and east Asia account for about 40%.

States, but close to China and ahead of India, Egypt, Brazil, Mexico, and Pakistan.

Other Vegetable Fibers

The world's farms and plantations produce a wide variety of vegetable fibers in addition to cotton. Many of these are, so far, mainly of local importance, but some are well-established items in a broad world trade. Chief among the latter are flax, hemp, jute, and sisal.

Flax is grown for two main purposes: oil and fiber. Most of the "oil flax," furnishing linseed oil, is produced in dry areas. Flax used for fiber, mainly linen cloth, is grown in cool, damp regions. The leading fiber flax areas are in Europe, extending from the central Russian Plain and the eastern shore of the Baltic to

northern France. Western Europe is the manufacturing area of practically all linen cloth.

Hemp is in demand for string, large cords, fishing lines, and thread, and finds important use in the manufacture of carpet and coarse cloth. It is grown mainly in the central part of the southern Russian Plain and from there southwestward as far as Italy. Somewhat smaller production occurs in the North China Plain and in Korea.

Jute is grown almost entirely in the Ganges–Brahmaputra delta of East Pakistan and India, although minor amounts are produced in Brazil and in Taiwan. It is the cheapest of the commercial fibers and is used for burlap bags (gunny sacks), carpet and linoleum base, webbing, and twine.

Sisal is used predominantly as binder twine

in the world's major wheat regions. Unlike flax, hemp, or jute, sisal is derived from a drought resistant plant. Yucatán, in Mexico, and Tanganyika, in Africa, are major producers. Important production also occurs in Kenya, Brazil, Angola, and Mozambique.

In addition to those noted˙above, there are other commercial vegetable fibers. One of them, Manila hemp, is produced chiefly in the Philippines. Manila hemp is derived from a plant related to the banana; being stronger than other hemp and, further, having greater resistance to the deteriorating effects of exposure to salt water, it is used extensively for ship ropes and cables.

Another fiber of some commercial importance is kapok, used in pillows, mattresses, and life preservers. This light, resilient, waterproof fiber is obtained from the pods of a tree produced commercially chiefly in Java and the Philippines. It has its widest use in the United States and western Europe. Ramie, sometimes called China grass, produces a fiber which is highly adaptable for both coarse and fine cloths, as well as threads, twines, and ropes. It is waterproof and very durable. As far as physical requirements are concerned, it could be produced widely in warm, humid regions. However, labor requirements, both for cultivation and processing of the fiber, are such as to limit its production almost entirely to its native areas in South China. It is possible that cheaper and more effective methods of growing and preparation may allow ramie to compete in the future with the major commercial fibers, even cotton.

Rubber

Columbus found the Indians of the West Indies playing with a ball that bounced. This was the white man's introduction to rubber. During the following three hundred years rubber was little more than a curiosity. In the early 1800's it had some use in the form of erasers and a Scotsman by the name of Macin-

17-27

COTTON field and a mechanical picker in the South. Machines help the United States compete with low-cost cotton-producing areas.

tosh learned how to apply it to cloth to make raincoats. Then, in 1839, Goodyear discovered how to vulcanize rubber and thus render it simultaneously pliable, durable, and nonsticky. However, not until the coming of the automobile and the widespread use of rubber-insulated electric wiring did demand become large. Today, rubber has myriad uses ranging from insulation, shock pads, and battery cases to mattings, cushions, and wearing apparel, but it is the use in the automobile, especially for tires, that consumes the greater part of the production.

Except during World War II, when Japanese forces occupied the main producing re-

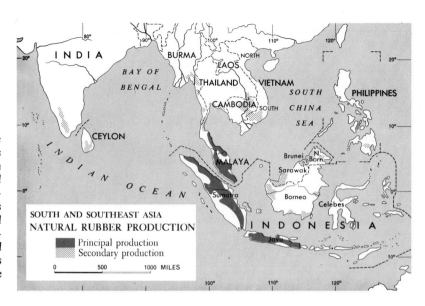

17–28

ABOUT 98 per cent of the world's natural rubber is produced on plantations in south and southeast Asia and Indonesia. Exports are principally to the United States and Europe. The United States imports about one-third of the world's total while Indonesia exports about one-third of the world's total.

SOUTH AND SOUTHEAST ASIA
NATURAL RUBBER PRODUCTION

Principal production
Secondary production

0   500   1000 MILES

gions, commercial rubber had been almost entirely natural rather than synthetic. Following the war, synthetic rubber production declined for a year or so, but afterward greatly increased.

Today, about 53 per cent of world consumption is natural rubber and about 47 per cent is synthetic. However, in the United States alone the consumption ratio is about 34 per cent natural to 66 per cent synthetic.

In 1900, all commercial rubber was derived from trees which grew wild, and nearly all of it came from the Amazon Basin. Most of it was obtained by tapping a native tree of the rainforest, the *Hevea brasiliensis*. At present, probably less than 3 per cent of commercial rubber is wild. It is collected partly in the Amazon Basin and partly from the rainforests of Africa. The latter region furnishes rubber juice, or latex, derived from vines, which is referred to as liana rubber. The remaining 97 to 98 per cent of present commercial rubber is plantation grown; about 95 per cent of it is obtained from southeastern Asia and Indonesia (FIG. 17–28).

The Far Eastern plantation production began with the introduction of hevea from the Amazon. In 1910, Brazil still held a rubber

monopoly, producing nearly 90 per cent. By 1920 plantation rubber accounted for about 90 per cent and by 1930 for nearly all. The shift occurred largely because plantations proved more economically advantageous to the consumers; rubber was produced more cheaply than was possible under the haphazard methods of forest exploitation. Further, the product was "standardized." Plantation rubber, produced using scientific methods, is a cleaner and higher quality product (FIG. 17–29). Many of the plantations are foreign owned and operated, although there is ever-increasing production from those owned and operated by natives. The major advantage of the Far East over the Amazon or the Congo lies mainly in the availability of cheap labor, plus, of course, the fact that production is so well established there that new production elsewhere faces great difficulty in breaking into the market. Indonesia is the chief producer, followed closely by nearby Malaya. Together, Indonesia and Malaya supply the bulk of the world's natural rubber. Lesser production occurs in Thailand, Ceylon, Vietnam, Sarawak, and Cambodia. Singapore is the major collecting and export center and London is the chief financial center. The flow of export natural

17-29

NEW *"tapping cut" on a rubber tree in a Malayan plantation.*

rubber goes primarily to the United States and secondarily to western Europe, including the British Isles. The United States is by far the leading consumer of natural rubber, and leads in both the production and the consumption of synthetic rubber.

Tobacco

This is the only one of the key agricultural commodities which is, so to speak, nonessential. The others, with the debatable exceptions of tea and coffee, are either essential foodstuffs, essential raw materials for manufacturing, or both. Despite its luxury nature, tobacco is grown in many regions and it enters importantly into agricultural trade.

There are many varieties of commercial tobacco, most of which fall into the categories of cigar tobacco or cigarette tobacco. The tremendous increase in the use of cigarettes has boomed tobacco production and created a billion-dollar manufacturing industry as well, particularly in the United States. Tobacco is grown in the tropics, subtropics, and mid-latitudes, depending on specific varieties, and it occupies fields which range in size from "tobacco patches" to large plantations. Even where grown in small fields and in small amounts it is an important cash crop, furnishing either the major cash income or an important addition to income derived from other crops or pursuits.

Because of its many varieties, tobacco has a very wide spread climatically. The St. Lawrence valley represents tobacco's farthest poleward extension in the Americas as southern Sweden and central Russia do in the Old World; in contrast, Sumatran production is virtually on the equator. Similarly, tobacco is grown in many different types of soils, ranging from deep loams to light sands. Some of the best cigarette tobaccos, where the demand is largely for light-colored, aromatic leaf, are grown on soils which naturally are light and shallow.

The United States, China, India, and the U.S.S.R., in that order, are the leading producers. The chief districts are widely scattered in China and India; in the United States they are concentrated in a belt which runs from southern Ohio through Kentucky to northwestern Tennessee and in the Virginia-Carolinas section east of the Appalachians. Another major district extends from southern Georgia into northern Florida; and lesser districts, devoted to dark cigar tobacco, occur in the Connecticut valley and southern Wisconsin. In the U.S.S.R., the main districts are chiefly in the central and southern portions of the Russian Plain.

The United States is the leading exporter; other exports come from many countries, such as Indonesia, Greece, Turkey, Brazil, and Cuba. Except for the United States, the leading producers are not leading exporters. For export tobacco the British Isles and western Europe are the leading consumers. The United States imports some tobacco from Turkey and southeastern Europe, chiefly for cigarette blends, and some from Indonesia and several of the West Indian islands, chiefly as cigars or cigar filler and wrapper.

ANIMAL HUSBANDRY

NO ONE knows when man first learned to tame wild animals as sources of food, materials for clothing and shelter, beasts of burden, and for companionship. Certainly it was tens of thousands of years ago. Most of the world's domestic animals were first tamed somewhere in Asia. Today the distribution of livestock is extremely wide. It includes the reindeer of the tundra, the water buffalo of the Oriental tropics, the many cattle, sheep, and other animals of the mid-latitudes and subtropics, as well as the highland-dwelling yak of Tibet and the llama and alpaca of the Andes. There are few parts of the present-day, permanently inhabited world where animals of some sort have not been put to active use by human beings.

Domestic animals vary greatly in size, ranging from small fowl to hogs, cattle, horses, camels, and elephants. They are found in greatest number in the more densely settled agricultural regions, but they use the largest amount of land in areas of sparse population, mainly in dry lands, savannas, and tundras. Where population is extremely dense, and, at the same time, supported almost entirely by agriculture, only the smaller domestic animals can be maintained. Examples are the scavenger hogs and chickens of China. India, on the other hand, has more cattle than any other region, yet it has practically no "meat cattle" industry. The reason lies in religion: the majority of the population is Hindu and cattle are sacred to them. The millions of cattle contribute to the overcrowding of India; they seem to be everywhere, whether in rural areas or in city streets and temples of worship. However, the cattle do furnish some milk, and many are used as beasts of burden and, when they die, as a source of hides.

Domestic animals, like crops, are raised either for subsistence or for commerce. Subsistence animal industry usually is termed nomadic herding; the production of animals and animal products for sale usually is termed commercial animal husbandry. The latter includes commercial grazing, the feeding of animals on farms and in feed lots, and dairy production.

Nomadic Herding

Nomadic herding affects tremendous areas, but relatively few persons; and the number of animals and the amount of products obtained are small when compared with those of commercial animal husbandry. With the world pressed for area suitable for crops, nomadic herding, which requires a great deal of space, is confined to regions which are essentially nonagricultural. When human ingenuity renders formerly nonagricultural land capable of crop production, or when the stage of settlement develops from extensive to more intensive land use, migratory herding gives way.

CHIEF REGIONS • Most of the areas of migratory grazing are in cold lands or dry lands (FIG. 17-4). Their correspondence to most of the regions of Polar (E) and Dry (B) climates is striking, just as it is to the regions of tundra grass and steppe and desert grass supported by those climates. Within the dry land portions, the areas of migratory grazing are more likely to occur in the Semiarid (BS) climates and steppe grass than they are in the drier Arid (BW) climates and the sparser desert grass and desert shrub.

In two major regions of the earth the migratory herdsman and his flocks and herds dominate the geographical scene. One is the Eurasian tundra and certain parts of the American tundra, which support a one-animal economy based on the reindeer. The other is the vast dry belt which extends from the Atlantic shore of northern Africa across Asia Minor and the heart of Asia to the plains of Manchuria. This is a multi-animal economy, based on such animals as goats, sheep, cattle, horses, and camels.

REINDEER ECONOMY • Reindeer are native to the Eurasian tundra and it is only in the past half century that they have been introduced to parts of the American tundra, in northern and western Alaska and in the Mackenzie Delta and adjacent sections (FIG. 17–4). The Eskimos, primarily fishermen and hunters, have not taken readily to the herdsman's way of life and its perennial responsibilities. Quite to the contrary, the native groups of northern Europe and Asia have lived "for and by" their animals for many centuries.

The reindeer is a most useful and likable animal. Its docility and its ability to live on the tundra, both in its frozen state during the coldest season and in its "mushy" state during the warmer period, make it easy to care for. From it are obtained food, clothing, shelter, and transportation. Live animals furnish milk, part of which is used to make cheese; dead animals furnish lean meat, fat, and blood, as well as skins for tents and certain clothing, and sinews and small bones for thread and needles. When the time comes to move, as it does so often in a land of scant and slow-growing pasturage, reindeer carry the family goods on their backs or pull them on crude "drags." Moving is no great chore, because possessions are, and must be, few and simple.

MULTI-ANIMAL ECONOMY • Within the second major area of the pastoral nomads (FIG. 17–4) the way of life is based on a comparatively large variety of animals, not only for the area as a whole, but within individual sections. Goats, furnishing milk, cheese, meat,

hair, and skins, are most numerous in northwest Africa, western Asia Minor, and the Pamir Highlands. They are able to live in the sections of roughest terrain and scantiest feed. There is a saying to the effect that, "Where cattle can't live, sheep can; where sheep can't live, goats can; and where goats can't live, nothing can." Although an exaggeration, the saying contains a great deal of truth. Sheep, supplying wool as well as mutton, have wide distribution, with more of them in Russian Turkestan than in other sections. The sections possessing the more abundant and nutritious feeds support cattle. Cattle are most numerous in the cooler portions; they are not commonly found in Africa and Asia Minor. The great mountain arcs which comprise the Himalayas, Kunluns, Tien Shans, Altais and, in the southern part, the Tibetan Plateau are the homeland of the yak. The yak can be ridden and used to carry burdens and pull carts, and it supplies meat, milk, and wool. It is very sturdy and well adapted to cold, scant feed, and high altitudes. However, it cannot live in lowlands and is seldom seen below five thousand feet. Horses are numerous and used primarily for riding, whether in traveling or in herding other animals. In some sections they furnish meat and hides, as well as milk. Some of the finest riding horses in the world have been developed in this area, particularly in Arabia. In the driest and sandiest sections of Gobi, Russian Turkestan, Arabia, and the Sahara, are many camels. The ability of the camel to travel well in sand and go long distances without water or food makes it a very useful animal for peoples who must "follow the feed" and often make long journeys from one water hole to another.

Even more than the reindeer herdsmen, the nomads of central and southwestern Asia and northern Africa must be on the move. When feed is especially scanty, they must move day after day. When it is more plentiful, their rude encampments may stay in one place for days or weeks at a time. In the warmest and driest sections, they literally "follow the showers," which bring short-lived grasses for the animals to feed on. In some sections, mainly in central Asia, they move northward during the summer and southward during the winter. Where the grazing lands are associated with mountains, herds and flocks are driven to alpine pastures in the summer and brought back to the warmer and less stormy lowlands in the winter. Such migration thus has a vertical as well as a horizontal aspect and it represents a rather nice adjustment to seasonal atmospheric changes and to the distribution of vegetation types.

Commercial Animal Husbandry

The parts of the earth in which animals and animal products are raised for market include the beef areas of Argentina, the sheep country of Australia, the beef and hog region of the United States Corn Belt, and the dairy regions of the northeastern United States and northwestern Europe. Latitudinally, they range from the warmer edge of the northern forests and cold, wind-swept Patagonia to the margins of the rainforests. Climatically, they range from all except the coldest and the hottest humid lands to the margins of the hot deserts. Some of the regions of commercial animal husbandry are associated with highly developed agricultural areas, such as the United States Corn Belt (FIG. 17–3); others are the livestock ranching areas of the "wide open spaces," such as the Great Basin of the United States (FIG. 17–12) or the Great Plains of Argentina. The chief animals raised, whether on vast ranges or in constricted pasture fields and feed lots, are beef cattle, dairy cattle, hogs, and sheep.

BEEF CATTLE • While beef cattle are raised primarily for meat, they also furnish large amounts of beef extract, hides, tallow, bone and bone meal, blood meal, and hair. The better varieties are produced in the mid-latitudes and the cooler margins of the subtropics. The cattle raised in savanna regions, such as the Orinoco Llanos, furnish inferior meat and are,

comparatively, more useful for other products, especially hides. Neither beef nor dairy cattle thrive in the rainier tropics, although other kinds of "cattle," such as the water buffalo of southeastern Asia and Indonesia, are well adapted. India's cattle, previously mentioned as being more numerous than those of any other country, are there because of religious belief and not because they are necessarily well adapted or of major commercial significance (FIG. 17–30).

Argentina usually exports nearly as much beef as all other nations combined. A mild subtropical climate, a vast area of rich soils and nearly level land, and widespread production of alfalfa, coupled with relatively sparse population, enable the Argentine Pampas to produce a large surplus. Other major beef export areas in South America are in Uruguay and the Brazilian Highlands. Far away Australia also exports large amounts of beef. Most of it comes from the eastern third of the country, partly from the humid coastal region and partly from the semiarid lands west of the Great Dividing Range. Like South America, Australia has abundant range, abundant feed, and relatively few persons to consume the meat at home. New Zealand, especially North Island, also produces a considerable surplus for export. Other producers of beef cattle, chiefly the United States and western Europe, have little or no surplus. The United States has more beef cattle than any other nation, yet home consumption is so great that there is practically no export in normal times. Many United States beef cattle, noted for their high quality, are raised on the western range lands and then transported to the Corn Belt for fattening. They are found in greatest concentration in the western part of the Corn Belt and immediately adjacent sections (FIG. 17–31).

At least half of the people of the world have never tasted beef; it is a high-priced food that can be afforded only by those with comparatively high purchasing power. Where poverty and dense population combine, as they

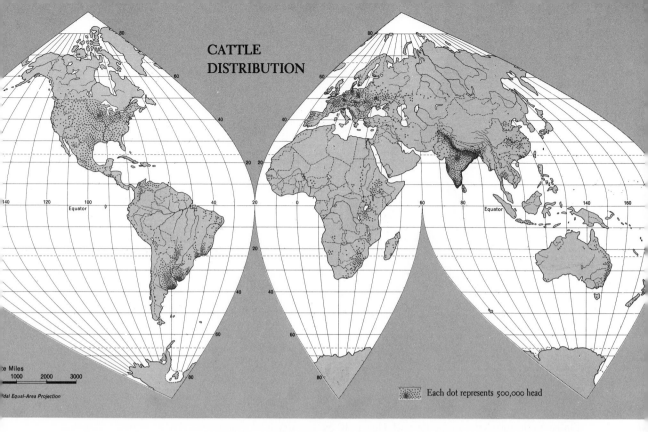

CATTLE
DISTRIBUTION

Mate Miles
1000 2000 3000

dal Equal-Area Projection

Each dot represents 500,000 head

17–30   TWO main types of cattle are found in the world—European cattle which predominate in temperate zones and zebus, or humped cattle, which predominate in the tropics. Cattle produced primarily for milk and meat are especially concentrated in western Europe, the United States, and east-central South America; cattle produced primarily for work purposes predominate in tropical Asia. India has the largest number of cattle in the world, with nearly a fifth of the world's total—though objects of religious worship, they are still used as work animals.

do in most of the Orient, beef imports are out of the question and land at home must be used to produce foods which can be directly consumed. Religion, too, forbids the use of beef to millions of people, such as the Hindus. The large exports of beef from the Southern Hemisphere travel mainly to the British Isles. These little isles normally import about three-quarters of the world's export beef. Other importers, definitely minor, are France, Belgium, and West Germany.

DAIRY CATTLE • Dairy cattle are concentrated chiefly in northern Europe and the northeastern quarter of the United States. Smaller concentrations are in southeastern Canada, southeastern Australia, and New Zea-

land. Most dairy cows are raised in cool or cold climates which are capable of producing abundant pastures, hays, and other feeds. The dairy business began in western Europe, where the Mid-latitude Marine (Cfb) climate, with its cool, moist conditions, encouraged the growth of lush pastures and hay crops, as well as the growth of the cattle themselves. Dairy cattle there are most numerous in the coastal and near-coastal belt from southern Sweden to northwestern France and in the British Isles. Denmark and the Netherlands are particularly noted as "dairy countries."

Dairy cattle are so numerous in the portion of the United States which extends from Minnesota and Iowa to New England that the re-

Animal Husbandry | 433

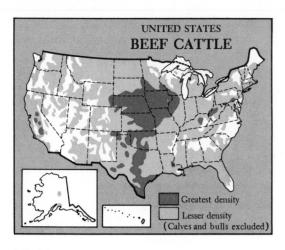

UNITED STATES
BEEF CATTLE

Greatest density

Lesser density
(Calves and bulls excluded)

17–31

BEEF *cattle are raised in most sections of the United States, but they are most numerous in the western part of the Corn Belt and in parts of the Great Plains.*

gion is known as the Dairy Region, or, recognizing the importance of feed, as the Hay and Dairy Belt (FIG. 17–12). A part of this belt extends into the Lower Great Lakes and Upper St. Lawrence valley sections of Canada. Both in Europe and the United States, dairy cattle are raised mainly within or next door to regions of dense population (FIG. 17–32). This enables the more perishable dairy products, milk and

cream, to be placed quickly on the large urban markets. Butter and cheese are also produced in large amounts, but they are much less perishable and hence easier to ship. Production of dairy products outside of Europe and the United States and far away from major markets is largely limited to butter and cheese. On refrigerator ships they accomplish the long journey from Australia and New Zealand without spoilage.

Commercial dairying is a full-time job. Between the pastures and hayfields, the care and milking of the cattle, and the preparation of the milk and cream for market, the dairy farmer finds himself busy the year around. Thus, this activity and this region become highly specialized, rather than diversified. Some diversification occurs in the chief dairy regions of Europe, where hog and poultry production is closely integrated with the dairy industry.

A very few nations monopolize the export trade in dairy products. New Zealand, Denmark, Australia, and the Netherlands account for most of the butter export. New Zealand alone may export as many as 375,000,000 pounds in a year. Export butter, regardless of source, is consumed mainly by the British Isles and Belgium. New Zealand and the Netherlands supply close to half of all export cheese;

17–32 A TYPICAL *modern dairy farm in the Hay and Dairy Belt of the United States. Note the cattle in the pasture, the huge barns, milking sheds, and silo.*

N.Y. MILK INDUSTRY FOUNDATION

the remainder is supplied by several countries, especially Denmark, Switzerland, France, Italy, and Australia. As with butter, most of the export cheese is sold in the British Isles and Belgium.

HOGS • Hogs, or swine, are much more adaptable than either beef or dairy cattle, although some of the most highly bred varieties of hogs require much care, including scientific feeding, protection from excess sun, and inoculation against diseases. Hogs are raised all the way from the tropics to the northern forests and in lowlands and highlands alike. It is possible that China has the greatest number, but these are scavengers and their commercial significance, as opposed to their significance in local subsistence economies, rests largely on the production of bristles. Other concentrations occur in Europe, the United States, the U.S.S.R., and Brazil. Hogs, regardless of type, would undoubtedly be much more widespread in the world if it were not for religious beliefs which exclude them from large areas stretching across northern Africa and southwestern, central, and southeastern Asia.

Commercial hogs are produced chiefly in Europe and the United States, which account for the bulk of bacon, ham, and lard output, whether for home or export markets, and for fresh pork, which enters very little into export trade. While commercial hog production is specialized to a certain degree, it is, of course, carried on in connection with crop production and other animal industries. In the United States, it is mainly a part of the complex crop and animal economy of the Corn Belt, where hogs consume about 42 per cent of all corn grown (FIG. 17–33). Corn-fed hogs furnish not only ham and bacon, but large amounts of lard as well. Hogs also occupy the corn regions of Europe, but they are most numerous in the noncorn areas. They are especially important in the dairy economy of Denmark and the Netherlands, where they are fed partly on skim milk, and in the general farming sections of Germany and Poland, where potatoes are

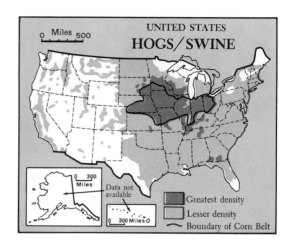

17–33

THE chief hog/swine-producing section of the United States corresponds closely to the area of greatest corn production.

major items in their diet. Hogs fed on potatoes and skim milk produce comparatively little lard, but they are noted for ham and bacon of fine quality.

Four countries control the bulk of the foreign trade in hog products: Denmark, Poland, the Netherlands, and the United States. Danish bacon is especially famous for its high quality. The United States is the only significant exporter of lard. The European exports go largely to the British Isles, and those from the United States to the Caribbean area and Middle America. Unlike the other exporters, the United States consumes most of its hog products at home as bacon, ham, lard, and fresh pork.

SHEEP • The mid-latitude and subtropical regions contain most of the world's sheep, although some occur in tropical highlands, notably the Andes (FIG. 17–34). The tropical lowlands are not suitable for sheep: a "wool coat" and hot, wet climates do not go together. Large numbers of sheep per unit area are found in the countries of western and southern Europe, and in parts of the United States, Argentina, Uruguay, South Africa, Australia, New

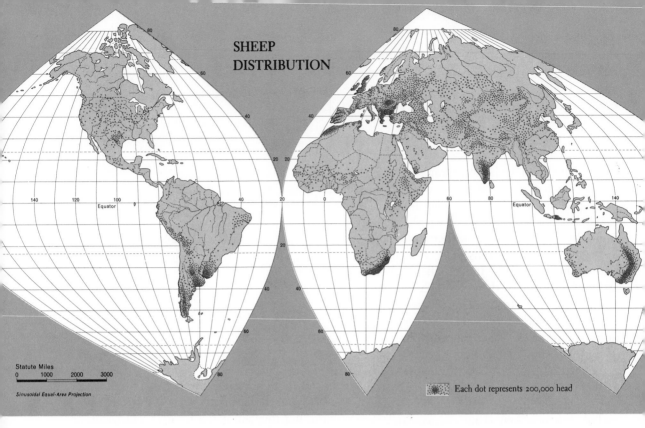

SHEEP
DISTRIBUTION

Statute Miles

0   1000   2000   3000

Sinusoidal Equal-Area Projection

:::: Each dot represents 200,000 head

17–34   SHEEP *are raised predominantly in the mid-latitudes and subtropics (including the steppes as well as humid regions) throughout all the continents along these latitudes. Sheep are raised mainly for meat and for wool, with Australia being the leading sheepland of the world, while the U.S.S.R., Argentina, India, New Zealand, the Republic of South Africa, and the United States follow, each with sizable numbers.*

Zealand, the U.S.S.R., China, and India. They are sparse in eastern Asia, mainly because of the lack of land that can be afforded for grazing. In general, sheep occupy lands which are inferior for crops and for the grazing of most animals except goats. The ability of sheep to produce both food (mutton, lamb) and clothing (skins, wool) has made them very useful, whether in dry lands and areas in the initial stages of development or in the poorer spots in regions which are well developed and generally favorable for agriculture.

A short while ago most of the world's sheep were raised either for meat or for animal fiber; they were either "mutton sheep" or "wool sheep," but not both. Today, as a result of crossbreeding, many of them produce both

meat and wool. In general, there is still a tendency to produce sheep primarily for wool in broad, semiarid range lands and principally for meat in more densely populated humid lands, but the distinction is disappearing as more dual-purpose sheep are raised on ranges and farms alike. In the United States, there has been an increasing specialization, in some sections, in the growing of lambs. Spring lambs are marketed from such areas as Nebraska, Colorado, Wyoming, and Tennessee. California, with its mild winters, is able to market winter lambs.

Three countries share the bulk of the mutton export trade. New Zealand exports more than all other nations combined, with Australia and Argentina supplying most of the

436 | *Agriculture and Animal Husbandry*

remainder. Again, as with beef, butter, cheese, and ham exports, most of the mutton goes to the food-deficient British Isles. Wool exports are derived chiefly from Australia (about 40 per cent); the remainder comes largely from New Zealand, Argentina, Uruguay, and South Africa (FIG. 17–34). The wool goes primarily to the textile districts of England and secondarily to those of France, Germany, Italy, Belgium, Luxembourg, Japan, and the United States. It will be noted that the chief exporters of mutton and wool, as well as of beef, have relatively sparse populations and large amounts of semiarid grazing land or humid pastureland; and, again, that the United States, a large producer, does not enter importantly into the export trade.

ANIMAL FIBERS • Wool is the world's most important animal fiber, although it is a poor second to the leading vegetable fiber, cotton. Woolen textiles are in high demand in regions with cold winters and in those regions with comparatively mild winters where there is a combination of coolness and a high degree of dampness. Thus, wool clothing and woolen blankets are in demand in Canada, the northern United States, and northern Europe, as well as in the British Isles and western and interior Europe. The chief drawback to greater consumption of woolen products is cost. Wool costs more to produce and manufacture than cotton; many persons need it, but cannot afford it, whether in the poorer sections of Europe or the still poorer sections of eastern Asia. Even in the northern United States, there would undoubtedly be a greater consumption of woolen goods were the price not so high.

The second of the two major commercial animal fibers is silk. This is often discussed in connection with crop production, because silkworms are raised on farms and fed on farm-raised mulberry leaves, and proceeds from the sale of silk are counted as a part of farm cash income. Yet silk is strictly an animal fiber. Compared to wool, silk production is highly localized. Also, silk textiles are so high in price that they are in demand in only a few luxury markets. Silk is one of the most ancient items of trade. It was a compact, high-value commodity in the earliest trade within the Orient itself. Later, it played the same role in trade between the Orient and Asia Minor and the Orient and Europe. The most famous of the ancient caravan routes which wound across Asia from China to southeastern Europe was called the Silk Road.

Silkworms can be raised in most subtropical regions, but most of the commercial production occurs in the milder parts of Japan and China. The decisive consideration in raw silk production is very cheap labor. The silkworms must be carefully raised and fed, and the unwinding of the fine fibers from the cocoons produced by the worms is a laborious process requiring considerable skill. The worms are actually raised in the farmhouses of Japanese and Chinese peasants, where they receive as much care as though they were human infants. Japan produces about 60 per cent of all commercial raw silk, as compared to China's approximately 20 per cent. The silkworm industry, technically known as sericulture, has been placed on a much more scientific basis in Japan, and Japanese silk generally is higher in quality than Chinese.

Most of the products manufactured from raw silk are made in those countries of the world able to buy luxury textile goods. Some silk textiles are manufactured in Japan and China for export, but most of the commercial raw silk moves to factories in the United States and western Europe. The United States alone makes about 30 per cent of all commercial silk cloth. In Europe, the chief manufacturer is France.

The animal fibers, particularly silk, continue to face increasingly stiff competition from certain vegetable and mineral materials. Artificial silk in the form of rayon and nylon has virtually replaced silk for stockings, dresses, or underclothing. Real silk cannot compete in price with these more cheaply made materials. Rayon is made from wood pulp or cotton linters, and nylon from coal, air, and water. Dacron and Orlon, too, as well as many other synthetic fibers and textiles continue to reduce the significance of silk, particularly in North America and Europe. Another competitor which may affect both animal fiber production and cotton fiber output is glass. Modern science has already learned how to make light and flexible glass cloth which is hardly distinguishable from certain silk, rayon, and cotton cloth. It has the major advantage of being fireproof and it is in wide use, especially for draperies, curtains, wall hangings, carpets, upholstery cloth, and decorations in crowded public places, where sudden fire has many times taken a heavy toll because of the use of highly inflammable paper or cotton decorations and furnishings.

Despite new substitutes which appear from time to time, the demand for domestic animals and their products continues to increase. In particular, the demand for meat, dairy products, and wool indicates a favorable future for commercial animal husbandry. It is difficult to foresee a time when the keeping of animals, whether as a source of food or of industrial raw materials, will become unimportant for mankind.

Commercial Animal Husbandry   HOGS
     BEEF CATTLE   SHEEP
     DAIRY CATTLE   ANIMAL FIBERS

• REVIEW QUESTIONS •

1. Discuss some of the effects of the Industrial Revolution on agriculture. Have they been strongly felt wherever agriculture is practiced?

2. Give some examples to show that agriculture and manufacturing are now closely related in many parts of the world.

3. What are the major physical factors which "limit" agriculture? Can any of these factors be modified by man?

4. Is there justification for considering cultural inheritance as a limiting factor to agriculture?

5. Do you know of any significant recent developments in plant selection and breeding? See what you can find out, for example, about hybrid corn and its implications.

6. Should we spend millions of dollars to irrigate or drain lands for crop production, when other lands which do not require irrigation or artificial drainage could be brought into production or, if in production, could be made more productive? Explain your answer.

7. In your area, is there competition with agriculture on the part of other land uses?

8. Compare and contrast types of subsistence agriculture with commercial types.

9. Describe the general agricultural economy of your home area or the agricultural area that is closest to your home. What is it like? Why is it that way? What are the trends?

10. What are the world's chief food crops? Where is the major commercial production region of each one?

11. Why did maize play such an important part in the Westward Movement in our country?

12. Discuss the physical requirements for large-scale commercial corn production.

13. Contrast wheat and maize in terms of what happens to them after harvesting.

14. Determine the location of the chief *surplus* wheat-producing regions of the world. What enables them to produce significant surpluses? Where are these surpluses sent? Why?

15. Can you account for the fact that international trade in barley is very small?

16. Are most of the world's vegetables raised for sale or for home consumption?

17. What enables the vegetable-producing areas of California to compete with vegetable-producing areas located in the chief consuming regions of the United States?

18. Where are the world's major citrus fruit production areas? With what types of climate do they correlate?

19. The United States could grow enough sugar beets to satisfy its sugar needs. Why doesn't it do so?

20. Trace the geographical shifts in commercial coffee production. Why does Brazil stand out so sharply in world coffee production?

21. Why do we not grow the tea we use in this country rather than import it from Asia?

22. What caused cotton to change from the "king's cloth" to the "people's cloth"?

23. Why did commercial rubber production shift from the Amazon Basin to southeastern Asia? Why is rubber in such great demand, particularly in the United States?

24. See if you can determine the present status of "synthetic versus natural rubber."

25. What are the chief domestic animals?

26. In general, what types of climate occur in the regions of nomadic herding?

27. What are the factors responsible for Argentina's leadership in beef exports?

28. Why do comparatively few of the world's people consume appreciable quantities of meat?

29. Where is our Hay and Dairy Belt? How do you account for its existence?

30. We commonly speak of "corn-fed" hogs. Are there any important hog-producing regions where the feed is not corn?

31. Explain the statement, in reference to hogs raised in the United States Corn Belt, that, "everything is used but the squeal."

32. Why is there such a large world demand for wool when cotton is cheaper?

33. Why is there so much mention of the decreasing importance of silk?

18 Utilization of Forests

U.S. FOREST SERVICE

❲ MORE *than a half-century of education and legislation has made the American public, even the city-dwelling segment, very much aware of the continuing need for protection, reconstitution, and wise utilization of forests. On a strictly practical basis alone, it is now well recognized that wood and wood products are holding their own even in the so-called Age of Metals, and that the resources of the forests are still economically vital. It is virtually impossible to foresee a time when trees and forests will become unimportant.*

GENERAL SIGNIFICANCE OF FORESTS

DESPITE thousands of years of use and abuse, forests still constitute one of the major geographical patterns. Their readily visible presence is especially marked in the northern portions of North America and Eurasia and in the rainier parts of the tropics. Over the whole world forests of one sort or another cover about one-fourth of the earth's land surface, an extent greater than that of the world's deserts and nearly as great as all deserts and steppes combined. However, the area that is classified as "productive" forest is only about one-sixth to one-seventh of the land surface of the earth.

Forests have many uses. In some parts of the world, they are the main sources or source regions of food for human beings; in other areas, they provide food both for man and for domestic animals. They are sources of spices, medicines, fuel, building materials, and raw materials for manufacture. They provide habitats for many kinds of wild animals. They are significant as agents of water conservation. And they offer opportunity for recreation. Clearly these manifold uses make forests of the greatest significance to man.

Foods, Spices, and Medicines

From time immemorial man has turned to the forest for part or all of his food; today, many primitive and semiprimitive peoples still depend heavily on the forests for food. The dependence is generally twofold: the forest furnishes such products as fruits, nuts, and roots; it also supplies edible insects, snakes, birds, fish, and game animals. There are, for example, many native tribes in the rainforests of Africa, South America, southeastern Asia,

and Indonesia who depend almost entirely on the vegetable and animal products of the forest for their livelihood. The same is true for a number of native groups in the northern forest regions of Canada and Siberia.

Where agriculture is practiced in forested areas, the farmer still turns to the forest for what it can offer. Thus the migratory farmer of the Amazon Basin seeks out forest fruits and game to add to the products of his small clearing. In similar fashion, the farmer of the warmer parts of the northern forests depends upon wild berries, a few tree fruits, and fish and game to augment his food supply. In the Great Lakes region and eastward practically to the Atlantic, the Indians obtained sugar from the sweet sap of the maple tree; today, in some of the "sugar-bush" areas, the white man has developed the production of maple sugar into an important local enterprise. Where domestic animals occur, the forest furnishes forage for them, either in the form of browse from trees and bushes, grass from forest-protected glades, or mast from nuts and roots.

While many of the spices which season and preserve foods are now produced on farms or plantations, some of the supply still is obtained from the forests, either from parts of trees or from bushes and vines which can exist only in the presence of numerous trees. Examples are pepper, cloves, nutmeg, ginger, and cinnamon. Chicle, one of the bases for chewing gum, also comes from the forest.

Scores of forest plants, both trees and smaller growth, furnish substances used in both primitive and modern medicine, either for the cure of disease or the alleviation of pain. Again, many of the plants are now farm and plantation products, but the collection of wild plants from the forest is still important. Here one may mention such items as cinchona bark for quinine, coca leaves for cocaine, kola nuts for stimulants, white pine bark for cough medi-

18–1

[OPPOSITE, TOP] SELECTIVE *cutting in ponderosa pine forest in Oregon helps to preserve a natural resource.*

cines, and timbo roots for rotenone to relieve muscular spasm (as well as to use in insecticides). Indians of the Canadian forest use spruce needles to make a medicinal tea.

Fuel

How much of the world's population depends mainly on trees for fuel cannot be stated accurately, but it is a large proportion, and authorities estimate that nearly 40 per cent of the world's wood output is used for fuel. In the tropics, wood, or charcoal made from wood, is practically the only fuel. Because of the climate, such regions require fuel primarily for cooking rather than for heating, especially in rural areas. It is estimated that between 60 and 70 million cords of wood are used annually for fuel in the United States alone, even though the chief sources of energy for heating and cooking are coal, natural gas, petroleum, and hydroelectricity.

Construction Materials

The use of trees as a source of piling, beams, and lumber of many sizes and shapes is well known. In those parts of the world where trees of "stick-timber" size are present or readily brought in, most buildings, wharves, bridges, and other structures are of wood. Where forests are not present, or are greatly depleted, lumber is scarce and high in price. In these regions, wood is reserved for smaller items, such as furniture, sills, panelings, and certain tools and household utensils. Some areas have purchasing power sufficiently high to allow large lumber imports from distant production regions. A good example of this is the Los Angeles metropolitan region. Here all except the larger buildings are constructed primarily of wood, despite the fact that all the lumber must be imported, most of it from the forests of northern California, Washington, and Oregon, which are from 600 to 1700 miles away. Lumber in Los Angeles is not cheap, even

though the greater part of the haul is by water.

In recent years, many new wood-processing techniques have been perfected, which have increased the utility of wood for building and many other purposes. Wood is now impregnated with substances which make it fireproof and termiteproof. Plywood, or laminated wood, can now be made nearly as strong as steel. It is used for building walls, panels, trimmings, containers, furniture, boats, and a wide variety of small articles.

Paper and Other Cellulose Materials

During the nineteenth century, paper made from rags gave way to paper made chiefly from wood pulp, that is, from trees, particularly spruce trees. The result was less expensive paper and a tremendous increase in paper consumption, not only for writing paper, newspapers, and magazines, but also for bags, cartons, separators, and packings. The greatest increase in the use of paper made from the cellulose fibers of trees has come since 1900. The increasing demand for pulpwood has further emphasized the importance of forests and the problem of the depletion of the forests of the United States. At present, the United States, which produces somewhat more than one-third of all the world's paper, must depend on foreign sources, mainly Canada, for much of its pulpwood supply.

Cellulose materials derived chiefly from trees are also used for the manufacture of rayon, plastics, and explosives. Present demands for cellulose for other than paper uses are so great that many areas previously logged-over for lumber are now being combed for the wood which the original lumbermen left behind. In some areas, stumps and even partly burned or partly rotted logs are being utilized.

Game Protection

Forests, particularly if they are not too dense, furnish habitats for many species of game animals and game birds (FIG. 18–2). Forests also protect streams and, hence, game fish. There are parts of the world where such game and fish are worth literally millions of dollars each year. Examples are to be found in much of the northeastern United States, parts of the Appalachian Uplands, and the mountainous regions of the West. Game attracts hunters and fishermen, who spend huge sums for licenses, equipment, transportation, guides, food, and housing. While some of the money is spent in cities and some goes into state treasuries, much of it goes to the local inhabitants. The amount is often almost enough to support permanent populations, some of them in areas which might otherwise have to be abandoned.

Water Conservation

The surest way to squander water resources and to encourage flood damage in a forested region is to remove the forest. Forests break the impact of torrential rains; they shade snow on the ground and enable it to melt slowly. Forest undergrowth and litter prevent rapid surface runoff and encourage more water to sink into the ground. In one fashion or another, they reduce floods and insure the preservation of underground water supplies. These things are significant not only within the forested areas themselves, but often many miles away; many a section, for example, has been struck by disastrous floods whose origin lay in deforested regions upstream. In addition, forests help to hold the soil in place (FIG. 18–3), so that it does not move with every rain to glut the valleys or to choke and clog streams which flow into other areas. For such reasons, forests should be preserved or even re-established over many parts of the earth. If they had nothing but water and soil conservation

18–2

AN example of a forest (a mixture of dense and more open growth) that is an excellent game habitat, near Lutzen, Minnesota.

to contribute, their maintenance still would be worth the cost.

Scenery and Recreation

Forests are also important just to be in and to look at. They are cool and restful; they please the eye and the spirit and help to restore energy to tired bodies. The truth of this is attested by the millions who vacation in them each year and by the many thousands who go to forest sanitariums to regain their health. Again, all this has economic importance, for vacationers and health-seekers spend millions of dollars annually to be among the trees.

M. S. TALBOT, U.S. FOREST SERVICE

18–3 SEVERE *gullying on unprotected land in the Tehachapi area in California. Note the lack of gully-ing on the surface protected by the tree.*

MAJOR FOREST REGIONS OF THE WORLD

THERE are three major forest regions in the world: the tropical, the mid-latitude, and the northern forests (FIGS. 13–13 and 14–2). Their distribution correlates with the definitely humid climates. The tropical forests are found chiefly in regions with 60 inches or more of average annual precipitation; the mid-latitude forests chiefly in regions with 20 or more inches; the northern forests mainly in regions with 10 or more inches. In general, the effectiveness of a given amount of precipitation increases with increased latitude (see p. 229). Thus, 10 inches of average annual precipitation in the higher latitudes is sufficient to insure a climate humid enough to support the growth of trees. In the somewhat warmer mid-latitudes, with increased evaporation, at least 20 inches is necessary. In the tropics, with their high evaporation rates, at least 60 inches normally is needed, except where swampy condi-

tions prevail or where soils locally are highly retentive of moisture.

The Tropical Forests

The area occupied by the tropical forests today does not differ greatly from that of the past, except that removal has been complete, or nearly so, in large parts of southeastern Asia, as in India and Java, areas of high population density. However, most of the tropical forests and their margins have suffered considerably in quality and density because of grazing, migratory agriculture, and fires. That the tropical forests do not have greater commercial importance is largely a reflection of the many difficulties of exploiting them. These difficulties include distance from major markets; competition from more favorably located forest regions; inadequate labor supply; hot, wet climates; health problems; and a world lumber demand which is mainly for softwoods rather than tropical hardwoods. However, the tropical forest regions are large and contain approximately one-half of the world's productive forest area, and the day may come when they will be more actively and more extensively utilized.

Roughly one-third of the world's hardwood forests are located in South America, mainly in Brazil. They sweep across the Amazon Basin from the Atlantic to the slopes of the Andes and from the northern edge of the Brazilian Uplands into and across much of the Guiana Highlands to the margins of the plains of the Orinoco Basin. Other similar forests occur in parts of the Brazilian Uplands, along the southeast coast of Brazil, and in much of western Colombia. Elsewhere in the Americas, they occur chiefly along and near the Caribbean shore, from Colombia to the Gulf of Mexico, and in parts of the West Indies. Africa possesses about one-sixth of the world's hardwood forests, practically all of which are tropical. Most of them lie in the area between the Gulf of Guinea and the equatorial mountain and lake district and along the northern shores of the Gulf of Guinea. In Asia, the bulk of the tropical hardwood forests is found in the southeastern corner, from Burma to Vietnam and south into the Malay Peninsula. The remainder of those in the Eastern Hemisphere are in Indonesia, chiefly in Sumatra, Borneo, Celebes, and New Guinea, and in scattered patches along the northern fringe of Australia.

The Mid-latitude Forests

The mid-latitude forests have suffered more from the ax, saw, and fire than the tropical forests. At present these forests comprise only a small part of the world's forested area. In China proper, the removal has been almost complete except in the hillier sections of the south. In Europe and the United States, all except the higher and rougher sections have been largely cleared or at least logged heavily, although there are many forests or woodland areas in the lowlands, mainly in the form of farm wood lots, forest strips along some of the steep valley sides, or relatively extensive stands in swampy or very sandy areas. Also, there now are many man-made forest districts, where trees are raised as a kind of crop, as in parts of Europe and portions of our South. The mid-latitude forests are "mixed"—a mixture of hardwoods and softwoods. Admitting many exceptions, where soils are sandy there are apt to be solid stands of conifers; where soils are high in clay there are apt to be hardwood stands. But, in general, any large mid-latitude forest area contains both softwood and hardwood varieties. Most of the mid-latitude forest was removed to make way for crops, although it also served as fuel, fencing, lumber, and so forth. In many sections, the forest was merely in the way and most of it "went up in smoke." For example, the early settlers in Ohio, Indiana, and southern Michigan cut and burned great piles of black walnut just to get rid of it. Today, black walnut is very scarce and, in the commercial market, almost "worth its weight in gold."

What is left of the mid-latitude forests is chiefly in the United States and Europe. Those of the United States are mainly in the Appalachian Uplands, the western mountains, the northern Great Lakes states, and parts of the Atlantic and Gulf Coastal Plains. Those of Europe are also mainly in uplands and a few lowland sections, especially in the north. The major occurrence is in a broken belt from Spain to central western Russia and east into Siberia. Elsewhere in the Northern Hemisphere they are chiefly in widely scattered hilly and mountainous areas, from the Caucasus to South China and northward in northern China, Korea, and Japan. The Southern Hemisphere had little mid-latitude forest to begin with, and it too has been greatly altered by burning and cutting.

The Northern Forests

Most of the remaining forests outside the tropics are in high latitude regions of the Northern Hemisphere (PLATE VI). In North America they lie chiefly on the poleward side of the 50th parallel; in Eurasia chiefly poleward of the 55th parallel. They extend northward until they gradually disappear, merging with the tundras of the Arctic. In a few places, they actually send out fingers which stretch north to embayments of the Arctic Ocean, as for example, in the delta of the Mackenzie river. The northern forests are predominantly coniferous, although hardwoods are not uncommon along the warmer margins. Mid-latitude market demands have eaten heavily into these forests, especially in Canada and Europe. In area the northern forest lands are equal to about three-quarters of the tropical forest area. In wood content, however, their reserve is much less than that of the tropical forests because the northern forests are patchy and broken and trees are comparatively small, except along the warmer margins where growing conditions are better. Very often the trees are of pulpwood rather than lumber size. Replacement by new growth is very slow because of the shortness of the growing season in these areas of long and severe winters.

FOREST REGIONS OF THE UNITED STATES

VIRGIN forests originally covered nearly half of the conterminous United States (FIG. 18–4), sweeping almost unbroken from the Atlantic to the prairies of the far interior and from the Gulf into Canada. Farther west, they occupied large sections of the central and northern Rockies, parts of the Colorado Plateau, and an extensive area in the Cascades, Sierra Nevada, and Coast Ranges. Today, the eastern virgin forests are more than 90 per cent removed and those of the west about half removed. The entire virgin forest, eastern and western combined, is now about 90 per cent depleted, and what areas remain have been virtually robbed of certain types of trees. Depletion of United States forests is most marked in the Corn Belt and east to the Atlantic, and in the eastern half of the Cotton Belt. It is least

18–4 THESE two maps, including the bar graphs at the bottom, indicate what has happened to the virgin forests of the conterminous United States since Colonial days.

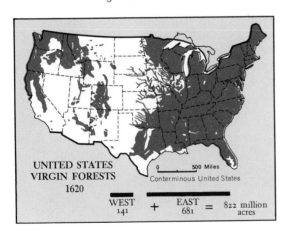

UNITED STATES VIRGIN FORESTS 1620

0   500 Miles
Conterminous United States

WEST 141 + EAST 681 = 822 million acres

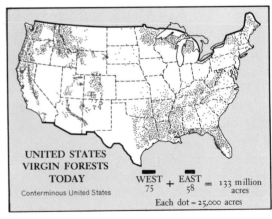

UNITED STATES VIRGIN FORESTS TODAY

Conterminous United States

WEST 75 + EAST 58 = 133 million acres

Each dot = 25,000 acres

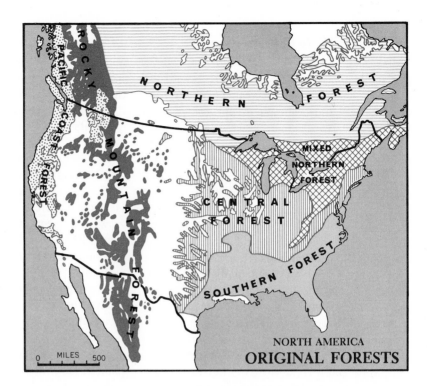

NORTH AMERICA
ORIGINAL FORESTS

marked in the western mountain and hill regions, the northern fringe of the country from
Minnesota to Maine, the southern Appalachian
Uplands, and the sandier and swampier portions of the Gulf Coastal Plain. Most of the
depletion has occurred within the past one
hundred years and much of it within the past
seventy years. Large areas which were cut over
and burned over have grown new forests, but
much of the new timber is inferior to that
of the virgin stand.

The major forest regions of the United
States are six in number: the Mixed Northern
Forest Region, the Central Hardwood Forest
Region, the Southern Mixed Forest Region,
the Rocky Mountain Forest Region, the Pa-
cific Coast Forest Region, and the Central
Alaska Forest Region (FIG. 18–5).

The Mixed Northern Forest

The Mixed Northern Forest extends chiefly
from Minnesota to Maine and from the latitude of the northern Great Lakes to that of
the southern Great Lakes. In addition, it sends
a narrow finger southward along the higher and
cooler parts of the Appalachian Uplands (FIG.
18–5). Its major remnants, mingled with areas
of new but inferior growth, are chiefly in the
northern Lake region, the Adirondacks, central
Maine, and the southern Appalachians (compare FIGS. 18–4 and 18–5). Dominant, or "key,"
genera of trees are spruce, balsam, fir, hemlock, cedar, pine, birch, poplar, beech, and
maple.

It is generally agreed that the northern,
rougher sections of this forest region are better suited to the growth of trees than to any
other use. Already there are some national forests, as well as some under control of state
and local governments, but the percentage of
the original area under such control is small.
As is usually true, it is much easier to destroy
a resource than it is to replace it or substitute
for it. Unfortunately, appreciation of a resource
comes, all too often, after its destruction.

Forest Regions of the United States | 447

The Central Hardwood Forest

The main body of the Central Hardwood Forest Region (FIG. 18–5) extends from the southern margin of the Great Lakes to the Cotton Belt and from all except the higher parts of the Appalachian Uplands to the interior prairies. An eastern portion, east of the higher parts of the Appalachians, extends as a strip from southern New England to northern Georgia. In the northern half this strip extends to the Atlantic; in the southern half it lies considerably inland. The western fringe of the forest region extends from Canada to Mexico. This is the forest-prairie transition: fingers of the forest reach westward along the damp valley bottoms, and fingers of the prairie originally reached eastward along interstream areas.

So much of the Central Hardwood Forest Region proved to be excellent for agriculture that there is little forest cover left (compare FIGS. 18–4 and 18–5). Most of the region has become the Corn Belt and the Corn and Winter Wheat Belt; a great deal of it was cleared to make way for fields of corn. The chief remnants of mature forest growth, and the chief areas which should be reforested, are in the rougher sections, particularly in major portions of such states as Kentucky, Tennessee, and Missouri. Dominant trees are oak, hickory, maple, elm, yellow poplar, and some pine.

The Southern Mixed Forest

Much of the Southern Mixed Forest Region (FIG. 18–5) has become the Cotton Belt, and another portion has become the Subtropical Fruits Belt and the southern part of the Middle Atlantic Truck Crops Belt (compare FIGS. 17–12 and 18–5). Even so, about half of the South is still in forest of one type or another. The region extends from the Atlantic to the southern part of the hardwood forest–prairie transition, noted above, and from the Gulf to the Corn and Winter Wheat Belt. Dominant trees are yellow pine, oak, cypress, tupelo, red

gum, and swamp maple. The last four occur in damp or wet sections, particularly in river flood plains and the northern edge of the Mississippi Delta. Their largest occurrence is in the broad flood plain of the Mississippi, from the Delta to the mouth of the Ohio. The chief remnants of the original Southern Mixed Forest are in the Mississippi drainage area and in Florida (compare FIGS. 18–4 and 18–5). More is left of this forest than of the Mixed Northern Forest and much more than of the Central Hardwood Forest. By reason of its ability to grow new trees rapidly, the Southern Mixed Forest Region probably has more to offer than any other forest region of the United States, with the possible exception of the northern part of the Pacific Coast Forest Region and the southern part of the Alaskan Forest Region. Many believe that eventually they will become our major forest reserves. Already there are numerous sections in which trees are planted and harvested as though they were ordinary crops. Undoubtedly this practice will become more general, especially on those lands which are nonoptimum or definitely submarginal for agricultural purposes.

The Rocky Mountain Forest

The Rocky Mountain forests are mainly in the central and northern Rockies, separated by the broad gap of the Wyoming Corridor (FIG. 18–5). They lie far from the main lumber-consuming markets of eastern United States and far from the ports and shipping facilities of the Pacific coast. Because of their comparative isolation and the difficulty of locating and logging the characteristically scattered mountain stands, they have survived largely intact to the present. However, most of the interior West has "boomed" in recent years and this has meant a more rapid cut of the mountain forests, to serve not the mountain areas themselves but rather the populations of growing Western towns and cities.

Huge portions of the Rocky Mountain For-

18–6

THIS *map shows only the National Forests of the United States, not National Parks nor National Monuments. The mountainous and plateau areas of the West contain most of such forests, although the number is slowly increasing in the East.*

UNITED STATES
NATIONAL FORESTS

est Region have been incorporated in national forests and national parks (FIG. 18–6). Some individual national forests are larger than some of the smaller eastern states. Thus, many of the forests of the Rockies will be preserved and used rationally and many adjacent lowland areas will have essential protection of their domestic and irrigation water supplies and their mountain-located hydroelectric power resources. These large forest reserves also insure a steady flow of lumber from such typical trees as spruce, Douglas fir, and yellow pine.

The Pacific Coast Forest

The Pacific Coast Forest Region occupies the Sierra Nevada, the Cascades, and the Coast Ranges north of San Francisco (FIG. 18–5), as well as mountainous Alaska. It is much less patchy in distribution than the Rocky Mountain Forest Region, and timber growth is heavier at lower elevations, including some valley lowlands. At first glance, this forest region appears to be largely untouched. Forested slopes meet the eye in almost any direction, and they stand up too abruptly and cover too much of the view to be ignored. Closer ex-

amination reveals widespread removal in the more accessible areas and tremendous "burns" in nearly all areas. One would hardly speak of this forest as consisting of remnants, yet it is already more than half destroyed. The dominant tree north of California is the Douglas fir. Others are spruce, red cedar, and yellow pine. In the California section, giant redwoods—the famous *Sequoia sempervirens*—occur along and near the shore in what is often referred to as the fog belt. Farther inland are the yellow pine and sugar pine, with some interior redwoods—the *Sequoia gigantea*—on the western slopes of the Sierra Nevada, where they occur as redwood patches in what is generally a sugar pine and yellow pine forest. The California forests have suffered greatly from cutting and fire. They are located closer to major West Coast markets, are generally drier than the forests of the heavy precipitation belt of Oregon, Washington, and Alaska, and are closer to great numbers of people, many of whom have never learned to be careful with fire.

As in the Rockies, national forests and national parks are numerous (FIG. 18–6). This offers considerable hope for the Pacific Coast Forest Region; however, fire is no respecter of man's boundary lines and each year thousands of acres of national forest, as well as of private forest, go up in smoke. Much of the private forest land, logged or now being logged, should be further reforested and given greater protection. Nowhere else in the United States is there so much land "all in one piece" which should be devoted permanently to forest cover, both for wood and for the many other uses which forests serve. The Pacific Coast Forest Region is now our chief reserve of trees of saw-timber size. It contains about half of all timber trees in the nation (FIG. 18–7). It would be complete folly to use it in such a manner that it might cease to contribute importantly to the national economy.

The Central Alaska Forest Region

The Central Alaska Forest Region occupies much of the interior of Alaska between the Alaska Range in the south and the Brooks Range in the north. Approximately two-thirds of the area is covered by relatively open woodland. Compared to the Pacific Coast forest, this woodland is dwarfed and scrubby. Trees of small trunk diameter and little height dominate. Only about half of this woodland, mostly near the Alaska Range, is estimated to have timber suitable for commercial purposes. Further, the location of the region and the lack of transportation facilities make utilization for other than local needs uneconomic. The chief

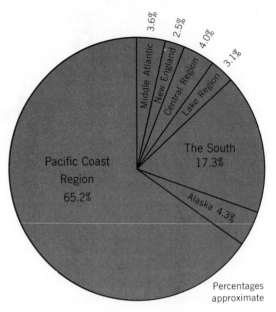

UNITED STATES DISTRIBUTION OF TIMBER OF SAW-TIMBER SIZE TODAY (BY VOLUME)

Middle Atlantic 3.6%
New England 2.5%
Central Region 4.0%
Lake Region 3.1%
Pacific Coast Region 65.2%
The South 17.3%
Alaska 4.3%

Percentages approximate

18–7

THE West, especially the Pacific Coast region, contains most of the trees of saw-timber size today in the United States.

species present are spruce, birch, poplar, tamarack, and aspen. Because growth is so slow in a location in such high latitudes, as well as for the reasons just suggested, this region does not appear to have any considerable potential as a future major source of forest products.

LUMBERING

THE world's large-scale commercial lumbering industry has developed only within the past century or century and a half. Prior to the early 1800's operations were crude and small. There were a few small sawmills in Europe as early as the middle of the 1300's, but most of the world's lumber was cut and used close to home and mainly shaped by the ancient methods of splitting and hewing logs. Some of it was produced by pitsawing. This method utilized a pit or, sometimes, a slightly elevated platform. The logs were placed over the pit or on the platform. Two men, one standing below and the other above, operated a long, two-handled saw which "whipped" logs into planks and boards.

18–8   MODERN *pulpwood operations in a section of the Mixed Northern Forest Region. The big "stick timber" is largely gone and the cut is now "smaller stuff."*

Shortly after 1800, sawmills became numerous in Europe and the era of modern lumbering began. Steam power as well as water power was used, new machinery was invented and utilized, and mills grew to greater size. Methods of logging and getting the logs to the mills slowly improved and the products of the mills began to move longer distances as land and water transportation facilities increased and the forests closest to markets were used up. The great changes in lumbering kept pace with those in agriculture, animal husbandry, and manufacturing. Lumbering, too, was caught up in the Industrial Revolution. By 1840, the "lumber boom" was on in the United States, generated and maintained by the great westward surge of population.

In the United States

Lumbering in the United States had its beginnings along the Atlantic seaboard, particularly in New England, in the early 1600's. As the better and more accessible stands of the East were used up, the loggers began a westward march through the Mixed Northern Forest Region (FIG. 18–8). The center of production shifted from New England to New York and then to Pennsylvania; by 1890 it was in the Great Lakes region, and by 1910 that region was practically "logged off." The chief demand then, as now, was for softwood lumber, and it was the stands of pine which suffered first and most heavily. In the wake of the "pine cutters" came the "hardwood cutters," both leaving great slashings and burns and abandoned lumber towns. The loggers stopped their westward trek and turned south. By the time they turned in this direction the Central Hardwood Forest Region was largely a thing of the past. It had made way for many thousands of farms and hundreds of hamlets, villages, and towns, as well as a few great cities. Thus, the loggers, except for those who went to the Pacific Coast Forest Region, jumped over the Central Hardwood Forest Region and

Lumbering | 451

began their work in the Southern Mixed Forest.

The Southern Mixed Forest Region came into its own with the beginning of the present century. For some twenty years it was the center of lumbering operations. Again, the softwoods suffered most, especially the extensive pine stands on the more sandy lands, but hardwoods were also cut in large numbers and used for more purposes than previously. The several varieties of southern oak were in particular demand for use in furniture and railroad ties. Today the southern forest furnishes about 35 per cent of the United States lumber supply, although much of the recent cut is based on second-growth and, in some sections, third-growth timber. Second-growth timber also is responsible for a large part of the supply obtained from what is left of the forest resources of the Northern Mixed Forest Region. Only in the Pacific Coast and Rocky Mountain Forest Regions is second-growth timber unimportant.

The lumber boom in the Pacific Coast Forest Region began during World War I. The Rocky Mountain forests, scattered and mainly inaccessible, were by-passed. The jump, extending into Canada, brought into major production a region far from the chief lumber markets of the United States (FIG. 18–9). Either by land or water, it was a long expensive haul to eastern markets. But softwood lumber was still in greatest demand and it was the Northwest which now had the only large supply. The markets, including growing foreign markets for United States lumber, were able to pay the rising costs, and from the Pacific Coast Forest Region moved the greatest flow of softwood lumber that the world had ever witnessed. Most of it moved, and still moves, to the eastern part of the United States, but large amounts traveled to rapidly growing southern California, to Australia, the Orient, South America, and Europe. The Pacific Coast Forest Region possesses about half of our saw timber and supplies about 45 per cent of our lumber.

Looking to the future, it is pertinent to note

SILVER SKAGIT LUMBER COMPANY, CANADA

18–9

LUMBERING *activity in British Columbia, Canada. The loading device is known as a hayrack boom. The head loader, standing on the logs, has the responsibility for even loading of the truck.*

that the South possesses the largest potential forest area. This area comprises about 25 per cent of all the land in the United States that is suitable for, and should be used for, forest purposes. The South's closest rival in this respect is the Pacific Northwest, where only about 13 per cent of United States land suitable for forests (and not better for other purposes) lies. On the basis of land and climate suitable for forests, it is easy to understand why the South may be expected to continue furnishing much of the United States timber supply.

In addition to the cutting of trees for lumber, American forests have already been heavily cut for pulpwood. It is pulpwood that supports the modern paper industry and furnishes wood fibers for such products as rayon, cellophane, wallboard, and certain explosives. World demand for paper, both for newsprint and containers, has increased by leaps and bounds since 1900. Inasmuch as most of the world's paper is made from wood, the forests have been subjected to an additional drain. In many areas, the pulpwood cutters have finished up what the saw-timber cutters left behind; they also have utilized previously untouched forests which were not suitable for lumber, but whose small trees are satisfactory for pulp.

Until the early 1920's, nearly all wood pulp produced in the United States was processed in the Northern Mixed Forest Region. Northern spruce, practically the only source of pulpwood, was obtained from sources within or very close to the Northeastern Manufacturing Region. Today, over half of the wood pulp secured in the United States comes from the South and the Pacific Coast Forest. Spruce still furnishes the material for more than half our wood pulp, but much of it is imported from southeastern Canada and some from northwestern Europe. Newer techniques of manufacturing have allowed the use of balsam fir, western hemlock, southern yellow pine, and southern poplar. Most of the mills which transform pulpwood into wood pulp are located in the source regions (FIG. 18–10). This is because

pulpwood itself is bulky and of low value, while wood pulp is more concentrated, easier to handle and ship, and of comparatively high value. Some of the mills which make wood pulp also make paper, but much paper is manufactured in mills located in or near the large cities of northeastern United States, particularly in those which do the most printing and make the largest numbers of paper bags and cartons. Such mills draw not only on distant sources of wood pulp but also depend greatly on wastepaper. Paper mills are concentrated particularly in a belt that begins in New England and extends to the northern edge of Chesapeake Bay, though they are numerous as far west as the Mississippi (FIG. 18–11).

In Europe and the Soviet Union

Nearly all of Europe and most of Soviet Asia were once covered with forests (see PLATE VI). In terms of climate, soil, and drainage conditions, trees represented the natural cover for most of the land. Widespread removal first began in the Mediterranean and in the eastern and southeastern portions of the Continent. As Europe developed, particularly as

18–11

18–10

THE *general distribution of pulp mills in the conterminous United States.*

THE *general distribution of paper mills in the conterminous United States. These mills are much more concentrated in or near large cities than are the pulp mills* (FIG. 18–10).

agriculture spread and towns and cities became numerous, forest destruction increased rapidly, except in the northern forests of what are now Norway, Sweden, Finland, and Soviet Russia. Today, virgin forest occurs only in the north, including Soviet Asia, or in some of the highlands. Much of Europe, unlike other forested portions of the earth, has practiced scientific forestry for more than a century. This is especially true in western Europe, where the pinch of insufficient wood and lumber supplies was felt first. Scientific methods have included reforestation, particularly of areas not well suited to other uses. Some sections have more trees now than they had fifty or one hundred years ago. Europe has fully recognized for centuries the importance of forests. There a forest, or even the smallest patch of trees, is seen as a very valuable thing. Rules and regulations concerning forest use are stringent and rigidly enforced. Nothing is wasted; small branches and twigs are carefully gathered and bundled and, ordinarily, each tree cut down means several young trees planted in its place. The contrast between forest use in Europe and the United States is startling. The United States is just beginning to grasp the significance of forests; it has barely reached the stage Europe was in a century ago.

The proportion of land in forest varies widely from one section of Europe to another. Finland is about seven-tenths forest. No other country in the world is so much a land of forests, forest workers, and forest products. About eight-tenths of Finland's exports are forest products, ranging from beams, lumber, and pulpwood to paper, safety matches, and small wooden articles. Sweden is more than half forested and is second only to Finland in her dependence on trees. The Soviet Union is about three-tenths forested, Germany about one-fourth, and France about one-fifth. Less than one-twentieth of England is in forest cover. Except in the north, the present forests of Europe are mainly man-planted and man-tended; the virgin forests disappeared long ago.

Despite some imports from Africa, the United States, and Canada, Europe's forests have been sufficient to take care of its needs in normal times. The chief consuming areas have been in the west and south; the chief supplying areas have been in the north and east. The major exporters have normally been those east of a line drawn between Sweden and Norway, Poland and Germany, and Yugoslavia and Italy. Chief among them are Finland and Sweden. The major importers, all west of the line, have been Great Britain, Germany, France, and Italy.

Like the United States, Europe and the Soviet Union draw upon their forests for pulpwood, as well as for lumber and fuel. Most of the pulp is processed in the supply areas of the northern forest and in West Germany. About half of it is manufactured in Sweden and Finland alone. Paper manufacture, again as in the United States, is concentrated in the more densely populated regions, either in or near the large printing centers, of Great Britain, France, West Germany, southern Sweden, and the U.S.S.R.

Elsewhere

Considering wood that is cut for all purposes (lumber, pulp, paper, fuel, etc.), the United States cuts about 20 per cent of the world total; the Soviet Union about 29 per cent; and non-Soviet Europe, chiefly Sweden, Finland, and West Germany, about 18 per cent. This adds up to nearly 70 per cent of the world's "wood cut." It emphasizes not only the relative importance of the major producers, but also the comparative insignificance of the cut in the remainder of the world, including the tropical forests.

Canada supplies an important amount of wood for world export, but her annual cut is less than one-third that of the United States. In southeastern Canada, pulpwood predominates, while lumber is most important in the Pacific Coast Forest Region. Japan produces significant amounts of both hardwoods and softwoods from her predominantly hilly and mountainous lands. China, although woefully deficient in forests, is still able to produce some lumber from the more rugged lands of the south and southwest. The remaining world timber cut occurs chiefly in widely scattered parts of the tropical forests. The nontropical parts of the Southern Hemisphere never did possess substantial forest resources. Chile is the only country that carries on major lumbering operations and then only in small sections to the south.

As pointed out previously, about half of the world's present forest area is in the rainy tropics. The difficulties of lumbering in tropical forests, plus the long haul to major markets and the fact that the demand is primarily for softwood, have left these vast hardwood forests largely untouched. Most of the timber that is obtained is for special purposes. So far, such trees as teak, mahogany, Philippine mahogany ("false mahogany"), ebony, and Spanish cedar have been most sought after. "Sought after" is a good way to express the matter, for most of the tree species of the tropical forests do not occur in solid stands, but here and there among a wide variety of other tree species. Thus, logging has been of the "selective" type, rather than the "over-all" or general "slash-log-ging" type practiced in mid-latitude and northern forests. Teak is obtained from southeastern Asia, mainly from Burma, Thailand, Vietnam, and Indonesia. It is hard, heavy, durable, and highly resistant to attacks of boring insects. Most of it is used in small boats or in the wooden parts and trimmings of large vessels, notably the decks.

Mahogany comes chiefly from Middle America and the islands of the Caribbean. Because of its hardness and durability and its capacity to take a smooth, lustrous finish, it is in demand for furniture. The somewhat similar Philippine mahogany is also used for certain types of furniture, particularly on the West Coast of the United States. Ebony is a very hard, almost black, wood. It is used chiefly for chests, carved figurines, and the backs of such articles as hair brushes and hand mirrors. The best ebony is obtained from the forests of southeastern Asia; other ebony or ebonylike woods are secured from central Africa and the West Indies. Spanish cedar, unlike the bulk of tropical woods, is soft and easy to work. In addition, it is light and highly fragrant. Its qualities make it useful for such things as interior trim, closet linings, chests, cigar boxes, and pencils. It is widely produced in the tropical forests, particularly in the Caribbean region, central Africa, and southeastern Asia.

NAVAL STORES AND TANNIN

NAVAL stores, representing another group of products secured from forests, are obtained by tapping, rather than cutting down, trees. Naval stores are pine pitch, or resin, and the rosin and turpentine derived from it. Their name goes back to the days of wooden ships, when large amounts of pine pitch and pitch products were needed to render wooden vessels waterproof and to protect them and their gear from wear and the elements. Pine forests in many sections of the world were tapped to enable merchantmen and ships of war to sail the seas. Today, only a few regions specialize in naval stores and the stores themselves are used mainly for other than ship purposes.

The two major production regions for naval stores are in our South and in the Landes region of southwestern France. United States output comes chiefly from Georgia, Florida, and Alabama. The Landes district is a good example of "much made from nothing." Formerly it was a barren sandy area; now it is a scientifically managed pine forest furnishing a permanent "crop" of pitch. The pine forests of the sandy lands of our South have not been so well managed. However, scientific methods are becoming more prominent: proper care of the trees and careful methods of tapping are putting more sections on a permanent production basis, as well as increasing the yield per tree (FIG. 18–12). The resin obtained by tapping is collected in barrels and hauled to local distilleries, where the turpentine is distilled from it, leaving a residue called rosin. While naval stores are still consumed in the small-boat industry, most of them now go as semi-raw materials to the large manufacturing districts. Turpentine is used in a wide variety of paints and varnishes, and rosin in chemicals, soaps, polishes, and paper surfacers.

The securing of vegetable tanning solutions, unlike naval stores, requires destruction of the plant. Sometimes, leaves, twigs, nuts, and other fruits are used as a source of the tannic acid solutions, but usually it is either the bark or the wood, or both, that furnishes the necessary material. If wood is used it must be chipped or ground before being soaked to obtain its tannin. Oak bark, still in common use, is one of the older sources. Other major sources are hemlock bark, chestnut bark, and quebracho wood. In the United States, oak bark and hemlock bark are of major importance. Most of the oak bark is obtained from the forests of the southern Appalachians and most of the hemlock bark from the remnants of the Mixed Northern Forest, especially in the northern Great Lakes region. The United States leather industry also depends partly on foreign sources of tannin, particularly quebracho extract from Argentina. Quebracho is a tree of very hard wood (its name means "axbreaker") which grows only in the Chaco region of northern Argentina and adjacent portions of Paraguay. Its tannin content is about double that of hemlock bark. Formerly, whole logs were sent

FLORIDA FOREST SERVICE, AMERICAN FOREST PRODUCTS INDUSTRIES

18–12

SCIENTIFIC *tapping of a pine tree for resin for naval stores.*

to the United States and Europe, but now most of them are ground up and the solution obtained in scores of small mills located on the banks of the Rio Paraguay. The extract is readily shipped by river boat to Buenos Aires and thence abroad by ocean vessels. In the leather centers of the United States and Europe, the quebracho extract is mixed with that from oak bark and hemlock bark. Mineral tanning solutions are now used in the production of most of the leather made in the United States, but the remainder is based on vegetable solutions supplied from forest trees, such as American oak and hemlock or Argentine quebracho.

Utilization of Forests

GENERAL SIGNIFICANCE OF FORESTS
Foods, Spices, and Medicines
Fuel
Construction Materials
Paper and Other Cellulose Materials
Game Protection
Water Conservation
Scenery and Recreation

MAJOR FOREST REGIONS OF THE WORLD
The Tropical Forests
The Mid-latitude Forests
The Northern Forests

FOREST REGIONS OF THE UNITED STATES
The Mixed Northern Forest
The Central Hardwood Forest
The Southern Mixed Forest
The Rocky Mountain Forest
The Pacific Coast Forest
The Central Alaska Forest

LUMBERING
In the United States
In Europe and the Soviet Union
Elsewhere

NAVAL STORES AND TANNIN

· REVIEW QUESTIONS ·

1. Explain and substantiate the statement that ". . . this is still very much a 'world of wood.'"
2. Distinguish between "forest" and "productive forest."
3. List and discuss the ways in which forests are significant.
4. Describe the general pattern of distribution of the three major forest regions of the world.
5. Compare and contrast general climatic conditions in the world's three major forest regions.
6. What is meant by a "mixed forest"?
7. Name and locate the forest regions of the United States. Give examples of dominant or "key" tree species in each region.
8. Which of the United States forest regions is physically so constituted as to be able to grow trees most rapidly? Why?
9. About how long has it taken virtually to wipe out the virgin forests of the United States? Where is most of the remaining virgin forest in this country today? Why is it in that area?
10. Trace briefly the history of lumbering, including geographical shifts, in the United States.
11. What sections of the United States supply nearly all of our commercial lumber at present?
12. Why are most of the wood pulp mills located near pulpwood supplies while most of the paper mills are located in or near large cities, especially in northeastern United States?
13. What is meant by "timber cropping"?
14. Western Europe has been far ahead of the United States in the practice of scientific forestry. Why?
15. Where are the surplus and deficiency areas of Europe as far as forest products are concerned?
16. Why are certain tropical woods sought after? Why is their cost comparatively high?
17. Is world demand primarily for softwood or hardwood? Explain.
18. Discuss the nature and methods of production of naval stores.
19. What is tannin? Comparatively, are mineral or vegetable tannins increasing in importance?
20. It is estimated, on the basis of cubic feet of wood alone, that the forest regions of the United States are now growing about as much wood as is needed. Why, then, is so much heard about decrease in our lumber resources?

19 Products of the Sea

❡ *THROUGH the ages fishing has grown from crude and simple beginnings into a world-wide industry with complex apparatus and installations. The earliest known records of China, Mesopotamia, and Egypt indicate fishing as an important occupation and certain groups of persons as specializing in obtaining food from adjacent waters. The Bible contains many references to fishing and fishermen. The folklore of the Eskimos and the South Sea Islanders is replete with tales of fishing and of the mighty fishermen whose cunning and heroism enabled them to wrest from the sea its bounty. The history of Norway and other countries of western Europe contain many tales of fishing and the voyages of the fishing fleets. Much of the story of early New England is one of fish, fishing vessels, and fishermen. Large sections of the Pacific Coast*

of North America are chiefly known for their salmon fisheries. Even in ordinary conversation the always interesting topic of fishing trips and of the "big one that got away" emphasize that fishing continues to manifest its importance in the lives of many people. Dependence upon the earth's waters as a source both of food and of raw materials for manufacture is increasing. Obtaining what the waters had to offer was in the past largely a matter for individuals or small groups; today, it often is a large and complicated activity.

NATURE AND LOCATION OF FISHERIES PRODUCTS

THE commodities which man obtains from the oceans, seas, lakes, and streams are more numerous and varied than is commonly supposed. Some are animal, some vegetable, and some mineral. In this chapter we discuss primarily the animal products, although some vegetable products are mentioned. Later on we shall discuss certain minerals obtained from the sea, such as salt and magnesium. All the activities associated with the securing of animal and vegetable products from the earth's waters come under the heading of *fisheries*, even though it is obvious that vegetable materials are not fish—nor are some of the animals, such as seals and whales. Fisheries products include such items as fish, clams, oysters, lobsters, shrimp, eels, turtles, seals, and whales; they also include pearls, sponges, coral, shells, and seaweed.

The fisheries of the world are varied and widely scattered: some are in fresh water, others in salt water; some are in very shallow water, some in comparatively deep water; some are in warm water, others in cold water. The water areas from which the products themselves are obtained are called *fishing grounds*. The chief ones are, as a rule, on the fringes of the

land masses with the widest continental shelves (FIG. 19–2). Certain of the fishing grounds are called *fishing banks*. Well-known examples are the Grand Bank near Newfoundland and the Dogger Bank of the North Sea. Water depths over the major banks range from as little as 20 to 40 feet to as much as 300 to 600 feet. Some fishing is carried on in deeper waters, but this is "open-sea," rather than "banks," fishing. The most important banks are located where both warm and cold currents meet to bring a wide variety of fish food into one relatively restricted area. For example, the Grand Bank is supplied with a great variety of minute plants and animals (known collectively as *plankton*) brought by the cold Labrador Current and the warm Gulf Stream (FIG. 4–6).

The leading fishing nations, on the basis of tons of fish caught, are Japan, mainland China, the United States, the U.S.S.R., Peru, Norway, Canada, the United Kingdom, and India. In Japan, Norway, and the United Kingdom, fishing is comparatively more important among the chief occupations and involves a greater percentage of the population. Its comparative importance in these three countries is a reflection, more than anything else, of meager agricultural resources and hence a greater dependence on the sea for food. Japan is more dependent on the bounty of the sea than is any other major nation.

19–1

[OPPOSITE, TOP] FISHING boats at Petersburg, Alaska. Small fishing ports dot the coast of southeastern Alaska.

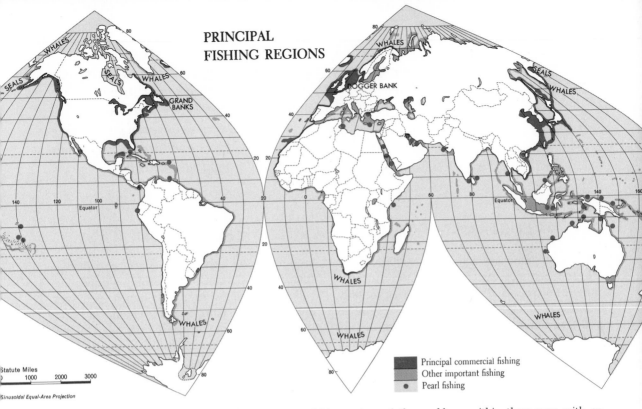

PRINCIPAL
FISHING REGIONS

Principal commercial fishing
Other important fishing
• Pearl fishing

Statute Miles
0   1000   2000   3000

Sinusoidal Equal-Area Projection

19–2   NEARLY all of the principal ocean fishing regions of the world are within those areas with approximate water depths of 0–600 feet (0–100 fathoms). Compare this map with FIG. 4–4 which shows ocean depths of 0–600 feet.

USES OF FISHERIES PRODUCTS

N O SINGLE statement to the effect that fisheries supply fish and that fish are used for human food can do justice to the multitudinous products of the world's fisheries. The wide variety in fisheries products leads to many uses—and new uses are constantly appearing.

Human and Animal Foods

The utilization of fisheries products for human food leads all other uses. The amount consumed varies greatly from one nation or local group to another. It also varies with general economic conditions. When meat is scarce and high in price, the consumption of fisheries foods increases, provided they are or

can be made available. Disregarding primitive peoples, consumption normally is high in such nations as Japan, mainland China, Norway, the United Kingdom, and the Catholic countries of Europe. It is comparatively low in such countries as the United States, Mexico, Australia, and Argentina.

Food fish, including cod, mackerel, halibut, herring, salmon, and many others, as well as oysters, clams, crabs, lobsters, shrimp, and even octopuses, are prepared for consumption in many forms—as fresh, frozen, salted, dried, smoked, pickled, or canned foods (FIG. 19–3). From the livers of such fish as cod, halibut, and shark come oils high in vitamin content. The roe of the sturgeon, when processed, becomes caviar. Other fish supply lard substitutes.

19–3   LOBSTERS *from the waters of the North Atlantic.*

Seaweed furnishes vegetable food, in Japan for example, and also agar-agar, which is used in ice-cream mixes and salad dressings.

Livestock and poultry are fed large amounts of fish meal and fish cake, foods high in essential proteins as well as fats.

Other Uses

Fish oils, including whale and seal oils, are used in the manufacture of soaps, cosmetics, special lubricating oils, and margarine. They supply certain ingredients of many paints and varnishes. Also, they are used in the manufac-

ture of linoleum, leathers, waterproofing compounds, and glues.

Fertilizer is prepared in the form of fish powder and fish cake. Seaweed furnishes potash fertilizer and iodine.

Shells supply material for inlaid tables, combs, and brushes, as well as for curios and certain kinds of costume jewelry. They also furnish millions of so-called "pearl" buttons. Real pearls are used for jewelry, and coral for curios and necklaces. Sponges are used for cleaning, surgical, and wall-finishing purposes. In one way or another, the modern fisheries industry allows little to be wasted.

MAJOR FISHERIES OF EURASIA

FISHING on a local and subsistence basis has been widespread in the world from time immemorial. Fishing on a large and truly commercial scale began in Europe. Of all the con-

tinents Europe is most intimately associated with salt water. Not only are there marine coasts on three sides, but there are many large and deep-reaching embayments which extend

19–4   FISHING *boat of the North Atlantic.*

far inland from the open oceans. Europeans have always been intensely aware of the sea and the foods it has to offer. It was only natural that they should learn how to build sea-going fishing boats that enabled them to secure more fish than could be obtained by fishing from the shore or in the streams and lakes. Thus, incidentally, Europeans laid the basis for later navies and commercial fleets. To the European peoples, ability to move over the sea gave a start toward development of sea lanes which have become world highways. In addition, several parts of western Europe, such as rocky Norway and Brittany and sandy Denmark, had such meager agricultural resources that the inhabitants were, in a sense, forced to the sea for at least part of their livelihood. Fishing operations led to the first real knowledge of the Mediterranean Sea. Fishing paved the way for the forays and explorations of the Vikings. Fishing fleets, particularly from France and Portugal, began making annual voyages across the Atlantic to the Newfoundland banks almost on the heels of John Cabot.

Some of the earliest arguments over control of North America revolved around the possession of fishing grounds.

Western Europe

While fishing is carried on across most of Europe, in streams and lakes as well as adjacent seas, it is most important along or relatively near the shores of western Europe (FIG. 19–2). The chief fishing grounds are in the North Sea, along the coast of Norway, and around Iceland. Others of importance are in the Baltic Sea, the waters west and south of the British Isles, the Bay of Biscay, and far to the north, the White Sea. As noted earlier, the chief fishing nations of western Europe are Norway and the United Kingdom; combined, they account for about one-third of the total catch of Europe.

The waters fringing western Europe provide many kinds of fish; chief among them are herring, mackerel, cod, and haddock. Herring is the most important.

19–5

FISHING *station and fleet,
Lofoten Islands, Norway.*

Fishing operations are conducted in a very efficient and scientific manner. The vast majority of the vessels, whether large or small, are powered by steam, gasoline, or diesel engines, and many different types of nets and other gear are used (FIG. 19–4). Shore installations are equipped to carry out rapidly many different processes, such as salting, smoking, canning, oil extraction, or fish-meal preparation (FIG. 19–5). Experts in fish life are employed to advise the fishermen; airplanes and radar are often used to locate the schools of fish.

The Mediterranean Sea

The Mediterranean lost long ago its one-time leadership in Europe's fishing business, although the tuna and mackerel catches are still important. Many of its fishing grounds are badly overfished and modern techniques and scientific knowledge are not widely used. Many Mediterranean countries, like Spain, Italy, and Greece, are so sorely pressed for food that fish, regardless of size and future propagation needs,

are caught wherever possible, even in the smallest quantities.

Japan

The extensive fishing grounds of western Europe are matched on the opposite side of Eurasia by those directly next to or near Japan (FIG. 19–2). Japan is the world's chief fishing nation, and the bulk of the catch is taken from waters south of Japan and Korea. Even more than in western Europe, the meager agricultural resources of Japan, accompanied by high population densities, force great reliance on the resources of the sea. In addition to waters near the homeland, the Japanese fish far afield, not only in the North Pacific, but in the waters of Antarctica and the South Seas.

Japanese fisheries produce a greater variety of products than those of Europe. Among them are sardines, salmon, cod, mackerel, tuna, shark, and bonito, as well as shellfish, cuttlefish, and crabs. The manufacture of fish oils and fish meals is a prominent side-industry of

Major Fisheries of Eurasia | 463

19–6 JAPANESE *coastal fishing is carried on with small boats and simple equipment. Note the fish drying in the sun.*

the fisheries. In addition, the Japanese secure pearls and coral from tropical waters and whales from Arctic and Antarctic waters. Cultured pearls are also produced in pearl-oyster "farms" located in shallow waters along the southerly portion of the homeland. Seaweed is harvested in large quantities. It has a variety of uses; it is an important vegetable food for humans, as well as a source of fertilizer, animal fodder, iodine, and stuffing for certain types of upholstery.

The equipment of the Japanese fisheries industry combines the ancient and the very new. Most of the boats are small and depend on sail power (FIG. 19–6). The larger vessels, which range far waters, have powerful modern engines and are equipped to stay at sea for months at a time. Not only do they possess

refrigeration facilities, but some of them are huge floating factories; some of these can catch, process, and pack thousands of cases of salmon and crabs, while others can catch and process whole whales. As it did in Europe, the fishing industry taught Japan to build and operate boats, and to explore ever more distant waters, laying the foundation for a huge merchant marine.

China (Mainland)

China is a close second to Japan in world fisheries. It produces about 85 per cent of Japan's total and nearly twice as much as the United States and the Soviet Union.

The general scarcity and high price of meat in China has long encouraged a heavy fish consumption. In a sense, fish is a meat substitute in a land which must use practically every square inch of arable land for heavy-yielding crops, rather than for animals and the raising of animal food.

The fish consumed in China are secured from rivers, coastal embayments, and open-sea fishing grounds in the Yellow Sea, East China Sea, and South China Sea. Even ponds and flooded rice fields contribute their share, especially in east-central and southeastern China. Practically all the catch is made from small boats using simple gear. Chinese fisheries definitely are not characterized by large modern vessels, scientific methods, or world-ranging fleets.

Soviet Union

During the past decade, the Soviet Union has greatly expanded its fisheries. Today, it secures just about as many tons of fisheries products as does the United States.

The Soviet ocean-fishing fleet, including huge "factory" ships, is large and modern, and its vessels range from the Arctic waters of Eurasia to the Newfoundland banks of the Atlantic, the waters of the Bering Sea and Gulf of Alaska in the North Pacific region, and the whaling areas near Antarctica. In addition to the ocean fisheries, important quantities of fish are obtained from the rivers of the Soviet Union and from Lake Baikal and the Aral and Caspian Seas.

Other Fisheries

Other Eurasian fisheries occur along the southeastern and southern coasts of Asia. Their westernmost extension is found in the Persian Gulf and the Red Sea (FIG. 19–2). Nearly all of them are coastal rather than deep-water. Fishing vessels are small and of ancient design and they engage in fishing primarily for subsistence rather than for commerce. Some pearls are obtained along the southern coast, especially in the Persian Gulf and the Red Sea. Important pearl fisheries also occur in Indonesia and along the northern coast of Australia. India, producing somewhat less fish than either Canada or the United Kingdom, obtains them from fishing grounds along both coasts of the Indian Peninsula and around Ceylon.

MAJOR FISHERIES OF THE AMERICAS

NORTH AMERICA has rich fishing grounds on three of its shores: Atlantic Coast, Pacific Coast, and the Gulf Coast–Caribbean–Bahamas area (FIG. 19–2). Inland fisheries, of far less value, are widespread: those of the Great Lakes and of the Mississippi and its tributaries are most significant. The North American ocean fisheries, coastal and deep-water, are controlled chiefly by the United States and Canada. Together, they produce about two-thirds as much as the Japanese fisheries. The United States, including Alaska, produces nearly three times the tonnage of fisheries products that Canada does, about half the tonnage of Japan, and almost as much as the tonnage of western European countries collectively.

South American fisheries are comparatively minor (FIG. 19–2). Only in Peru in the Southern Hemisphere are fisheries as highly developed as they are in the Northern Hemisphere. Some coastal fishing occurs on both eastern and western sides of South America (that on the western side is more important), especially in the colder waters of the south. Whales are obtained in the adjacent waters of Antarctica and the Falkland Islands. Stream fishing, mainly noncommercial, is important

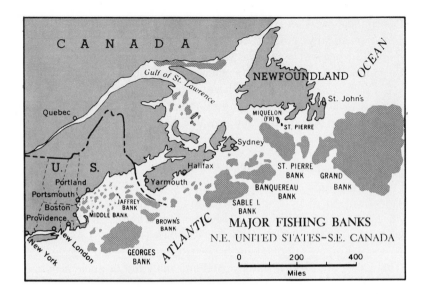

19-7

THE tinted areas are the major fishing banks of the northeastern United States and southeastern Canada.

in the Amazon river, the Paraná river, and their tributaries.

United States

The commercial fisheries of the United States began with Plymouth Colony in the early 1600's. In fact, Plymouth sent a cargo of fish, preserved by salting, to England as early as 1624. Plymouth also traded in fish with other settlements, including the Dutch colony of New Amsterdam. The importance of fish as food and as a profitable trade item resulted in the establishment of many fishing villages and towns and in the spread of the industry to new and more distant fishing grounds. The success of the New England fisheries encouraged the development of fishing activities farther south, at many places along the entire Atlantic coast. When the thirteen colonies became the United States, fishing rights were retained not only in the waters directly off the coast of New England, but also those off the Canadian Maritime Provinces and Newfoundland.

The Atlantic fisheries of the United States extend from the Grand Bank of Newfoundland to Florida (FIG. 19-2). They are both less and

more important than in the past: less important because they occupy a smaller place among all present-day occupations; more important because the annual catch and annual value of the catch is greater than in the past. As in most other commercial fisheries of the world, modern boats and gear have made larger catches possible, both in deep-water and shallow-water fishing grounds. Also, modern methods of processing and marketing, including a greatly increased sale of "iced" and quick-frozen fish to markets located far inland, permit large catches to be disposed of quickly. Fishing ports are strung from Portland, Maine, to Jacksonville, Florida, but the major ones are Boston, Gloucester, and Baltimore. The leading fishing grounds extend from the latitude of Virginia northward to the Grand Bank (FIG. 19-7). Typical products are cod, halibut, haddock, herring, and mackerel, as well as oysters, clams, and lobsters. Farther south, menhaden, mullet, bass, and bluefish, among others, are obtained; these have less value for food purposes, but are used in the preparation of fish-meal fertilizer, fish-meal and fish-cake animal feeds, and fish oils. The menhaden is a particularly good source of oil and fertilizer.

19–8   A FLOATING *salmon cannery in one of the many coves along the steep, forested shore of south-eastern Alaska.*

The warm waters of the Gulf Coast–Caribbean–Bahamas region supply a wide variety of commercial fisheries products. Included are mackerel, mullet, red snapper, flounder, sheepshead, oysters, some pearls, shrimp, and a few sponges. Gulf of Mexico shrimp, which grow comparatively large, are of increasing importance. The major sponge-fishing region of the world is in the waters of the Bahama Islands, those of the east and west coasts of Florida, and those to the north of Cuba and Haiti. Recently, widespread sponge disease plus the manufacture of synthetic sponges have greatly injured the sponge industry. The fishing industry as a whole centers in a few major ports located here and there from Jacksonville, Florida, to Galveston, Texas.

Gulf Coast and Atlantic fisheries combined account for roughly 76 per cent of the tonnage and 65 per cent of the value of all United States fisheries.

The Pacific Coast fisheries account for about 21 per cent of the tonnage and about 30 per cent of the value of United States fisheries. Some commercial fishing has been practiced there for approximately a century. Tuna and salmon, nearly all canned, lead by a wide margin. The salmon is obtained in immediate coastal waters and river mouths all the way from northern California to southern Alaska (FIG. 19–8). The heaviest catch is in Alaskan waters and the bulk of it is canned, almost as soon as caught, in small cannery towns which bustle with activity during the summer "salmon run" and are practically deserted the rest of the year. Large amounts also are canned in the cities of Seattle and Portland. The numbers of salmon have declined, particularly in

Major Fisheries of the Americas | 467

19–9   FISHING vessels and canneries in Los Angeles harbor, California. The canneries shown handle chiefly tuna, sardines, and mackerel.

the southern section, and the future of the industry is precarious. Unwise fishing practices, based on the impulse to "get rich quick" and the idea that "there will always be plenty of salmon," plus pollution of the river spawning grounds, the damming of rivers, and widespread river logging operations, are major factors in the decline. As salmon fishing has declined somewhat, tuna fishing has increased. Like salmon, tuna is marketed almost entirely in canned form. California produces nearly all the tuna "pack" in the United States, and Los Angeles is the chief tuna port and canning center. Much of the tuna is caught off the West Coast of Mexico and even as far away as off the northwest coast of South America. Other important commercial fish taken along or near the West Coast include pilchard (sardines), herring, and mackerel. The major fishing ports of the Pacific Coast are San Diego, Los Angeles (FIG. 19–9), Monterey, San Francisco, Portland, and Seattle, as well as the many small and scattered cannery towns of southeastern Alaska. It is pertinent to note that the Pacific Coast fisheries supply the

greater bulk of canned and otherwise preserved fish produced in the United States.

Inland fisheries account for only a small part of the United States catch. Nearly all the inland production is from the Great Lakes and the Mississippi river. While these fresh-water fisheries are comparatively insignificant, it may be surprising to learn that their production equals just over 50 per cent of the value of the famous Alaskan fisheries. The production of the Great Lakes fisheries alone is over one-fourth that of Alaska. Also, the average price per pound received for Great Lakes fish is higher than in any of the other United States fisheries. The chief fish are herring, trout, perch, chub, and whitefish. The Lower Lakes account for most of the catch, but Lake Superior is famous for its trout and whitefish, which command high prices in the hotel and restaurant trade. Some of them, packed in ice, are shipped by express and airplane to cities as far away as New York and San Francisco. The greater portion of all Great Lakes fish is sold fresh in large cities located along or near the Lower Lakes. Nearly 2000 small craft, known as "fishing tugs," carry on the Lakes fisheries. They operate both from small towns and fishing villages and from large city ports. Seldom do they travel more than a few miles from their home docks. The total catch is declining. Again, it is the old story of overfishing, insufficient protection of small, young fish, and pollution of waters. Added difficulties are the spread of certain fish diseases and the recent invasion of the lakes by a kind of sea lamprey, an eel-like creature that fastens itself to a fish's side and feeds until the fish dies. The Mississippi river fisheries supply local towns and cities with such products as catfish, carp, and buffalo fish. They also contribute important amounts of mussels (river clams) which are used chiefly for buttons and "pearl" inlays. Mussels also contribute a few "river pearls."

A separate and unique portion of the United States fisheries is carried on in the Pribilof Islands. This is the fur-seal industry. The Pribilofs are in the Bering Sea about 250 miles west of the Alaskan Peninsula and a like distance north of the arc made by the Aleutian Islands. From the Pribilofs come practically all of the world's fur-seal pelts.

Canada

Of the various Canadian fisheries, it is the ocean fisheries, both shallow and deep-water, that are of chief commercial importance (FIG. 19–2). The major fishing grounds lie near Newfoundland, Nova Scotia, and Labrador, in the Gulf of St. Lawrence, and along the shore of British Columbia (FIGS. 19–2 and 19–7).

Salmon is king in the west; cod is king in the east. Other important fish on both coasts are herring and halibut. Some seals (not fur seals) are hunted in Hudson Bay.

Newfoundland, first of the British colonies in the New World, long has been synonymous with good fishing. Fishing still occupies approximately one-third of the population, including practically all the population of the Labrador coast. Meager agricultural resources, combined with the abundance of fish in the nearby sea, have kept fishing in a position of great prominence. Fishing still is relatively much more important in Newfoundland than in other Canadian provinces and the United States. The chief fish are cod, herring, and halibut; there are a few salmon, and seals are hunted off the Labrador coast.

OTHER FISHERIES

IN ADDITION to the world fisheries discussed in the preceding pages there are others which should at least be mentioned. These are the whale and seal (nonfur) fisheries.

Commercial whaling began as a near-shore activity in Europe nearly a thousand years ago. Since then it has spread into deep waters and across all the oceans. Whaling reached its peak during the nineteenth century and then went into decline when petroleum and petroleum products largely supplanted whale oil and when metals and synthetic materials came to replace whalebone in women's apparel. But decline did not mean oblivion. Some demand continues for whalebone in clothing and for use in mechanical brushes; the oil is used in soaps, leather preservatives, special lubricants, and edible fats; the meat is used as human food; and the "waste" is processed as meal and cake for animal feed, poultry feed, and fertilizer. Following World War II, the shortage of edible and industrial fats and oils, as well as meat, gave new encouragement to the whaling industry.

Modern whaling is carried on by large, specially equipped ships quite unlike the sailing whalers of the past century. While some whales are still towed to port and processed

19–10   Above: Norwegian whalers in Sandefjord, Norway, their home port; the larger vessels are factory ships and the smaller ones are hunting ships. Below: Scene aboard a factory ship during the processing of a whale carcass.

in shore "stations," many of them are processed at sea in huge factory ships (FIG. 19–10). Some whales still are captured in Arctic waters and in the North Atlantic and North Pacific, but most of them are now found in commercial numbers only in Antarctic waters and along the southwestern coast of Africa (FIG. 19–2). Japanese vessels now dominate the whaling industry; others are mainly Norwegian, British, and Soviet.

Seal fisheries, in addition to the fur-seal industry previously mentioned, are carried on mainly in the Arctic Ocean, the Hudson Bay–Labrador Coast region, and the Antarctic waters near South America. Like whales, many of the varieties of nonfur seals have become extinct, or nearly so. Those of present commercial importance are obtained chiefly in northern waters and are mainly of the group known in the trade as "hair seals." These seals are sought for their oil and hides. The oil is used primarily for special lubricants and in-dustrial dressings and the hides for the manu-facture of such goods as shoes, handbags, and luggage. The industry is almost completely dominated by Russian, Norwegian, and British sealers.

FISHING SETTLEMENTS

THE human settlements associated with fishing vary greatly from one place to an-other. Those of a more primitive sort are small and simple. They are represented by such set-tlements as the South Sea Island fishing village and the Eskimo fishing village of northwest Greenland. Some of them are seasonal and temporary, like the summer fishing encamp-ment of the Indians in the portion of Canada west of Churchill. Equipment is simple, usually no more than small boats, spears, and crude nets. Processing, too, is simple. Fish not im-mediately consumed may be dried, salted, or smoked, but there are no special buildings or machinery. Nor are there problems of market price, transportation, or special handling.

Nonprimitive fishing settlements are quite different, whether they are comparatively sim-ple or highly complex. Their function is to supply commercial, rather than subsistence, fish. Some of them are small and simple, like the fishing villages of rocky Labrador or those found in parts of northern Norway, but no matter how small, they possess specialized gear and processing grounds or buildings and they are connected with the channels of world trade. Somewhat larger settlements are very highly specialized as to gear, processing equip-ment, and types of wharves. They also are well integrated with the world's transport system, including sometimes even air service. Exam-ples are to be seen in Norway's Lofoten Is-lands towns and villages (FIG. 19–5), the fishing towns of the Bay of Biscay coast of France, or the whaling and sealing stations of the Falkland Islands (FIG. 19–11). Some of the highly specialized settlements are, in a sense, seasonal. A good example is seen in the typical cannery town of southern Alaska.

Today, the most important fishing centers can hardly be called fishing settlements. The handling of fish is only one of many economic activities. All of the intricate operations in-volved in receiving, processing, and distribut-ing fish and fish products represent but a small part of the total commercial and industrial work performed by large seaport cities. One can hardly refer to Boston as a fishing settle-ment, or Baltimore, or New Orleans. The same is true of Los Angeles, even though that city or, rather, its harbor section, is the leading fishing center of the United States. Fishing, like so many other occupations, has become largely mechanized and urbanized. Commer-cially at least, fishing is now chiefly a "big town" and "big city" enterprise, despite the fact that the fish or other fishery products may be secured many miles away.

19–11   A WHALING *station in the Falkland Islands, in the South Atlantic.*

· CHAPTER OUTLINE ·

Products of the Sea

NATURE AND LOCATION OF FISHERIES PRODUCTS

USES OF FISHERIES PRODUCTS
Human and Animal Foods
Other Uses

MAJOR FISHERIES OF EURASIA
Western Europe
The Mediterranean Sea
Japan
China (Mainland)

Soviet Union
Other Fisheries

MAJOR FISHERIES OF THE AMERICAS
United States
Canada

OTHER FISHERIES

FISHING SETTLEMENTS

· REVIEW QUESTIONS ·

1. Why is the term "fisheries" somewhat inappropriate and ambiguous?
2. List the commercial products obtained from the earth's waters, excluding mineral products.

3. Locate the chief fishing regions of the Americas. How do these correlate with water depths?
4. What is plankton and why is it important?

472 | *Products of the Sea*

5. Which are the leading fishing nations of the world?
6. Why are sea products such a major item in the diet of the Japanese?
7. Where are Europe's major fishing areas? What two countries lead in Europe's fishing industry?
8. Discuss the significance of fishing in the development of New England and its business.
9. What are the chief commercial uses of cod? Of menhaden?

10. Are there any major reasons for the recent decline in the United States sponge fisheries?
11. What are the major problems of the Great Lakes fisheries?
12. Contrast the "old" and the "new" in world whaling activities. What nations dominate the whaling industry?
13. Why is it that today's chief fishing ports cannot be referred to as "fishing settlements"?
14. See if you can find recent articles on the future importance of the sea and of fresh waters in terms of food supply for man.

20 Coal and Petroleum: The Chief Sources of Industrial Energy

STANDARD OIL CO. (N.J

❨ So far in this book, attention has been focused primarily, although not entirely, on the surface of the earth. For another important part of the geographical complex it is necessary to go beneath the surface, into the upper portion of the earth's crust. Here are the minerals which have played and are playing a major role in man's material and cultural progress. From raft to ocean liner, from wooden hoe to tractor and gang plow, from foot and horseback to streamliner and airplane, from home workshop to mammoth factory, man's story is inextricably entwined with minerals. Even his very leisure, so essential to progress, reflects the manner in which resources from within the *earth have helped to free him from unending drudgery. Among these resources none have proved more important than coal and petroleum.*

Industrial power in the future may well be derived from uranium and certain other man-made elements—atomic energy, in fact, is already in limited use in both factories and homes. But the fact remains that the modern industrial civilizations have been built on coal and petroleum and these are still, practically speaking, the mainstays of industrial power.

COAL

IT HAS been said that "coal is the lifeblood of modern industry" and that "no modern nation has become a world power unless it has had abundant coal." Neither statement is exaggerated. Coal is so vital to the highly industrialized parts of the world that any insufficiency in supply creates serious problems; sudden and complete stoppage of supply brings quick paralysis. Why this is so may be appreciated readily by considering the uses of coal.

Production and Uses

No one knows when man first discovered that certain "black stones" would burn and provide more heat, and more lasting heat, than wood. One authority believes that coal was used to smelt copper in Manchuria as early as 1100 B.C. If that is so, it probably was used for domestic purposes long before that. Coal cinders are contained in the remains of a Roman wall constructed near Manchester, England, about 100 A.D. Newcastle, England, had a coal mine in operation as early as 1238 A.D. Even the American Indian knew of coal and used it slightly. From him, the colonists learned about the existence of some of the coal deposits of eastern Pennsylvania.

20–1

[OPPOSITE, TOP] DERRICKS *of the Tia Juana oil field rise from the shallow waters of Lake Maracaibo, Venezuela.*

The beginning of the Industrial Revolution (about 1750) marked the real start of commercial coal production. This was in the British Isles, where man first turned from the making of goods by hand at home to their manufacture by machines in factories. Machines needed power, and coal was the answer. Burning it under boilers supplied steam and steam ran the machines. As the Industrial Revolution spread to Europe and the United States, so did the mining of large quantities of coal. By 1850, the United States was on its way to becoming the world's leading coal producer, a position it attained about 1900. In Europe, at about the same time, Germany surpassed the United Kingdom in coal production and rivaled the United States for first place. A marked decrease in Germany's coal production resulted after partition at the end of World War II. Since that time, coal production in both the Soviet Union and mainland China has increased enormously so that they compete with the United States for first place. While actual tonnages mined vary from year to year in response to economic forces within any country, the United States currently produces about 20 per cent of the world total of bituminous and anthracite coal and is followed by the U.S.S.R. and the United Kingdom. West Germany contributes another 7 per cent. Production figures for mainland China generally include lignite as well as bituminous and anthracite. Hence, they are not properly

TABLE *18*

Selected List of Products Obtained from Coal

COKE

Blast-furnace coke
Smelting coke
Foundry coke
Domestic fuel
Industrial fuel
Briquette coke
Carbon dioxide
Water gas
Boiler gas
Calcium carbide
Carbons
Electrodes
Graphite
Washing soda

AMMONIA

Pyridine
Nitric acid
Nitrous oxide
Ammonium phosphate
Ammonium sulfate
Ammonium chloride
Ammonium carbonate
Ammonium nitrate

LIGHT OIL

Benzene
Solvent naphtha
Benzaldehyde
Benzyl alcohol
Carbon disulfide
Varnish
Toluene

HEAVY OIL

Carbolineum
Carbazole
Anthracene
Anthraquinone
Phenanthrene

GAS

Fuel gas
Illuminating gas
Naphthalene
Cyanogen
Sulfur

HARD PITCH

Insulation
Electrodes
Core compounds
Pitch coke
Pitch gas

SOFT PITCH

Roofing
Waterproofing
Paving
Batteries
Paint

TAR ACIDS

Phenols
Cresols
Carbolic acid
Flotation agents
Naphthalene

comparable with those of the other countries listed.

Today, on the basis of tons consumed, there are five major uses of coal. The two chief ones are the running of factories and the manufacture of coke and other coal-derived products. The extent to which coal enters into the production of particular materials and goods is partly indicated in TABLE 18. The other major uses of coal are to heat homes and public buildings, to generate electricity, and as fuel for locomotives.

Comparative Importance

Coal is the main source of energy for the industrial nations of the world as a whole, although there are some exceptions, such as

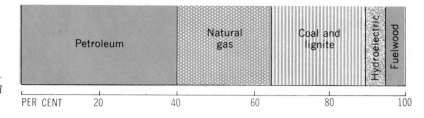

20–2

THE *principal sources of energy production in the United States.*

Norway, Switzerland, and Italy. In those countries, lack of coal has stimulated the use of electricity obtained from water power. In the world as a whole, coal is as important as all other sources of energy combined. In the United States, coal is one of the main sources, supplying about 25 per cent of the energy used (FIG. 20–2). Petroleum, coal's main rival, supplies about 40 per cent, and natural gas an additional 25 per cent. Hydroelectric power and other fuels, like wood and peat, account for the remaining 10 per cent. It is well to remember that in the United States, as in most countries of the world, far more electricity is produced in plants burning coal than in those using water power, despite the considerable increase in hydroelectric plant development which has taken place during the past thirty-five years.

It seems evident that coal, even with increasing competition from other energy sources, will continue to play a major part until the as yet unknown potentials of atomic energy are realized. Also, more efficient mining and utilization of coal will enable it to meet competition more effectively. A significant development was the perfection of the coal-burning gas turbine, which can use finely powdered coal of low as well as high quality. It is said that a locomotive powered by the gas turbine is three or four times as efficient as the older coal-burning steam locomotive. In the face of diminishing reserves of petroleum and natural gas, such an invention may have far-reaching consequences and may cause coal to increase, rather than decrease, in significance. Still another possibility is the use of coal as an important source of gasoline.

Origin

Coal represents a long evolution from plant remains to the "black rock" which we know today. It began its existence in extensive swamps where lush tropical vegetation grew. As plants died, muds and water prevented their complete decay. Running water carried other muds and sands into the swamps, to bury and press down upon the layers of organic material. The result was alternate layers of plant remains and earth materials. As time went on, pressure from overlying earth materials, plus the heat derived from those pressures and from deeper burial, caused the organic materials to evolve into some kind, or stage, of coal. Instrumental, too, were the great pressures and high temperatures which accompany deformation of the earth's crust. Such deformation did not occur in all areas where coal was being formed, but, where it did take place, it speeded up the evolutionary process. When sufficiently severe, it produced types of coal that could not otherwise have come into existence.

Stages

Each kind or type of coal represents one stage in the evolution of plant remains. The first stage is *peat*, which is found in the bogs of Ireland. Peat is not truly coal, but it may be called "incipient coal." Acted upon through time by heat and pressure, it slowly changes into *lignite*, or *brown coal*. Lignite is soft, woody, high in water content and volatile gases, and low in "fixed carbon" (FIG. 20–3). Its low quality and low value normally limit its

Coal | 477

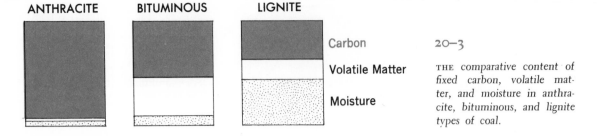

ANTHRACITE BITUMINOUS LIGNITE

Carbon

Volatile Matter

Moisture

20–3

THE *comparative content of fixed carbon, volatile matter, and moisture in anthracite, bituminous, and lignite types of coal.*

use to local areas and to simple domestic purposes. However, Germany has made important use of her lignite deposits for industrial and manufacturing purposes. This was done at large expense of time and money, since it involves special processing as well as mixing with coals of higher quality.

When lignite is subjected to further metamorphosis, it becomes *bituminous coal,* the exact type and quality depending on how far the evolution is carried. Bituminous coal is higher in fixed carbon and lower in water content than lignite. It is also hard enough to stand shipment without too much breakage. Bituminous is the coal of major use. The higher the grade of bituminous, the less are the wastes in ash, water, and volatile gases (FIG. 20–3), and, in general, the greater are the possibilities of use. Some grades of bituminous are of "coking quality." This is important in the manufacture of iron from iron ore, for which large quantities of coke are required for blast furnaces. Inasmuch as steel is made from iron, coke is also essential to the steel industry. Coke is coal that has been baked in "coke ovens" until part of the volatile gases have been released, leaving material which is high in fixed carbon. The volatile gases, formerly wasted, are now carefully collected and used as "artificial" gas in homes and factories. Nations which, like the United States, possess large tonnages of bituminous coal, including that of coking quality, are richer than they would be if they owned instead all the gold mines of the world.

Some coal has evolved to the stage in which it becomes very hard, shiny, and comprised

largely of fixed carbon. This is *anthracite,* a clean, slow-burning coal. Its "dustless" and "smokeless" nature makes it an excellent fuel for the heating of dwellings and public buildings in cities. Such use is greatly encouraged because it minimizes the smoke pall or smog which distresses large urban areas. However, anthracite is very expensive. It occurs in few places in the world and is so interbedded with complexly folded and faulted rocks that mining costs are high.

In a few places, coal has evolved to the point where it is no longer coal. Virtually all volatile matter has been eliminated, leaving little more than carbon, or graphite. The "graphitic coals" are insignificant commercially as energy sources.

Geologic and Geographic Location

Many things determine the usefulness of a given coal deposit—and of deposits of other minerals as well. Very important among them are geologic and geographic location. Geologic location refers to the actual position of the coal layers, or seams, within and among other rocks, and to distance from the surface of the ground. Some coal seams are near or at the surface, and are arranged horizontally or nearly so. If they are also thick and of high quality, conditions for mining are optimum. Cheap strip-mining methods can be used; the regolith or, in some instances, solid rock is removed by power shovels and draglines (FIG. 20–4), and the coal is scooped up and loaded into trucks or railway cars.

Most of the world's coal is not so conven-

20–4

STRIP *mining of coal, like open-pit mining of iron ore, is less expensive than shaft or tunnel mining. Here is the world's largest coal shovel in operation in a strip mine in Ohio.*

iently located. It occurs in layers at various depths and in various degrees of deformation. Often the coal seams outcrop on the sides of valleys, so that the easiest way to obtain the

coal is to make tunnels or "drifts" which reach back, following the given seam, into the valley side. Tunnel mining demands supporting timbers to prevent cave-ins, proper aeration and drainage, and small tracks and cars for hauling the coal out of the mine. Much of the Appalachian coal of the United States is mined in this fashion (FIG. 20–5A). Obviously, it is much more expensive than strip mining. Some coal seams are intricately folded and faulted and, in part, deeply buried (FIG. 20–5B). This is particularly true of the anthracite seams of eastern Pennsylvania. In attempts to follow the weaving, broken seams into the earth, a combination of shaft and tunnel mining is necessary. Anthracite has to be lifted through the shaft to the surface by elevators, and the deeper the mine, the greater is the cost of getting the coal up. Thus, purely geologic location is an especially prominent factor in the price of anthracite.

Geographic location refers to the place in the world where coal occurs, as in western Germany or southern Wales. This is just as important as geologic location. There are large deposits of high-quality bituminous coal in Antarctica, for example, but from the point of view of economical exploitation, they are in the wrong place. Much the same is true of Alaskan coal and of many deposits in the interior of Asia. However, a region does not necessarily remain inaccessible. There was a time when the Illinois coal was inaccessible,

20–5   CROSS *sections showing positions of coal seams among other earth materials. A is fairly typical of the Appalachian bituminous coal fields; B is representative of the Pennsylvania anthracite fields.*

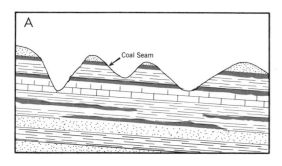

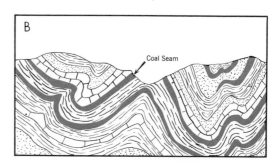

Coal | 479

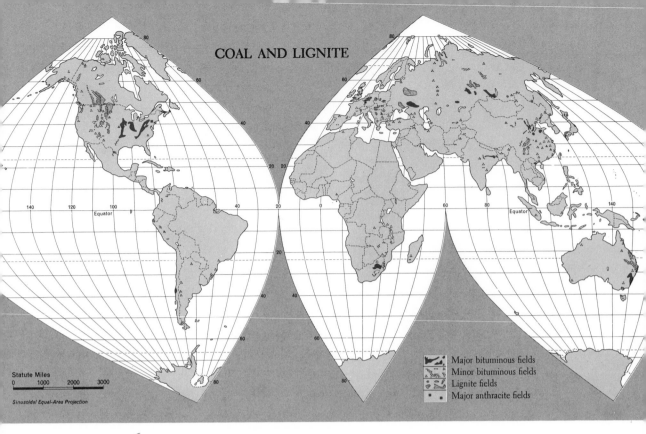

COAL AND LIGNITE

Statute Miles
0 1000 2000 3000

Sinusoidal Equal-Area Projection

Major bituminous fields
Minor bituminous fields
Lignite fields
Major anthracite fields

20–6 THE *Northern Hemisphere is the coal hemisphere. All coals consist of the altered remains of former plant life, and the extent to which nature has altered these plant remains is a measure of the "stage," or "maturity," of the coal.*

but the westward spread of industrialization and improved methods of transportation completely changed the picture. A few years ago, the coal of the Kuznetsk Basin in Siberia was inaccessible, but now it is being actively mined. However, the mining of Kuznetsk coal is not simply a matter of transportation, railway coal cars, and availability of miners, but a matter of government policy as well. The Soviet Union runs the mines and the operations do not have to be "economical"; they do not have to meet open commercial competition from other coal mines, either in the U.S.S.R. or in foreign countries. Thus it is sometimes difficult to state which coal deposits are "favorably" located in a geographic sense and which are not. The same applies partly to geologic location, for a government may order that

certain deposits be mined, regardless of mining difficulties.

Granted all this, the optimum conditions occur in those areas where thick, high-quality seams lie horizontally near the surface and near, or with convenient access to, large markets.

Major Coal Fields

Coal occurs in all continents and in nearly all countries, but most of the world's proven reserves and the largest deposits are found in only a few countries (FIG. 20–6). These are the United States, the U.S.S.R., and China, in order of importance. Together, these three countries have over three-fourths of the total estimated world reserves of coal. South Africa,

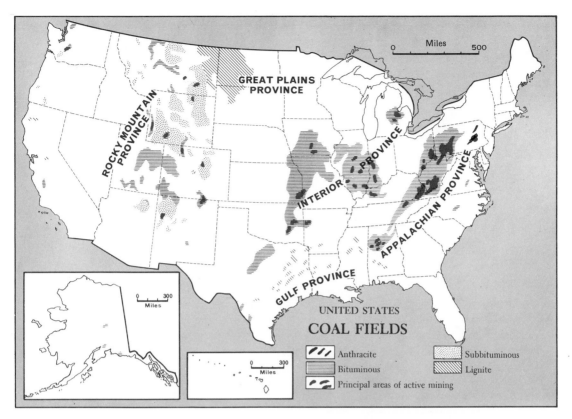

20–7   THE *United States is a coal-rich nation. Highly active mining, especially in the fields east of the Mississippi river, accounts for its prominent position in world coal production.*

the United Kingdom, Poland, West Germany, India, and Canada combined have a total of about 15 per cent of the world's reserves. This leaves less than 10 per cent in all other countries of the world together. These figures include coal of all types (anthracite, bituminous, and lignite).

UNITED STATES • This nation possesses, despite heavy past withdrawals, some of the largest and richest coal deposits of any country. Distribution of the various types, including low-quality bituminous and lignite, is shown in FIG. 20–7. The coal fields of the eastern (Appalachian) province extend from northern Pennsylvania to the Birmingham district of Alabama. Most of the coal is high-quality bituminous, including abundant coking coal. The world's chief anthracite deposit occurs in

eastern Pennsylvania, in the Scranton–Wilkes-Barre district. The eastern province is the world's outstanding example of "enough of the right kind of coal in the right place." The interior province extends from Michigan to central Texas. It also is comprised of bituminous coals. So far, the chief mining areas are in Illinois and parts of adjacent Indiana and Kentucky, areas which are most favorably located in terms of market and where the coal is in the more favorable geologic positions. The coal fields of the remaining provinces are more broken and scattered and definitely inferior in quality of coal, although the tonnage is tremendous. The Gulf province is a lignite province. The Great Plains province is chiefly lignite. The Rocky Mountain province, very much scattered, contains numerous deposits

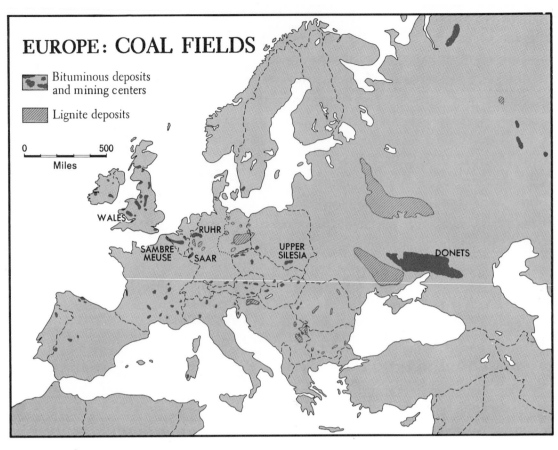

EUROPE: COAL FIELDS

Bituminous deposits and mining centers

Lignite deposits

0 — 500 Miles

WALES

RUHR

SAMBRE MEUSE   SAAR   UPPER SILESIA   DONETS

20–8   EUROPE *has a few large and many small coal deposits. In Western Europe, Ruhr valley coals lead in both high quality and great quantity. The U.S.S.R. now leads the world in coal production.*

of bituminous and subbituminous coal. The Pacific province is more a name than an actuality (FIG. 20–7).

The world prominence of the United States, beginning about 1900, is based on the coal in the eastern half of the country, particularly in the Appalachian region. The chief coal-mining states, in order of production, are West Virginia, Pennsylvania, Kentucky, and Illinois. The first two produce about 50 per cent of the total for the United States and the last two, about 24 per cent.

EUROPE • The major coal fields of Europe are in the United Kingdom, West Germany, Belgium, Poland, and the U.S.S.R. Small and scattered fields are found from the Mediter-

ranean to the Baltic and from the Atlantic to the Urals (FIG. 20–8).

The United Kingdom held first rank in world coal production from the beginning of the Industrial Revolution until about 1900, but since then it has fallen behind the United States, and, in recent years, behind the U.S.S.R. British coal fields, although heavily mined for a century and a half, are not exhausted. Reserves are said to be sufficient for several hundred years, but the coal which remains is much less accessible and, as mines are pushed deeper and deeper, mining costs increase. The chief fields lie among the margins of the Pennine Chain and in southern Wales. Significant deposits also occur in the Central

Lowland of Scotland (FIG. 20–8). The Welsh coal was particularly useful in Britain's seaborne commerce, not only to fuel her merchant marine but also as an item of foreign trade. High in quality and located practically on tidewater, Welsh coal is still found on the wharves of many of the world's major seaports. When one recalls the world position of the United Kingdom in manufacturing and trade, it is easy to appreciate the role of coal in the British economy.

Germany's rapid rise to power before World War I was based as much as anything else on plentiful bituminous coal, including coking coal. While she had several small fields, the bulk of her production came from the famous Westphalian fields in the Ruhr valley (FIG. 20–8). From 1870 until 1914, Germany possessed both the Ruhr coals and the Lorraine iron ores, two major sinews of modern industry—and of modern warfare. Following World War I, Lorraine was returned to France, but Germany still retained the Ruhr coals as well as important fields in Upper Silesia, next to the southwestern border of Poland. At the end of World War II, Germany lost the Upper Silesian fields to Poland, and, for a time, the Saar Basin coal field which is located along the Franco-German border next to Luxembourg. But West Germany has continued to hold the Ruhr field, largest and richest producer on the Continent.

The European coal fields of the U.S.S.R. are mainly in the Donets Basin, in the Ukrainian portion of the Russian Plain and a bit to the north of the Sea of Azov (FIG. 20–8). They are chiefly bituminous; some of them are of coking quality, but not of highest coking grade. Other fields are the Tula field, just south of Moscow, and several small ones at the southern end of the Urals. The former is comprised of lignite and low-quality bituminous; the latter contains bituminous of noncoking nature. The U.S.S.R. "came out of nowhere" in terms of world coal production. In 1918, its name did not appear on the list of important coal-pro-

ducing nations; by 1939, at the start of World War II, it held fourth place, and today is first in the world. The sharply rising curve of its coal production practically coincides with the curve of Soviet industrial progress. As will be noted later, a significant part of Soviet coal is now mined in Siberia.

Belgium and France share coal fields which extend roughly east-west through central Belgium and barely into northern France: the Sambre–Meuse fields (FIG. 20–8). Smaller fields occur in northeastern Belgium and in several parts of France, chiefly around the edges of the Massif Central. The Sambre–Meuse coals are excellent for most purposes, but they have to be mixed with imported coals in order to manufacture high-grade coke. Both France and Belgium have had to depend greatly on coal from the Ruhr and the United Kingdom.

ASIA • The coal of Asia extends in a sort of broken ring around the margins of the upland heart of that continent (FIG. 20–6). Most of it is in Siberia, China, and India. Lesser amounts occur in scattered fields in the Japanese islands and elsewhere.

Significant activities in world coal mining and utilization have taken place recently in Soviet Asia. Among them is the use of the coal of the Kuznetsk Basin (Kuzbas), a region in the southeastern part of the Ob Basin, in the foothills of the Sayan Mountains and a bit south of the main line of the Trans-Siberian Railway. Here and nearby are several new industrial centers which draw on Kuznetsk coal. Other important coal fields, some of them being utilized, occur across much of southern Siberia, from the region north of Lake Balkhash (especially the Karaganda field) nearly to the Pacific Ocean. Still others lie in central Siberia and on the fringe of the tundra region.

The bulk of the coal of China lies in the North China hill country, west of the North China Plain, in the provinces of Shansi and Shensi. The coal has been only slightly utilized; it is expensive to mine, hard to reach, and far from the market. As China becomes much more industrialized, the Shansi–Shensi coal deposits will increase in importance. Actually much more coal has been mined in southern Manchuria than in any other part of China. However, Manchurian reserves are meager compared to those of the rest of mainland China.

Japan's coal fields are small and scattered. Hokkaido has the largest reserves, followed by Kyushu and Honshu, the latter a poor third. Japanese coals are bituminous of medium quality, so that Japan has had to import coking coal for its iron and steel industries.

Most of the coal fields in India lie to the west of Calcutta. By far the largest lie in the hills of the Damodar valley area in the northeasternmost part of peninsular India, close to the Ganges Lowland. Other fields lie in the upper Son valley and the upper Mahanadi valley, immediately west and southwest of the Damodar valley area. Still others are located in the lower Godavari valley and the valley of its tributary, the Pranhita, in central India. India's coal, particularly that in the Damodar valley, is enabling her to make significant strides towards an industrial economy.

SOUTHERN HEMISPHERE • Coal fields are few and far between south of the equator (FIG. 20–6). Australia and South Africa are the principal producers. Some of Australia's coal is of coking quality and is unique in this respect among Southern Hemisphere coals. The chief fields occur near the important ports of Sydney and Brisbane. Newcastle, a bit northeast along the coast from Sydney, is the chief coal center. It takes its name from a more famous Newcastle, the ancient coal-mining city in England.

South Africa has coal of medium grade in parts of Natal and Transvaal, which can be moved readily to Port Natal and less easily by longer hauls to Cape Town. Its importance rests largely on the facts that it is excellent for railway and steamship purposes and that no other coal is available within thousands of miles.

South America is "coal poor." Only in the southern part of middle Chile is there coal which is both accessible and of good quality (FIG. 20–6). Even there, reserves are small. Some high-grade coal exists in the Peruvian and Colombian Andes, but it is so isolated as to be of little use. Southern Brazil possesses coal, but of low quality.

PETROLEUM

THE commercial uses of petroleum are both old and new. In certain places, where the "rock oil" seeped from the ground, it has undoubtedly had minor use for thousands of years. Historical records mention it as early as four centuries before the birth of Christ. In early trade, it was a rare and costly substance.

Production and Uses

Primitive man used crude petroleum obtained from "seeps" to caulk small boats, waterproof the roofs of dwellings, dress his hair, and anoint his skin. Later, as evidenced in the trade of the Middle Ages (roughly 500–1500 A.D.), it was used as a medicine. Petroleum derived from coal and oil shales began to serve importantly for lighting purposes by 1800, gradually replacing whale oil and tallow candles. Modern production from drilled wells started just prior to the American Civil War and increased by leaps and bounds after 1900. Accompanying the rapid upsurge in production there was great progress in drilling and refining methods as well as in transportation and marketing.

In recent years, the story of petroleum parallels that of automobiles, airplanes, and modern

TABLE *19*

Selected List of Products Obtained from Petroleum and Natural Gas

NATURAL GAS

Domestic fuel
Industrial fuel
Butadiene
Butylene
Acetylene
Ethylene
Methyl alcohol
Formaldehyde
Chloroform
Carbon tetrachloride
Carbon black

HYDROCARBON GASES

Fuel gas
Petroleum ether
Liquefied gases
Solid carbon dioxide
Carbon black
Light naphthas

WHITE, INTERMEDIATE, HEAVY DISTILLATES

Naphthas
Refined oils
Kerosene
Signal oil
Diesel fuel
Flotation oils
Transformer oils
Lubricating oils
Waxes (paraffins)

RESIDUES

Greases
Lubricating oils
Fuel oils
Road oils
Waterproofing oils
Oil coke
Medicinal oils

REFINERY SLUDGES

Sulfonic acids
Sulfuric acid
Asphalts
Binders
Wood preservatives
Fuel oil
Fuel coke

SPECIAL USE PRODUCTS

Rocket fuels
Penetrating oils
Skin and hair oils
Colored smokes

---

ships. It is a story of tremendous demand for petroleum and petroleum products to run and to lubricate engines and machines. In addition, petroleum is used to supply paraffin, vaseline, cleaning fluids, kerosene, dyes, and scores of other products. TABLE 19 indicates most of the present-day uses. Looking at this table, one can appreciate why world production has risen from less than 7000 barrels in 1859 to about 7,650,000,000 barrels in 1960 and why production in the United States, major home of the automobile and the airplane, rose from 2000 barrels in 1859 to 63,000,000 barrels in 1900,

1,350,000,000 barrels in 1940, and approximately 2,600,000,000 barrels in 1960—over 7,000,000 barrels a day.

Just before World War II, the United States produced as much as 61 per cent of the world total of petroleum, but, by 1960, this had been reduced to approximately 33 per cent. This changed position resulted mainly from great increases in the production of such countries as Kuwait, Saudi Arabia, and Venezuela. For the future, the United States has proven reserves approximating 12 per cent of the world's total.

Comparative Importance

Petroleum alone furnishes about 40 per cent of the energy used in the United States (FIG. 20-2). It has become so important that any sudden stoppage of supply would paralyze the nation almost as quickly as would lack of coal. Not only is it necessary to a peacetime economy, but it is extremely critical during time of war. Air fleets, mechanized armies, and navies require huge quantities of fuel oil, gasoline, and lubricants. In World War I, it was said that the Allied nations "rode to victory on a sea of oil." This was doubly true in World War II. Considering the significance of petroleum in peace and war, one can easily understand why there has been, and still is, a "world struggle for oil." Nations with little or no oil struggle to insure themselves supplies from foreign countries. Thus, the United Kingdom is vitally interested in the rich oil fields of the Middle East and in protecting the pipelines and sea lanes which bring the oil to the British Isles. Other nations, temporarily rich in petroleum, seek large supplies elsewhere for use in the future or to help conserve their own

deposits. This partly explains why a nation like the United States is vitally concerned with the huge oil reserves of faraway Arabia; it partly explains the interest of the U.S.S.R. in the affairs of Iran. When two strong nations are attempting to gain control of oil in the same foreign country, the possibilities of conflict, even open warfare, are great. Iran was a case in point, for both Soviet and British interests are strong there, and Iran, until it nationalized its oil in 1951, was in a sense "caught in the middle." Someone has said that the worst thing that can happen to a weak, undeveloped country is the discovery of large and rich oil deposits within its boundaries.

Geologic Occurrence

Petroleum is found in only very restricted portions of the earth's crust. First of all, it is limited to regions of sedimentary rocks. Thus there is no possibility of its discovery in such vast areas as the Laurentian Upland of North America, the equatorial uplands of eastern Africa, or most of western Australia. Even in regions of sedimentary rocks there are few de-

20-9 SOME of the types of geologic structures which trap petroleum. A. Anticlinal trap. B. Fault trap. C. Trap in a lens structure. D. Traps formed by deformation of strata by a volcanic "neck."

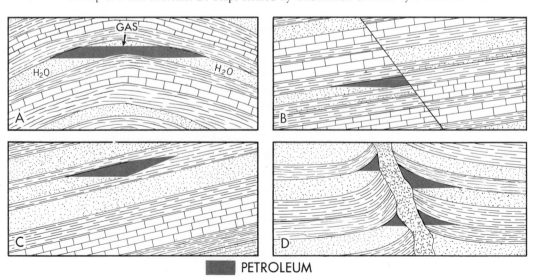

PETROLEUM

20–10 OIL field south of Oklahoma City. The wells are spaced so that there is only one well to each 40 acres of land.

posits, at least in commercial quantities. Either the oil was not formed, or it was lost as a result of seepage, erosion, or extreme diastrophism.

For petroleum to exist in commercial amounts, in the form of oil "pools," special rock structures are required. These must trap and hold the oil particles as they migrate within sedimentary rock layers. FIGURE 20–9 illustrates some of the more common possibilities. It will be noted in each example that the rocks are so arranged, because of folding, faulting, or both, that any oil particles which may be present are literally trapped in a portion of the structure. Here they remain, under great pressure resulting from the weight of the rocks above and from the natural gas which is usually entrapped with the oils. When an oil prospec-

tor locates a "pool" and drills into it, the oil and gas usually rush up the drill hole with great force, often with a roar which can be heard for several miles. Such oil wells are "gushers"; they must be capped in order to control the flow of oil and gas and to prevent complete loss. Later, as pressures lessen, such wells must be pumped.

Geographic Distribution

UNITED STATES • The United States has the most actively exploited of all the world's petroleum deposits. Commercial production began in 1859, when the initial well was drilled near Titusville, in northern Pennsylvania. This was the first drilled oil well in the world. Oil

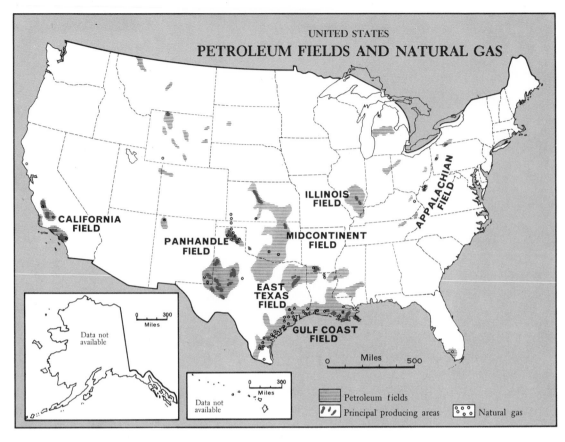

UNITED STATES
PETROLEUM FIELDS AND NATURAL GAS

CALIFORNIA
FIELD

PANHANDLE
FIELD

ILLINOIS
FIELD

MIDCONTINENT
FIELD

APPALACHIAN
FIELD

EAST
TEXAS
FIELD

GULF COAST
FIELD

Data not
available

Petroleum fields
Principal producing areas
Natural gas

20–11   PETROLEUM *deposits in the conterminous United States are well distributed. By use of pipelines and other conveyances, petroleum products and natural gas are readily made available to most sections of the country.*

was obtained at a depth of only 69 feet. As equipment improved, it was possible to tap deeper-lying pools, both in Pennsylvania and elsewhere (FIG. 20–10). Today, man is able to reach far into the earth for petroleum: a well drilled in southern California is over 22,000 feet deep—more than four miles!

The petroleum fields of the United States are sufficiently scattered to insure most of the nation easy access to the oil and the products derived from it (FIG. 20–11). Moreover, petroleum and its products are relatively easy to transport, whether by pipeline, tank car, tank truck, oil barge, or ocean-going tanker. Most of the refineries, of which the United States possesses nearly as many as are found in all the

rest of the world, are located at the junctions of major pipelines and at points where foreign oil arrives at the seaboard. The greatest single refining district extends from New York to Baltimore. Much of the crude oil used there comes by tanker from Venezuela and many of the refined products travel by water to western Europe. Other major refining centers are at the southern end of Lake Michigan, along the Texas-Louisiana Gulf Coast, and in the south coastal section of California.

U.S.S.R. • Russia became an important producer of petroleum about 1873. In some years, she produced more than did the United States, although this was not true after 1901. The Soviet Union's total production in recent

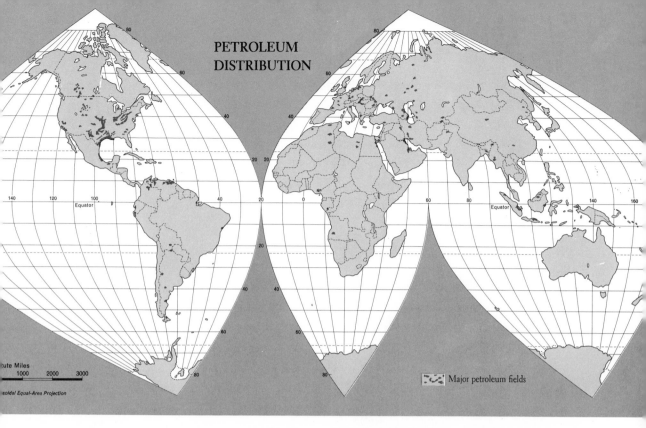

ute Miles
1000   2000   3000

soidal Equal-Area Projection

Major petroleum fields

20–12 PETROLEUM *is found principally in areas of sedimentary rocks, such as sandstone and limestone, and is pumped from wells from depths ranging from a few hundred feet to about four miles.*

decades has been less than one-half that of the United States, but she does have important reserves nearly as large as, if not larger than, those of the United States. Still, the Soviet Union is vitally interested, as are many countries, in acquiring access to and control of foreign sources, especially in the Middle East.

The Baku fields, located where the Caucasus Mountains meet the Caspian Sea, were until recently the principal producers within the U.S.S.R. Far more important at present is the so-called Ural-Volga Field, stretching from the Volgograd area along the middle Volga to the central Urals (FIG. 20–12). This field is now responsible for 70 to 75 per cent of the total production within the U.S.S.R., while the Baku Field produces about 20 per cent. Other producing fields in the Soviet Union occur on the northern slopes of the Caucasus, on the

southeastern and northeastern shores of the Caspian Sea, and in the area just north of the Pamir Mountains, in interior Asia. Other known reserves are not in production in significant amount. Outside of these areas, Romania has the only other oil fields of significance in the Soviet-controlled portion of Europe. Currently, the total production within the U.S.S.R. approximates 14 per cent of the world total.

VENEZUELA • It was not until 1919 that Venezuela entered importantly into the world petroleum scene; yet by 1928, she was in second place, although producing only slightly more than one-eighth as much as the United States. In 1959 Venezuela produced more than one-third as much as the United States and a little less than 14 per cent of the world total.

The rapid increase in Venezuelan oil output

20–13

PART of a large oil refinery on the island of Aruba, Netherlands Antilles.

largely reflects improved technology. By the time her pools were discovered, the petroleum industry had developed modern techniques for drilling, pumping, and transporting oil in large quantities. In addition, American capital was readily available and there was a great world demand for the oil.

Although there is some production elsewhere in Venezuela, as in the lower Orinoco Basin, most of the country's oil comes from the Lake Maracaibo fields (FIG. 20–12). Shallow-draft tankers carry the oil out into the Caribbean to the nearby Dutch islands of Aruba and Cu-

raçao. There some of the oil is run through mammoth refineries (FIG. 20–13) and shipped to the United States and Europe; the remainder, pumped into large ocean-going tankers, proceeds to refineries located on the Gulf and Atlantic Coasts of the United States and to those located in Britain and adjacent sections of western Europe. Venezuela's proved reserves, probably about one-half those of the United States, are the second largest in all the Americas and, in 1960, appeared to be about 80 per cent of those that are known in the U.S.S.R.

MIDDLE EAST • The Middle East now produces about one-fourth of the world's crude petroleum, somewhat more than Venezuela. The chief producing countries are Kuwait, Saudi Arabia, Iran, and Iraq.

The real significance of the oil of the Middle East lies in the future, and, evidently, the near future. The greatest proved reserves are here; Kuwait, Iran, Saudi Arabia, and Iraq collectively have fully 60 per cent of the known world reserves. This is approximately five times the reserves in the United States. Much of the reserve, particularly in Kuwait, Saudi Arabia, and Iran, is located close to cheap water transportation and even more of it is so placed that the oil can move to the sea's edge by means of relatively short pipelines. Long pipelines have already been used to transport oil to the eastern end of the Mediterranean.

OTHER AREAS • The countries and fields noted above produce about 86 per cent of the world's petroleum and possess over 85 per cent of the petroleum reserves. Thus world oil production will continue to be associated primarily with the United States, Venezuela, the U.S.S.R., and the Middle East, with the last gaining in prominence. However, production will continue for some time in the other areas which appear on FIG. 20–12. Chief among these are Canada, Indonesia, Mexico, Romania, Argentina, Algeria, and Colombia.

Coal and Petroleum: The Chief Sources of Industrial Energy

COAL
Production and Uses
Comparative Importance
Origin
Stages
Geologic and Geographic Location
Major Coal Fields
    UNITED STATES
    EUROPE
    ASIA
    SOUTHERN HEMISPHERE

PETROLEUM
Production and Uses
Comparative Importance
Geologic Occurrence
Geographic Distribution
    UNITED STATES
    U.S.S.R.
    VENEZUELA
    MIDDLE EAST
    OTHER AREAS

• REVIEW QUESTIONS •

1. Why is coal so important in this so-called Age of Electricity?
2. See if you can determine how important coal is in the community in which you live.
3. Discuss the origin and the "stages" of coal.
4. Distinguish between geologic and geographic location of coal.
5. Identify coal fields now actively mined which were formerly unused because of unfavorable geographic locations. What happened to make their use possible?
6. Is it possible to overcome a poor geologic location of coal? Explain.
7. What is the relative position of the United States among the nations as far as possession of high-quality coal is concerned?
8. List the major coal fields of Europe. Which one of them will undoubtedly be exhausted last?
9. What are some of the major reasons why China's Shansi province coals have been mined so little?
10. Compare the Northern and Southern Hemispheres as to quality and quantity of coal.
11. Account for the comparatively sudden large demand for petroleum.
12. Explain the statement, "Petroleum may be one of the major causes of future wars."
13. In recent years, much has been heard about petroleum discoveries in Canada. What would your attitude be if you were asked to invest money in exploration for petroleum deposits in the interior of Quebec? Give the reasons for your attitude.
14. Is the geographic location of petroleum in the United States favorable or unfavorable? Explain.
15. Compare the mining and transportation problems of coal and petroleum.
16. What is the world position of the United States in petroleum production and reserves?

21 Iron Ore and the Ferroalloys

U.S. STEEL CORPORATION

❲ NO IRON ore, no iron—no iron, no steel. *Thus, briefly and directly, may be stated the significance of iron ore in the present-day world. While coal and petroleum run most of the world's machines, the machines themselves are made chiefly of iron, or of steel, which itself is made from iron. The same is true of common tools from knife and ax to saw and hammer. When it is remembered that iron is one of the more abundant elements in the earth's crust, it would seem that no country, region, or district need lack for iron. But such is not the case.*

IRON ORE

Chief Ores

IRON has practically no "free" or pure occurrence in nature. It exists in many compounds which, in turn, are greatly mixed with other rock materials. Most of the iron compounds do not constitute ores; that is, they do not occur in sufficient quantities or in sufficient purity to bear the expense of commercial development. Thus, there is much iron in the earth, but there are relatively few deposits of iron ore.

The chief ores of iron are *hematite, magnetite, limonite,* and *siderite.* They are mainly compounds of iron, oxygen, and carbon, plus, of course, varying amounts of impurities. The first three ores named are oxides, whereas the last is a carbonate. If impurities, such as phosphorus, are present in too great amount, the ores are inferior or perhaps unusable. Iron ores vary considerably in the proportion of iron per ton of ore. Some run as high as 60 or 70 per cent, others as low as 25 to 40 per cent. A few countries, such as the United States and Sweden, have been fortunate in the possession of large tonnages of ore high in iron content. Others, like France, have large tonnages of low-grade ore. Still other countries, such as Italy, have little or no iron ore.

To date, most commercial mining of iron ore has been done in three nations: the U.S.S.R., the United States, and France (FIG. 21–2). Together these countries now produce about two-thirds of the world's annual output. Other producers are Sweden, Canada, Venezuela, India, West Germany, the United Kingdom, and Brazil. Some major iron-ore deposits as yet produce relatively little. Most important among such large reserves are those in

Brazil, eastern Canada, India, southeastern Cuba, Venezuela, the Republic of South Africa, central Siberia, and China (FIG. 21–2). The Indian, Venezuelan, Canadian, Siberian, and Chinese ores are now undergoing rapid development.

Iron Ranges of the United States

Districts containing usable iron deposits are known as *iron ranges.* There is no necessary connection between iron ranges and ranges of hills and mountains. Some iron ranges do occur in hilly areas, as do those in northern Sweden and northeastern New York State; some small ranges are found in mountainous country; but many, like those of the Cleveland district in England or the Dnieper Basin of the U.S.S.R., are located in plains.

The chief iron ranges of the United States are located in northeastern Minnesota and northern Michigan. Other important ones lie in central Alabama, northeastern New York, southeastern Pennsylvania, and northern Wisconsin (FIG. 21–3). All of them, from Minnesota to New York and south to Alabama, are either in or close to the margins of the northeastern manufacturing region of the United States—the greatest manufacturing region in the world. In addition, the major iron ranges have easy access to cheap water transportation on the Great Lakes. Lesser ranges, scattered and isolated, occur in Wyoming, Utah, Colorado, New Mexico, and California.

LAKE SUPERIOR RANGES • Located in a broken arc around the western margins of Lake Superior are the large, high-grade deposits which gave the United States first rank in the mining of iron ore in the past (FIG. 21–4). These ranges normally account for from 80 to 90 per cent of United States output and about one-fourth of that of the entire world. Ordinarily, from 50,000,000 to 75,000,000 tons of iron ore move down the Great Lakes each year, chiefly

---

21–1

[OPPOSITE, TOP] OPEN-PIT *iron ore mine at Hibbing, Minnesota, in one of the great iron ranges of the world, the Mesabi. Electric shovels scoop up the ore and load it onto the cars which then "spiral" up out of the pit.*

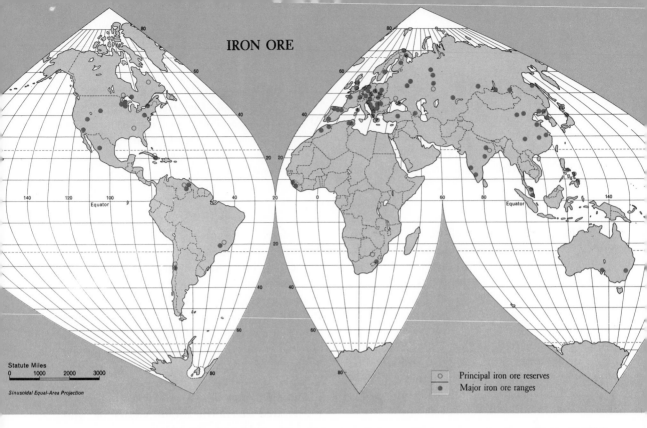

IRON ORE

Statute Miles
0   1000   2000   3000

Sinusoidal Equal-Area Projection

21–2   THE *Northern Hemisphere accounts for most of the world's iron ore production, with the U.S.S.R., the U.S., France, and Sweden producing nearly three-quarters of the total. Other large iron reserves known to exist in many parts of the world will become important in future production.*

to the blast furnaces and steel mills strung from Chicago to Buffalo and from the southern margins of the Great Lakes to the upper Ohio valley. But there are warnings in the air: we have drawn so heavily on the Lake Superior ranges, both in peace and in war, that the readily procured reserves of high-grade iron ore may be exhausted by 1975. The period of the richest harvest is about ended. To be sure, there are tremendous reserves of low-grade ore, but they will demand expensive processing and perhaps the importation of high-grade foreign ores to be mixed with them as "enrichers." The low-grade ores are known as *taconites*.

The iron ore of the Lake Superior country was discovered in the Upper Peninsula of Michigan in 1844; this was in the section which soon became known as the Marquette Range (FIG. 21–3). Movement of ore from this range to eastern manufacturing districts was greatly facilitated by the opening, in 1855, of the Soo—the Sault (pronounced "soo") Sainte Marie Canal. The Menominee Range came into production in 1872 and the Gogebic Range in 1884. Then, in 1892, the greatest of them all was opened—the world-famous Mesabi Range, which lies in northeastern Minnesota, within short and easy rail haul of the ports of Duluth and Two Harbors (FIG. 21–4). In recent years, this range alone has supplied more than half of all iron ore mined in the United States. When other Minnesota ranges, the Vermilion and Cuyuna, came into production, Minnesota far outdistanced Michigan as an iron-ore producer.

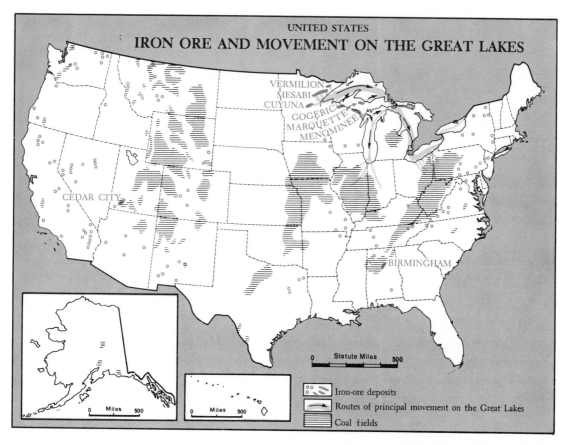

IRON ORE AND MOVEMENT ON THE GREAT LAKES

VERMILION
MESABI
CUYUNA
GOGEBIC
MARQUETTE
MENOMINEE

CEDAR CITY

BIRMINGHAM

Statute Miles
0   500

Iron-ore deposits
Routes of principal movement on the Great Lakes
Coal fields

Miles   500

Miles   500

21–3   THE *largest concentrated flow of iron ore in the world is from the shores of the upper Great Lakes to the iron and steel plants strung along the lower Great Lakes, near the great coal fields of the United States, from Illinois to Pennsylvania.*

The importance of the Mesabi Range is based on more than tonnage of high-grade ore. "Geology was kind" to the Mesabi: the high-grade ore lies at or near the surface and in continuous deposits which are so soft that they can be mined with power shovels (FIG. 21–1). In sharp contrast, the ores of the Michigan ranges occur mainly in tortuous, faulted, and deep-reaching veins and pockets within masses of hard rock (FIG. 21–5). Thus, while Minnesota ores are mined by relatively cheap open-pit methods, the Michigan ores demand the use of slower and more costly shaft-mining procedures (FIG. 21–6). Shafts, often 2000 feet deep, reach down into very hard rocks, and

from the shafts several tunnels or drifts extend out to intersect the weaving and pockety ore bodies. Special equipment is needed to operate elevators or lifts, to pump out water, and to supply a steady flow of clean, cool air. When demand for iron ore is high, the shaft mines operate at a profit; when demand is low, they must close or operate at a loss. Thus, the Mesabi continues to produce during years when most of the shaft mines are closed. To be sure, the open-pit operations cease for three, four, or five months each year, depending on the severity of the winter, but the ore is not perishable and enough can be mined during the "open season" to fill each year's orders.

Iron Ore | 495

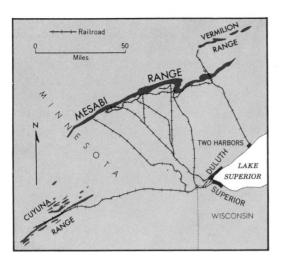

21–4

MAIN *rail lines which connect Minnesota's iron ranges with the Lake Superior shipping ports.*

ORE ON THE GREAT LAKES • It is hardly possible to discuss the Lake Superior iron ranges without mentioning the Great Lakes. These great bodies of water effectively connect our richest iron ores with our most useful coal deposits (FIG. 21–3). Over these lakes, from April to December, move the long ships, called ore carriers or ore boats, which transport the reddish ores "down-lakes" and the black coal "up-lakes" (FIG. 21–7). When blizzards blow and cold strikes, violent storms sweep the lakes and thick ice forms in the canal locks at the Soo and in the harbors of the upper lake ports. As the winter season progresses, large ice packs shift back and forth over the lakes, blown first one way and then the other by the winds. This is the "closed season" and during this time the ore carriers are tied up in long rows in several ports of the lower lakes. There they await the "spring breakup" which again will send them shuttling back and forth in long processions between such ports as Duluth and Buffalo, and Escanaba and Gary.

To reach the carriers, iron ore must travel short distances by rail. It moves in open-topped cars which are hauled to tall and massive ore docks at Duluth and Two Harbors in Minnesota, Ashland and Superior in Wisconsin, and Marquette and Escanaba in Michigan. Cars are hauled up long ramps to the tops of the docks; there the bottoms of the cars open to drop the ore into huge cylindrical bins embedded vertically in the sides of the docks. Ore boats move into position below the bins and the ore slides from the bottoms of the bins into the holds of the boats by means of long metal chutes. Most carriers can contain about 10,000 to 11,000 tons, although a few of them are capable of transporting as much as 15,000 tons at one time. One boat, built a few years ago, has a capacity of nearly 20,000 tons! The happy combination of short rail haul, mass handling, and cheap lake transportation is basic to the ability of the United States to produce iron and steel in such great quantities and at such low cost.

After loading, the boats begin the long journey down-lakes. Some of them go to the Chicago-Gary district at the southern end of Lake Michigan, but most of them proceed to ports

21–5 DIAGRAMMATIC *expression of the occurrence of ore in the Lake Superior iron ranges. A is typical of the Mesabi Range in Minnesota; B is typical of the Marquette Range in Michigan. In B, the bedrock is both intricately folded and faulted.*

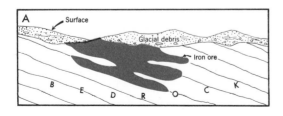

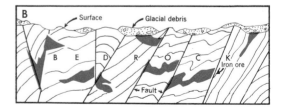

21–6   Left: *Shaft house, crusher, and iron ore stock pile in the "Iron Country" of northern Michigan. Right: One of the tunnels in a hard-rock iron ore mine.*

located along the southern shore of Lake Erie. Chief among the latter are Toledo, Cleveland, and Ashtabula, all in Ohio; Buffalo in New York; and Erie in Pennsylvania. The most lengthy haul is from Duluth to Buffalo, a distance of approximately 1000 miles, requiring about four days' travel time. From the Lake Superior ports to those of the lower lakes, the ore vessels make use of Lakes Superior, Huron, St. Clair, and Erie. In addition, they must "lock through" the Soo, follow the narrow and winding St. Marys river and the straight and full streams of the St. Clair and Detroit rivers. Much of the ore shipped out of Esca-

naba moves over Green Bay and then south to the southern end of Lake Michigan; the remainder proceeds, via the Straits of Mackinac, into Lake Huron and thence down-lakes to Lake Erie.

At either upper or lower lakes ports, most of the ore carriers are unloaded by machines located on the edges of the wharves. However, some vessels carry their own unloading machines, which are permanently fastened to parts of their long steel decks. Unloading may require from four hours to half a day, whereas the original loading by means of chutes took only two or three hours. The ore may be

21–7   LOADED *ore carrier leaving the harbor at Duluth, Minnesota, to begin its journey down-lakes.*

Iron Ore | 497

placed in huge stock piles on the wharves, close to the blast furnaces, or it may be dumped into railway cars and shipped to Pittsburgh and other iron and steel manufacturing districts. Whether the ore is used at the ports or at inland centers, the flow of ore down-lakes has no parallel in any other part of the world.

BIRMINGHAM DISTRICT • Second only to the Lake Superior iron mines, albeit a poor second, is the string of iron mines which lies immediately east of Birmingham, Alabama, and extends southwest to nearby Bessemer and Woodstock. Most of the ore is mined by shaft methods, although there are a few small open-pit mines near Woodstock. Birmingham ore varies considerably in quality, but there is enough high-grade ore to mix with that of low grade to bring the resultant mixture up to blast-furnace standards.

The Birmingham district is unusual and fortunate in that both coking coal and limestone lie close together near the iron ore (FIG. 21–8). This is significant because the blasting of iron ore to make iron requires coke as a fuel and limestone as a purifier. In addition, some of the Birmingham ores actually contain enough lime to make them self-purifying or self-flux-ing. Mainly because of the proximity of vital

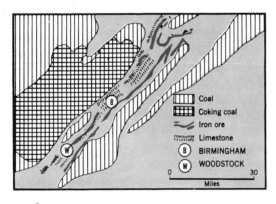

21–8

THE *Birmingham district of Alabama, showing the general distribution of coal, coking coal, iron ore, and limestone.*

raw material, the Birmingham district can produce metallic iron more cheaply than any other part of the United States, although it has no local markets comparable to those of Pittsburgh, Cleveland, Gary, or the many other cities which lie along or near the Great Lakes.

OTHER RANGES • The relative insignificance of the other iron ranges of the United States can be appreciated when it is pointed out that all of them combined mine less than 10 per cent of the United States output. These other ranges are scattered here and there from New York to California. Chief among them are the iron-mining districts of the Adirondacks and the ridges and valleys of eastern Pennsylvania.

Iron Ranges of Europe

European iron ores occur in many places, but the major deposits are in France, the U.S.S.R., Sweden, and the United Kingdom (FIG. 21–9). Other important deposits are located in Luxembourg, northern Spain, southern Poland, and eastern Austria.

FRENCH ORES • France possesses the largest deposit of iron ore in Europe. This Lorraine deposit is in the northeastern part of the country, close to the German border (FIG. 21–9). Some of the ore extends into Luxembourg. France has other iron-ore deposits in several places, but they are comparatively insignificant. It was the Lorraine ores, plus Ruhr Valley coal, which largely made possible the industrialization of the Continent. From the time of the Franco-Prussian War (1870) to the end of World War I (1918), Germany had both the Ruhr coal and most of the Lorraine ores, a combination which enabled her to become a world power. Since 1918, France has again controlled all of the Lorraine ores, but is still greatly dependent on coking coal from the Ruhr.

As mentioned earlier, French iron ores are low grade. They contain only 25 to 40 per cent of metallic iron, in contrast to the Lake Su-

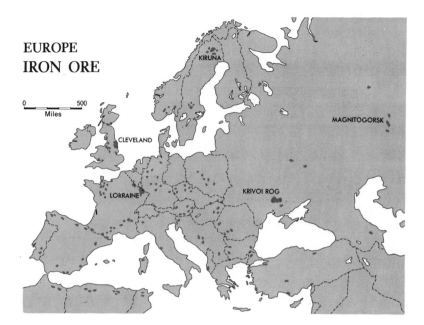

EUROPE
IRON ORE

0 — 500
Miles

KIRUNA

MAGNITOGORSK

CLEVELAND

LORRAINE

KRIVOI ROG

21–9

EUROPE *possesses many small and scattered iron ranges and a few major ones. The latter are labeled on the map. The Krivoi Rog range of the U.S.S.R. is the most recently developed.*

perior ores of the United States, which run in excess of 40 per cent iron—some as high as 60 and 70 per cent. Then, too, French ores are high in phosphorus, so that they had to await the invention of special processes before they could be used fully. About 1880, the basic *Bessemer* and the basic *open-hearth* methods of steel-making appeared. These processes allowed ready use of iron derived from high-phosphorus ores. As a result, the value of the Lorraine ores increased immeasurably. Germany, however, was the first to profit, for the processes came into use only ten years after she seized the deposits. Lorraine still gives France leadership in the iron-ore mining of western Europe. In the world, France ranks third, well behind the U.S.S.R. and the United States.

SOVIET ORES • Much of the startling industrial progress made by the Soviet Union is based on the relatively recent exploitation of its iron ores. At present, the Soviet Union ranks first in tonnage of iron ore mined, although only a few years ago she was not even mentioned among important iron-ore producers.

Most of the Soviet Union's iron ore is obtained from four districts: Krivoi Rog in the Dnieper Basin of the southern Ukraine (FIG. 21–9), the southern and central sections of the Urals, the Lake Balkhash area, and the Kuzbas region of central Siberia. Krivoi Rog is by far the most important. Its ores are high in iron and low in phosphorus, and are in such a geologic position that the relatively inexpensive open-pit method of mining is used. These advantages, coupled with government ownership and operation—the manner in which the government can force production regardless of ordinary economic considerations—have brought Krivoi Rog to a high position among the world's iron ranges.

SWEDISH ORES • Sweden's dominant iron range lies in her north country, in that inhospitable region where the northern forest gives way to the tundra. The district is known as Kiruna or Kiruna-Gällivare (FIG. 21–9). The ores are hard and phosphoric, but they are surface-mined. They are rich in iron—rich enough so that, despite geographical position and the rigors of the long winters, they are much sought after in western Europe. They are exported to West Germany, England, Czechoslovakia, Belgium, and France, and even to the United States. During the summer, the ores move to the Gulf of Bothnia by rail and thence to ports in west-central Europe and the British Isles. In the cold season, their chief outlet is the Norwegian port of Narvik, for that port remains open while the Gulf of Bothnia is in the grip of thick ice.

Other Swedish iron ore, roughly 25 per cent of the country's output, is mined near and northwest of Stockholm, chiefly in the Grangesberg district. This ore is the basis for Sweden's small iron and steel industry. There is no lack of iron ore, but coking coal is not available. This lack forces Sweden to use charcoal in place of coke for smelting iron ore in blast furnaces, and hydroelectricity as a source of energy in the manufacture of "electric-furnace" steel. The end product is the world-famous "Swedish steel," but total production is meager, and production costs are very high.

BRITISH ORES • The iron ores of Europe were first commercially used in England and Scotland. There the "ironstone," along with coal and coke, furnished the sinews for the Industrial Revolution which was to sweep into western Europe and, a bit later, into the United States. Because of many years of mining, the best of the ores have been used up and Britain finds herself forced to import about 40 per cent of her requirements. The imported ore comes mainly from the Bilbao district in northern Spain, from several small districts in the Atlas country of northwestern Africa, and from northern Sweden.

Today, the bulk of British ore is mined in the Cleveland district of Yorkshire (FIG. 21–9). Lesser amounts come chiefly from the Midlands area at the southern end of the Pennines. Most British ores average only 30 per cent iron and are high in phosphorus. Mining

costs are high, partly because the ores are so situated that open-pit methods cannot be used, although there are a few places where "ironstones" are quarried. Despite all this, Britain still furnishes about 60 per cent of her iron-ore needs.

Other Iron-Ore Sources

Particular attention should be directed to certain other sources of iron ore. Though present output from these sources is only a small fraction of total world production, the potential is high. The sources are eastern central India; the Itabira region of Brazil; the Newfoundland, Labrador, and Lake of the Woods areas of Canada; eastern Cuba; southeastern Venezuela at Cerro Bolívar and El Pao; the northern part of the Republic of South Africa; central Siberia; and central China. India has about 30 per cent of the total iron-ore reserves of the world, the largest of any single country. For comparison, this is four times the reserve of the United States, six times that of the U.S.S.R., and eight times that of China.

Ore now moves from the Schefferville area on the Quebec-Labrador boundary of eastern Canada by rail approximately 400 miles to the St. Lawrence river and thence by water to east coast ports of the United States and to Great Lakes ports of both the United States and Canada. Ore moves in increasing amount from west-central Chile, from the northern edge of the Guiana Highland in southeastern Venezuela, and even from southeastern Brazil to the iron and steel centers of the eastern United States. High iron content in the ore from all of these sources makes it especially attractive; developing solutions to problems of economic transportation, as, for example, the Great Lakes–St. Lawrence Seaway, suggest greater future significance.

THE FERROALLOYS

STEEL cannot be made from iron alone. To the iron must be added other ingredients in order to obtain steels of wide commercial use. Because such ingredients will unite or "alloy" with iron, they are called iron alloys or, more properly, ferroalloys. Chief among the ferroalloys are manganese, chromium, tungsten, molybdenum, vanadium, and nickel. Each imparts some particular quality to the final steel and enables the production of many types of steel for many different uses.

Manganese

This ferroalloy has been called "the Achilles heel of the steel industry." Without it, truly useful steel cannot be made. On the average, 14 pounds of manganese are required for each ton of steel manufactured. In addition, larger amounts are needed to purify the materials as they "cook" in the steel furnace.

In one way or another, the steel industry consumes about 90 per cent of the world's production of manganese. About 5 per cent is used to alloy with other metals, such as copper and nickel, and another 5 per cent is used in the manufacture of a wide variety of paints, varnishes, glass, disinfectants, and batteries.

As a purifier in the steel furnace, manganese cleans the molten steel of oxides and sulfur. This use accounts for the bulk of manganese consumption. The part which remains in the final steel is essential in providing the vital qualities of hardness and toughness. If larger amounts are purposely kept in the steel, the resultant metal is particularly resistant to shock and abrasive wear; such manganese steels are very useful for heavy-duty steel rails, railroad switches, digging and crushing equipment, and many types of tools.

Like iron, manganese is widespread in the rocks of the earth's crust, and, like iron, it is also found in commercial deposits in relatively few places. It is important to realize that the United States, leading steel-maker of the world, produces little manganese. The interest of United States steel manufacturers in foreign manganese ores, including ease of access to them, can hence be readily appreciated.

The "Big Four" of world manganese production are the Soviet Union, India, Brazil, and the Republic of South Africa (FIG. 21–10). The major Soviet deposit, largest in the world, is in the Caucasus region; another important one lies just to the north of the Black Sea, close to the Krivoi Rog iron ores. These two deposits usually produce over one-third of the world supply; the U.S.S.R., India, Brazil, and the Republic of South Africa together produce about three-quarters of the total. Other countries of world significance in manganese output are Ghana, the Republic of the Congo (Léopoldville), Morocco, and Japan.

Chromium

Chromium makes steel hard, tough, and highly resistant to heat and corrosion. Chrome steel is used for such purposes as high-speed tools, machine parts, acid-resistant containers, rust-resistant trimming, and armor plate. Chromium is also used in certain iron-nickel and cobalt-tungsten alloys. As a nonalloy, it is used to line furnaces and to make certain chemicals. Important uses in the chemical industries are for dyes, pigments, and tanning extracts (hence, chrome leather).

Five countries produce over three-quarters of the world's chromium ore (FIG. 12–10). They are the U.S.S.R., the Republic of South Africa, the Philippines, the Federation of Rhodesia and Nyasaland, and Turkey. The United States has little chromium. The U.S.S.R. is the only major steel-manufacturing country which is self-sufficient in chromium, as well as in the essential manganese.

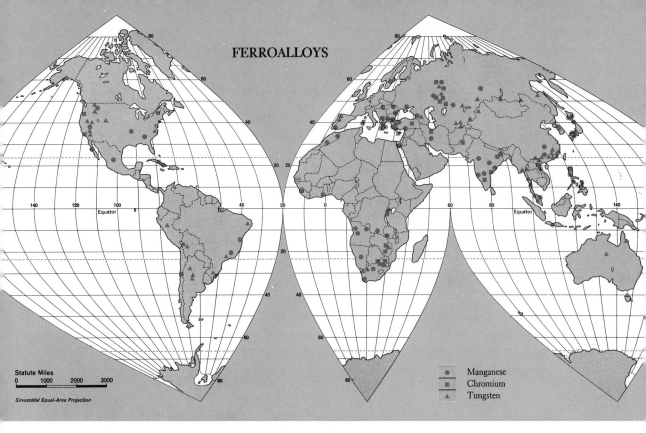

FERROALLOYS

Manganese
Chromium
Tungsten

Statute Miles
0   1000   2000   3000

Sinusoidal Equal-Area Projection

21-10 FERROALLOY *ores are generally widely dispersed throughout the world, being produced within both the major steel-making countries and the industrially underdeveloped countries.*

Tungsten

The addition of tungsten to steel insures a metal which remains hard and strong even at high temperatures. Hence, tungsten steel is especially useful for high-speed cutting tools, saw blades, files, engine valves, and the linings of big guns. In addition, it is valuable for use in the manufacture of razor blades, knife blades, and armor plate. Some tungsten is also used in copper alloys and in alloys of cobalt and chromium.

China has long been the world's chief producer of tungsten ores, mainly from the southeastern provinces. The U.S.S.R. is second, and the Republic of Korea and the United States vie for third place. Among other major producers are Bolivia, Portugal, and Australia (FIG. 21-10).

Molybdenum

Molybdenum steels ("Molly steels") are strong in proportion to their weight and are highly resistant to shock. They also remain strong at relatively high temperatures, a characteristic which enables them to serve, at least partly, as substitutes for chromium and tungsten steels. "Molly steels" have many uses, ranging from gears, tools, and pistons to magnets and oil-drilling equipment.

The United States, though short on manganese, chromium, and tungsten, leads the world in the mining of molybdenum ore. Approximately 70 per cent of the world supply comes from a famous deposit at Climax, Colorado. The U.S.S.R., Chile, and mainland China are the other significant producers (FIG. 21-11).

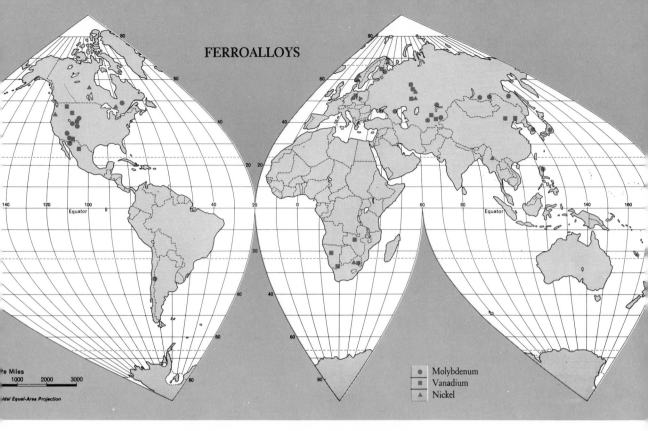

●	Molybdenum
■	Vanadium
▲	Nickel

21–11   FERROALLOY ores are generally widely dispersed throughout the world, being produced within both the major steel-making countries and the industrially underdeveloped countries.

Vanadium

Vanadium steels are very resistant to repeated shocks and flexings, particularly if vanadium is added to chrome steel. Such steels are highly useful for springs and axles in automobiles and railway equipment.

About 70 per cent of the world supply of vanadium ore is mined in the United States, almost entirely in southwestern Colorado. Minor producers are the Republic of South Africa and Finland (FIG. 21–11).

Nickel

Nickel steels are highly resistant to heat and corrosion. Their uses range from cooking utensils, steam cabinets, and chemical apparatus to bullets and heavy machinery. Nickel is also mixed with copper to make Monel metal, used in the manufacture of equipment for restaurants, hospitals, and laundries.

Several ores of nickel exist, and nickel is also found in ores of copper, iron, gold, and platinum. Although this may seem to imply widespread occurrence of nickel production, the fact is that one limited area normally produces over one-half of the world nickel supply. This area is the Sudbury district of Canada, located in the eastern portion of Ontario, not far north of Lake Huron and Georgian Bay (FIG. 21–11). Other producers worthy of note are the U.S.S.R., New Caledonia, and Cuba. The United States produces only modest amounts of nickel, but fortunately the Sudbury district is "next door" and supplies are readily obtainable in large amount.

The Ferroalloys | 503

Other Elements Used with Iron and Steel

Besides the ferroalloys mentioned above, there are several other metals used to greater or lesser degree in the steel industry: copper, lead, zinc, tin, and antimony. However, their most important uses are in connection with other industries than iron and steel manufacture, and hence they are not normally considered as ferroalloys. Along with several others, they will be discussed under the general heading of nonferrous minerals.

• CHAPTER OUTLINE •

Iron Ore and the Ferroalloys

• REVIEW QUESTIONS •

1. Iron is one of the more abundant elements of the earth's crust. Why, then, are not iron ores widely distributed in each country or region of the world?
2. What is meant by "free" occurrence of a mineral? Illustrate.
3. Demonstrate that iron ore is essential to modern industry.
4. Name the "Big Three" nations in iron-ore production. About what per cent of total world iron-ore production is normally supplied by these nations combined?
5. Which nations own the fortunate combination of abundant coal and abundant iron ore?
6. Compare the geologic location and condition of the Minnesota and the Michigan iron ores. Discuss the effect of these differences on mining methods and costs.
7. Trace a shipment of iron ore from the Mesabi Range to Buffalo, New York. Include handling methods as well as ports, water routes, etc. Do the same for a shipment of coal from western Pennsylvania mines to Milwaukee, Wisconsin.
8. Why is it that Birmingham, Alabama, can produce metallic iron (pig iron) cheaper than any other iron center in the United States?
9. Discuss France and Germany in terms of coking coal and iron ore.
10. Why does Sweden, with large, rich deposits of iron ore, export most of that ore to other countries? Also, why does most of the Swedish

iron ore go out through the Norwegian port
of Narvik?

11. What is meant by the term "ferroalloy" and
what, specifically, are the chief ferroalloys?

12. Illustrate the imparting of special qualities to
commercial steels by ferroalloys.

13. What is the "Achilles heel" of the United
States steel industry? Explain.

14. Discuss the United States from the standpoint
of self-sufficiency in coal, iron ore, and the ferroalloys.

22 Some Significant Nonferrous Minerals

NATIONAL FILM BOARD, CANADA

¶ IN ADDITION *to coal, petroleum, iron ore, and the ferroalloys, many other resources are obtained from within the earth. Some of them are like coal and petroleum in that they are nonmetallic. Others are, in a sense, more closely related to iron ore and the ferroalloys in that they are metallic in nature. Nonmetallic minerals include salt, pottery clays, and building stone. Metallic minerals are exemplified by aluminum, copper, tin, and gold. All of them, metallic and nonmetallic alike, serve important purposes in those portions of the world which have become highly commercialized and industrialized. A few of them are also important in those sections of the earth which are still marked by primitive economies. Here one thinks almost immediately of such minerals as salt, clay, and stone.*

SOME NONMETALLIC MINERALS

Salt

SALT is essential to life. It is a "food mineral." Wild animals often travel long distances to natural salt licks or live close to them. Many primitive peoples do the same. Others choose to live near the sea or a briny lake where salt can be scraped up along the margins of shallow pools or lagoons. In addition to being a food, salt is a seasoner and preserver of food in the dry form or in pickling solution.

Even our word "salary" is derived from salt. This goes back to the days when Roman soldiers were paid their wages in salt instead of money. The expression, still commonly used, "He is not worth his salt," refers to a person who is not worth the salary paid him. Salt is still a common medium of exchange. There are a good many places in the world where money is refused but salt is eagerly accepted—as in the Sudan region in Africa and the forest lands to the south.

While we usually hear of salt as a food or in connection with foods, it is also a very important product in the chemical industries. Several chemical products, such as soda ash and caustic soda, are made from it, and the manufacture of many others demands the use of large amounts of salt.

Most countries, either by mining or extraction from sea water, supply themselves with all the salt they need. For this reason, salt does not normally appear in international trade. This in no way detracts from the importance of salt, but merely indicates that it has wide geographical distribution and that man has no great difficulty in obtaining it.

22–1

[OPPOSITE, TOP] PORT RADIUM and the Eldorado Mine on the bleak shores of Canada's Great Bear Lake. The Eldorado Mine is a major source of pitchblende from which radium and uranium are secured.

Abroad, one hears of the salt mines of China's Szechwan Basin, those of Russia's Ukraine, and those of East Germany and Poland. In the United States, most of the salt is produced in Louisiana, Texas, Michigan, New York, and Ohio. The order given is that of rank in production. Some of the salt is obtained by mining, as the term mining is ordinarily understood, but most of it is "mined with a pump." Hot water is piped into underlying salt deposits and the resultant brine is pumped back to the surface to be evaporated and refined. Some iodine often is left in, or added to, the refined salt as a preventative of simple goiter in humans. Most salt-producing districts look like oil fields because the derricks used in pumping operations closely resemble oil derricks. Where salt is derived from sea water, the "workings" look much like small fields flooded with irrigation water.

Clays, Sands, Gravels, and Stone

Like salt, these mineral resources are ordinarily taken for granted. Locally, they may be so common that even heavy utilization causes no comment. But whether they occur in local abundance or not, they are among the commercially significant minerals. The fact that a small clay deposit or larger deposits of sand and gravel, or a stone quarry may sell for thousands of dollars is a direct indication of commercial importance. As they are bulky and low in value per ton, such minerals can seldom bear the cost of long-distance shipment; they do not appear in foreign trade records. However, certain products made from them possess relatively high value and may be shipped long distances.

CLAYS • Beds of clay furnish raw materials for many kinds of products: ordinary brick, firebrick, tile, pottery, chinaware, and so on.

Brick and pottery clays are widely distributed in the United States, but are mined, or dug, mainly in Ohio, Pennsylvania, Illinois, Georgia, and California. Ohio leads in both brick and pottery manufacture. In Europe, Germany is well known for chinaware and porcelains, the porcelains being produced chiefly for use in scientific laboratories. The chinaware of England, such as Spode and Wedgwood, is famous all over the world. It is exported to other countries, especially to the United States. Denmark, Czechoslovakia, and Austria have made their clays well known in the form of pottery, dishes, and laboratory vessels. China, ancient home of chinaware, and Japan make and export clay-derived products which are known for their artistic shapes and colorations.

SANDS AND GRAVELS • It is anyone's guess as to how many million tons of sand and gravel are used in the world each year. Certainly the tonnage is tremendous. Most of it is used in the construction of roads, bridges, buildings, and airfields—private as well as public. Some of it is used directly as in certain types of roads, but much of it is used in cement and concrete, sand for exterior and interior plastering, and certain sands—the glass sands—for the manufacture of many varieties of glassware.

While sand and gravel are extensively distributed, they do not occur in sufficient amounts in many localities. Thus, despite their bulk and comparatively low value, they are often moved considerable distances either by trucks or by gravel cars on railroads. Sands and gravels are usually abundant along ancient and modern shorelines, in regions of continental glacial deposition, and in the arroyos and alluvial fans of dry areas. Fortunately, the portion of the United States where construction of all sorts is greatest has ready access to the sands and gravels contained in vast glacial deposits and in lake-shore and seashore materials.

STONE • As used here, *stone* refers to both crushed rock and rock which is used in block form. In many sections of the world, particularly where sands and gravels are scarce, large tonnages of bedrock are drilled and blasted and then crushed for use in roads or concrete.

Limestone is a good example of rock which is commonly mined and crushed; also, it is often pulverized completely and used in the manufacture of cement. The cement industry has become a vital one in this age of cement and concrete construction, especially in the United States and in Europe. Bedrock which is quarried and shaped is represented by some limestones, such as the fossiliferous limestones of Indiana, and by marble, granite, and slate. These stones are used mainly in building construction either as actual building blocks or as ornamental trimming and flooring. Some slate is used in the form of roofing shingles, as well as for blackboards.

The world has thousands of stone quarries, ancient and modern, scattered from China and Egypt to the New World. Among them may be mentioned the famous marble quarries at Carrara, Italy, the granite quarries of Vermont (FIG. 22–2), and the slate quarries of eastern Pennsylvania.

Sulfur

Sulfur was used anciently as a medicine and less anciently for old-style sulfur matches. Today, most of it is consumed by the chemical and papermaking industries. The chemical industries are particularly dependent upon sulfur. From it is made sulfuric acid, often referred to as the key ingredient of modern chemical enterprise. In addition, sulfur is used, in one form or another, in fertilizers, insecticides, explosives, vulcanized rubber, wood preservatives, and medicines.

For many years, up to about 1912, the island of Sicily led the world in sulfur mining. Today, the United States produces approximately 70 per cent of the world supply. Mexico produces nearly 20 per cent and the remainder comes chiefly from the U.S.S.R., Japan, and Italy. Some sulfur is obtained as a by-product from smelters and chemical plants rather than from natural sulfur deposits, as in Canada and Norway.

22–2   WORLD'S *largest granite quarry at Barre, Vermont.*

Nearly all United States sulfur is obtained from thick deposits under part of the coastal plain of Texas and Louisiana. Like salt, the sulfur is mined with a pump. After the hot sulfur-charged water is brought back to the surface, it is led into huge bins where a process of drying out and hardening yields mammoth sulfur cakes. These are easily broken up and loaded into railroad cars by power machinery.

Mineral Fertilizers

As this and other countries have used and abused their vital soil resources, there has been an ever-increasing demand for fertilizers. These may be of several kinds: some are animal fertilizers, some are green fertilizers obtained by growing certain crops and plowing them under, and many of them are mineral fertilizers. Some

mineral fertilizers are obtained directly from the earth while others are by-products of smelting and chemical plants, or are made in special factories which draw upon the air for raw material. The chief mineral fertilizers are compounds of nitrogen, potassium, and phosphorus. For the market, these may be prepared separately, but more commonly they are mixed. When they are mixed, calcium, another essential plant food, is usually included as part of the bulk.

NITRATES • The nitrate fertilizers are those containing nitrogen. Natural nitrates, as opposed to synthetic, are obtained almost entirely from a few sections in the Atacama Desert of northern Chile (FIG. 22–3). There the *caliche* is dug and scraped from the upper portions of numerous playas, after which it is partially refined and shipped to Europe and the United

22–3

A TYPICAL nitrate oficina located on a small "island" in one of the playas of Chile's Atacama Desert. (From The Face of South America, published by the American Geographical Society)

States. Until about 1920, Chile had a virtual world monopoly of nitrates. These were useful not only for fertilizers, but also for explosives, including munitions of war. Dire need for nitrates from closer sources and at lower prices encouraged the production of synthetic nitrates from the air and the recovery of nitrogen-containing materials from industrial plants. Much of the synthetic production, as in Germany and especially in Norway, is based on cheap and abundant hydroelectricity. Today, synthetic and by-product nitrates control the world market. Chile, once supreme, now produces only about 6 per cent of the world's annual supply. The United States is the leader, although only one of many producers.

POTASH • Compounds of potash, containing potassium, are secured from factory wastes, seaweed, and mineral deposits. The chief mineral deposits of potash occur as buried beds in the upper portion of the earth's crust and in surface deposits and brines of desert salt lakes.

The United States ranks first in world potash production, producing some 25 per cent. Its mineral potash comes chiefly from the Carlsbad area in southeastern New Mexico and the Searles Lake area on the northern margin of the Mojave Desert of California (FIG. 22–4); Utah and Michigan follow New Mexico and California in potash production. West Germany ranks second, producing about 21 per cent. East Germany and France each produce about 19 per cent. East Germany controls the famous potash deposits in the Harz Mountains and the nearby Stassfurt area. The French deposits are in Alsace. In fifth place is the U.S.S.R., supplying about 12 per cent of the world's total production from mines in the central Urals.

PHOSPHATES • Phosphorus-containing compounds are derived from phosphatic limestones; thus two critical plant foods, phosphorus and calcium, may be obtained from the same material. Great amounts are also obtained from the slag of blast furnaces, particularly in the iron and steel manufacturing districts of Europe, where phosphoric iron ores are used more than in the United States.

The United States produces more than half of the world's phosphates, most of the supply coming from the South, particularly Florida and Tennessee. Minor amounts are secured in Idaho, Montana, and Arkansas, and huge reserves are available in the Rocky Mountain states, from Utah to Montana. Northwest Africa mines about two-thirds as much as the United States, with Morocco supplying the most, followed by Tunisia and Algeria. The United States production is used at home, whereas the African production flows to western Europe. Other important producers are the U.S.S.R. and some of the Pacific islands, like Nauru.

22—4 AN air view of the "chemical" town of Trona located on the edge of Searles Lake, a "dry lake" in the northern part of the Mojave Desert, California. The edge of the lake appears at the left. From its deep, layered deposits are pumped the brines from which potash and other chemicals are extracted.

PRECIOUS METALS AND DIAMONDS

Gold

GOLD, more than any other mineral, has fired the imagination of man and sent him scurrying to the far reaches of the earth in attempts to find it. The lure of gold played a large role in the exploration of the continents and islands and sent many a vessel across unknown seas. It may be recalled that Spain was interested in the New World primarily for the gold (and silver) which its galleons might bring back to the homeland. Pizarro conquered Peru for Inca gold; Cortez subdued Mexico for Aztec gold; and Coronado explored much of what is now our Southwest in a vain attempt to find the imaginary Seven Golden Cities of Cibola. Much later, it was gold which caused the sudden and great interest in little-known California. Still later, gold brought Alaska into the world spotlight. Even today, gold is bringing people in large enough numbers to establish modern settlements in

22–5   Left: *Gold dredge in operation in Yuba County, California. Right: The debris-drowned land that is left behind after dredging.*

several isolated sections of Canada and Australia. For countless centuries, gold has represented wealth, whether to nations or to individuals, and man and nation alike have striven to find and amass as much of it as possible.

Gold usually occurs in the free state, either by itself or in mixture with other minerals. It may be in the form of flakes, dust, or sometimes nuggets; or it may be mixed with quartz in veins of solid rock, or with ores of other metals, particularly those of copper, lead, nickel, and silver.

When gold is found in quartz veins or in conjunction with ores of other minerals, it is mined by shaft and tunnel methods. But when it is found in loose materials, *placer mining* techniques are used. Placer mining may be carried on in a small way by panning. The pan is merely a shallow basin in which water and gravels are scooped and then rocked back and forth by hand until the water and gravels spill over the sides and the heavier gold remains in the bottom of the pan. Another method involves the use of a long trough with cleats on its bottom. Water and gold-bearing sand and gravel are sent down the trough and the gold collects against the upper side of the cleats. In large undertakings, huge hoses break loose the sand and gravel and wash them into the troughs. The most modern and large-scale method entails the use of mammoth dredges (FIG. 22–5), which suck up gold-bearing materials, remove the gold from them, and drop the waste material in great piles. While efficient and comparatively inexpensive, dredging turns whole countrysides into debris piles. When one views an area which has been dredged over, one wonders whether the gold was worth it.

World leadership in gold production has changed hands many times. Once it belonged to Egypt with gold from fabulous Ethiopia; later to Greece; still later to Spain, and so on through many countries and their colonies. Soon after the discovery of gold in California, the United States became an important producer, but it remained second to Russia, the leader. Russia continued to lead until the discovery, near the turn of the present century, of the South African gold fields. South Africa now holds first rank without question. The richest fields are located in the Transvaal of the Republic of South Africa, particularly in the district known as the Rand and centering on the city of Johannesburg. The Rand produces, depending on the year, from 40 to 45 per cent of the world's gold production. The U.S.S.R. holds second place with about 23 per cent; Canada third with 10 per cent; and the United States fourth with 4 per cent.

Nearly all the gold mined in the United States comes from west of the Mississippi, especially from the Black Hills of South Dakota, and from the states of Alaska, Utah, and California.

Silver

Whether for jewelry, plating, or money, silver has been sought after nearly as much as gold. Much more of it, ounce for ounce, has been mined than gold, but its value has been consistently far less. Much of the world's silver is obtained from ores of other metals, particularly ores of copper, lead, and nickel. In fact, Mexico is the only country with any appreciable number of silver mines. Other countries have chiefly copper mines, lead mines, or other mines, where silver is extracted as a by-product.

Mexico's silver mines gives it first place in world production, with about 20 per cent of the annual supply. The total North and South American production exceeds 65 per cent of the world total. Canada produces about 15 per cent of the world total, Peru about 11 per cent, and the United States about 10 per cent. Nearly all the United States supply comes from the states of Idaho, Utah, Arizona, and Montana. Outside the Americas, the leaders are the U.S.S.R., with about 12 per cent of the world total, and Australia, with about 7 per cent.

Diamonds

Diamonds, like gold and silver, symbolize wealth. Although chiefly famous as jewels, including the crown jewels of many an ancient and modern ruler, their greatest usefulness is in connection with certain modern industrial activities. The diamond is the hardest of minerals and this quality makes the diamond, and diamond dust, uniquely useful in the manufacture of cutting and abrasive tools. Specifically, diamonds are used in the cutting points of well-boring and rock-drilling tools, etching tools, abrasive wheels, and glass cutters. In addition, fine wires, such as copper wires, are manufactured by being drawn through very small holes pierced in pieces of diamond.

Although known and prized for many centuries, diamonds did not become especially desired and valuable until special cutting processes which enhanced their beauty and utility were invented. Successful commercial diamond cutting was not common until just before the time of Columbus. Furthermore, it was not until the discovery of the rich African fields, nearly a century ago, that diamonds became at all numerous in world markets (FIG. 22–6). Present major producers, in order of importance, are the Congo (Léopoldville) with over 55 per cent, Ghana, the Republic of South

SOUTH AFRICAN INFORMATION SERVICE

22–6

A DIAMOND mine near Pretoria in the Republic of South Africa. From this mine, the Premier, came the famous white jewel known as the Cullinan diamond.

Africa, Angola, Sierra Leone, and South-West Africa. Most of the cutting and marketing is done in western Europe, the United States, and Israel. The main cutting centers are Antwerp, Amsterdam, New York, Natanya (Israel), and Johannesburg.

SOME METALLIC MINERALS

Aluminum

ALUMINUM is more abundant than iron in the rocks of the earth's crust. Yet as recently as a century ago, metallic aluminum was rare and costly. Even at the beginning of the present century, it was so scarce that the selling price was $2 per pound. Today it is a common and inexpensive metal with many uses. The change occurred because modern techniques allowed rapid and ready transformation of aluminum ore to alumina (aluminum oxide) and the transformation of alumina into metallic aluminum. When the industrial world discovered the many useful properties of metallic aluminum, the demand for more and more aluminum at lower prices rapidly increased.

Aluminum is light in weight, strong in proportion to weight, relatively noncorrosive, an excellent conductor of both heat and electricity, and capable of high polish. Little wonder that it has many uses and that production has increased so greatly. At present, its major uses, as exemplified in the United States, are for transportation equipment, foundry and metallurgical industries, electrical equipment, chemical industries, construction, and cooking utensils and appliances.

Most significant has been the great increase in the use of aluminum in the manufacture of aircraft, streamlined trains, and long-distance electrical transmission lines. Much aluminum is used in alloy form with other metals and materials. Duralumin, or dural, is an alloy of aluminum and copper, a metal much stronger than aluminum or copper alone. Powdered aluminum and iron oxide, mixed, are the in-

gredients of incendiary bombs. Carborundum, a well-known abrasive, is aluminum carbide.

Despite its common occurrence as an element in earth materials, large deposits of commercial aluminum ore are rare (FIG. 22–7). Practically all aluminum is obtained from one ore, known as *bauxite*. The ore takes its name from Les Baux, a town in southeastern France. France for many years mined more bauxite than any other nation. Now, Jamaica produces about 26 per cent of the world bauxite supply and Surinam (Dutch Guiana), about 15 per cent. The U.S.S.R. probably ranks third, with about 13 per cent. The United States, France, and British Guiana are rivals for fourth place, with a little over 7 per cent each. Other relatively important producers are Hungary, Greece, Yugoslavia, and the Dominican Republic. United States bauxite comes predominantly from Saline County, Arkansas. However, imported ore, mainly from Jamaica and the Guianas, supplies about two-thirds of the needs of the United States.

After bauxite is dug from the earth, chiefly by large power shovels, it is crushed, washed, and screened. Most of the bauxite is then shipped to other lands to be smelted into alumina and refined into metallic aluminum. For this reason the chief producers of bauxite are not the major producers of aluminum metal. The United States alone produces some 43 per cent of the world's metallic aluminum. The others of the aluminum "Big Three" are the U.S.S.R. (about 16 per cent) and Canada (about 13 per cent). Beyond these, France, West Germany, Norway, and Japan are significant.

The principal smelters in the United

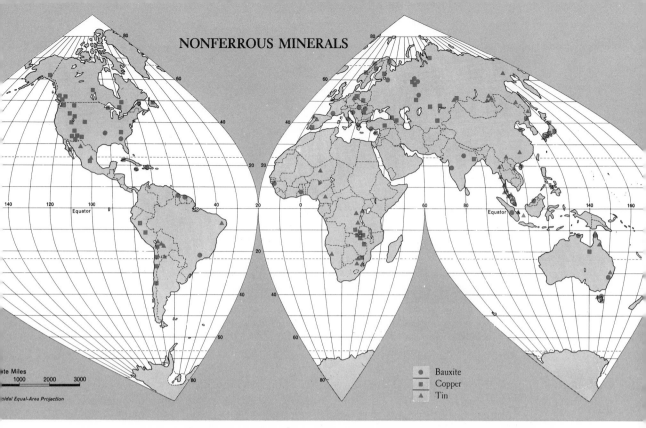

Bauxite
Copper
Tin

Spindal Equal-Area Projection

te Miles
1000   2000   3000

22–7   NONFERROUS *mineral ores are generally widely dispersed throughout the world, being produced both within the industrially advanced and the industrially underdeveloped countries.*

States are at East St. Louis, Illinois; Baton Rouge, Louisiana; Hurricane Creek, Arkansas; and Mobile, Alabama. The alumina travels from these smelters to places of cheap and abundant electric power where it is refined into metal—for example, to the Ohio Valley, Louisiana, Tennessee (FIG. 22–8), New York, Washington, and Oregon. Canada's production of aluminum is based on abundant hydro-electricity provided by large plants located along north-bank tributaries of the St. Lawrence and in British Columbia.

Magnesium

Within recent years, particularly since 1939, magnesium has become very important. It is a sort of "twin brother" to aluminum, both in properties and uses. Like aluminum, it occurs in many minerals, yet has few ores. Similarly, it must be elaborately processed in order to transform it into a metal.

Because magnesium is lighter than aluminum, but just as strong, it is used primarily in aircraft engines and plane parts. Today, a single large plane contains as much magnesium as was produced in an entire year some fifty years ago. Comparatively small amounts of magnesium are still obtained from the ore known as magnesite, but most of it now comes from buried salty or briny deposits and, strangely enough, chiefly from sea water. The U.S.S.R. probably produces some 42–43 per cent of the world's metallic magnesium and the United States, about 30 per cent. Other important producers are Norway, Canada, Italy, and the United Kingdom. The United States supply comes mainly from Texas, Michi-

22–8   ONE of the huge plants, at Alcoa, Tennessee, which transforms alumina (aluminum oxide) into metallic aluminum.

gan, California, New Jersey, Washington, and Nevada.

As a strong "light metal" in an age demanding less weight and more and more speed, magnesium would seem to have a promising future.

Copper

Unlike aluminum and magnesium, copper has been known and used for several thousand years. With the possible exception of gold, copper was the first of the metals to be used by man. Certainly it was used in Egypt as early as 5000 B.C. and it entered importantly into the early trade of the Mediterranean, Asia Minor, and northeastern Africa. Bronze, an alloy of copper and tin, was probably known by 2000 B.C. In North America, copper was used to some extent by the Indians of the Lake Superior region, and was traded by them in small amounts to Indian groups farther south.

Native or free copper occurs as chunks of pure copper which are practically indistinguishable from the refined metal. It is found mainly in the Keweenaw Peninsula of northern Mich-

igan. Because of its location near the shores of Lake Superior, copper of this sort is often called Lake copper. The metal is found occasionally at the surface, although most of it has to be mined expensively by means of shafts, some over a mile in depth. It was the surface occurrence which enabled the Indians to discover it and, later, to make use of it. They learned that it was soft enough to be hammered into various shapes for use as axheads, arrowheads, spear points, bowls, and ornaments.

Nonfree copper occurs in a wide variety of ores. The ores occur either as veins, as in the famous Butte district of Montana, or widely scattered among other rocks, as in the copper districts of Utah, Arizona, and Nevada. Most of the ores of the western United States contain only a small percentage of copper per ton, but, except for the rich veins at Butte, they can be mined by the cheap open-pit method (FIG. 22–9). Open-pit production of western ores took the leadership away from Michigan's Keweenaw Peninsula.

While processes vary somewhat, there is much that has to be done to copper ore be-

22–9

WORLD's *largest open-pit copper mine near Bingham, Utah.*

located, they demand large amounts of electricity, since the refining process is an electrolytic one.

The United States leads the world with 20 per cent of the annual smelter copper production (FIG. 22–7). The Federation of Rhodesia and Nyasaland is second, followed by Chile, the U.S.S.R., Canada, and the Congo (Léopoldville). The rank is practically the same whether one is thinking of tons of copper mined or tons of copper coming from smelters. In refining, the United States is far ahead of any other nation; it is the only one of the major copper-ore producers which refines more copper than it mines. This is made possible by imports, chiefly from Chile. The bulk of the African copper is refined in western Europe, especially in West Germany.

The world's metallic copper is used in scores of ways. Pound for pound, most of it is used in the electrical industries (for generators, mo-

fore it is available as pure, metallic copper. Western ores, for example, have to be crushed, concentrated, smelted, and refined. The first three steps are usually performed near the mines. The copper which comes from the smelters, called "blister," is about 98 per cent pure. The blister, smaller in bulk and much higher in value than the original ores, travels long distances to refineries (FIG. 22–10). Thus, copper from Arizona, Utah, Montana, Nevada, Michigan, and New Mexico, the leading copper-producing states in that order, is refined chiefly at places along the Atlantic seaboard, particularly in the New York–Baltimore area. These same places are importing centers for copper from foreign sources. Exceptions to the Atlantic seaboard location of refineries are to be found at Great Falls, Montana; El Paso, Texas; Inspiration, Arizona; and Hubbell, Michigan. No matter where the refineries are

22–10

INTERIOR *of a New Jersey copper refinery, showing anodes being lowered into the cells used in the electrolytic refining process.*

Some Metallic Minerals | 517

tors, switchboards, etc.) and in telephone, telegraph, and power lines. The Bell Telephone System has in use at one time enough copper wire to reach almost from the earth to the sun! Other uses include wire cloth and screen, rods, ordinary electric wire, sheathing, munitions, cooking utensils, and alloys. It will be recalled that bronze is an alloy of copper and tin. Brass is an alloy of copper and zinc. Duralumin, mentioned before, is an alloy of copper and aluminum.

Tin

Tin, like copper, is a metal of both ancient and modern use. It was used in the making of bronze nearly 4000 years ago. Like gold, tin was one of the reasons why man "went places." Phoenician traders, perhaps as early as 1200 B.C., journeyed in their small Mediterranean craft all the way from Asia Minor to the tin mines of Cornwall in Britain. Cornwall tin became an important item in the bronze trade of the Mediterranean world.

Tin is relatively easy to melt, sticks readily to other metals, is resistant to vegetable and fruit acids, and is nonpoisonous to man and animals. Thus one can easily understand why nearly half of all the tin produced in the modern world is utilized in the manufacture of tin plate, almost all of which is used for tin cans. Strangely enough, tin cans are mainly steel cans. They consist of thin sheets of relatively soft steel with only a thin coating or plating of tin. This becomes apparent when tin cans are used and discarded: the rusting which ensues is evidence of the deterioration of steel, for tin does not rust. Another major use of tin is in the manufacture of solders. In addition, tin is used in the manufacture of bronze, tin tubing, foil, printing type, and terneplate. The last is an alloy of tin and lead; while it cannot be used for food containers, for fear of lead poisoning, it is very useful in the form of containers for oil and gasoline, as well as for roofing material.

Commercial deposits of tin-bearing materials normally occur in loose, easily mined form (FIG. 22–11). By means of power shovels or huge dredges, these materials are picked or sucked up, washed, and concentrated. Concentrates are moved to smelters, most of which are near the "tin pits," and the product then travels long distances to refineries which produce metallic tin. In some tin-mining districts —those of lesser importance—tin ore occurs in a hard-rock form and must be mined by more expensive methods. Ores of this sort are merely concentrated and shipped to refineries without smelting.

For many years Malaya has led in the mining of tin ore (FIG. 22–7), producing about a quarter of the world supply. Other major producers are Bolivia, Indonesia, mainland China, the U.S.S.R., and the Republic of the Congo (Léopoldville). Malay ore is smelted at Singapore and Penang and then sent to the United Kingdom for refining; Indonesian ore is smelted locally and shipped to refineries in the United States. The major tin-smelting nations are Malaya, the United Kingdom, mainland China, the U.S.S.R., the United States, and the Netherlands. The United States, the world's major consumer of metallic tin, has virtually no tin ores. It must obtain foreign ores to smelt, and also buy smelted tin ores from Malaya and western Europe.

Lead and Zinc

Lead and zinc are commonly mentioned together because they often occur in the same mining districts.

Among the nations, Australia is first in lead mining, its production being about 14 per cent of the world total. Close behind is the U.S.S.R. Then come the United States, Mexico, and Canada. In lead-smelting, the current world ranking is the U.S.S.R., the United States, Australia, Mexico, West Germany, and Canada. The main source areas of lead within the United States are in Missouri, Idaho, Utah,

and Colorado. The United States and the U.S.S.R. run neck-and-neck in the use of metallic lead.

The United States leads in the mining of zinc (FIG. 22–12), producing about 13 per cent of the world supply, followed closely by the U.S.S.R. and Canada, and less closely by Mexico and Australia. In zinc-smelting, the United States is far ahead (about 25 per cent of the world total). Then come the U.S.S.R., Canada, and Belgium, and, in a third group, Poland, France, West Germany, and Australia. In terms of use of metallic zinc, the United States has no close rival. Sources of zinc within the United States are mainly in Tennessee, New York, Idaho, and Utah.

Most of the lead is used for storage batteries, coverings for electric cables, paints, and leaded gasolines. Other important uses include ammunition, foil, solder, printing type, and pipe. Lead's low melting point, its resistance to battery acid and other corrosives, and the ease with which it can be shaped or worked, account for the major part of its usefulness.

Zinc is used mainly in the manufacture of galvanized iron and steel. The major characteristic that accounts for this chief use is its resistance to oxidation, or rusting. Thus, a steel pail which is galvanized by coating it with zinc is rustproof, as are galvanized screens, wires, and pipes. Mixed with copper, zinc becomes brass, an alloy with many familiar uses. Zinc is also used in paints, fruit-jar covers, photoengraving sheets, and medicines.

Antimony

Usually one hears little about antimony, yet it is one of the important industrial nonferroalloy minerals. In recent years, the annual tonnage of antimony has greatly exceeded that of some of the well-known ferroalloys such as vanadium and tungsten. Antimony is often

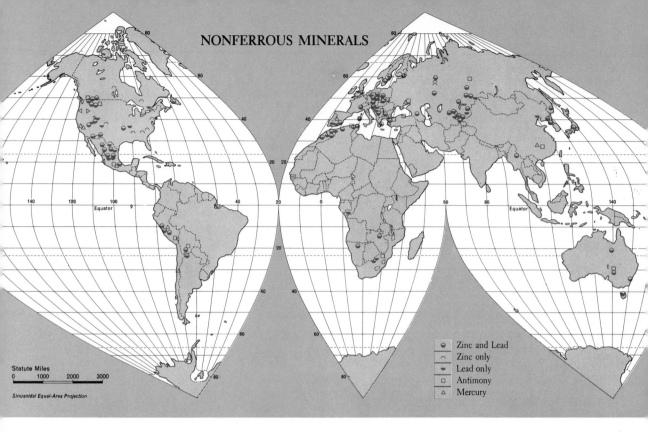

NONFERROUS MINERALS

	Zinc and Lead
	Zinc only
	Lead only
	Antimony
	Mercury

22–12   WORLD *distribution of the major producing areas for lead, zinc, antimony, and mercury.*

mentioned in connection with lead because some of it occurs in association with lead ores and because metallic antimony is used mainly in combination with metallic lead. In fact, its chief use is in the manufacture of what is known as "hard lead." Alloyed with tin and lead, antimony yields pewter and metal for bearings. Another use is in the making of chemical smoke screens.

Antimony is also essential in type metal, another lead-tin-antimony alloy. Perhaps the most important characteristic of antimony is that, unlike most metals, which contract on cooling from a liquid to a solid state, antimony expands. This makes it important in molding and casting where an exact shape must be preserved—as in type metal.

The major producers of antimony ore are mainland China and the Republic of South Africa (about 32 and 26 per cent respectively).

Lesser, but still important, producers are Bolivia, Mexico, and Yugoslavia (FIG. 22-12).

Mercury

Mercury is "the metal which is a liquid"; at least, it is the only metal which is in liquid form at ordinary temperatures. Often called quicksilver, it is familiar to everyone in the mercury thermometer. Because it occasionally occurs in the free state in miniature pockets within its ore, and because it can be easily "cooked out" of its ore rock, it was known early in the Mediterranean world. It was chiefly a curiosity, eluding the fingers when one attempted to pick it up and readily coating objects made of other metals, such as gold rings or copper coins. In modern times, it is used in a wide variety of scientific instruments, such as thermometers and barometers, and in paints, medicines, electrical control devices, and special types of lights.

The world's mercury supply is obtained mainly in Spain (20 per cent) and Italy (19 per cent). The oldest and most famous mines are those of Spain. They are located near the southern edge of the Iberian Plateau where an abrupt drop-off forms the Sierra Morena. Italy's mercury mines are in its northeastern mountains. The other major producers are the United States, the U.S.S.R., and mainland China (FIG. 22–12). In the United States, mercury is secured from several western states and Alaska, but California produces about as much as all others combined.

Uranium and Thorium

World attention has been strongly focused on atomic energy ever since the first atomic bomb was dropped over Hiroshima in 1945 and the ensuing "atomic race" among the world powers got under way. The atomic bomb's terrific explosive force is derived from radioactive minerals such as uranium and thorium. Atomic energy may someday supplement on a large scale, or even replace altogether, the energy now derived from our conventional sources such as water, coal, petroleum, and natural gas.

Uranium is the principal source element of atomic energy (fuel) and is secured from many different ores. It is a major constituent of over a hundred types of minerals which are widely distributed throughout the world. Formerly, only very high-grade ores, such as pitchblende, davidite, and uraninite, were used as sources. Today carnotite and even phosphate rocks and marine shales can be commercially exploited for uranium. The United States is the world's leading producer and Canada is a close second (FIG. 22–13). The United States production comes mainly from New Mexico, Utah, Colorado, and Wyoming. Many other countries, both large and small, produce considerable quantities; and many are capable of

increasing production tremendously. Of these, the U.S.S.R., the Republic of South Africa, the Republic of the Congo (Léopoldville), and France are currently the principal producers.

Thorium is the second most important source element of atomic energy (fuel). It is derived mainly from the mineral sources, monazite and thorite, though there are at least fifty source minerals. Thorium production is widespread over the world.

The peaceful uses of atomic energy in the future will be not only to meet the world's ever-growing needs for industrial power, but also to provide power sources for transportation. The United Kingdom probably leads the world in the use of nuclear power in the generation of electricity, but the United States, the U.S.S.R., Japan, and India all have atomic reactors for commercial generation of electricity. Many more will come into operation throughout the world within the next few years. The United States has several atomic-powered submarines and surface craft, and the U.S.S.R. has one. Other nations are experimenting along similar lines and most of them are working on the problems associated with atomic-powered aircraft and rockets.

The nations of the world may be divided into three groups on the basis of probable economic uses of atomic power in the future. One group includes such industrial countries as the United Kingdom and Japan. In the countries in this group, supplies of cheap conventional fuels are limited or lacking, and hence atomic power will probably come into large-scale use very soon. The second group includes newly developing countries like India and China, which require increased power supplies urgently and quickly. These countries may find atomic power production cheaper and more convenient than conventional power sources right from the start. The third group includes such countries as the United States and the U.S.S.R., which have large, developed supplies of the conventional fuels. These countries may not find it either economically attractive or

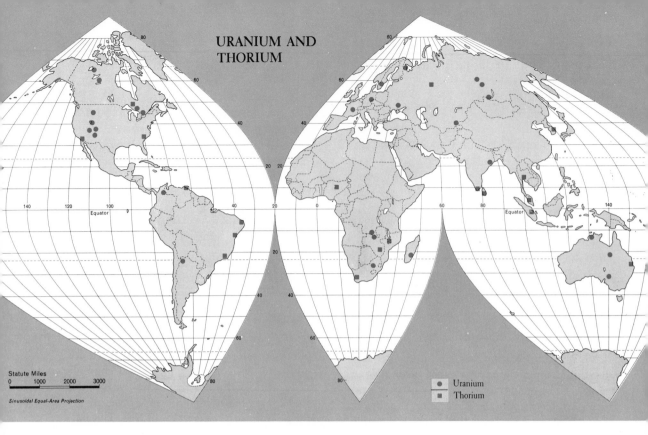

URANIUM AND THORIUM

● Uranium
■ Thorium

Statute Miles
0   1000   2000   3000

Sinusoidal Equal-Area Projection

22–13   URANIUM *is secured from many ores and is the principal source element of atomic fuel. Thorium is the second most important atomic fuel source.*

necessary to convert to atomic power on a large scale so soon as the countries in the first two groups. Thus, though the potentialities are great, it cannot be expected that atomic power will replace other types speedily or uniformly over the whole world.

· CHAPTER OUTLINE ·

Some Significant Nonferrous Minerals

SOME METALLIC MINERALS   Lead and Zinc
  Aluminum   Antimony
  Magnesium   Mercury
  Copper   Uranium and Thorium
  Tin

• REVIEW QUESTIONS •

1. Why is there practically no international trade in salt?
2. What large sections of the United States possess abundant sands and gravels? Why?
3. Explain the term "by-product sulfur."
4. Discuss "mining with a pump" in reference to salt and sulfur.
5. Is the reference to sulfur as the key ingredient of modern chemical enterprise justified? Explain.
6. Discuss sources of the mineral fertilizers used in the United States.
7. Account for the long-time importance of gold. Where are the chief gold-producing areas of the world today?
8. Discuss the importance of industrial diamonds.
9. What are the properties of aluminum which account for its great demand? What proportion of the world's presently known bauxite deposits are within the United States?
10. Trace the history of a shipment of copper from a "pit" in Arizona until it is placed on the eastern market as metallic copper. Explain the fact that the United States refines more copper than it mines.
11. Account for the commercial importance of tin. Discuss tin demand and sources of supply for the United States.
12. Why has the demand for lead increased so greatly within the past century and especially within the past 50 years?
13. Obtain the most recent information available on source areas, production, use, and control of uranium and thorium.
14. Construct a cross-reference table of minerals and producing countries. Across the table make a column for each mineral; down the left-hand side of the table, list the producers. Place an X in each column on a line with the name of the producer.

2 3 Industrialization

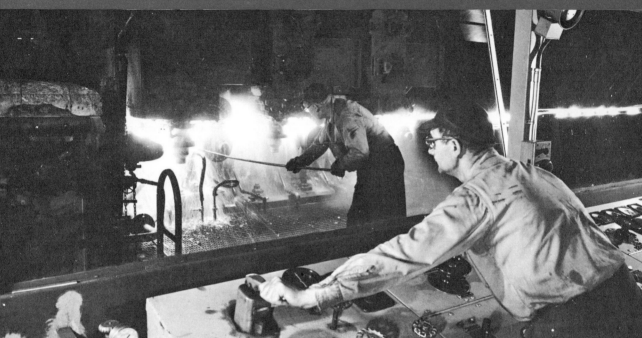

⟨⟨ CHANGES *in the ways of life and ways of making a living of many of the world's inhabitants are indicated by the change in meaning of the word "industry" itself. Today industry means the gathering, processing, combining, and fashioning of all kinds of nature's raw materials—with the use of modern machines and power—into finished products of every kind and description. Man has been making products of one sort or another for thousands of years, but only within the past two hundred years has he learned to let powered machines do most of the work. The entire time span of the Industrial Revolution, marking the significant change from using human power and the home workshop to using industrial power and the factory, is no more than the span of three or four generations. Such world-changing inventions as the steam engine, the diesel engine, the electric motor, the airplane, and the blast furnace, with their dependence on mineral fuels and water power to make them function, occurred in the life of the human race only yesterday.*

In those parts of the earth which have become highly industrialized, the old ways of life have changed with surprising rapidity; vast populations have shifted from farms to urban centers; factories have grown until they encroached upon, or swallowed completely, many rural areas; people by the millions have been thrust closer to each other in teeming, smoky cities. Some nations, such as the United States, have changed from wilderness and oxcarts to huge cities and jet planes within little more than a century—a few even within a single lifetime. The astonishing fact is not that the people of the world face so many problems of adjustment and readjustment in the modern industrial world, but that the problems are not more numerous and more devastating than they are. Even many of the world's "far-away places" have been deeply affected because some of the machines, literally space-eaters, have so shrunk the world that today there are no two spots on earth which are more than a day apart by jet plane. Isolation is rare today.

INDUSTRIAL REGIONS

MANY basic limitations of the physical and cultural landscape underlie the world distribution of major industrial regions. Most easily recognizable and measurable among them are availability of source materials, availability of power and fuel supplies, nature and size of markets, development of transportation facilities, availability of labor, and availability of capital. Other less easily measurable factors, often more influential than the whole range of so-called basic factors, include the predominant type of culture in an area, the stability of its government and the degree of government authority and control, its climate, and its terrain. In areas where manufacturing is a large contributor to the way of life, we say that industrial regions exist.

Source Materials

The creation of a major industrial region normally must be based on the local availability of certain basic source materials and the possibility of securing others. This situation differs from one section of the world to another, and differs considerably from one type of industry to another. For example, Denmark is so poor in basic industrial source materials that she has not, and probably cannot, become a leading industrial nation. On the other hand, postwar West Germany, with an abundance of high-grade coal but little else in the way of basic source materials, has become one of the outstanding industrial nations of Europe and the world.

Power and Fuel

To make industrial products in modern factories demands more than the energy of human and animal muscles; great amounts of controlled inanimate power are needed to make machines, and to run them after they are built.

23–1

[OPPOSITE, TOP] STEEL and steel products are the symbols of modern industrialization. Here an operator in the control pulpit oversees the action of a continuous pipe mill at the Fairless Works National Tube Division of the U.S. Steel Corporation.

So far, the world's industrial regions, both large and small, have developed mainly where abundant coal supplies have been readily available, although the use of atomic energy, solar power, or the long-distance transmission of energy by radio may eventually change this. This is true despite the importance of power derived from water or petroleum and natural gas in many parts of the world.

Markets

The world's most important industrial regions are those which have large and fairly stable markets within their own limits. Although the fact is not commonly recognized, each industrial region is its own best customer. The Western European Industrial Regions collectively consume most of their own products; the Northeastern Industrial Region of the United States does likewise. This in no way minimizes the importance of world trade in manufactured goods, because part of the flow, as in western Europe, crosses international boundaries. The sale of manufactured goods in far-distant markets by nations which have dependable home markets as well is very important. In general, the additional profit derived from distant foreign markets often makes a great difference in the nation's financial balance sheet; for example, the home market may "pay the bills," while the distant markets, perhaps consuming only a small portion of the total production, represent pure profit. To be sure, some industrial countries depend largely on distant foreign markets for the sale of the bulk of their manufactured products, but they are exceptional. The United Kingdom is the classic example, but even she sells many of her manufactures somewhere within the large European industrial area of which she is a part.

Transportation

To manufacture a variety of products requires the movement of raw materials and semimanufactured materials of many kinds from one geographic location to another over varying distances. Also, following manufacture, the products must be distributed near and far to consuming areas. Without modern types of transportation and a sufficient fineness, or detail, of transportation network, large-scale industry is impossible. So close is the relationship that one may easily ascertain the general world pattern of major industrial regions by noting the areas of the world in which transport lines, especially railroads, are numerous and are arranged in a fine-meshed network.

Labor

Modern industry, despite all the work done by machines, requires abundant labor of several sorts, from highly skilled, including managerial, to semiskilled and unskilled. Any industrial region needs varied types of labor. In general, a region which has all types readily available at comparatively low costs has a distinct advantage over regions which possess only limited types. The United Kingdom has long had all types of labor, as have France and Germany; so has the United States, although it has at times suffered in international competition because each of its labor types has been higher priced than those of other parts of the world. Contrariwise, certain other countries have had either insufficient industrial labor supply or an insufficiency of skilled and semiskilled labor, like Ghana or Peru, for example.

Capital

A modern industrial enterprise requires large financial resources. Buying source materials, providing power and machinery, paying salaries and wages, installing and maintaining transportation systems, and developing and retaining markets, not to mention paying taxes, upkeep on equipment, and other obligations, demand tremendous sums of money. Regions or nations with abundant capital or abundant credit (which amounts to the same thing) are in a position to become industrially important —others are not.

Other Factors

Many groups of people, even entire nations, hold beliefs and follow ways of life that do not readily allow for industrialization. China's long resistance to new ideas, emphasis on the family unit as opposed to national unity, and a high reverence for agriculture were cultural factors which slowed the growth of that country's industrialization until very recent years. Among other peoples and nations, by contrast, customs and ways of life have strongly promoted the development and growth of industrial enterprises. Britain's willingness to accept new ideas and methods two hundred years ago, coupled with a pronounced national unity and continuing political stability, were instrumental in pushing that country's industrialization to a high degree of development.

The foregoing paragraphs suggest the complex interplay which has produced the modern world pattern of industrial regions. To put it simply—perhaps to oversimplify—one may say that industrial regions grow up where the following combination of factors exists: source materials (large coal or iron-ore deposits, or both); sufficient labor and technical knowledge; transportation facilities; and an adequate supply of capital. Certainly no major industrial regions exist today where this combination is not present. This in no way implies that the present pattern is necessarily permanent. Cultures change, ideas spread, source materials are exhausted in some areas and new supplies are discovered in others, entirely new kinds of source materials or fuels come into use, populations grow or decline, and, with them, certain modifications of labor supply, market, and capital occur. The emergence of the industrial areas of the Soviet Union is a good example not only of change but of rapid change. Other recent examples of rapid change are to be found in India, China, Japan, and certain sections of Australia, Africa, and South America.

WORLD DISTRIBUTION OF INDUSTRY

MOST of the world's industrial development is located in the Northern Hemisphere, specifically, in three relatively small major regional concentrations: the northeastern United States, western Europe, and the western U.S.S.R. Other lesser regions of industrialization are widely scattered and include areas in the southern and western United States, Canada, central Siberia, India, China, and Japan in the Northern Hemisphere, and parts of Australia, Africa, and South America in the Southern. Outside these major and lesser regions there are scattered small concentrations of industry in many countries of both hemispheres. Within each of the major regions, and even some of the lesser ones, there are sub-regions distinguished by specialization of production, convenient proximity to source materials, transport facilities, or political influences (FIG. 23–2).

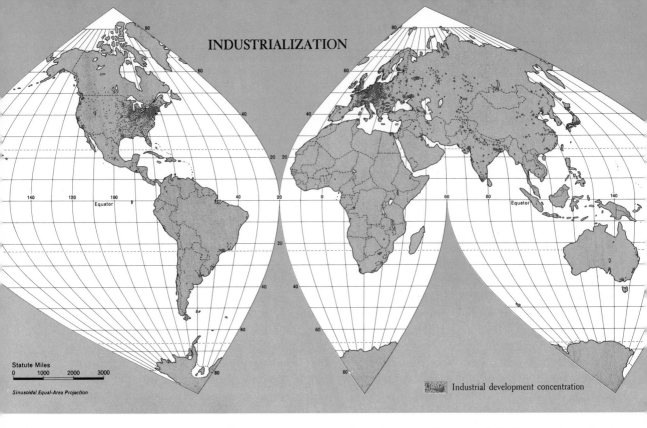

INDUSTRIALIZATION

Industrial development concentration

Statute Miles
0   1000   2000   3000

Sinusoidal Equal-Area Projection

23–2   INDUSTRY *is still concentrated in its traditional centers—Europe and the United States, but it is now rapidly spreading into the less developed countries of the world.*

INDUSTRY IN THE UNITED STATES

As a consequence of many factors, especially the greater abundance of source materials, better developed transportation, advances in mass-production techniques, greater availability and mobility of capital, and freedom from physical devastation by recent wars, shortly after World War II the Northeastern Industrial Region of the United States surpassed Northwestern Industrial Europe to become the world's most important industrial region at mid-twentieth century.

Several other lesser industrial regions in the United States developed considerably during the late World War II years, and have since continued to expand and diversify in response to changing local conditions and growing mar-

kets, as well as to general economic expansion throughout the nation.

Northeastern Industrial Region

From very small beginnings in southern New England during early colonial days, industry has spread westward and southward with the steady march of settlement and transportation across the United States, growing in intensity and diversity decade by decade. The great Northeastern Industrial Region today encompasses that portion of the United States in which industry is most highly concentrated and areally continuous; it extends from New England westward to the Mississippi valley and

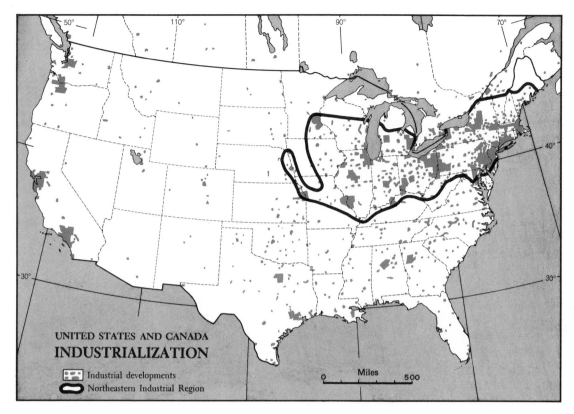

UNITED STATES AND CANADA
INDUSTRIALIZATION

Industrial developments
Northeastern Industrial Region

Miles
0   500

23–3   INDUSTRY *has spread across the conterminous United States and southern Canada from coast to coast but has its greatest concentration in the Northeastern Industrial Region, which is today the leading industrial region of the entire world.*

from the Great Lakes–St. Lawrence valley southward to beyond the Ohio valley (FIG. 23–3). If superimposed upon Europe, this portion of the United States would stretch from the United Kingdom to the western edge of the Soviet Union, and from southern Sweden to the Mediterranean Sea. Within the Northeastern Industrial Region are located eight of the nation's ten giant billion-dollar-a-year industrial cities, which contribute enormously toward making it the world's greatest industrial concentration.

Within the region are most of the coal mines, most of the electric power plants, and nearly half of the petroleum-refining capacity

of the United States. Close by are major source areas for petroleum, natural gas, iron ore, and a wide variety of other essential raw materials. The region contains nearly all of the coke ovens, blast furnaces, and steel mills of the United States. Within its limits are manufactured most of the automobiles, locomotives, railroad cars, and ships, as well as most of the machine tools, machinery, textiles, and clothing in the United States. With only a few exceptions, the familiar trade-mark "Made in U.S.A." could just as well be "Made in the Northeastern Industrial Region." Just as the region possesses great wealth in source materials, transport facilities, and machines, it also has the highest population density and largest total population of any part of North America. People are present in sufficient numbers not only to make, run, and repair the machinery of industry, but also to transport and buy a large part of the manufactured products which they produce; actually the region is its own best customer.

Within this major industrial region of the northeastern United States, scores of different products have become local specialties because of differing local factors. Not all of these will be discussed here, but some of the more important ones deserve mention. Most fundamental in many ways is the specialty production of iron and steel. The critical nature of these materials in our industrial economy has been made apparent often in many ways. Frequently, lack of steel has forced the closing of automobile factories, agricultural machinery plants, railway equipment and repair shops, and other industries. Of the many things needed to "feed" an industrial region and a modern industrial nation, steel is the most important one.

IRON AND STEEL • The United States has led the world in iron and steel production for the last half century. Nearly all of the nation's iron and steel has been made in three relatively small sections of the Northeastern Industrial Region (FIG. 23–3). The principal area is in western Pennsylvania and adjacent parts of Ohio and New York. This specialty area centers on the city of Pittsburgh, but fans out northward toward Lake Erie to include other important cities, such as Youngstown, Cleveland, Erie, and Buffalo, as well as eastward to Johnstown and southwestward to Wheeling. This area is known as the Pittsburgh–Youngstown region and normally produces about 40 per cent of the United States total of iron and steel. Its production is at least as great as the total production of any other single country in the world, even the U.S.S.R. Within this region are brought together the Lake Superior iron ores and the coals from Pennsylvania and West Virginia which are used to melt them (FIG. 21–3). The second important iron and steel concentration is in the Chicago–Gary area, which accounts today for approximately 30 per cent of the United States total. This relatively new development, started since the turn of the century, brings together iron ores from Lake Superior and coal from the nearby Illinois Basin. A third iron and steel area lies in southeastern Pennsylvania, New Jersey, and Maryland. It includes such cities as Baltimore (Sparrows Point), Philadelphia, Allentown, Bethlehem, and Trenton. This area receives much of its iron ore from foreign sources such as Venezuela, eastern Canada, Chile, and Sweden. Long ocean hauls from these countries are less costly than would be the short rail hauls necessary to move Lake Superior ores from southern Lake Erie ports to the Atlantic seaboard. Other small iron and steel producing centers of the United States are widely scattered: in Massachusetts, New York, Ohio, Michigan, Minnesota, Alabama, Missouri, Texas, and California, with numerous single plant locations in several other states such as Colorado and Utah. These other centers have local source materials and markets so far from the three major concentrations that production is economically feasible.

MACHINE TOOLS, MACHINERY, AND TRANSPORTATION EQUIPMENT • These manufactures are closely associated with the iron and steel industry proper, within the Northeastern Industrial Region. Combined, they have the highest value rating of any major group of manufactured products in the United States (FIG. 23–5).

Machine tools—forges, presses, drills, lathes, and the like—are the power-driven implements with which other machinery and finished products, such as automobiles, planes, tractors, typewriters, and locomotives, are made. Machine-tool production in any country indicates industrial maturity. The United States began production shortly after the Civil War and today leads the world, with centers in southern

23–4   THE *assembly section of a modern American aircraft plant.*

New England, New York, Pennsylvania, Ohio, Michigan, and Illinois (FIG. 23–5).

Textile machinery is manufactured primarily in southern New England and eastern Pennsylvania. This pattern still holds in spite of the fact that considerable textile manufacturing has spread into the southern Appalachian region in recent decades (FIG. 23–4). Electrical machinery and motors are manufactured rather widely throughout the length and breadth of the Northeastern Industrial Region, with the three principal concentrations between Chicago and St. Louis, between Cleveland and Cincinnati, and in the Baltimore–New York–Schenectady area (FIG. 23–5). Manufacturing of agricultural machinery is definitely oriented toward market, spreading from Ohio to eastern Iowa, with over half concentrated in Illinois (FIG. 23–5).

Most of the nation's automobiles and trucks are manufactured in southern Michigan, with much smaller production in adjoining areas of Ohio, Indiana, Illinois, and Wisconsin. Especially noted centers are the cities of Detroit, Pontiac, and Flint in southeastern Michigan, Toledo in Ohio, and South Bend in Indiana. Automobiles require so many kinds of materials and specially fabricated parts that many satellite industries have sprung up in and near the major automobile centers. Even distant places contribute certain materials and parts which make the complete automobile

Industry in the United States | 531

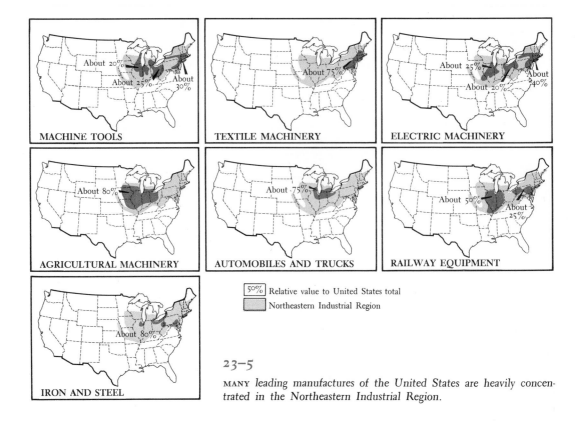

23-5

MANY *leading manufactures of the United States are heavily concentrated in the Northeastern Industrial Region.*

possible. The close connection between automobile manufacture and many other industries in the United States is illustrated by the fact that within recent years the automotive industry has consumed about 20 per cent of the nation's total steel, 20 per cent of its copper, 30 per cent of its nickel, 25 per cent of its lead, 75 per cent of its plate glass, and 80 per cent of its rubber products. In addition, the automobile industry uses large amounts of tin, zinc, aluminum, upholstery materials, and paint and lacquer—not to mention the heavy consumption of gasoline, lubricating oils, and greases by automobiles when they are put into operation. Thus, it is easy to appreciate the close relationship between Detroit automobile production and Arizona copper, Pittsburgh steel, Ohio plate glass and rubber tires, and many other production regions and products (FIG. 23-5). Many automobiles are as-

sembled in the East, the South, and the West —still, the major component parts such as bodies, motors, and power drives are manufactured in the Michigan region and shipped to the numerous assembly plants.

About half of the nation's railway rolling stock is manufactured in northern Illinois and Indiana, while the manufacture of locomotives is highly concentrated in Philadelphia and Schenectady (FIG. 23-5). Production of airplane frames and engines is scattered over practically the entire United States, from Connecticut to California, with a large portion within the Northeastern Industrial Region. Like the automobile, the airplane requires many kinds of materials and parts, involving the participation of many types of factories, both large and small. Its main assembly-plant locations (FIG. 23-4) are likely to be largely labor-oriented.

About half the shipbuilding of the United States is carried on along the lower courses of the Hudson and Delaware rivers and on the shores of Chesapeake Bay. There, launching facilities are excellent and the shipyards are not far removed from the major sources of iron and steel, machinery, and electric equipment needed to build large modern vessels. New England, where our shipbuilding industry began, is handicapped by lack of local steel and other essentials for large ships. The larger Gulf Coast ports, such as New Orleans, Mobile, and Beaumont, build both small and large craft. On the Pacific Coast, at Seattle and Tacoma in Washington and in the San Francisco Bay area in California, many ships are built and repaired. West-coast shipbuilding suffers from a lack of large local steel and machinery supplies, although the huge timbers used for forms and launching ways are readily procurable. The shipbuilding industry of the United States has had a long history of "ups and downs." In time of war, the output has been tremendous; during peacetime, production has frequently dropped virtually to nothing. The United States has a great shipbuilding capacity, but the high cost of labor and materials often makes competition with the shipyards of western Europe uneconomic. This situation stands in sharp contrast to production in the United States of other transportation equipment, such as automobiles, railway equipment, and aircraft.

FOOD PRODUCTS • The Northeastern Industrial Region processes and produces great quantities of foodstuffs, as well as special containers for canning and packaging the foods for market. Flour milling is done both within the region and on its western fringe in or near the chief wheat-growing regions. Important flour centers include St. Paul, Minneapolis, Kansas City, and Buffalo. In meat packing Chicago is the principal center, but there are many other cities of almost equal importance, such as Omaha, St. Paul, Detroit, and New York (FIG. 23–6). Special breakfast foods are made

23–6

U.S. GOVERNMENT *inspectors examining carcasses on the hog chain in a Chicago meat-packing plant.*

from a variety of cereal grains such as corn, wheat, oats, and rice; the principal processing centers are at Battle Creek in Michigan, and at Niagara Falls in New York. Canned, frozen, and dried fruits and vegetables are prepared throughout the Northeastern Industrial Region, from the western Great Lakes to the Atlantic Coast. Most of the canning of fruits and vegetables is done in small local plants located in rural areas very near the fields and orchards, rather than in large cities. Cheese and butter are made chiefly along the northern edge of the Northeastern Industrial Region within the Hay and Dairy Belt. Wisconsin, Minnesota, Iowa, Michigan, and New York are especially noted for dairy products.

A comparatively recent method of food preparation and processing is quick-freezing. In addition to huge plants with a national marketing area, there are literally thousands

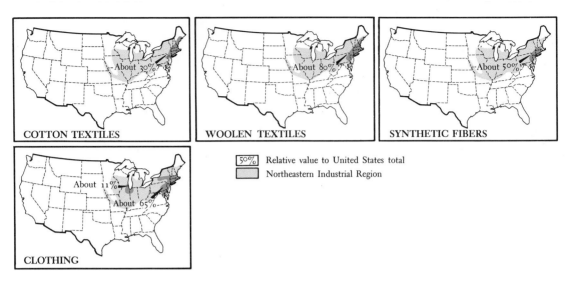

COTTON TEXTILES — About 30%

WOOLEN TEXTILES — About 80%

SYNTHETIC FIBERS — About 50%

CLOTHING — About 11%, About 65%

50% Relative value to United States total
Northeastern Industrial Region

23-7   MANY leading manufactures of the United States are heavily concentrated in the Northeastern Industrial Region.

of small plants which serve local communities, as well as thousands of deep-freeze lockers in farm and city homes. The opportunity to preserve fresh meats easily and to enjoy fresh fruits and vegetables in off-seasons through deep-freezing is revolutionizing the eating habits of millions of persons. That a person living in Chicago may sit down to a meal including fresh, locally grown vegetables while a January blizzard howls outside is something new.

Two facts stand out in this brief discussion of food processing: first, it is an important part of "big business"; and, second, the Northeastern Industrial Region is more than just a land of iron and steel, automobiles, machinery, airplanes, and ships.

TEXTILES AND CLOTHING • About a third of the United States cotton-textile production takes place in the southern New England–eastern New York–Pennsylvania area of the Northeastern Industrial Region, while over three-quarters of the nation's woolen goods and half of its rayon fabrics are produced in the same localities. A part of New England's production is based on imported cotton; this

cotton has a longer and silkier fiber than the cotton grown in the Cotton Belt and is used to make higher quality and costlier goods (FIG. 23–7).

The section of the United States from Maine to Maryland makes most of the nation's woolen goods, with New England alone producing about half of the total. New England's dominance in wool manufacture is considerably enhanced by the fact that Boston is the major raw wool market of the United States, a dominance which Boston acquired in colonial days and has maintained since that time. Many small woolen-goods factories, including those which make woolen yarns and woolen knit goods, are to be found outside New England in adjoining states (FIG. 23–7).

In recent years silk manufacture, based mainly on imports of raw silk from Japan, has declined significantly in the face of competition from rayon and other synthetic fibers. Production of synthetic fibers in the Northeastern Industrial Region is highly localized in eastern Pennsylvania and adjacent New Jersey, with New York and southern New

England accounting for the remainder. The necessary wood pulp, mainly from southeastern Canada, cotton fibers, and chemicals are readily procurable there. The United States produces about one-third of the world's rayon. Other synthetic fibers, such as nylon, dacron, orlon, and the like are rapidly increasing in importance, furnishing serious competition not only to natural silk and rayon, but also to cotton and wool. Some increase in the use of cotton has, however, come about through the development of textiles made from various combinations of cotton and artificial fibers (FIG. 23–7).

The designing, making, and selling of clothing is markedly concentrated in the New York City metropolitan area (FIG. 23–7). Other centers are in the Middle West, especially in and near Chicago. In the Far West, Los Angeles has become increasingly important, particularly in the designing and making of outdoor and sports clothing.

OTHER INDUSTRIES • The description of industrialization in the Northeastern Industrial Region of the United States could be greatly extended, a fact not surprising in a nation which has attained world leadership in industrial enterprise. Beyond the major manufactures mentioned so far, there are many others which are only relatively less significant. Chemicals are produced and mainly consumed in the section from Illinois to the Atlantic seaboard; they include some thirty basic materials, ranging from acetic acid to zinc oxide, and drawing upon a wide variety of source materials such as wood, sulfur, coal, petroleum, salt, borax, soda, and certain crops. Other industrial activities include petroleum refining, ore smelting, and the fabrication of clays and stone, while the printing of newspapers, magazines, and books is carried on in nearly all cities, with the greatest concentrations in New York, Boston, Philadelphia, Chicago, and St. Louis. Manufacture of furniture, both wooden and metal, is concentrated in the states of the southern Great Lakes, while rubber goods, which by bulk are mainly automobile and truck tires, are made chiefly in such centers as Akron and Detroit.

Southern Appalachian–Gulf Coast Industrial Region

The combined industrial production of all the other industrial regions and scattered individual developments which lie outside the mighty Northeastern Industrial Region totals no more than a quarter of the United States hundred-billion-dollar annual industrial output. These other lesser producing centers are widely scattered from coast to coast. The largest is the Southern Appalachian–Gulf Coast Industrial Region, which is dwarfed by its northeastern counterpart in industrial production, but surpasses it in size by encompassing a dozen states from Virginia to Texas (FIG. 23–3).

This is not a homogeneous region. Agriculture still dominates its economy, but industry is rapidly growing, changing the face of what was the "Old South." Here are indications of deep-seated economic and cultural changes within the United States which are felt strongly throughout the nation. Many of the states of this Southern Appalachian–Gulf Coast Industrial Region lead the nation in the manufacture of some important industrial product —Virginia in synthetic fibers, the Carolinas in tobacco products and cotton textiles, and Texas in petroleum, petrochemicals, synthetic rubber, and sulfur. Since the beginning of industrialization in the South, textiles have constituted the most important single category of product, and probably will continue to do so in the future. Textile production is concentrated largely in Virginia and the Carolinas, but recently has been spreading westward throughout the whole region.

The fourth most important iron and steel center in the United States has long been Birmingham, Alabama. This locality has the advantage that iron ore, coal, and limestone flux are all produced close by. Nearly half of the nation's production of aluminum is located in North Carolina, Tennessee, Alabama, and Arkansas, using local and imported bauxite and great quantities of local hydroelectric power. An immense new petrochemical industry is growing in the South, principally in the Texas and Louisiana coastal areas, based upon local source materials and natural gas. Half of the nation's new synthetic rubber production is now concentrated in the coastal areas of Texas and Louisiana and in northern Texas, utilizing the region's tremendous natural gas supplies as source material.

In textiles, iron and steel, tobacco, aluminum, furniture, lumber, and paper products the Southern Appalachian, or eastern, section is especially important, while petroleum products, chemicals, synthetic rubber, carbon black, magnesium, foodstuffs, and airplanes are produced in considerable and ever-increasing amounts in the western Gulf Coast section of the larger region. No other part of the United States, with the exception of southern California, is attracting industry in greater relative volume, or gaining more rapidly in relative wealth, purchasing power, and general well-being than is the Southern Appalachian–Gulf Coast Industrial Region.

West Coast Industrial Region

Far removed from the great industrial concentrations of the eastern United States are the recent industrial developments scattered along the Pacific Coast, through the states of Washington, Oregon, and California. These concentrations have developed primarily in response to local market demands in a newly developing part of the nation and have very little to contribute to nation-wide markets, except for the production of such items as aircraft, motion pictures, petroleum, and foodstuffs. The West Coast Industrial Region is considerably fragmented in areal pattern, and will require many years to "fill in" like its eastern counterparts. A few major cities, separated by sparsely populated countryside, contain most of the development. In the Pacific Northwest two cities, Seattle in Washington and Portland in Oregon, predominate, while in the Pacific Southwest three cities, San Francisco, Los Angeles, and San Diego in California, are the centers of major industrial concentration.

Important contributing factors for the location and development of varied industries in this region are: source materials such as petroleum, fibers, foodstuffs, and timber; markets that are rapidly expanding and remote from eastern suppliers; power and fuel supplies such as petroleum and hydroelectricity; and, lastly, a climate throughout that is highly attractive to many people. Today, the West Coast Industrial Region is important nationally for large-scale production of items previously noted, and locally for automobile assembly, meat packing, and the production of iron and steel, aluminum, tin containers, beet sugar, timber products, and clothing.

Other Industrial Developments

Scattered industrial developments, not included within the three large industrial regions noted above, are found in each of the western mountain and plains states. The areas near Denver in Colorado and Salt Lake City in Utah are the two of greatest individual importance in this otherwise sparsely industrialized vastness of the West.

INDUSTRY IN CANADA

CANADA, the second largest country in the world, covers a vast geographic area, but most of it is undeveloped, even largely undevelopable. Coal and iron-ore deposits are considerable, but for the most part inconveniently located. Other source materials such as timber and pulpwood, copper and uranium, meat and dairy products, and other foodstuffs, are the chief bases for Canada's growing industries.

Industrial developments of importance are found in only two regions in Canada; a major one extending along a narrow front on the lower Great Lakes–St. Lawrence Seaway, and a much lesser one on the Pacific, at Vancouver in southwestern British Columbia. Both of these are closely associated with, almost branches of, United States industrial regions across the international boundary (FIG. 23–3).

The lower Great Lakes–St. Lawrence Region has no Canadian coal of value closer than the New Brunswick and Nova Scotia fields far to the east. In consequence this area depends largely on conveniently nearby Pennsylvania coal from the United States when hydroelectric power is not available. Industrial production is concentrated primarily in the major city centers of Montreal and Toronto, and in the smaller cities of Hamilton, Windsor, London, Kitchener, Ottawa, and Quebec. Output includes such varied items as automobiles and parts, wood pulp and paper, aluminum, petroleum, meat products, tobacco, textiles and clothing, iron and steel, electric equipment, and processed foodstuffs.

The industrial development centered on Vancouver, with its saw timber and pulpwood, meat and fish products, petroleum and airplanes, and foodstuffs, is small by comparison with Canada's southeastern region, yet it is of considerable importance in this western part of the country far removed from other industry.

INDUSTRY IN WESTERN EUROPE

THE Industrial Revolution had its first small beginnings in northwestern England during the late eighteenth century. From there it spread gradually over much of western Europe and across the Atlantic to the United States at the end of the eighteenth century, and to many other parts of the world during the nineteenth and twentieth centuries.

Today, western Europe is dominantly industrial, with the exception of a few fringe areas. The heaviest concentration of industry has been in the portion of the continent which stretches from the United Kingdom to Poland, and from the Baltic to the Mediterranean (FIG. 23–8), often spoken of as the Northwestern Industrial Region. This region about equals its American counterpart in size, but it has recently been surpassed in total production by the Northeastern Industrial Region of the United States.

Throughout the broad area of the Northwestern Industrial Region are intensively cultivated farmlands and dairy centers, cultivated forests, large commercial cities, and some relatively unutilized hill and mountain areas. Still, the region is marked throughout by both large and small concentrations of modern industrial development. Nearly all of the western European industrial concentrations, like those of the rest of the world, lie on or near important coal fields or iron-ore deposits. The coal and iron ore of the United Kingdom, and the coal of the Ruhr District of West Germany coupled with the Lorraine iron ores of France, have played major parts in the development of the region. The oldest of the many industrial re-

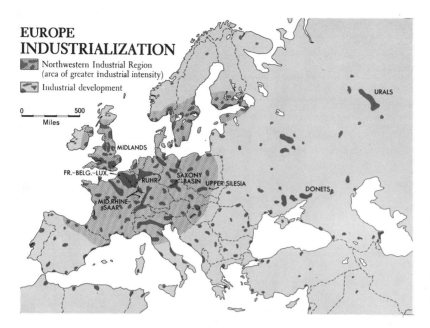

EUROPE INDUSTRIALIZATION

Northwestern Industrial Region
(area of greater industrial intensity)

Industrial development

0   500
Miles

URALS

MIDLANDS

FR.-BELG.-LUX.

RUHR

SAXONY
BASIN   UPPER SILESIA

MID.RHINE
SAAR

DONETS

23–8

INDUSTRY *has practically engulfed Western Europe, except for a few areas on the outer fringes, but has its greatest concentrations in the Northwestern Industrial Region, stretching from the United Kingdom to Poland and from the Baltic to the Mediterranean.*

gions of western Europe is located in the United Kingdom, still a highly productive area, yet surpassed in total output by some of the more recently developed centers on the Continent.

Industrial Regions of the United Kingdom

Throughout the United Kingdom, industry is widely dispersed, partly because of planned removal from the older and larger concentrations of the past and partly because of the changed character of the manufactures themselves. Destruction incident to war, plus a growing population which cannot be housed in existing centers and which is more and more dependent on employment in manufacturing for its livelihood, have contributed to the dispersal as well. Yet certain of the older concentrations, particularly those on the flanks of the Pennine Hills, still dominate (FIG. 23–9). At the southern end of the Pennines, in the area known as the Midlands and centering on the city of Birmingham, is found the greatest concentration of heavy industries—iron and

steel, heavy machinery, transportation equipment, machine tools, automobiles, and chemicals. Northwest of the Midlands, on the western flank of the Pennines, lies the Lancashire district, long the cotton-textile heart of Britain and her Commonwealth. The cities here, Manchester and its satellites, are still associated with cotton textiles, but diversification has reduced the importance of this type of industry. Liverpool and Birkenhead are no longer port cities only, but manufacturing centers as well. Northeast of the Midlands, on the eastern flank of the Pennines, is the Yorkshire district, stretching from Nottingham and Derby in the south through Sheffield to Bradford and Leeds in the north. Here woolen textiles, textile machinery, cutlery, hardware, and leather goods are the outstanding products.

In the northeastern part of England, again on the eastern flank of the Pennines, is the Newcastle district. Here heavy industry dominates, with the production of iron and steel, shipbuilding, and the manufacture of ancillary machinery. In addition, considerable glass manufacturing and flour milling are done there.

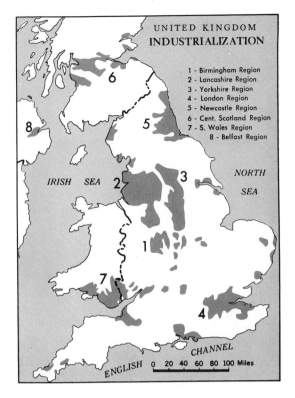

UNITED KINGDOM
INDUSTRIALIZATION

1 - Birmingham Region
2 - Lancashire Region
3 - Yorkshire Region
4 - London Region
5 - Newcastle Region
6 - Cent. Scotland Region
7 - S. Wales Region
8 - Belfast Region

IRISH SEA

NORTH

SEA

CHANNEL
ENGLISH 0 20 40 60 80 100 Miles

23–9

THE *oldest industrial regions of Europe, and of the world, are in the central and southern parts of the United Kingdom. Except for the London and Belfast regions, all of the United Kingdom industrial developments are located over or very near coal fields.*

The Midlands, Lancashire, and Yorkshire districts have continued to spread from original foci like Birmingham, Manchester, and Leeds so that the urban industrial landscape is nearly continuous within the triangle whose apexes are Birmingham, Leeds, and Liverpool.

In southeastern England is the London industrial concentration. Here is a tremendous and varied light industrial production of consumer goods for the district's own twelve million people as well as for Commonwealth export. Facing the English Channel are such increasingly industrial seaports as Portsmouth and Southampton, with a galaxy of manufactures for home and foreign markets, including machinery, chemicals, paper, printed materials, processed foods, leather, soaps, clothing, and petroleum products.

Outside of England, other industrial regions are located in Scotland, Wales, and Northern Ireland (FIG. 23–9). Scotland's industrial district stretches across the Central Lowland from the Firth of Clyde to the Firth of Forth, with Glasgow the principal center. Activities include iron and steel production, shipbuilding, manufacture of cotton and woolen textiles, and jute milling. Welsh manufacturing occurs mainly in the south, in the Cardiff area, and specializes in iron and steel, tinplate, and copper refining. In Northern Ireland a small concentration, centered on the city of Belfast, is well known for its fine linen, laces, and woolen goods, as well as for shipbuilding.

If the London and Belfast districts are excepted, there is a very close relationship between the presence of coal and iron on the one hand and the location of industry on the other. A map showing coal and iron-ore distribution serves almost as a map of the industrial regions (FIGS. 20–8 and 23–9). The fact that this relationship does not always hold must not be overemphasized, for although London is not "on coal," it is only a hundred miles from Birmingham coal and a hundred and twenty-five miles from Welsh coal—and there is an excellent low-cost connecting transport system.

Industry is more vital to the United Kingdom than to any other major nation of the world. Britain's area is so small, and she has turned so largely to the factory for a living, with a consequent de-emphasis on agricultural development, that most of her foodstuffs and raw materials must be imported from other parts of the world. Thus there is a constant flow of source materials into the United Kingdom, and an equally constant flow of manufactured goods out—exports to pay for the imports. With the people of the United Kingdom, it is a never-ending process of "import, manufacture, and export—for survival."

Northern France–Belgium–Luxembourg Industrial Region

Although made up of several independent and politically separate industrial areas, this northwestern continental development can best be treated as a single industrial region (FIG. 23–8). Underlying nearly the whole of this area are the extensive coal fields of Belgium and northern France; also the great supply of Lorraine iron ore is available with very short haulage requirements. The area does depend greatly on many other parts of the world for source materials. The portion of northern France abutting upon Germany, including Strasbourg, Nancy, and Metz, is important for its iron and steel production, making use of the vast supplies of Lorraine iron ores and local coal, while the portion facing Belgium, particularly the area about Lille, is noted for its cotton textiles. In Belgium industrial cities are spread over most of the country, but the intensity is greatest along the Sambre and Meuse rivers. Large cities like Brussels, Antwerp, Ghent, and Liége have large production capacities for iron and steel, machinery, railway equipment, machine tools, glass, textiles, and diamond cutting. Luxembourg has major iron and steel plants, textile factories, and breweries.

West German Industrial Regions

RUHR • Of the many industrial regions on the Continent, the one which has developed within the Lower Rhine–Ruhr valleys of West Germany is much the largest and most important (FIG. 23–8). This region is known as "the Ruhr." As with its American counterpart, "Pittsburgh," its name is synonymous with giant, modern heavy industry. The Ruhr and Pittsburgh are the two largest heavy-industrial concentrations in the world. Fed by its own high-grade coal and by nearby raw materials, such as Lorraine iron-ore, from northeastern France, the Ruhr region has long been the heart of European heavy industry. Here, concentrated in a small area, are such industrial cities as Dortmund, Bochum, Essen, Duisburg, and Düsseldorf, with a large production of iron and steel. This supply of steel, in turn, has spawned a wide range of ancillary manufactures such as machine tools, heavy machinery, locomotives, and armaments. Coal and other minerals, such as potash, have provided raw materials for the development of large chemical industries manufacturing dyes, caustic potash, synthetic rubber, synthetic gasoline, and many other important products. This industrial region was almost completely destroyed by intensive bombing during World War II, but it has been rebuilt so that it now surpasses its prewar magnitude; it is, furthermore, completely modernized.

MIDDLE RHINE–SAAR • A hundred miles southward from the Ruhr region is a somewhat less important industrial development along the middle reaches of the Rhine valley, which includes such well-known cities as Mainz, Frankfurt, and Mannheim, and extends westward to include the Saar Basin near the French border (FIG. 23–8). Iron and steel and their ancillary manufactures predominate here, based on local and imported coals and the large iron-ore supplies from nearby Lorraine.

East German Industrial Region

Situated upon the scattered coal and lignite fields of the Saxony Basin in southern East Germany, and including such urban areas as Dresden, Leipzig, and Magdeburg, is a considerable concentration of industry, which was second only to the Ruhr in prewar undivided Germany (FIG. 23–8). Some iron and steel is produced here from the local coal and the iron ore of the nearby Sudeten Mountains. Most of the large developments are, however, of the light-industry type, including machinery, textiles, chemicals, beet sugar, and optical equipment.

Southern Poland Industrial Region

The most easterly of the major industrial regions in Europe, outside the Soviet Union, has developed in southern Poland over the coal and iron-ore fields of Upper Silesia, near the Czechoslovakian border (FIG. 23–8). This piece of Europe changed hands politically several times during the World War II period, with Polish, Czechoslovakian, German, Russian, and then again Polish control dominating in rapid sequence. Here, in a roughly triangular region marked by the cities of Krakow, Katowice, and Czestochowa, is a relatively important center of iron and steel production, supplemented by ancillary heavy industry.

Northern Italy Industrial Region

Lacking practically every basic requirement for industrial development—such as coal, petroleum, natural gas, iron ore, and other strategic minerals—Italy has developed important light industries based on hydroelectric power, imported source materials, and plentiful cheap labor. Both the Alps and the Apennines supply the hydroelectric power which has made possible the industrialization of such cities as Milan, Turin, Genoa, Florence, and Padua.

Northern Switzerland Industrial Region

The Swiss have made the northern half of their country into a relatively important industrial region even though such commodities as coal, iron ore, petroleum, natural gas, strategic minerals, and even agricultural raw materials for industry are practically nonexistent. With highly skilled labor and imported materials, they have developed many high-value, small-volume light industries, such as clocks and watches, optical equipment, and professional instruments.

Southeastern France Industrial Region

With relatively large resources of iron ore and some supplies of local coal, a sizable industrial region has developed in southeastern France, particularly in the Rhône-Saône valleys between the cities of Lyons and Dijon. Light industries predominate, such as light machinery, textiles, and chemical products.

Other Industrial Developments

In addition to the major industrial regions of western Europe noted above, there are many other scattered centers which are of importance to the countries in which they are located. Their lesser importance is only relative within a great and varied industrial complex such as Europe. Many are larger and more important than some regions in other parts of the world which have acquired international recognition, because the latter are frequently industrial oases in vast underdeveloped countries. Significant among these lesser industrial centers of Europe are Stockholm, Copenhagen, Eindhoven, Hamburg, Bremen, Munich, Berlin, Warsaw, Poznan, Prague, Pilsen, Vienna, Budapest, Belgrade, Naples, Bilbao, and Barcelona (FIG. 23–8).

INDUSTRY IN THE SOVIET UNION

INDUSTRIAL developments in Czarist Russia were relatively insignificant. But the Soviet Union, built from the wreckage of the old Empire following the 1917 Revolution, has made rapid industrial progress in the last four decades, until it now stands second only to the United States in industrial development and production. Complete and ruthless control of

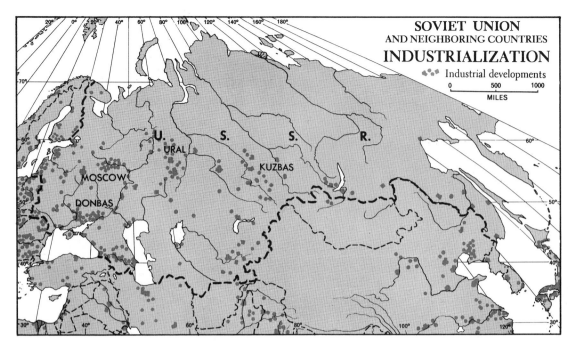

INDUSTRY *is spreading rapidly across the vast stretches of the Soviet Union but has its four great- est concentrations in the central and southern European areas and in the western and central Siberian areas.*

industry and labor, as well as all other phases of life, on the part of the Soviet government has had one main objective—to make the Soviet Union industrially strong whatever the cost.

Most of the Soviet industrial development is concentrated in four major regions, widely scattered across nearly five thousand miles of the country's tremendous east-west expanse of territory. Two of these major industrial regions, the Moscow Region, the oldest, and the Don- bas Region, the largest, are in European U.S.S.R.; while the Ural Region, the most nearly self-sufficient, and the Kuzbas Region, the newest, are in Asiatic U.S.S.R. (FIG. 23–10). Important factors which have contributed to the concentration and development of industry in these regions are: first, source materials, such as iron ore, manganese, bauxite, textile fibers, and foodstuffs; second, power and fuel supplies such as coal, petroleum, natural gas, and hydro- electricity; third, markets that are rapidly ex-

panding and locally oriented by virtue of lim- ited Soviet transportation; and fourth, a social- ist economy dedicated to the theory of regional self-sufficiency—"the Plan."

Moscow Industrial Region

The Moscow Industrial Region was the old- est and largest in Czarist Russia and had de- veloped, like many others in the world during the late nineteenth century, primarily because Moscow was the original nucleus of the old Empire (FIG. 23–10). Industry was, and still is, considerably varied, but the chief emphasis is on light industry and consumer goods to supply the capital city market with such items as textiles, clothing, automobiles, agricultural machinery, hardware, flour, paper, tools, and some iron and steel. The region is not par- ticularly well favored with high-grade coal or iron ore, but it does have large supplies of lignite, large foodstuff supplies from the surrounding plains, and wood from the forests immediately to the north.

Donbas Industrial Region

The Donbas Industrial Region is the principal single iron and steel and ancillary heavy-industry region of the entire Soviet Union. It stretches from Donetsk to Lugansk in the eastern Ukrainian S.S.R, near the famous coal fields of the Donets Basin. The rich iron-ore deposits of Krivoi Rog to the westward are easily available, as is the manganese of Nikopol in the same vicinity (FIG. 23–10). In addition to very large iron and steel production, the Donbas Region is important for other typical heavy-industry products such as steel rails, locomotives, railway cars, tractors, machinery, industrial chemicals, glass, cement, machine tools, and armaments. There is a railroad "shuttle system" between the Krivoi Rog iron-ore fields and the Donets coal fields which provides a heavy flow of coal to the iron as well as iron to the coal, thus allowing a development of iron and steel production in both areas. The outskirts of this giant Donbas Industrial Region reach beyond the immediate coal and iron-ore centers to include such heavily industrialized cities as Rostov-on-Don to the east, Kharkov to the north, and Kiev to the northwest. In this larger sense, the Donbas Industrial Region is interspersed and surrounded by the broad flat expanses of the Ukrainian Plains—the Soviet breadbasket—where agriculture is still the most intense within the Union.

Other Developments in Soviet Europe

In addition to the two major regions above, some lesser industrial regions and scattered centers have developed on the great Russian Plains of Eastern Europe. Leningrad, northwest of Moscow on the Gulf of Finland, has become a heavily industrialized city, while Minsk to the west, Volgograd to the southeast,

Kuibyshev and Gorki to the east, and the Kola Peninsula far to the north have all felt the impacts of modern industry. Leningrad manufactures range from iron, steel, ships, and machinery to paper, textiles, and furs. Minsk is noted for textiles, shoes, and light machinery, while Volgograd is important for iron and steel, tractors, agricultural machinery, and petroleum products. Industry has also expanded on a large and varied scale far southward in the Caucasus Mountain Region, with the cities of Batum, Tiflis, and Baku as important centers. Here are produced iron and steel, petroleum products, and foodstuffs (FIG. 23–10).

Ural Industrial Region

During Czarist days the Ural Industrial Region produced about a fifth of the Russian Empire's total iron and steel, as against two-thirds of the total produced in the Donbas Region. But the strategic interior location of the Urals has prompted the Soviet planners to push the country's industrial developments there as well as even farther eastward in the Central Asian regions. These regions of Asiatic U.S.S.R. now combine to produce half of the Soviet's total iron and steel, representing a significant planned shift in a major heavy industry. The Ural Industrial Region stretches for five hundred miles along the southern half of the low Ural Mountain range, and includes such heavily industrialized cities as Magnitogorsk, in the south, and Ufa, Chelyabinsk, Sverdlovsk, and Serov farther northward (FIG. 23–10).

Except for their almost complete lack of coal, the Urals probably form as nearly self-sufficient an industrial region as is to be found anywhere in the world: plentiful supplies of iron ore, manganese, copper, bauxite, nickel, chromite, phosphate rock, and petroleum are located there. Coal must be hauled by railroad largely from the Kuznetsk Coal Basin 1000 miles eastward, and from the Karaganda coal fields 600 miles southeastward. The scarcity of coal within the region itself is such an economic handicap that it is doubtful if this region would have become a significant iron and steel producer under a free economy. The mineral imbalance has been partially offset by the establishment of a railroad "shuttle system," similar to that in the Donbas Region, which moves coal westward and iron ore eastward between the Kuznetsk Basin and the Urals and thus allows the development of iron and steel production in both areas.

Kuzbas Industrial Region

The first large blast furnaces were blown in at Kuznetsk in 1932. This operation started the large-scale industrial development that created the Kuzbas Industrial Region in Central Asia, a thousand miles east of the Urals and halfway to Lake Baikal. Coal from the huge deposits of the Kuznetsk Coal Basin and local iron-ore and manganese deposits combine to form the base of this new industrial region. As has been noted, a railroad "shuttle system" moves coal from the Kuzbas to the Urals and on the return trip carries iron ore from the Urals to the Kuzbas to supplement the local ore supplies. The Kuzbas Industrial Region lies on and just south of the Trans-Siberian Railway, surrounding such growing cities as Novosibirsk, Krasnoyarsk, and Novokuznetsk.

Other Developments in Soviet Asia

Some lesser industrial regions and scattered centers have developed eastward of the Ural and Kuzbas Regions of Central Asia, at the southern end of Lake Baikal and even farther along the route of the Trans-Siberian Railway to its eastern terminus, Vladivostok, on the Sea of Japan. Even more important industrially is the Tashkent–Alma Ata region, southwest of Lake Balkhash, which is relatively rich in uranium ores and also possesses lead and zinc, petroleum, and some coal.

A characteristic feature of the change in the distribution pattern of Soviet industry, the iron and steel industry in particular, is its movement eastward toward Central Asia, where large supplies of nature's resources such as coal, iron ore, manganese, petroleum, and uranium are available for industrial purposes (FIG. 23–10).

INDUSTRY IN INDIA

BEFORE the period of British domination, India was famous in the world's markets for her cottage industry and handicraft production of luxury goods such as fine silks, muslins, and embroideries, as well as sandalwood and ivory carvings. However, during the one hundred and fifty years of British control, the small cottage industries and handicraft trades declined, though considerable compensating progress was made in the direction of large-scale modern industrialization during the first half of the present century. Still, the total industrial production in India during this time always fell short of the demand; even cotton textiles had to be imported from England's Lancashire district to clothe India's millions. Raw materials went west to the home country, and manufactures returned east to the colonial markets, not only in India, but in Southeast Asia and the Far East as well.

After long years of political and economic restiveness, India gained her independence in 1947 and became two separate political units, Pakistan and the Union of India. India's first efforts under independence were devoted to expanding consumer-goods production and bolstering capital-goods industries. Her most important industries were cotton textiles, jute materials, cement, iron and steel, paper, sugar, chemicals, and engineering goods, all established on a small scale in the period before independence. During India's first five years of independence, her industrial output increased by over 50 per cent in most commodities, and more in some. India was, and still is, moving with ever-increasing vigor, purpose, knowledge, and speed toward industrial maturity. Her source materials are plentiful: she has considerable cotton and wool, the world's largest jute production, plenty of manganese, the world's largest iron-ore reserves, coal, petroleum, hydroelectric power potential, rice, wheat, sugar, and the world's largest cattle population—and all this combined with the world's second largest potential market for industrial products—more than 400 million Indians.

Cotton textiles occupy the top position in Indian industry. Although production is countrywide, two-thirds of it is concentrated in the state of Maharashtra, centering on Bombay, and in Gujarat, in Ahmadabad. Production of jute materials occupies second place in Indian industry, and is almost totally concentrated in West Bengal, around the city of Calcutta. Iron and steel production is rising rapidly to form the backbone of India's new industrial economy. Although there are 140 large and small iron and steel works in India, most production is strung along a 500-mile line running roughly southwestward from Calcutta through the cities of Asansol and Durgapur in the state of West Bengal, Jamshedpur in the state of Bihar, Rourkela in the state of Orissa, and Bhilai in the state of Madhya Pradesh. Durgapur, Rourkela, and Bhilai are all newly established steel centers, coming into full production only in 1960–61, with the foreign financial and technical assistance of the United Kingdom, West Germany, and the U.S.S.R., respectively. American financial and technical assistance went into the original Jamshedpur iron and steel plant development a half century ago, and also into its recent expansion, which makes it now the largest integrated iron and steel plant in the British Commonwealth of Nations.

The greatest concentrations of industry in India are found in and around the three major cities of Calcutta, Bombay, and Madras. Industries of many types have developed over India during the past decade, and today three major industrial regions can be readily distinguished; these account for about 90 per cent of India's industry.

North India Industrial Region

The North India Industrial Region stretches 1000 miles along the Ganges–Indus Plains, from Calcutta near the mouth of the Ganges to Amritsar in the Punjab hard against West Pakistan, and juts southward onto the Indian plateau to form a triangular area with its apex at Nagpur (FIG. 23–11). Within this rapidly developing industrial region are dozens of important cities lying the length of the valley, such as Calcutta, Howrah, and Burdwan with jute and cotton textiles manufacturing; Asansol and Durgapur with iron and steel; Varanasi (Benares) with silk goods; Lucknow, Kanpur, and Agra with woolen and cotton textiles; Delhi with varied light industries; and Ambala and Amritsar with cotton and woolen textiles. On the adjoining northeastern section of the Indian plateau are the cities of Jamshedpur with iron and steel, Ranchi with machine tools, Rourkela and Bhilai with iron and steel, and Nagpur with cotton textiles (FIG. 23–12).

The small southeastern section of this region, on the Indian plateau, contains the large bulk of India's iron-ore, coal, and manganese deposits and features chiefly heavy industry, while the eastern, middle, and western sections, containing large resources of raw jute, wool, and cotton, feature light-industry developments. The orientation of manufacturing is, thus, primarily determined by the availability of source materials.

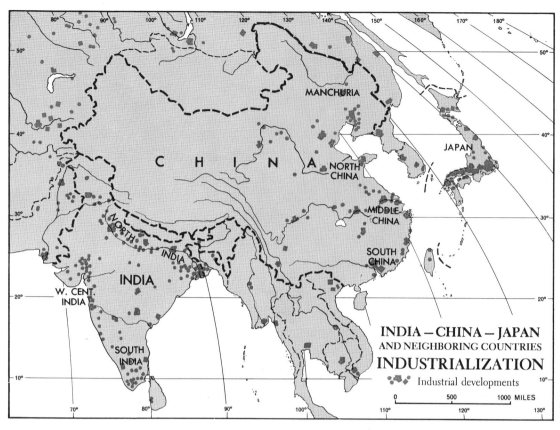

23–11   INDUSTRY *is spreading rapidly across the densely populated lands of India and China, as it did over Japan earlier this century.*

West-Central India Industrial Region

The West-Central India Industrial Region is small in area, and also small in production and variety, compared with the northern region. It stretches along the western coast of India for 400 miles, from Ahmadabad through Baroda, Bombay, and Poona to Kolhapur, and lies close to India's largest cotton-growing area. Consequently this is the area in which the bulk of India's large cotton-textile production, so important in the problem of clothing the nation's millions of people, takes place (FIG. 23–11). Here also has developed India's largest concentration of sugar refining, particularly in the Ahmadabad area. Farther south there is significant production of electric equipment, as well as other light industries.

South India Industrial Region

The South India Industrial Region blocks in the whole of south India from the tip of the peninsula northward to a line running from Madras on the east coast to Mangalore on the west (FIG. 23–11). Here are concentrated major resources of iron ore, very large amounts of hydroelectric power, large supplies of raw cotton, wool, and coir. Upon these are based major productions of cotton and woolen textiles, coir products, iron and steel, machinery, airplanes, electric equipment, and professional instruments, scattered within and among such industrial cities as Madras, Bangalore, Mysore, Mangalore, Coimbatore, and Madura. Variety rather than specialization is here the keynote of industrial growth.

23–12   SIGNS *of modern India: the Tata Iron and Steel Works, Ltd., at Jamshedpur, in Bihar.*

INDUSTRY IN CHINA

CHINA is the latest of the major countries of the world to undertake industrialization. No modern industries developed in China during the nineteenth century as they did in western Europe and the United States, nor even during the first half of the present century as they did in neighboring countries like the Soviet Union, India, and Japan. The long delay was due to a combination of many factors, the most significant of which were China's age-old weak and chaotic political structure, internal strife, recurring famines, poor transportation facilities, and economic weaknesses, all combined with a fervent resistance to "foreign" ideas and innovations from either the West or the East. But under the relentless control of totalitarian Chinese Communism since 1949, and strongly influenced by and modeled after the Soviet Union, China is attempting to industrialize quickly, in a "great leap forward." China's traditional industrial source materials are neither plentiful nor conveniently located for economic utilization. Still, economic handicaps may be politically manipulated when totalitarian governments undertake to promote industrialization at any cost. Industrial efficiency can be bought at the price of human freedom. China has substantial coal supplies, with three-quarters of its total resources in the northern provinces of Shansi and Shensi, appreciable amounts in Manchuria, and the rest scattered in small deposits in nearly every province of the country. China has moderate supplies of relatively low-grade iron ore, nearly two-thirds of which are in southern Manchuria. This distribution of coal and iron ore leaves southern China relatively poorly endowed for modern heavy industrialization. Petroleum and natural gas are still unknown quantities in China's industrial inventory, but her hydroelectric potential is considerable in many regions, especially in the remote and undeveloped fringes of the Tibetan plateau, in the Hwang Ho valley of the North, and in eastern Manchuria. Other significant minerals with which China is adequately endowed are copper, silver, manganese, tungsten, tin, and antimony.

During the last decade modern industry has made considerable inroads into some of China's age-old cottage handicraft industries, and today supply depends almost entirely upon "new factory" output. Cotton textiles are the most important single commodity now factory-oriented; home weaving has almost disappeared in China. Iron and steel, machinery, cement, railway equipment, foodstuffs, flour, ceramics, rubber goods, electric equipment, sugar, and ships are the major industrial items on which emphasis has been placed and in which production has been expanded.

China's modern industrial developments are located mostly along or near the country's east coast, with one extension reaching into central Manchuria, a second reaching into the Hwang valley, and a third a thousand miles

up the Yangtze valley to the fringe of the Tibetan plateau.

Manchurian Industrial Region

The Manchurian Plain and the southward jutting Liaotung Peninsula in northeastern China encompass the country's largest heavy-industry region (FIG. 23–11). With nearly two-thirds of the country's iron ore and appreciable resources of coal occurring in close proximity, the greatest industrial concentration is in the southern Manchurian Plain region where large iron and steel plants have been developed at Anshan (Japanese-built during Manchurian occupation) and at Penchi, a shale-oil reduction plant at Fushun, and an auto-truck factory at Changchun, as well as the largest railroad shops, shipyards, and cement plants in all of China.

North China Industrial Region

The loess plains and plateaus of North China were the ancient culture hearths of Chinese civilization. These same loess plateaus contain the bulk of China's great coal reserves in the provinces of Shansi and Shensi, but industrial development has so far been very slow. The triangular area including Peiping, Tientsin, and Tangshan, in the northeastern Hopei province plains, includes China's second-largest coal mines and associated industrialization. Here there are glass and cement plants, as well as major cotton-textile and flour-milling developments. Eastward, in the Shantung Peninsula, iron and steel, cotton-textile, flour-milling, and foodstuff productions have developed (FIG. 23–11).

Middle China Industrial Region

The Yangtze valley, extending from the great port city of Shanghai a thousand miles inland to Chungking, constitutes China's largest and most important industrial region

(FIG. 23–11). The lower Yangtze plain, with cities such as Shanghai, Suchou, Nanking, and Hangchou, is heavily industrialized, and accounts for two-thirds of China's textile output, as well as many other items of light industry. Shanghai, one of the world's largest cities, is China's largest industrial city; virtually every type of light industry, including textiles, food processing, printing, flour milling, and shipbuilding, is represented.

In the Central Lakes district local iron ore from the Tayeh mines, largest outside Manchuria, and nearby coal provide source materials and fuel for an important iron and steel and ancillary heavy-industry development at both Tayeh and Hanyang, near Wuhan (Hankou). Textiles, foodstuffs, and tea and flour processing also contribute to the development of the Middle China Industrial Region.

South China Industrial Region

On the delta of the Hsun (Si) river is concentrated a large amount of light industrial production, including silk and cotton textiles, ceramics, rubber goods, electric equipment, and sugar refining, to serve the large and varied markets of the southern part of China. Hong Kong, although still British territory, and Macao, still Portuguese territory, with their large and varied light industrial developments, both belong in this South China Industrial Region (FIG. 23–11).

INDUSTRY IN JAPAN

DURING the last half century Japan has made astonishing progress in commerce and industry. Stimulated by her victory over Russia in 1905, and by the new ideas and machines of the Western World, Japan changed from a feudal, underdeveloped agricultural nation into a highly organized progressive industrial state within the time-span of a generation. Over 20 per cent of Japan's labor force is employed in some capacity in industry. This is the highest proportion in all of Asia, and is comparable to the less than 30 per cent employed in industry in the United States.

In natural resources needed for modern industry, Japan came into existence a poor nation. It is still a very poor nation in most of the basic metallic minerals and in the modern fuel and energy resources of petroleum and natural gas. But, by a combination of peaceful and aggressive actions, Japan has reached out frequently in the past few decades for more territory and more and more natural resources in East and Southeast Asia and over the Pacific islands. The peaceful reaching netted raw cotton, petroleum, and scrap iron from the United States, manganese from India, and petroleum from Indonesia. Aggressive reaching started in 1932 and, for a time, netted iron ore from Manchuria, rubber from Malaya, and petroleum and tin from Indonesia. All these, combined with her own meager resources, provided an industrial base which enabled Japan to become the "Britain of the East" and to compete in many of the world's markets with the United States and the industrial nations of western Europe. However, Japan's ambitions to dominate the Asiatic world and thrust out established Western interests culminated in widespread conflict of the Pacific area in World War II, in which Japan was decisively defeated. In the years since military defeat, Japan has completely rebuilt her home industrial machine on more peaceful lines.

South Honshu Industrial Region

Present-day Japan is without her former iron and steel plants in Manchuria and her textile factories in China. For all practical purposes she has only one major industrial region today. This is the southern rim of the main island of Honshu and the adjoining tip of the southern island of Kyushu (FIG. 23–11). Included in this region, as the northern anchor, is the Tokyo–Yokohama center. Nagoya forms a second center two hundred miles southwestward, and Osaka–Kobe a third center facing the Inland Sea a hundred miles beyond. Okayama, Kure, and Hiroshima are strung farther along the Inland Sea coast, and the southern anchor of the region lies in a group of small industrial cities across the mile-and-a-half wide Straits of Shimonoseki in the southernmost island of Kyushu.

Before World War II the Tokyo–Yokohama center accounted for about 30 per cent of Japan's total production, and postwar percentages are even higher. Its manufactures are highly diversified, like those of other capital cities of the world, and include iron and steel, optical equipment, textiles, light machinery, electric equipment, printing, and the manufacture of professional instruments. Nagoya, with its surrounding cities, is the only major center of Japan in which textiles are the most important industrial products, but this is well supplemented by other light industry, machinery and pottery, as well as the heavier manufacture of airplanes and automobiles. The Osaka–Kobe center, including such other cities as Kyoto and Nara, is second only to Tokyo–Yokohama in volume of production, and equal to it in diversity. Manufactures emphasize the heavier industries such as shipbuilding, iron and steel, heavy machinery, chemicals, and cement, though textiles, lacquers, toys, and handicraft products are significant. The concentration at the Straits of Shimonoseki differs from the others in that textiles are of relatively little importance, while the heavier industries predominate; Japan's largest iron and steel plant is located there. Other heavy manufactures include machinery, chemicals, glass, and cement. This region, with its heavy-industry emphasis, is Japan's "Pittsburgh of the East," but without the wealth of source materials enjoyed by Pittsburgh itself.

INDUSTRY IN AUSTRALIA

Many of the industrial products used by the people of Australia are not produced within the country and must be purchased outside, from the United Kingdom, continental Europe, and the United States. Australia has plentiful supplies of coal, with large deposits in the southeast near Sydney and smaller ones near Melbourne, Brisbane, and Perth. However, she is not well endowed with iron ore, or most of the other basic necessities of industry. Small industrial regions have developed in southeastern Australia around the cities of Sydney, Melbourne, and Brisbane, and in southwestern Australia around Perth (FIG. 23–2), based upon the limited source materials available. Australian industry is diversified, but mainly of the light-industry type. Of chief importance to other parts of the world is the making of butter, cheese, and condensed milk, meat packing, and the processing of raw wool. Products for home consumption consist of shoes, textiles, clothing, flour, refined sugar, brewery products, small metal articles, and a small amount of iron and steel.

INDUSTRY IN SOUTH AFRICA

THE Republic of South Africa is primarily a seller of raw materials and a buyer of industrial products. Again, it is factories in the United Kingdom rather than local factories which supply most of South Africa's industrial needs. Small industrial regions center on Cape Town and Johannesburg, with other scattered developments, such as Port Elizabeth, East London, and Durban, along the southeastern coast (FIG. 23–2). Manufactures consist of clothing, processed foods, household equipment, books and newspapers, and a little iron and steel. Comparatively, the Republic has made rapid industrial progress in recent years.

INDUSTRY IN SOUTH AMERICA

IN SOUTH AMERICA, as in Australia and Africa, manufacturing is notably conspicuous by its near absence and its unimportance from a world point of view. The major South American concentration is in the Río de la Plata region. Important centers there are Buenos Aires, La Plata, and Rosario in Argentina, and Montevideo in Uruguay. The Río de la Plata region produces leather goods, shoes, textiles, paper, cement, flour, and packed meats. In Chile, small industrial developments are found in the central Santiago–Valparaiso region, the southern Concepcion–Valdivia region, and the northern Antofagasta region. In these centers, a wide variety of items, including shoes, clothing, wines, and smelted minerals, are produced. The only other industrial region of comparative significance is that centering on Rio de Janeiro and São Paulo in Brazil, with productions of textiles, clothing, machinery, cement, chemicals, and processed foods, as well as the assembling of automobiles.

THE short statements made above about industrial regions in the Southern Hemisphere has emphasized their small number and their small extent, as compared with those of the Northern Hemisphere. But it should be pointed out that comparatively small industrial regions may be of extreme importance to local regions, or to the entire country in which they lie.

• CHAPTER OUTLINE •

Industrialization

· REVIEW QUESTIONS ·

1. Discuss the effects of increasing industrialization on the distribution of population in the
United States.
2. Using other examples than those given in the
text, demonstrate that type of culture may
encourage or discourage the development of
industry in different regions or nations over
the world.
3. Is there justification for the statement that
Denmark cannot become a *leading* industrial
nation?
4. Explain the apparent paradox involved in referring to "scarcity of labor" in India.
5. Why do industrial regions and well-developed
railroad nets go hand in hand?
6. Where is the greater bulk of the goods manufactured in the United States consumed?
7. What "combination" is referred to in the

statement that, "Certainly no *major* industrial
regions exist where this combination is not
present"?
8. Give the location of the two major industrial
regions of the world. Which one is now the
leader? Why?
9. Demonstrate the critical importance of steel
in the national economy of the United States.
10. What and where are the four major iron and
steel manufacturing concentrations of the
United States?
11. Give examples of specialization centers in the
manufacture of machinery, tools, and transportation equipment.
12. Why did New England, once the leader,
lose its leadership in the shipbuilding industry
to the Chesapeake–Delaware–Hudson region?
13. Discuss the problems of the United States

shipbuilding industry in terms of meeting foreign competition.

14. On the basis of monetary value, what is the leading "product group" in the United States?

15. New England once held leadership in cotton textile manufacturing. What section of the United States now leads? In what textile does New England now hold leadership?

16. What were some of the principal reasons for the rise of the cotton textile industry in the South?

17. Discuss the distribution of coal and iron in relation to the Northwestern Industrial Region of Europe.

18. Why is industrial development "more vital to Britain than to any other major nation"?

19. Which of the important industrial regions of Europe are under the direct or indirect control of the Soviet Union?

20. Give examples of specialization centers within India's industrial manufacturing regions.

21. Attempt to secure recent information concerning India's industrial progress, especially in the Bombay and Calcutta districts.

22. What areas or regions stand as exceptions to the fact that the Southern Hemisphere is mainly a "raw materials hemisphere"?

24 The World Pattern of Routes

STANDARD OIL CO. (N.J.)

⟮ THE *endless variety of both physical and cultural elements of the human habitat from place to place suggests, at first thought, a sharp separation of the individual parts of the world. There is real danger of overemphasizing this notion of separateness. Actually, the whole human habitat is a single mosaic in which each tile contributes its bit to the over-all effect. It is the world network of routes, above all other features, that holds the pieces together. The pattern of routes is like the visible part of the matrix in which the individual tiles of a mosaic are set. Their function, like the material which holds one tile to the others in a mosaic, is to unite the whole—to tie together the great variety of the human habitat into one world pattern.*

The present world pattern of routes has evolved through the whole of human history; it reflects man's successes and failures in overcoming the handi-

caps of distance and barriers and in passing from simple to complex economic stages. Early man depended upon his own muscles to move about over the surface of the earth, primarily in search of food. His routes were irregular, perhaps radiating from his shelter throughout the area in which he hunted, or leading from his shelter to a source of water, and they were limited by the distance which he could conveniently cover on foot. With the taming of animals which could be used as beasts of burden, and the invention of navigation, range of movement became greater and routes more definitely fixed —a pathway from the dwelling to a fishing site on a lake or river, or the river itself when used to get from one hunting ground to another.

Routes followed by one group of people gradually extended to link up with those of neighboring groups. Overland roads for vehicles took the place of trails for men and animals. River routes formed links between land routes; then water routes were extended first to cross inland seas and later to cross open oceans. Artificial waterways, canals, amplified the natural water routes. Steam power brought the railroad and steamship. The internal combustion engine speeded movement overland and later brought air travel. At each step, the existing pattern of routes was amplified both in more intensive local coverage and in wider extent. Always the result was the closer tying together of the whole human habitat, the creation of one modern world mosaic from the scattered fragments of the prehistoric world.

The world pattern of routes is made up of lines of transportation and communication over the land, on the water, and through the air. The lines on the land leave permanent traces whether they are paths, trails, roads, or railroads. On the water, inland waterways, both natural and artificial, are as clearly marked as roads, but nothing permanent marks the passage of a ship over a sea or ocean. Nor is there a visible trace of passage through the air. Yet both ocean and air routes become as well defined as roads, for they exist because they link two places on the surface of the spherical earth. The shortest route between any two such points occurs along a great circle (see p. 31). As nearly as is physically possible and economically feasible, ships and aircraft follow these great circle routes.

24—1

[OPPOSITE, TOP] ROUTES create a world-wide net of increasingly close weave, linking all parts of the human habitat. Ports, like New York, are the focal points where intercontinental and intracontinental routes meet.

INTERCONTINENTAL ROUTES

Ocean Routes

THE great highways of the oceans and seas exist despite the lack of visible markings. Just as surely as though the way were marked by a broad expanse of pavement, a ship sailing from a port on the eastern coast of North America to one in northwestern Europe follows, within broad limits, the course of the ship which preceded it. Insofar as it is possible, this course is a great circle on the ocean's surface, because a great circle is the shortest distance between any two points on the globe. Similarly, certain other parts of the world's oceans become regularly traveled routes which can be indicated with exactness upon the map (FIG. 24–2).

Well-defined ocean routes were not so prominent in the past, when a far larger proportion of ocean traffic was handled by "tramps," those cargo-carrying vessels that plied from port to port where cargo was available. Nowadays, the role of the tramp steamer has dwindled; regular cargo services exist and vessels ply back and forth between fixed termini. Thus by far the greater part of trans-ocean traffic has been funneled into a few outstanding routes. These routes are the great strands which tie the densely settled portions of the human habitat together.

THE NORTH ATLANTIC ROUTE • The shape of the North Atlantic basin and the directions of the North American and European coastlines are such that the routes from all ports on one side of the ocean to all those on the other side follow essentially the same course—a great circle route across the North Atlantic. For example, ships from the ports of the southeastern United States must travel close to the coast for some distance northward if they are to follow the shortest route to western Europe.

This convergence of shipping lanes to form the North Atlantic route, and the nature of the lands at each end of it easily explain its rank as the most used ocean route in the world. Surplus raw materials, partially manufactured goods, and some wholly manufactured commodities flow eastward from industrial eastern North America and from the regions of surplus agriculture in the interior of the continent. Back from even more densely peopled northwest Europe flow manufactures, both complete and partial, and a few food items. In addition, millions of people have followed the route, the millions that moved westward from overcrowded Europe to help fill the empty interior of a new land in the past and since then the smaller stream returning, mostly for temporary visits or for business negotiations.

In winter, the North Atlantic route is exceedingly stormy, for at that season it lies athwart the zone of contact between Polar and Tropical air masses. Storm follows storm, with gale-force winds whipping the sea into tremendous waves and lowering temperatures below the freezing point. At all seasons, though somewhat more frequently in summer and autumn, fog is a hazard on the Newfoundland Grand Bank where the warm Gulf Stream encounters the cold Labrador Current. In summer, icebergs drifting southward from more northerly seas make necessary continued patrolling of the waters along this route so that the hundreds of ships that ply the track may be warned and escape danger. Despite these handicaps, the North Atlantic route has become the highway for a large share of the world's total shipping tonnage, and serves nearly half of the world's principal ports.

Branching from the main course of this route, a track followed by increasingly large numbers of ships leads by way of the Azores to the Straits of Gibraltar. There it joins with the second of the world's major ocean routes.

THE MEDITERRANEAN–ASIATIC–AUS-TRALIAN ROUTE • The route which is sec-

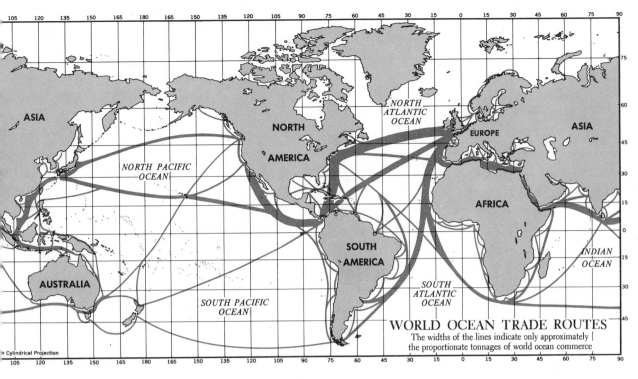

ASIA

NORTH AMERICA

NORTH PACIFIC OCEAN

NORTH ATLANTIC OCEAN

EUROPE

ASIA

AFRICA

AUSTRALIA

SOUTH PACIFIC OCEAN

SOUTH AMERICA

SOUTH ATLANTIC OCEAN

INDIAN OCEAN

WORLD OCEAN TRADE ROUTES
The widths of the lines indicate only approximately the proportionate tonnages of world ocean commerce

r Cylindrical Projection

24–2   THE *great ocean routes are as well defined as highways across the land.*

ond in importance to the North Atlantic water highway is the one leading from northwestern Europe to the densely settled areas of the Middle and Far East. This is known as the Mediterranean–Asiatic–Australian route. From the North Sea it leads through the Strait of Gibraltar and on to the eastern end of the Mediterranean Sea. Then by means of the man-made Suez Canal, it reaches into the Red Sea and through that into the Arabian Sea. Branch routes diverge to the eastern coast of Africa, to the Persian Gulf, and to the ports of West Pakistan and India (FIG. 24–2), but the main track leads on to Ceylon. There, three branches open out, one to southern Australia, a second through the Strait of Malacca past Singapore to Indonesia and the coastlands and islands of the eastern Asiatic fringe, and a third through Sunda Strait.

This route is much longer than the one which links the lands on either side of the North Atlantic. Furthermore, local traffic con-

tributes heavily to the total which flows along it, primarily because the route is close to the land throughout much of its course. For example, the exchange between the eastern and western ends of the Mediterranean is a significant element in total volume. In the past, this route was often called the "life line of the British Empire" for it tied industrial Britain to a large portion of her overseas dominions and colonies. It is still of great significance to the British Commonwealth, and the increased importance of Middle East petroleum has added another element.

Along this route lie nearly all the different kinds of lands, from the tropics to the higher middle latitudes; it has one terminus in an area of Western industrial economy and the other in the center of an Oriental agricultural economy. Yet the flow along it is smaller than that across the North Atlantic: southeastern Asia is a region of relatively little surplus production, and its buying power is still low in

Intercontinental Routes | 557

comparison to that at either end of the North Atlantic route.

OTHER MAJOR OCEAN ROUTES • Prior to the cutting of the Suez Canal (1859–1869), the way to the East lay around the Cape of Good Hope in southern Africa or around Cape Horn at the southern tip of South America. The Cape of Good Hope route is still important as one of the major routes of the world; economic and political ties between northwestern Europe and southern Africa are sufficiently close to provide considerable traffic.

The Europe–eastern South America route diverges from the Cape of Good Hope route off the Saharan coast of Africa. Along it flow the manufactured goods of northwestern Europe and the agricultural surpluses of southeastern South America. Though this route continues southward "round the Horn," the volume of traffic on it decreases materially south of Buenos Aires. The eastern South America–eastern North America route has been far less significant in the past than the one leading from South America to Europe, but it nevertheless is one of the prominent world routes.

The North America–western South America route owes its prominence to the Panama Canal, which was opened in 1914. Before the canal was constructed, the water route between the Atlantic and Pacific seaboards of North America had to follow the difficult way around Cape Horn. Now, the Panama Canal provides a cutoff and, in addition, allows easy contact of both eastern and western North America with all the coastlands of South America. The coastlands of Middle America and the islands of the Caribbean are also easily accessible to the arms of this Y-shaped route (FIG. 24–2).

From the Atlantic end of the Panama Canal, an increasingly important route leads directly to northwestern Europe. It provides direct communication between Europe and the Caribbean area and, by way of the Canal, the Pacific Ocean.

The tremendous expanse of the Pacific Ocean is spanned by several main ocean highways. The North Pacific route swings far to the north, close to the Aleutian Islands and more than a thousand miles north of the Hawaiian Islands, to provide the shortest course between the ports of western America and those of Japan and eastern Asia. A longer route stretches from western North America through the Hawaiian Islands to the ports of the Far East. A still longer route reaches from Japan through Hawaii to the Pacific end of the Panama Canal. The North America–Australasia route cuts boldly southwestward from west-coast ports by way of the Hawaiian Islands to cover the 7000-mile distance to New Zealand and Australia. Secondary routes make a crossroads station of the Hawaiian Islands. But the volume which flows over the Pacific routes is far less than that of the previously mentioned ones, except under the stress of war. The routes are "marked out," but they have not become the heavily traveled "Main Streets" of world transportation.

The routes that have been listed form the skeleton of ocean transportation (FIG. 24–2). From all of them, innumerable branches spread out. The coastwise shipping of almost every maritime nation merges with the main flow along one or the other of these routes in some parts of its course. About the edges of all of the continents, except Antarctica and the Arctic fringes of North America and Eurasia, oceans and seas are well-used routes. Even the Arctic fringe of Eurasia is subject to sporadic use: the Arctic sea route from northern European Russia to eastern Siberia has been used in summer since 1936. The coastal fringes feed to the main ocean highways which, in turn, link together the permanently inhabited parts of the globe.

Air Routes

Approximately thirty-five years ago, the ocean routes were without competition in

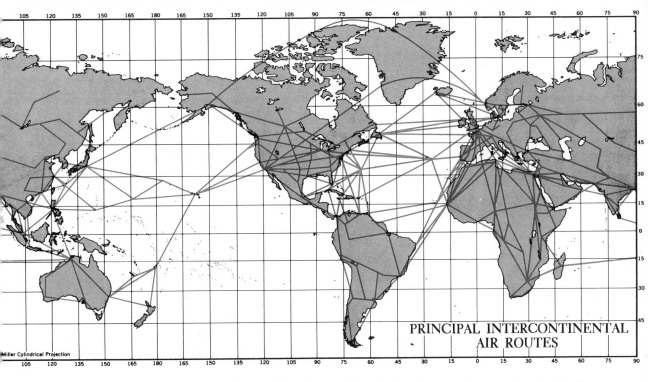

24-3 TODAY's *intercontinental air net has as its prominent foci northwestern Europe and eastern North America.*

intercontinental transportation. Since then, a rapidly growing net of scheduled airways has spread over much of the human habitat, so that air routes are outstanding transport lines linking the continental areas ever more closely together than before (FIG. 24-3). For many human beings, for mail, and for high value—small bulk goods, air transport has come to be preferred, especially since the development of the jet plane. But, for many other human beings and for bulky goods, either for economic reasons or through human choice, the ocean lanes remain the essential links.

GENERAL FACTORS IN AIR-ROUTE LOCATION • Like a ship crossing an ocean, an airplane leaves no permanent trace of its passage. The atmosphere extends alike over land and sea. Passage through it is possible in any direction. It would seem, therefore, that there would be no restricting influence to the development of air routes between any two points on the earth's surface. Further, it might appear that there would be no tendency to establish regular channels of flight now that long-range aircraft have been developed. But air routes have become more or less fixed just as have ocean routes. Some examination of the causes must here be made.

Economic reasons help to account for the close-knit appearance of the air net over some parts of the world and its fragmentary nature in others. Airplanes of the present day travel at speeds scarcely conceivable thirty years ago. Though their size has increased greatly in the same period, they can carry only relatively small loads as compared with ocean vessels, especially since much of an airplane's carrying capacity has to be used to transport the huge loads of fuel necessary to drive it at high speed over long distances. Thus, the airplane's use normally must be restricted to the transport of human beings or goods of great value per unit weight. Here, then, is a restriction placed upon the location and growth of intercontinental air routes.

The highly industrialized and commercialized portions of the world—northwestern Europe and the northeastern United States—are the chief destinations for high-value goods. In most instances, the goods also originate from these same regions. It is in these regions, too, that human travel, either for business or for recreational purposes, is most common. Hence, northwestern Europe and the northeastern United States constitute prominent foci for the strands of the intercontinental air net (FIG. 24–3). The strands themselves are heaviest over the North Atlantic basin.

Southward from both the North American and European foci, air routes lead to South America and Africa. Western North America and Asia are tied across the North Pacific. By way of the Hawaiian Islands, North America is tied to the southwest Pacific area, to New Zealand and Australia, and to eastern Asia. From northwest Europe routes extend to southern and eastern Asia. Finally, there are several routes reaching from northwestern Europe across the Arctic to western North America and the Orient, thus almost completing the girdling of the globe (see FIG. 24–3 and PLATE IX). In general, the pattern of airways corresponds closely to the distribution of areas most influenced by Western industrial civilization.

SPECIFIC FACTORS IN AIR-ROUTE LOCATION • The growth of air routes is affected not only by economic developments, but also by certain technical difficulties peculiar to air travel. The most critical periods in any airplane flight are, ordinarily, the take-off and the landing. Adequate facilities, especially large cleared areas suitably surfaced and with unobstructed approaches, are essential at both ends of a flight. Intercontinental aircraft need ports just as ocean vessels do. These ports must be accessible to both passengers and high-value goods, in quantity. Essentially this means a location in or near great cities or groups of cities. Commercial centers were already established and the flow lines of both passengers and goods to them were well fixed before the airplane came into being. It is to these centers that airports have had to be attached. The terminal points of significant intercontinental air routes were, thus, fairly well predetermined.

Yet, the very places on the earth's surface which are the most logical terminal points for air routes create many difficulties for efficient air operation. In the first place, space in the world's great cities is at a premium. Usually this means relegation of the airport to a location at some distance from the city's center. Local transportation which will make movement easy and rapid between the urban center and the airport becomes an essential. Even if easily accessible space is available, the mere presence of the city imposes physical obstacles to approach and departure. Tall buildings and power lines are two of these; the smoke of heavy industrial plants is another.

Then, too, since cities date from an earlier period in transportation history, presence of a good ocean harbor may have outweighed other features in the choice of site. Level land is often not present except at some distance from the urban center. Yet despite this difficulty, it is where the break between overland and ocean routes provides a collecting and distributing center that air routes must be tied down to earth.

Local weather conditions must also be taken into account in the detailed location of air routes. Weather phenomena like frontal activity, visibility, and icing conditions are troublesome. Man is not yet able to control the weather. In two ways, however, he has sought to overcome its effects. First, progress has been made in understanding atmospheric conditions and probable atmospheric changes. Second, even greater progress has been made by numerous inventions to cope with unfavorable weather conditions. De-icing and pressurizing equipment, radio, radar, and the like have all made air transport possible in extremely adverse weather. Yet, even now, weather causes flight cancellations or changes of destination in midflight. Where regularly followed air routes become well established, subsidiary airfields or emergency landing fields must also be available.

Meteorological observations are more plentiful and more complete on either side of the North Atlantic and along the great route followed by ocean shipping between North America and Europe than in any other part of the world. Despite the fact that in these areas the atmosphere is a zone of intensive cyclonic activity and hence a zone of extremely variable weather, it is nevertheless better understood than almost any other portion of the earth's atmospheric blanket.

National frontiers present another obstacle to international air routes. The segment of the atmosphere above a country is considered to lie within the jurisdiction of that country. Once an ocean vessel clears port, it may proceed on any determined course across the open ocean. Movement over the world's oceans, except in the immediate vicinity of the coast, is recognizedly open to ships of all nations. Airplanes, however, if they fly the shortest course, often have to pass over, perhaps more literally through, the domain of different nations.

For example, the air route from New York to Europe may lead to the British Isles or, by way of the Azores, to Portugal. Newfoundland's location, close to main great circle routes across the North Atlantic, made it a logical junction point in the earlier period of transoceanic flight, and Gander became truly an international air-route junction. Nevertheless, another country—Canada—has sovereignty over the port and all of its approaches. With the advent of direct jet flight from the United States to many parts of other continents, the position of ports like Gander became less significant, but the problem posed by air sovereignty still remains. Examples are to be seen in the limitation of air corridors into Berlin, and along the boundary between Turkey and the U.S.S.R. Thus it is easy to see that great international air routes are subject to restrictions in a way that ocean transportation is not.

INTRACONTINENTAL ROUTES

WHERE the great transoceanic routes by air or sea reach the continental edges, they join networks of routes leading inland, networks which tie even the most remote fixed human habitation into the world transportation pattern. Roads, waterways, and railroads exist as visible evidences of the flow lines of people and goods. Airfields indicate the most recent addition to the transport scheme. All of these forms, with the vehicles which move along them, are among the more prominent man-made features on the land. In this respect alone, intracontinental transportation is immediately different from intercontinental, which has as its major evidence only the urban terminal ports.

The culture of the inhabitants of an area, largely their economy and the stage of development within that economy, determines the nature of the network of routes and the intensity of its use. To the self-sufficient farmers of South China, for example, roads are of little significance. The few that exist are mere tracks or paths leading from the villages to the fields. They are not main-traveled thoroughfares between large urban centers, nor do large quantities of goods flow along them. On the other hand, to an industrial society like that in the northeastern United States, first-class highways with many surfaced and unsurfaced feeders, numerous railroads, and a growing system of airlines are "musts." Along all of these, as well as along inland waterways, flow the necessaries upon which industrial life is based. Food and raw materials for manufacture constantly travel inward to the urban centers, while manufactured goods move outward. The net of transportation must not only be of the highest quality; it must also be closely woven.

The location of any route is subject to the strong effects of both the physical and the cultural elements of the habitat. Since its function is to tie together two given points, any route follows the most direct path feasible between those two points. The obstacles which force deviation from the straight-line path are numerous. Some of them are physical features like steep slopes, swamps, or lakes; others are man-made like property lines or international boundaries. Nevertheless, whether it is the rude footworn path of the Chinese farmer or the wide, gleaming pavement of the most modern superhighway, the straight-line trajectory is the goal.

Roads

FUNCTION • The main function of the road is to facilitate the movement of human beings and their goods from one place to another on the face of the earth. This function means different things to different groups of people. The needs of the migratory farmer of the Amazon forest are met by a crude system of pathways: from his jungle-crowded garden patch to his dwelling, from a fishing place along a river to his dwelling, and from a hunting or collecting place in the forest to his dwelling. Perhaps animal trails through the areas of lighter forest are also roads for him, for they lead him to and from the places where he can supplement his meager agriculture. All of these pathways are his "roads"; the function of them all is to facilitate his movement.

In the intensive industrial region of northwestern Europe, as in that of the northeastern United States, the "road"—it may be a mag-

nificently paved and boulevarded highway— has essentially the same function. The differences between the primitive path and the modern highway are differences in magnitude and not in function. For the migratory farmer, it is not important that his roads connect with those of other groups or go beyond the area of his immediate use. But for the people of a modern industrial center, the roads must extend beyond the confines of the immediate area in which the center is located. They must extend far enough and in a sufficiently tightly connected design to make possible the accumulation of huge supplies and the distribution of equally huge amounts of manufactured produce.

Until relatively modern times, the road was developed and operated primarily on a local scale. Perhaps the first departure from this was the conception and creation of the famous system of Roman roads. In the days of the Roman Empire, surfaced roads were built throughout much of western and southern Europe, all of them focusing eventually on the city of Rome itself. Main trunk lines led from that city to all major parts of the Empire and to key points on the frontier. The function of this system was to facilitate primarily troop movements. The roads welded together the territory throughout which Roman military authority extended.

With the decline of the Roman Empire, the road system became the line of movement of armies despoiling the lands formerly under Roman control. Later, the system fell into disuse and decay. For a long period, roads again served only local areas. Later still, particularly in the seventeenth and eighteenth centuries, roads became the framework for the spread of political control, a device for the centralizing of power, as in the creation of the modern French state. Yet through these many centuries, the prime function—to facilitate the movement of peoples and goods for short distances—did not change. When the spread over larger areas became necessary for carrying on a certain way of life, long-distance transportation by road was developed.

PATTERN OR DESIGN • Landforms, water features, vegetation, and soil all have their effect on the position of the road upon the land. Similarly, features of the cultural milieu, the locations of settlements, the system of land survey, the type of economy, and intangibles like law have equally strong effects upon the location of the road in any given area.

Relief features stand out perhaps more prominently than any others in controlling road location. Roads across mountain ranges, for example, are fixed in part by the location of low sections of the crest line—the passes, like Brenner Pass in the Alps. There, not only the position of the pass, but the possible means of access to it, determine where the road goes. A wide glacial trough leads back into the Alps from the plain of the Po river in Italy and gives easy access to the pass. Likewise, another glacial trough leads northward from the pass itself to the hill zone of the Alpine foreland of southern Germany and Austria. Thus, the easiest gradient across the whole width of the Alps provides the obvious line to be followed and practically fixes the road's location.

To be sure, engineering skill has made it possible to have less regard for terrain barriers. Instead of steep, zigzag climbs and descents over abruptly sloping ridges, tunnels have been driven through the ridges, as along the Pennsylvania Turnpike or in the western ascent to Newfound Gap in the Great Smoky Mountains. Still, the approaches are largely determined by the location of valley ways back into the heart of mountain country. In the instance of the highway tunnel now under construction from Chamonix, France, to Courmayeur, Italy, under Mont Blanc, the approach on both sides is up the glacial troughs which flank the northwestern and southeastern sides of the Mont Blanc Massif.

Other features of the physical setting, like swamps, marshes, and lakes, all contribute to the location of a specific roadway. A jog may indicate avoidance of land which is seasonally flooded, or it may lead around a patch of exceptionally clayey soil where passage would be easy in dry weather but almost impossible in wet. Roads often depart from the direct route to approach an easy river crossing instead of a difficult one. Many of the roads which had their origin in early days avoided wooded areas and chose instead to follow from one open grassy area to another. Nowadays there often seems to be no reason for such routes. In earlier days, however, when political power extended only over small areas and was not too strong even within them, as, for example, in the Europe of the Middle Ages, there was no policing of the highway. As a result, woodland often gave cover to highwaymen. Travel was dangerous and wherever possible the road led across country in which nothing offered cover for ambush.

But features of the physical setting have by no means been the only elements influencing the location of roads. The existence of a market town offering commercial facilities for a considerable countryside has often formed a focus toward which roads led, subject always to the physical barriers to be overcome. Sometimes the design was planned, as in the building of the system of *Routes Nationales* in France (FIG. 24–4). There, the great system of highways which radiated to all parts of the nation from Paris was primarily a planned way of extending royal influence to all parts of the territory nominally subject to the French king. The road was in this instance a political and military device. The pattern imposed was the radial one, by which everything was directed toward the seat of government, Paris.

In the Midwest and West of the United States, a cultural element was in large part responsible for the road pattern which developed. The rectangular land survey, used in the Northwest Territory and later in the area which became our western states, created a gridlike pattern. Even in this area departures from the rectangular pattern are numerous

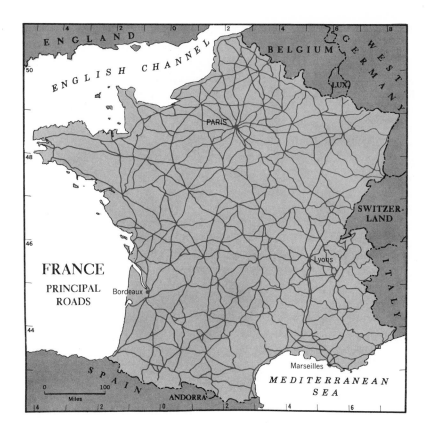

24-4

THE *basic road pattern of France radiates from Paris to all parts of the country. This map shows only the main Routes Nationales.*

where it became necessary to avoid certain water or landform features or where settlement preceded survey. Yet over much of the land, the roads extend straight for miles on end and are crossed at right angles by other equally straight roads. The motor age has brought some modification, for high speeds and right-angle turns are not compatible. Where sharp turns occur on main-traveled roads, they are being replaced by wide, sweeping curves, so engineered as to allow high speed to be maintained.

QUALITY · Early roads were essentially tracks marked on the land by the passage of men, beasts of burden, and primitive vehicles. There was no idea of road construction, nor were there special works like bridges, culverts, fills, and cuts. There was no special or organized effort to maintain the road once it came into being. In rare instances roads were paved locally, as by the Incas in Peru, but far and away the greater part of the roads were simple, natural tracks across the land.

To the Romans belongs the credit for the first constructed roads in areas of Western civilization; to them likewise belongs the credit for the development of the first road system. Heavy rock foundations, causeways, bridges, and culverts were introduced to make the roads passable at all times of the year. And pavement of the stone-block type created a new and less ephemeral feature on the land. The highway net which the Romans spread through western and southern Europe was more firmly fixed than any of the roads which preceded it, and more completely knit together. Then, too, the roads were maintained during the whole period of ascendancy of the Roman Empire. Maintenance was planned, not haphazard. Even after the decline of the Empire had set in, as has been suggested previously, many of the Roman roads were maintained locally. So well were they built, and in many places so well kept up, that they form the base of many of the modern roads of Great Britain, Belgium, France, and Italy.

By and large, however, road systems declined during the Middle Ages. It was not until near the end of the fifteenth century, and then in France only, that any attempt was made at organized road maintenance. In France, Louis XI created *Les Postes Royales*, which was actually a system of relay stations along routes traveled by royal messengers. The creation of this system brought to the forefront the notion of road-surface improvement and road maintenance. From that time on, the quality of a road became the object of greater and greater care.

The toll road was one of the early devices introduced to better the quality of the road. Private individuals or companies were given the right to charge for travel over a certain length of highway in return for maintaining the highway in the best possible condition. As often as not, this "best possible condition" was little better than earlier cross-country tracks (FIG. 24–5). Yet the system of toll roads did develop commonly used ways that were

24–5

THE *Washington–Richmond road near Quantico, Virginia, some forty years ago.*

more extensive than any local network. And where travel was sufficiently heavy, it led slowly to improvement.

Not until the coming of the automobile, however, was progress in road improvement rapid. Higher speed of travel and longer distances to be covered—in short, greater mobility—brought the demand for more and more surfaced roads, and for surfaces of greater and greater smoothness. It is really only in this century that road systems have been built to tie together areas which are relatively far apart.

The extent to which high-speed movement between major focal urban areas has developed has created the need for "superhighways" in both western Europe and in North America. The "thruway," "expressway," and "parkway" are all expressions of the expanding function of roads (FIG. 24–6). It is curious to note that the building of the superhighway has, in many instances, brought a return to the old device, the toll road, to carry the cost of construction.

GENERAL WORLD PATTERN • A network of high-quality roads for a large area is best illustrated in the United States. The great number of motor vehicles in the United States as compared with the rest of the world suggests a reason. Just over two-thirds of the approximately 3,100,000 miles of rural roads in the United States are classed as surfaced roads. The remainder are ordinary dirt roads. Of the roads with some type of surface, such as gravel, crushed stone, macadam, or any of the other types of surfacing, only about 300,000 miles are the highest quality, hard-surfaced type (FIG. 24–6). Thus, despite the fact that United States roads are the best in the world, only about 10 per cent of all roads in the country have the high-quality surface which we commonly think of as a usual feature of our roadway system.

The highest density of roads is encountered in Japan. Great Britain, Denmark, France, Ireland, and Belgium follow in order. All of these countries are small in area; they are comparable to individual states in the United States. When large areas are considered, two great areas of

24–6

THE *Tappan Zee Bridge which carries the New York State Thruway over the Hudson River at Nyack, New York.*

high road density stand out above all others: the United States and northwestern Europe (FIG. 24–7). The nets loosen to fray out in widely spaced strands in eastern and southern Europe on the one hand and in Canada and Mexico on the other.

In Asia, the eastern and southern fringe areas, like Japan and parts of China in the east and sections of Pakistan and India in the south, include some areas of tightly woven road net. From these, isolated stringers reach out toward the interior. A few lines cross the continent to connect with the European pattern in the U.S.S.R.

Of the other continents, Africa shows a fairly dense road net in the Atlas lands and in the Cape region. Elsewhere long stringers criss-cross the continent at wide intervals. In South America, a high density marks Southeastern Brazil, most of Uruguay, the Argentine Pampas, and parts of Chile. Along the coasts over the rest of the continent, an occasional road reaches back from coastal settled regions to a nearly empty interior. Southeastern Australia

is the focal region on that continent though there the net is less tightly woven than in other centers mentioned.

Where human beings live in a commercial or an industrial economy, an elaborate net of roadways is a necessity. Where human groups exist in an economy which is self-sufficient, the road net is fragmentary. The stage of cultural and economic development largely determines both the density and the quality of the network of roads.

Waterways

Men have been using rivers and lakes as natural routes for ages. Today, rivers and lakes still remain almost the only highways in some of the less densely peopled parts of the world. For example, the Amazon river is the only real "road" throughout a large part of the South American continent. At the same time, rivers and lakes remain very important in the transportation system of the most highly industrialized regions of the world. To be sure, artificial works like canals have been introduced to bypass obstructions like falls and rapids. And it is a far cry from the small and hazardous dugout of the tropical forest dweller to the huge vessels of modern design which ply certain of the world's great inland waterways like the Great Lakes.

Waterways are most useful today in the movement of bulky goods of low value per unit weight and of goods which make no call upon speedy transportation. In North America, the magnificent waterway of the Great Lakes is an essential link between the Midwest, with its supplies of mineral and agricultural raw materials, and the manufacturing regions of the East, with their huge demands for "food" for both human beings and machines. The thousands of tons of iron ore from the Lake Superior mining region are brought to the coal of the Appalachian region cheaply and efficiently. So are huge tonnages of wheat brought from farms to the eastern milling and

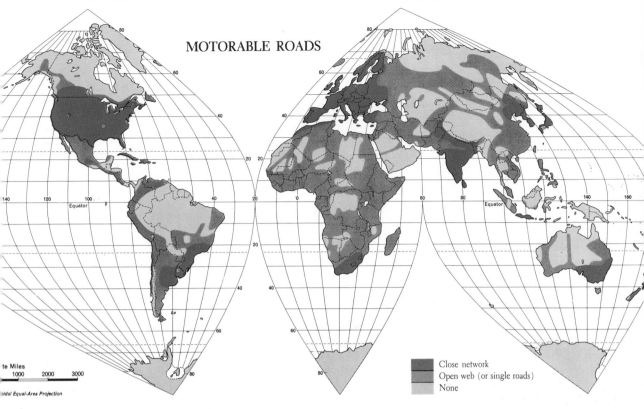

Close network
Open web (or single roads)
None

24–7   A GENERALIZED *world map showing relative density of the net of motorable roads.*

shipping centers. By use of this waterway other lines of transportation are freed to move other goods, many of them requiring faster means of conveyance. The opening of the St. Lawrence Seaway tied this magnificent system to the intercontinental route pattern and thus further increases efficiency. Similarly, the Rhine with its navigable tributaries and associated canals is still, as it has been for centuries, a main artery of transportation in western Europe. The Yangtze still funnels the produce of interior China to the coast, where there is access by coastal routes to other parts of China.

Where new land or relatively sparsely populated land is being opened either for exploitation or for settlement, the waterway is a cheap, ready-made route. The early opening of the interior of the United States was facilitated by the existence of the widespread system of the Mississippi and its tributaries. The produce of

frontier farms could be floated downstream to New Orleans and the needed goods brought back upstream by river boat. Again, the exploitation of the Congo forest was greatly facilitated by the presence of an extensive network of water routes. Even today, in the opening of northern Siberia by the U.S.S.R., water routes are the most practical expedient yet available. The great northward-flowing rivers of Siberia—the Ob, the Yenisei, and the Lena —though unnavigable for much of the year because of ice, are the best routes from the Trans-Siberian Railway northward or from the Arctic coast southward. By far the most used waterways of the modern world are those of northwest Europe. A plains surface in this region of humid climate where winters are not too severe provides many rivers which are not seriously interrupted by rapids or waterfalls nor frozen for extended periods. Flow in most of them has been regularized and the courses have

Intracontinental Routes | 567

24–8 THE Rhine river is one of the main traffic arteries of Europe. Barges are passing the town of Kaub in the Rhine Gorge section of West Germany. Note the terraced valley side with Gutenfels fortress overlooking the town and the castle of Pfalzgrafenstein on an island in midstream.

been straightened and deepened. The Seine, the Meuse, the Rhine (FIG. 24–8), the Weser, the Ems, the Elbe, the Oder, and the Vistula are the main ones giving access to the Atlantic or to its marginal seas, the North and Baltic. Not too far from the headwaters of all of these streams, the Danube offers a line which leads to the Black Sea and thus to the Mediterranean. Between the northern rivers, canals were easily built linking the whole North European Plain. By means again of a canal, the northern rivers were linked to the southward-flowing Rhône and through it to the Mediterranean. A whole network of waterways fills in the parts of this general pattern so that few sections of European industrial regions are far from water transportation of some sort.

In the United States, waterways play a smaller role. The Great Lakes, of course, are an exception. There are, in addition, a few canals, like the New York State Barge Canal, which links the Hudson river with the Great Lakes. Important too is the main stem of the Mississippi river and some of its tributaries, especially the Ohio. Beyond that, there is the system of coastal waterways leading from Long Island Sound to the Gulf Coast. But, throughout the greater part of the country, roads and railroads carry the loads.

Railroads

All peoples have roads of some sort. Waterways too are used by primitive peoples as well

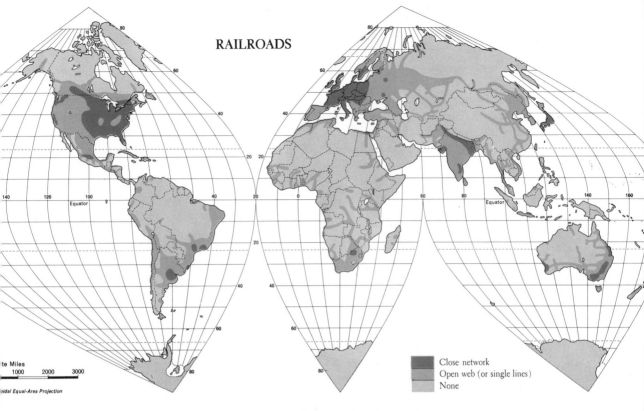

Close network
Open web (or single lines)
None

te Miles
1000 2000 3000

sidal Equal-Area Projection

24–9   A GENERALIZED world map showing relative density of railroads.

as by the most advanced or complex civilizations. But the railroad is the distinctive transportation feature of Western industrial civilization (FIG. 24–9).

The railroad made possible the movement of huge volumes of goods over long distances at high speeds. Through the use of railroads, industrial nuclei could draw their raw materials for manufacture and their foods from areas increasingly larger and increasingly farther away. And the products of the industrial centers could be distributed in volumes and at speeds previously unattainable.

Railroads are little more than a century old, and it is hard to imagine just how our present-day great cities could exist, how any sizable urban agglomerations could ever have existed, without them. Today, other means of transportation have, at least in the United States, taken over much of the local business from the railroads. Motor trucks, buses, and airplanes

have taken over the functions of the railroads for short distances and small hauls and for passengers. In 1940, for example, railroads carried 63 per cent of the intercity freight traffic in the United States. In the same year, commercial motor vehicles accounted for 10 per cent; inland waterways, for 18 per cent; and pipelines, for 9 per cent. The volume of air freight was negligible (.002 per cent). In 1960, the share of the railroads was just over 46 per cent; motor vehicles, just under 22 per cent; inland waterways, 15 per cent; and pipelines, 17 per cent. Air freight, though it had increased notably, still accounted for only .05 per cent of the total. Most passenger traffic used private automobiles in both years. The passenger traffic using public carriers in 1940 was divided as follows: railroads, 46 per cent; commercial motor vehicles, 38 per cent; airways, 14 per cent; and inland waterways, 2 per cent. Marked changes were evident in 1960

Intracontinental Routes | 569

when railroads carried only 29 per cent; commercial motor vehicles, 26 per cent; airways, 42 per cent; and inland waterways, 3 per cent. The railroad, however, remains as the long-distance method of shipping the bulk of the world's industrial goods.

RAILROADS IN THE UNITED STATES • From a scant 5000 miles in 1840, the railroads of the United States extended so that there were approximately 250,000 miles of line in 1930. Since that year, mileage has decreased to 218,000. The first steam locomotive in regular service began its operations in December of 1830 on a six-mile line from Charleston to Hamburg in South Carolina. From this small beginning, American railroads have grown so that they now make up about one-quarter of all the railroads in the world.

The rail net (FIG. 24–10) focuses upon the industrial northeastern part of the country. Nearly all of the eastern seaboard region is crossed by lines linking the large eastern cities and extending inland from them. Notable concentrations cross the Appalachian system by the Hudson–Mohawk corridor in the north and by more devious routes between Philadelphia and Pittsburgh. Once the rough land of the Appalachians is crossed, the net of lines becomes denser in the interior plains, with a major focus at Chicago. To the south and west of that city a relatively closely woven net spreads over the land as far as the 100th meridian except for the rough land of the Ozark Highlands. Then quite suddenly the rail net frays out and only a few long stringers stretch across the plain, mountain, and plateau country of the west to link Pacific Coast centers with the east. It is in the humid east that rail lines are most numerous and most evenly spaced over the whole surface.

The pattern of rail lines does not reveal their true significance from one region to another within the United States. A line may be single track or multiple track; it may carry one train per hour or one train per week. When the distributions of these elements are added

to the pattern, it can be clearly appreciated that rail traffic counts most heavily in the Northeastern Manufacturing Region.

RAILROADS IN THE REMAINDER OF NORTH AMERICA • Canadian railroads seem almost to be extensions of the net within the United States. The route between Buffalo and Detroit —through Ontario—is an example as is also the northward extension of the Hudson valley lines to Montreal. Southern Ontario and the middle St. Lawrence valley in the east have closely woven nets.

The second concentration of rail lines in Canada is that of the so-called Prairie Provinces, from Winnipeg in Manitoba in a wide-sweeping belt westward through the wheat-producing lands of Saskatchewan and Alberta.

There are finally the cross-continent lines between the Pacific and Atlantic coasts. These lines hold together the widely separated, more highly populated parts of the country. From them extend a few long tentacles like that to Prince Rupert on the British Columbian coast, Churchill on Hudson Bay, and Moosonee on James Bay.

The Mexican rail net is fragmentary. It is best developed in the vicinity of Mexico City. Lines lead from that center to the Gulf Coast at Veracruz and Tampico. Likewise, lines lead northward to join with railroads of the United States along the Texas and Arizona boundaries.

RAILROADS IN EUROPE • Northwestern Europe has an even closer network of rail lines than the United States (FIG. 24–9). It was, of course, in England that the world's first railroad was built and operated in 1825. As industrialization spread from England to the northwestern part of the Continent, railroads quickly followed. An increasingly widely spaced net extends eastward across the Plain of North Europe to fray out toward the Ural Mountains. The net likewise thins out southward and southeastward from the North Sea shores to become especially thin in the Iberian and Balkan areas.

Over much of Europe, the handicaps of

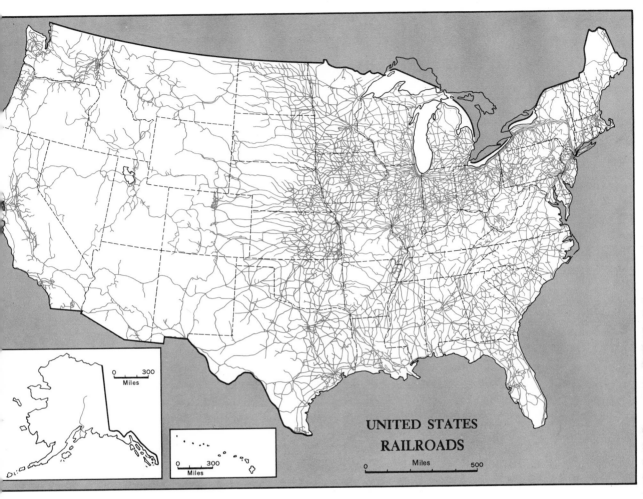

24-10　THE rail net in the United States is most nearly complete in the northeastern quarter of the country. It is fragmentary in the rougher lands of the East, in the drier Great Plains, and in the mountain and plateau country of the West. For other relationships, compare this map with FIGS. 17–12 and 23–3.

rugged terrain are absent. Only in the Alps are there serious landform obstacles, and even in those mountains great engineering feats like the Saint Gotthard, Simplon, and Mont Cenis tunnels extended rail communication tying Italy closely to northern Europe. In extreme northern Europe, the almost complete absence of railroads reflects the low density of population.

Two features distinguish the European railroad pattern. First, railroads came after the land was thoroughly settled, so that they followed already existing routes. Hence the effect of the railroad was to increase the importance of existing centers of manufacture and commerce rather than to create new ones. For example, the supremacy of Paris among French cities was already established well before the railroad era. The fact that rail lines over the whole country converge toward Paris has strengthened that city's position so that no other French city even approaches it in size,

24–11

THE railroads of France converge on Paris.

in importance as a center of manufacturing, or as the commercial and economic heart of the country.

The second feature of the European rail pattern is that railroads radiate from capital cities in each country; France provides a good example (FIG. 24–11). The railroad has been developed throughout Europe with military needs in mind. Each country, faced with the military needs of the nineteenth century, sought ease of access from the capital city to all points on the frontier. Military convenience became the leading influence in the development of railroads within each of the separate countries of the Continent. International routes were, of course, made available, but they were relatively few in number and their planning and construction were secondary to the internal lines. Further, difficulty of articulation of one country's net with another's be-

came a problem with the use of different rail gauges by different countries. For example, most of the railroads of France are standard gauge (rails 4 feet 8½ inches apart) while much of the railroad system of Spain is broad gauge (rails 5 feet 5¾ inches apart).

RAILROADS IN ASIA • The tremendous expanse of Asia has hardly been penetrated by the railroad. Only in a few sections of the continent is the pattern sufficiently intensified to be called a net. Western influence has created the net in those places where one exists.

On the west, Asiatic railroads are linked to the frayed edge of the European pattern. One thin strand was early extended eastward from Moscow across Siberia to the Pacific Coast at Vladivostok (FIG. 24–9). Later, under the Soviet regime, other lines were built linking with the Trans-Siberian Railway to bring the newer mining and industrial areas of the

Central Urals, Kuznetsk, and the like into closer touch with the European portions of the U.S.S.R. A tie has also been made across the Mongolian People's Republic to the expanding net of China's rail lines.

Throughout Japan, railroads came with industrialization. It is there more than in any other part of the Asiatic sphere that the railroad is a common means of transportation. In Manchuria, Korea, and northern China there are lines which are really amplifications of the eastern end of the Trans-Siberian line. The Indian peninsula has as completely developed a pattern as is to be found on the Asiatic mainland. The broad lowland of the Ganges is the most intensively covered part, with major termini at Calcutta and Delhi. An east-coast network centers upon Madras, while Bombay and Karachi are termini in the west. Over the Deccan Plateau stretches a net which is less dense than that of the Ganges lowland, but which ties the parts of the peninsula together.

RAILROADS IN THE OTHER CONTINENTS • Of the other continents, South America is perhaps best equipped with railroads, though it has no truly continental development. Three networks stand out clearly in the east-coast regions: they center on Rio de Janeiro, São Paulo, and Buenos Aires. All have tentacles reaching toward the interior and there are weak links between the three nets. In Chile in the west, a north-south line extends nearly the whole length of the central valley and from it lead spurs eastward into the Andes and westward to the Pacific. Beyond these few, the railroads of South America are mostly isolated lines reaching from a port into the interior or from one navigable portion of a river to another.

In Africa, two areas have moderately well-developed rail patterns. The French tied together the North African lands of Morocco, Algeria, and Tunis with an east-west line stretching the whole length of the Atlas lands. From this, skeletal spurs lead from the coast into the desert. In the Republic of South Africa, the more humid lands of the Cape Town area, Natal, Orange Free State, and Transvaal are closely joined by railroads. The main line northeastward from Cape Town leads ultimately by way of the Rhodesias to the important mineral region of Katanga. From this main line, spurs lead to coastal termini like Port Elizabeth and Durban in the Republic, and Beira and Lourenço Marques in Mozambique.

In Australia, the greatest development is in the southeast, between Adelaide, Melbourne, Sydney, and Brisbane. A smaller net centers on Perth in the southwest, with a single line tying the two together. Elsewhere, long fingers reach from ports toward the interior.

Airlines

The density of scheduled-flight airlines is greatest in the most highly urbanized portions of the earth, as in the United States. The commercial operation of airlines so far deals mainly with passengers and with mail. Increasingly important, especially for high value–small bulk goods, are the commercial cargo lines. Though cargo planes still carry a far smaller portion of total freight than do other public carriers, as indicated on page 569, total tonnage in the United States was 25 times as great in 1960 as it was in 1940. Speed has been the great asset; limited load capacities, the greatest handicap. As has previously been stated, it is in the urbanized portions of the earth that both passengers and mail are plentiful enough to ensure economic operation of the airlines.

Here and there other means of transportation are so costly as to make air transport economically feasible. For example, in South America the trip from the coast of Colombia up the Magdalena river valley and into the eastern Andes to the capital city of Bogotá is so time-consuming when made by rail and river that the airline can compete successfully. Still, passengers and mail make the bulk of the cargo. Similarly in Africa, travel to such places as Elisabethville in southeastern Katanga is so time-consuming by surface routes that the airplane offers, in the end, the most efficient transport agent. Airplanes can and do function over such sparsely populated areas as northern Canada or Alaska where other means of transportation are lacking. But most bulky goods still are transported by other carriers.

Other Transportation Forms

To the roads, waterways, railroads, and airlines of intracontinental transportation must be added such forms as pipelines, telephonic and telegraphic wires, cables and power lines, radio and television in their various types. Pipelines carry natural gas and oil from the producing fields to the consuming areas, as from the mid-continent and Texas–Oklahoma fields to the urban northeast. Again, it is the urban areas of the world, especially those of the United States, which have brought this transport agent into being. In the same way, the industrialized portions of the world have brought wires and cables into use for transportation purposes—transportation of electric energy and electric impulses.

There has come likewise the transmission of words and images with and without the use of wires. These forms of communication are primarily a part of the industrial urban way of life; they are most numerous and most commonly used in North America and northwestern Europe. Yet they too are stretching out to new regions, tying those fragments of the human habitat into closer and closer relation with one another.

THE WORLD PATTERN OF TRANSPORTATION AS A FEATURE OF WESTERN CULTURE

BY ONE means or another, the great number of fragments of the human habitat have come to be more and more closely linked, largely as a result of the development and spread of Western culture. In the early periods of human history, the people of one small part of the world spread over increasingly larger areas until they came in contact with other groups. Through contact, a limited habitat came to be more than an isolated fragment. For example, a weak tribe of South European peoples once occupied the "Hills of the Tiber" in west-central Italy. Through centuries, they extended their little world beyond the hills on which they settled, through the Italian peninsula, across the mountain barrier of the Alps, and even across the water barrier of the English Channel. All of this they welded together, the greater part of western Europe and northern Africa, into the Roman Empire. They used "roads" to do it—the land road and the route provided by the Mediterranean Sea.

From the western European base, the nations which were the descendants of the Roman Empire sought out overland "roads" to the Orient. Later they ventured out onto the "Western Sea." Water routes supplanted land roads and brought more of the human habitat into the European—the Western—sphere. At the same time, Western economy underwent radical changes and became the industrial economy. A need was present for continued expansion over still more of the world, the need of supplying increasing urban populations with food for themselves and raw materials for their machines. The means of linkage between the parts of the world were the roads, the waterways, the railroads, and, newest of all, the airways. Thus the transportation pattern of the world grew to its present form.

Imperfect though it still is over many parts

of the world, this pattern has profoundly affected our concept of the whole human habitat. For Western people especially, the world is no longer a jumble of little pieces separated from one another by unknown voids; it is a mosaic of great variety of detail in some portions and of great coarseness in others, but all held together in a matrix, the visible evidence of which is the world transportation pattern.

• REVIEW QUESTIONS •

1. Why do most ships crossing the North Atlantic Ocean follow essentially the same course?

2. Why is the North Atlantic route the most traveled intercontinental route in the world?

3. What conditions account for the location of intercontinental air routes?

4. In what parts of the world are intercontinental air routes most numerous and most frequently flown? List some of the reasons.

5. What are some of the factors which place detailed limitations upon the location of air routes?

6. Why are the patterns of intracontinental routes of different quality, intensity, and design in different parts of the world?

7. What is the main function of the road? Illustrate by specific reference to different parts of the world.

8. What factors contribute to the determination of road pattern in various parts of the world? Give specific examples.

9. What part of the world has the densest network of high-quality roads for a large area? For a small area?

10. With what kinds of areas are high-quality roads normally associated? Why?

11. What waterway is of major significance in the United States today? What gives it its importance? Explain.

12. In what parts of the world are there relatively dense networks of railroads? With what other

distributions may that of railroads be associated?

13. Describe the main features of the railroad pattern of North America.

14. What two features distinguish the European railroad pattern?

15. In what parts of the world is the intensity of scheduled-flight intracontinental airlines greatest? Give some of the reasons for this distribution.

16. What are some transportation forms other than those of road, waterway, railroad, and airline?

IV

THE VARIED AND CHANGING SCENE

25 Physical and Cultural Variety and Change

FAIRCHILD AERIAL SURVEYS

⟨⟨ MODERN *man's knowledge of his world is relatively thorough. To be sure, some portions of the earth are still unexplored and many others inadequately mapped. Also, many problems of living and making a living on the earth are only vaguely recognized or are far from solution. But, by and large, the earth as man's habitat is well understood and fully appreciated. As man sizes up his present-day world, he can hardly fail to see its amazing variety and be aware of its many changing conditions.*

VARIETY AND CHANGE IN THE PHYSICAL SCENE

THE physical variety of the earth is such that no two parts are identical. This presents man with many opportunities and many problems: opportunities to live and gain a livelihood in different fashions, problems of how best to meet physical conditions as they occur in a given region or in all regions. Bewildering as the physical variety may be, close examination soon indicates certain broad comprehensible patterns. The complexities of the air resolve themselves into recognizable types of weather and climate. The variations of the land surface itself become identifiable kinds of major and minor landforms. The details of natural vegetation merge to produce major vegetation associations. Finally, the various types of climate, landforms, natural vegetation, and other physical elements themselves combine to constitute certain physical complexes of one size or another. Thus, as one gains a working notion of such environments as the world's Dry Lands, Mountain Lands, Northern Forest Lands, or Tropical Rainforest Lands, ultimately one gains a grasp of the physical earth as a whole (FIG. 14-2). Or, on a more detailed scale, one gains insight regarding the physical setup of such areas as the Argentine Pampas (FIG. 25-2), the Paris Basin (FIG. 16-10), or the Central Valley of California (FIG. 14-4).

Men often refer to "the unchanging physical scene." The reference reflects the shortness of the individual life span and general unawareness of such change as does take place, often in a single lifetime. In terms of one man's life there are many conditions which change only a little: the Rocky Mountains "stay there"; the climate of England remains the same; the state of Iowa still has its black prairie soil; glacial lakes continue to dot the Laurentian Upland. Yet, the Rockies represent only one temporary phase in the succession of landforms of that particular segment of the earth's crust; England's climate has been different in the past and undoubtedly will be different in the distant future; Iowa's black prairie soil is, in terms of earth's history, only a fleeting phase of the regolith; the glacial lakes of the Laurentian region are being filled with sediment and aquatic vegetation, many of them already have become swamps, and some of the swamps have become dry land.

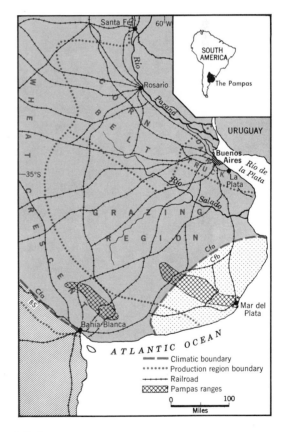

THE Argentine Pampas, with its fertile soils, nearly level lands, and mild, humid climate, is one of the world's great food baskets.

25-1

[OPPOSITE, TOP] A TRAFFIC cross-over at Rochelle Park, New Jersey. How different from the crossroads of the past!

25-2

25–3

A MINNESOTA *spruce swamp which has resulted from the filling in of a former glacial lake.*

25–4

AIR *view of a recent fault scarp, which may be seen as the pronounced line extending from upper left to lower right, near Indio, California. The parts of the scarp which cross canyon mouths are buried by alluvial materials washed from the hills.*

The vast majority of the major changes in the physical scene result from processes that accomplish their work very slowly in terms of man's common concept of time (FIG. 25–3). However, there are some which occur with comparative rapidity, especially in localized areas. A flash flood in the desert may carve a large arroyo within a few hours. Faulting of the earth's crust may create a new escarpment within a few minutes (FIG. 25–4). A fire set by lightning may devastate hundreds of square miles of forest in a matter of days. River channels change position overnight and the local character of a shore may be transformed appreciably by one storm. Rapidly or slowly, the physical complex changes.

In addition to the physical changes wrought naturally, there are many more caused by man himself, particularly in those areas where he has lived a long time and in sizable numbers. In extensive areas he has wiped out forests or turned seas of grass into seas of wheat. He has brought water to deserts and transformed

25–5

A SECTION *of reclaimed land in the Pontine Marshes along the west coast of Italy, near Rome.*

sterile wastes into densely populated garden lands. He has leveled hills and filled valleys, drained marshlands (FIG. 25–5) and constructed huge reservoir lakes. In large metropolitan areas, he has changed virtually everything, including the conditions of the lower atmosphere. Too often, he has wrought destructive change, as witness farmlands eroded beyond possibility of cultivation (FIG. 12–8), fire-blackened wastes of former forest lands, and "dried-out" regions with lowered water tables and dwindling streams. Unthinkingly or by design, man has played a large part in changing the physical world.

VARIETY AND CHANGE
IN THE CULTURAL SCENE

JUST as no two parts of the earth are physically identical, no two parts are culturally identical. Again, man is presented with opportunities and with problems: opportunities to share the best from many cultures, problems of what to do when cultures clash with one another or fail to function when transferred to new environments. Like the physical variety, cultural variety often seems bewilderingly complex—perhaps the term "cultural complex" has much deeper meaning than the term "physical complex." Yet on one scale or another, or with one objective or another, we can grasp the manifold cultural patterns and their individual elements.

We may recognize Western as opposed to Oriental cultures, primitive as opposed to advanced cultures, machine as opposed to non-machine cultures, nomadic as opposed to sedentary cultures, and so on. In a more restricted sense, we may recognize rice culture as opposed to maize culture, or hoe culture as opposed to plow culture. All of these cultures, singly and intermixed, provide the variety of the earth's cultural scene. Geographically, they appear as populations of different patterns, densities, and "races," as various types of structures, settlements, major occupations, and ways of transportation and communication, and as different types of land-use complexes (FIG. 25–6). Certainly, the variety in the cultural scene at least matches that of the physical scene. If it is a variety more difficult to grasp, there is good reason for it is fraught with many elements which do not readily lend themselves to quantitative measurement and with changes which are, more often than not, disconcertingly rapid and unexpected.

Until the Age of Exploration and the Industrial Revolution, cultural change was relatively slow. Ideas, persons, and goods moved at a snail's pace. Some cultures were so isolated that they grew and gave their particular impress to the land for thousands of years before the rest of the world was aware of their existence. Within the past 150 to 200 years, change has been the order of the day and man has witnessed greater change than took place within the preceding 2000 years. Some areas have been affected much more than others, but there is hardly a region, no matter how remote, that has not changed, or been forced to change, its way of life to some degree. Change has been so rapid for the earth as a whole that cultural evolution has been replaced by cultural revolution.

The growth and application of technology lie at the root of the rapid changes occurring in the present-day world. Ideas can now spread very rapidly and persons and goods are sped across land and sea at ever-increasing rates. The results are to be seen almost everywhere. Grasslands, long stubbornly resistant to the hoe and wooden plow, have capitulated to the steel plow and tractor-drawn gang plow; deforested areas are replanted and placed under

25–6   Top: Man and his works dominate the landscape in some sections of the world, as in the California seaport of San Francisco. Below: In other parts of the world, man's presence is less noticeable, as in this Vermont village.

25–7 NIGHT *view of modern Pittsburgh—a far cry from little Fort Pitt of Colonial days—showing blast furnaces and steel mills along the steep, crowded banks of the Monongahela river. In the left background, the lighted tops of two tall buildings mark the position of Pittsburgh's famous "Golden Triangle," where the Monongahela and Allegheny join to form the Ohio river.*

scientific management; regions of subsistence farming become highly specialized commercial farming districts; open rural countryside becomes a crowded city (FIG. 25–7); airplanes serve regions which have never seen a highway or a railroad; and automobiles provide economic and social mobility for whole populations.

In today's world, political boundaries change; empires decline; mass population movements occur; whole systems of land use are modified; nationalism clashes with internationalism; the released energy of the atom promises man a better way of life—or threatens to annihilate him. In one fashion or another, all these changes affect the cultural scene; coupled with the variety and transformations in the physical scene they present us with a fascinating, even though often disconcerting, world.

Variety and Change in the Cultural Scene | 583

APPENDICES

BEGINNING OF INTERVAL *(Millions of Years)*

Scale (top): 0 10 20 30 40 50 60 70 80 90 100 110 120 130 140 150 160 170 180 190 200 210 220 230 240 250 260 270

ERA	PERIOD	EPOCH	BEGINNING OF INTERVAL (Millions of Years)
CENOZOIC	QUATERNARY	Recent (11,000) / Pleistocene	1
	TERTIARY	Pliocene	13
		Miocene	25
		Oligocene	36
		Eocene (UPPER / MIDDLE / LOWER)	45 / 52 / 58
		Paleocene	63
MESOZOIC	CRETACEOUS (UPPER)	Maestrichtian	72
		Campanian	81
		Santonian / Coniacian	84 / 88
		Turonian	90
		Cenomanian	
	CRETACEOUS (LOWER)	Albian	110
		Aptian	120
		Neocomian	135
	JURASSIC (UPPER)		
	JURASSIC (MIDDLE)	Bathonian	166
		Bajocian	
	JURASSIC (LOWER)		181
	TRIASSIC (UPPER / MIDDLE / LOWER)		200
	PERMIAN (UPPER / MIDDLE / LOWER)		(230)
			260

Scale (bottom): 0 10 20 30 40 50 60 70 80 90 100 110 120 130 140 150 160 170 180 190 200 210 220 230 240 250 260 270

Geologic Time Scale

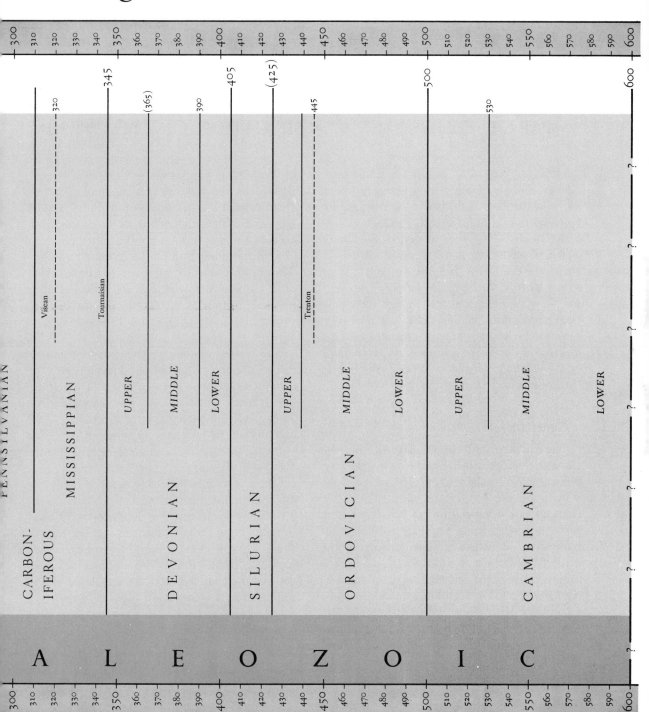

APPENDIX

B Climate

PART I. THE KÖPPEN CLASSIFICATION OF CLIMATES

Origin

THE most commonly used classification of climates is that devised by a Russian meteorologist, Wladimir Köppen (1846–1940). As early as 1900, Köppen suggested a climatic classification based on plant cover. It was in 1918, however, that he first formulated the actual scheme. In its major aspects, this original plan has not been altered though there have been many minor modifications. The final form specified by Köppen himself appeared in 1936 as a section of a five-volume work, *Handbook of Climatology*, of which Köppen was one of the authors and an editor.

General Features

The Köppen classification deals with the two climatic elements which are most obviously significant to man as he attempts to live and make a living on the face of the earth. These two elements are temperature and precipitation. Long-time records of each are available for numerous and widely scattered places on the earth. When these records are analyzed, it is found that certain outstanding combinations regularly occur. For example, some places show a combination of "hot and moist"; others are "hot and dry"; still others are "cold and moist"; and so on, through many temperature and moisture combinations. It is such recognized combinations, or types, that constitute the Köppen "system" of climatic classification.

This system recognizes five *major* categories.

To each of these a letter symbol is given. One of the major categories, for example, is expressed by the letter **A**, which signifies moist climates that are perennially hot. Subdivisions are made within each of the major classes, and each of these in turn is given a letter symbol. One of the subdivisions of the **A** climates is **Af**. The addition of the **f** indicates one special type of **A** climate, one which is not only hot and moist, but moist to the degree that there is no season of true drought at any time during the year.

The type of climate, or the *climate-formula*, to use Köppen's designation, is expressed as a combination of two or more letters. The letters are defined specifically as well as generally. Thus, direct measurements of degrees of heat and amount of moisture are provided.

In the use of the complete system, many detailed differences can be indicated by the addition of as many letter symbols as apply to the measurements at hand. For purposes of a general world survey, the subdivisions of the climatic types usually involve a third letter. Thus, a given climate may be symbolized as **Cfa**. The third letter in this instance signifies hot summers, and it, too, is capable of exact definition in a quantitative fashion. To go beyond a third symbol is, *for general purposes,* unwise and cumbersome.

Significance of This Classification

The Köppen classification of climates is extremely useful, first, because it is a quantitative and wholly objective device for the categorization of observed climatic phenomena. As has been indicated, it makes use of temperature and of precipitation amounts and of temperature and precipitation distribution through the year. These are measurable facts which are commonly observed over a large part of the earth's surface. When the Köppen definitions are applied to the observed facts, there is no question as to which category those facts represent. Given a set of climatic statistics, any individual, no matter from what part of the world he may come, can arrive at the proper climate-formula for his own, or any other, climate. The classification thus provides a sort of climatic Esperanto, or an international climatic shorthand.

Second, the Köppen classification is an extremely useful geographic tool for world or continental study. The definitions are stated in exact amounts which are capable of accurate representation on maps. It is therefore possible to construct maps on which the areas of different climatic types may be specifically delimited. From these maps, direct comparisons between one part of the world and another, or between one part of a continent and another, may be made. Further, these comparisons are standardized by the quantitative nature of the definitions. On a world-wide or on a continental scale, the patterns disclosed by a map of climatic types are basic to an understanding of the variety which exists. It must here be noted, however, that the classification is of much less value in disclosing significant patterns within smaller areas.

Third, the Köppen classification is easy to apply. It does not require any special knowledge, either of meteorological details or of mathematical processes. It can, therefore, be used by nonspecialists fully as easily as it can by professional students.

Finally, the Köppen classification has come into such common use throughout the world that it may now be considered a standard. Nearly all of the many current classifications

of climate are variants of the Köppen system. In some variants, names have been substituted for combinations of letter symbols. Thus, it is fairly common to speak of an **Af** climate as a Tropical Rainforest climate, of a **BW** climate as a Desert or Saharan climate, and of a **Cs** climate as a Mediterranean climate. In other variants, there have been different definitions proposed for those of Köppen while the main framework remains unaltered. Whether they be descriptive-type variations or definition variations, no one of the alternative classifications has had the world-wide acceptance which has been accorded the Köppen system *as a useful geographic tool.* This is not to suggest that there are no weaknesses in the Köppen system —for example, the definitions specify types that are far too broad for purposes of climatological research. But despite difficulties of this sort, the system remains an extremely useful and a widely accepted tool for geographers.

Plan of the Classification

MAJOR CATEGORIES • The five major categories of climate are given the letter symbols **A, B, C, D,** and **E.** Climates which are moist and are always hot, showing no appreciable seasonal changes of temperature, are designated the **A** climates. Those in which potential evaporation exceeds precipitation, dry climates, are given the symbol **B.** Moist climates in which there is a definite, though mild, winter are called **C** climates. Moist climates with severe winters use the letter **D.** And climates which have no summer season are known as **E** climates. For convenient reference, a tabular summary of general meanings of all symbols is given in TABLES A and B in this part of the appendix. In addition, exact definitions for each symbol are given in Part II of this appendix. The method of determination of the climatic symbol represented by any set of temperature and precipitation statistics is included in Part III of this appendix.

The choice of the particular letters is purely

arbitrary. It should be noted that the first letter symbol in the classification is always a capital letter. This is important because, in the definition of subdivisions of the major categories, some of the letters are used again, but they are always written or printed as small letters.

The **A**, **C**, and **D** climates are moist; that is, they are climates in which, regardless of the temperature, there is normally no problem of insufficient precipitation. In contrast to these three, the **E** climates are so cold that the problem of moisture is not significant. Only in the **B** climates do we find, as a normal condition, the problem of moisture deficiency.

Moisture deficiency, or dryness, must be defined on a sliding scale. Efficiency of precipitation, from the point of view of the cover of vegetation which it produces, is closely related to the rate of evaporation. More water will evaporate at high temperatures than at low ones. If evaporation is high, water available for plants is decreased. Hence, the amount of precipitation which is adequate for plant growth in a cool area is altogether insufficient in an area of constantly high temperatures. Likewise, an area which receives most of its precipitation during the warm growing season when the evaporation rate is high must have more water available than an area where most of the precipitation comes during the cooler season when evaporation is low. If evaporation records were kept as frequently and as accurately as are those of temperature and precipitation, it would be possible to determine directly the location of the line along which evaporation equals precipitation. This would permit exact definition of the boundary between climates which are moist and those which are dry. Unfortunately, records of evaporation are few in number and the points of observation are widely scattered. For these reasons, it has been necessary to introduce into the classification a definition which is not predicated upon a single amount of precipitation, but which is in reality a crude estimate of evaporation. This definition makes allowance for temperature, for yearly

---

◆◆◆◆◆◆◆◆◆◆◆◆◆◆◆◆◆◆◆◆◆◆◆◆◆◆◆◆◆◆◆◆◆◆◆◆

TABLE A

Tabular Summary of Twenty-five Main Climatic Types of the Köppen System

Af	Always hot, always moist climate
Am	Always hot, seasonally excessively moist climate
Aw	Always hot, seasonally droughty climate
BSh	Semiarid, hot climate
BSk	Semiarid, cool or cold climate
BWh	Arid, hot climate
BWk	Arid, cool or cold climate
Cfa	Mild winter, always moist climate with long, hot summers
Cfb	Mild winter, always moist climate with short, warm summers
Cfc	Mild winter, always moist climate with very short, cool summers
Cwa	Mild winter, moist summer climate with long, hot summers
Cwb	Mild winter, moist summer climate with short, warm summers
Csa	Mild winter, moist winter climate with long, hot, droughty summers
Csb	Mild winter, moist winter climate with short, warm, droughty summers
Dfa	Severe winter, always moist climate with long, hot summers
Dwa	Severe winter, moist summer climate with long, hot summers
Dfb	Severe winter, always moist climate with short, warm summers
Dwb	Severe winter, moist summer climate with short, warm summers
Dfc	Severe winter, always moist climate with very short, cool summers
Dwc	Severe winter, moist summer climate with very short, cool summers
Dfd	Severe winter, always moist climate with short summers and excessively cold winters
Dwd	Severe winter, moist summer climate with short summers and excessively cold winters
ET	Polar climate with very short period of plant growth
EF	Polar climate in which plant growth is impossible
H	Undifferentiated mountain climates

Relationship Between the Major Categories of Climate and Their Subdivisions

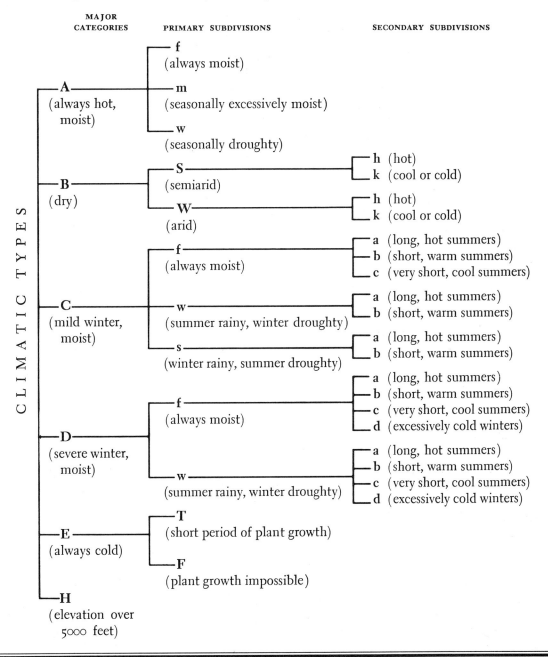

MAJOR CATEGORIES | PRIMARY SUBDIVISIONS | SECONDARY SUBDIVISIONS

CLIMATIC TYPES

A (always hot, moist)
- f (always moist)
- m (seasonally excessively moist)
- w (seasonally droughty)

B (dry)
- S (semiarid)
  - h (hot)
  - k (cool or cold)
- W (arid)
  - h (hot)
  - k (cool or cold)

C (mild winter, moist)
- f (always moist)
  - a (long, hot summers)
  - b (short, warm summers)
  - c (very short, cool summers)
- w (summer rainy, winter droughty)
  - a (long, hot summers)
  - b (short, warm summers)
- s (winter rainy, summer droughty)
  - a (long, hot summers)
  - b (short, warm summers)

D (severe winter, moist)
- f (always moist)
  - a (long, hot summers)
  - b (short, warm summers)
  - c (very short, cool summers)
  - d (excessively cold winters)
- w (summer rainy, winter droughty)
  - a (long, hot summers)
  - b (short, warm summers)
  - c (very short, cool summers)
  - d (excessively cold winters)

E (always cold)
- T (short period of plant growth)
- F (plant growth impossible)

H (elevation over 5000 feet)

TABLE C

Some Climatic Type Equivalents

TYPE NAME USED IN THIS TEXT	KÖPPEN TYPE	PLACE NAME EXAMPLE
Tropical rainforest	**Af**	Upper Amazon
Tropical monsoon	**Am**	Malabar
Savanna	**Aw**	Southern Sudan
Semiarid	**BSh** and **BSk**	Lower Rio Grande and Northern Great Plains
Arid	**BWh** and **BWk**	Tarim Basin and Sahara
Humid subtropical	**Cfa**	Gulf states
Mid-latitude marine	**Cfb** and **Cfc**	Northwestern Europe
Subtropical monsoon and tropical upland	**Cw**	South China and Ethiopia
Mediterranean	**Csa** and **Csb**	Mediterranean countries
Humid continental with hot summers	**Dfa** and **Dwa**	Iowa and North China
Humid continental with warm summers	**Dfb** and **Dwb**	Northern Great Lakes and Northern Manchuria
Subarctic	**Dfc, Dwc, Dfd,** and **Dwd**	Central Canada, Amur Lowland, and Northeastern Siberia
Tundra	**ET**	Northern Alaska
Icecap	**EF**	Greenland

precipitation, and for seasonal distribution of precipitation.

SUBDIVISIONS OF THE MAJOR CATEGORIES • The **B** climates are subdivided into arid climate which is represented by the secondary symbol **W**, and semiarid climate which is represented by the secondary symbol **S**. These are written as capital letters when they are used with **B** and they have no tie with the letters **w** and **s** as those are used with the **A, C,** and **D** types. Beyond the classification as arid or semiarid, a further difference within the **B** climates is made in terms of temperature; those dry climates which are always hot use the symbol **h**

and those which are cold or have a pronounced winter season use the symbol **k.**

In each of the **A, C,** and **D** types, the second symbol is one which specifies the nature, the amount, and the distribution of precipitation through the year. There are three possibilities so far as the distribution of precipitation throughout the year is concerned; either the precipitation is rather evenly spread through the year, or it is concentrated in the cooler part of the year, or it is concentrated in the warmer part of the year. The symbol which indicates an even spread through the year is **f;** that which indicates concentration in the cooler part of the year is s; and that which shows concentration in the warmer part of the year is **w**. Theoretically, any of the three might be used following the first letter of the climate-formula. Actually, s occurs so infrequently with either **A** or **D** that it may be omitted so far as those two major categories are concerned. Within the **A** climates, another letter, **m**, is used to indicate an intermediary position between **f** and **w**.

Only in the **C** and **D** climates is a third symbol essential to the generalized world pattern. Since in those two categories the nature of the winter and of the summer have great effect upon the vegetation, the symbols should indicate the nature of each of those seasons. The first letter does this in part; the third letter completes the statement. Three of the letters used in third place characterize the summer and one of them, the winter. Where the summers are long and hot, the symbol **a** is used; for short and warm summers, **b** is used; for very short and cool summers, **c** is the symbol; and where winters are ex~~~~~ ~~~~ ~~old and severe, the sym-~~~~~~~ ~~~~~~

Within the climates which have no true summer, **E**, a distinction can be made between areas of continuous frost, **F**, and those in which temperatures are occasionally high enough to permit a spotty vegetation cover of tundra, **T**.

Summary of Types

GENERALIZED DESCRIPTION • In summary, twenty-four climatic types are recognized. These are listed in TABLE A in this part of the appendix, each with a generalized résumé of its major features. TABLE B shows the relationship between the major categories and their subdivisions. It also indicates the relative position within the whole scheme of each of the types.

EQUIVALENT CLIMATIC TYPES • It is common practice to refer to climatic types by descriptive names, as has been done in the body of this text, or by names of places in which the climates occur. For convenience, certain of these equivalent names are listed in TABLE C of this part of the appendix. It should be pointed out that, even though they are rough equivalents, the descriptive or place-name climatic types lack the uniformity and convenience of detailed, standard definition which the Köppen types possess.

PART II. DEFINITIONS OF CLIMATIC SYMBOLS

Primary Types

A Average temperature of the coolest month 64.4° F. or over.

B Precipitation less in inches than the amount .44t − 8.5 when it is evenly distributed through the year; or less than the amount .44t − 14 when it is concentrated chiefly in winter; or less than the amount .44t − 3 when it is concentrated chiefly in summer. In all of these amounts, t equals average annual temperature in degrees F. These amounts are worked out in TABLE D. See note regarding meaning of "concentrated" in TABLE D.

C Average temperature of the warmest month over 50° F. and of the coldest month between 64.4° F. and 32° F.

D Average temperature of the warmest month over 50° F. and of the coldest month 32° F. and below.

E Average temperature of the warmest month below 50° F.

Secondary Types

As they occur with A

f Precipitation of the driest month of the year at least 2.4 inches.

w Precipitation of the driest month of the year less than the amount shown in TABLE E.

TABLE D

This table gives the amount of precipitation in inches at the boundary between the **B** climates and the other primary types for each average annual temperature from 32° F. to 90° F., and for the three possible distributions of rain through the year.

AVERAGE ANNUAL TEMPERA-TURE	PRECIPITA-TION CONCENTRATED CHIEFLY IN WINTER ($.44t-14$)	PRECIPITA-TION EVENLY DISTRIBUTED THROUGH THE YEAR ($.44t-8.5$)	PRECIPITA-TION CONCENTRATED CHIEFLY IN SUMMER ($.44t-3$)	AVERAGE ANNUAL TEMPERA-TURE	PRECIPITA-TION CONCENTRATED CHIEFLY IN WINTER ($.44t-14$)	PRECIPITA-TION EVENLY DISTRIBUTED THROUGH THE YEAR ($.44t-8.5$)	PRECIPITA-TION CONCENTRATED CHIEFLY IN SUMMER ($.44t-3$)
32	.08	5.58	11.08	62	13.28	18.78	24.28
33	.52	6.02	11.52	63	13.72	19.22	24.72
34	.96	6.46	11.96	64	14.16	19.66	25.16
35	1.40	6.90	12.40	65	14.60	20.10	25.60
36	1.84	7.34	12.84	66	15.04	20.54	26.04
37	2.28	7.78	13.28	67	15.48	20.98	26.48
38	2.72	8.22	13.72	68	15.92	21.42	26.92
39	3.16	8.66	14.16	69	16.36	21.86	27.36
40	3.60	9.10	14.60	70	16.80	22.30	27.80
41	4.04	9.54	15.04	71	17.24	22.74	28.24
42	4.48	9.98	15.48	72	17.68	23.18	28.68
43	4.92	10.42	15.92	73	18.12	23.62	29.12
44	5.36	10.86	16.36	74	18.56	24.06	29.56
45	5.80	11.30	16.80	75	19.00	24.50	30.00
46	6.24	11.74	17.24	76	19.44	24.94	30.44
47	6.68	12.18	17.68	77	19.88	25.38	30.88
48	7.12	12.62	18.12	78	20.32	25.82	31.32
49	7.56	13.06	18.56	79	20.76	26.26	31.76
50	8.00	13.50	19.00	80	21.20	26.70	32.20
51	8.44	13.94	19.44	81	21.64	27.14	32.64
52	8.88	14.38	19.88	82	22.08	27.58	33.08
53	9.32	14.82	20.32	83	22.52	28.02	33.52
54	9.76	15.26	20.76	84	22.96	28.46	33.96
55	10.20	15.70	21.20	85	23.40	28.90	34.40
56	10.64	16.14	21.64	86	23.84	29.34	34.84
57	11.08	16.58	22.08	87	24.28	29.78	35.28
58	11.52	17.02	22.52	88	24.72	30.22	35.72
59	11.96	17.46	22.96	89	25.16	30.66	36.16
60	12.40	17.90	23.40	90	25.60	31.10	36.60
61	12.84	18.34	23.84				

NOTE: Precipitation is said to be concentrated in summer when 70% or more of the average annual amount is received during the warmer six months. It is concentrated in winter when 70% or more is received in the cooler six months. If neither season receives 70% of the annual total, the precipitation is considered to be evenly distributed. Division of the year into six-month periods is made between March and April on the one hand and between September and October on the other.

TABLE *E*

This table gives the amount of precipitation in inches during the driest month of the year along the boundary between **Am** and **Aw** climates for differing amounts of yearly precipitation. If the amount in the driest month is 2.4 inches or more, the symbol **f** is used; if the amount in the driest month is between 2.4 and the amount shown in this table, the symbol **m** is used; and if the amount in the driest month is less than that shown in this table, the symbol **w** is used.

TOTAL YEARLY PRECIPITATION	PRECIPITATION IN DRIEST MONTH	TOTAL YEARLY PRECIPITATION	PRECIPITATION IN DRIEST MONTH	TOTAL YEARLY PRECIPITATION	PRECIPITATION IN DRIEST MONTH	TOTAL YEARLY PRECIPITATION	PRECIPITATION IN DRIEST MONTH
38.5	2.40	54	1.78	69.5	1.15	85	.54
39	2.38	54.5	1.77	70	1.13	85.5	.51
39.5	2.36	55	1.75	70.5	1.11	86	.50
40	2.34	55.5	1.73	71	1.10	86.5	.48
40.5	2.32	56	1.70	71.5	1.08	87	.46
41	2.30	56.5	1.68	72	1.06	87.5	.44
41.5	2.29	57	1.66	72.5	1.03	88	.42
42	2.26	57.5	1.64	73	1.02	88.5	.40
42.5	2.24	58	1.63	73.5	1.00	89	.37
43	2.22	58.5	1.60	74	.98	89.5	.36
43.5	2.20	59	1.58	74.5	.96	90	.34
44	2.18	59.5	1.56	75	.94	90.5	.32
44.5	2.16	60	1.55	75.5	.92	91	.29
45	2.14	60.5	1.53	76	.90	91.5	.28
45.5	2.12	61	1.51	76.5	.88	92	.26
46	2.10	61.5	1.48	77	.86	92.5	.24
46.5	2.08	62	1.47	77.5	.84	93	.22
47	2.07	62.5	1.45	78	.81	93.5	.20
47.5	2.04	63	1.42	78.5	.80	94	.18
48	2.02	63.5	1.41	79	.78	94.5	.16
48.5	2.00	64	1.38	79.5	.76	95	.14
49	1.98	64.5	1.36	80	.74	95.5	.11
49.5	1.96	65	1.34	80.5	.72	96	.09
50	1.94	65.5	1.33	81	.70	96.5	.07
50.5	1.92	66	1.30	81.5	.68	97	.06
51	1.90	66.5	1.28	82	.66	97.5	.04
51.5	1.88	67	1.26	82.5	.63	98	.02
52	1.86	67.5	1.24	83	.61	98.5	.00
52.5	1.85	68	1.22	83.5	.59		
53	1.82	68.5	1.20	84	.58		
53.5	1.80	69	1.18	84.5	.56		

NOTE: If the total yearly precipitation is 197 inches, there can be two whole months without rain and the symbol **m** used; if the yearly amount is 295.5 inches, three months may be dry and the symbol **m** used; etc. The symbol **m** signifies that the dry period is compensated by excess rain at another time whereas **w** indicates a lack of compensating amounts. Hence, the dividing amount in the driest month becomes smaller as the total for the year becomes larger.

m Precipitation of the driest month of the year less than 2.4 inches, but more than the amount shown in TABLE E.

As they occur with B

W Precipitation for the year less than half the amount shown in the definition for **B**. See TABLE D.

S Precipitation for the year less than the amount shown in the definition for **B**, but more than half that amount. See TABLE D.

As they occur with C and D

s Precipitation for the driest month of the summer half of the year less than 1.6 inches and less than ⅓ the amount which falls in the wettest month of the winter half of the year.

w Precipitation of the driest month of the winter half of the year less than ¹⁄₁₀ the amount which falls in the wettest month of the summer half of the year.

f Precipitation not satisfying the definitions for s or w.

As they occur with E

T Average temperature of the warmest month of the year between 50° F. and 32° F.

F Average temperature of the warmest month 32° F. or below.

Tertiary Types

As they occur with B

h Average annual temperature 64.4° F. or above.

k Average annual temperature below 64.4° F.

As they occur with C

a Average temperature of the warmest month 71.6° F. or above.

b Average temperature of the four warmest months 50° F. or above, and average temperature of the warmest month below 71.6° F.

c Average temperature of from one to three months 50° F. or above, and average temperature of warmest month below 71.6° F.

As they occur with D

a Same as with **C**.

b Same as with **C**.

c Same as with **C**.

d Average temperature of the coldest month below −36.4° F. (*Note:* **a**, **b**, and **c** do not specifically exclude **d**, *but* when **d** can be used, do *not* use **a**, **b**, or **c**.)

PART III. THE DETERMINATION OF CLIMATIC TYPES

General Procedure

PRIMARY TYPES • In order to determine the climatic type at a given place, it is necessary to have available average temperatures for every month and for the year as well as average precipitation for each month and for the year. When these statistics are at hand, the actual classification can most easily be accomplished by following the routine procedure stated below. It is essentially a process of elimination.

To determine the first letter of the climate-formula, proceed according to the following questions.

1. Is the average temperature of the warmest month below 50° F.? If it is, the climate is of the E type; if it is not, proceed to the second question.
2. Is the amount of precipitation less than the amount specified as the limit of the **B** climates in TABLE D? If it is less, the climate is of the **B** type; if it is not, proceed to the third question.
3. Is the average temperature of the coolest month 64.4° F. or above? If it is, the climate is of the

A type; if it is not, proceed to the fourth question.

4. Is the average temperature of the coldest month between 64.4° F. and 32° F.? If it is, the climate is of the C type; if it is not, or, in other words, if the average temperature of the coldest month is below 32° F., the climate is of the D type.

Thus by following through a sequence of, at most, four questions, it is possible to determine which one of the five primary climatic types is represented by any set of temperature and precipitation statistics.

SECONDARY TYPES • Once the primary type is determined, similar routines are followed to obtain the second and third letters of the climate-formula. Secondary characteristics of each of the main types are most easily determined by applying the following questions.

1. If the climate is of the E type, is the average temperature of the warmest month over 32° F.? If it is, the secondary symbol is T; if it is not, the secondary symbol is F.
2. If the climate is of the B type, is the yearly precipitation over one half the amount specified as the limit of the B climates in TABLE D? If it is, the secondary symbol is S; if it is not, the secondary symbol is W.
3. If the climate is of the A type:
   a. Is the precipitation of the driest month 2.4 inches or more? If it is, the secondary symbol is f; if it is not, refer to the next question.
   b. Is the precipitation of the driest month more than the amount specified in TABLE E? If it is, the secondary symbol is m; if it is not, the secondary symbol is w.
4. If the climate is of the C or D type:
   a. Is the driest month of the year in the summer six-month period and is its precipitation less than 1.6 inches? If both conditions are satisfied, proceed to question b; if either is not satisfied, proceed to question c.
   b. Is the precipitation of the driest month of summer less than ⅓ that of the wettest month of winter? If it is, the secondary symbol is s; if it is not, the secondary symbol is f.
   c. Is the precipitation of the driest month of winter less than 1⁄10 that of the wettest month

of summer? If it is, the secondary symbol is w; if it is not, the secondary symbol is f.

TERTIARY TYPES • Tertiary characteristics of each of the C and D climates are determined most easily as follows. If the climate is of the C or D type, apply the following questions.

1. Is the average temperature of the coldest month below −36.4° F.? If it is, the symbol is d; if it is not, proceed to the next question.
2. Is the average temperature of the warmest month 71.6° F. or above? If it is, the symbol is a; if it is not, proceed to the next question.
3. Are the average temperatures of the four warmest months 50° F. or above? If they are, the symbol is b; if they are not, the symbol is c.

Application of the Procedure of Classification

FIRST EXAMPLE • The first example is Maracaibo, Venezuela. The statistics are given below.

Beginning with the primary types, we must first ask the question, "Is the average temperature of the warmest month below 50° F.?" The warmest month is August, with an average of 84.4°. This is well above 50° and hence the type cannot be E. We have eliminated one of the primary types.

Second, we must ask the question, "Is the amount of precipitation less than the amount specified by definition as the limit of the B climates?" It is simplest here to refer to TABLE D. To use the table, we must know three things about the place in question. These are: (1) the average annual temperature, (2) the average annual precipitation, and (3) the distribution of the precipitation through the year—for example, does 70% or more of the precipitation come in the winter six months? Does 70% or more come in the summer six months? Or does 70% come in neither season?

Items 1 and 2 are given in the statistics: Maracaibo has an average annual temperature of 82.3° F., and an average annual precipitation of 18.2 inches. To secure the necessary

	J	F	M	A	M	J	J	A	S	O	N	D	YEAR
Maracaibo													
TEMP.	80.7	81.0	81.2	82.5	83.2	83.5	84.1	84.4	83.5	82.0	81.3	81.0	82.3
PREC.	0.1	0.1	0.3	0.5	2.4	1.6	1.4	1.3	3.3	4.3	2.5	0.4	18.2

third item requires the application of simple arithmetic.

The warmer six months at Maracaibo are April through September. During these months, the precipitation in inches is as follows: April, .5; May, 2.4; June, 1.6; July, 1.4; August, 1.3; and September, 3.3. The total for this season is 10.5 inches. Since the total for the year is 18.2 inches and that for the warmer six months is 10.5 inches, the amount which falls in the cooler six months must be 18.2 minus 10.5, or 7.7 inches. The summer, or warmer season, precipitation is 10.5 inches; the winter, or cooler season, precipitation is 7.7 inches. Is either of these amounts equal to or more than 70% of the total for the year? Seventy per cent of 18.2 is 12.74. Since neither the warmer season precipitation nor that of the cooler season is equal to or greater than 70% of the total, the precipitation is considered to be evenly distributed throughout the year.

Now, the three items necessary for the use of TABLE D are available: average annual temperature, 82.3° F.; average annual precipitation, 18.2 inches; and evenly distributed precipitation. Consulting TABLE D we find in the first column average annual temperatures in whole numbers. The nearest to 82.3 is 82. The third column is headed "Precipitation evenly distributed through the year." We follow down this column until we come to the figure on the same line as 82 in the first column. That figure is 27.58. Now we can answer the question, "Is the amount of precipitation less than the amount specified by definition as the limit of the **B** climates?" The precipitation at Maracaibo (18.2 inches) is less than the limit figure (27.58 inches). Hence, Maracaibo has a **B** climate.

We need go no further with the primary types for no set of statistics will fulfill the re-quirements for more than one. The task is now to determine the secondary symbol.

For the second symbol, only one question is necessary. "Is the yearly precipitation over one half the amount specified in TABLE D?" The amount specified in TABLE D in this instance is 27.58. One half of that is 13.79. Is the annual precipitation at Maracaibo (18.2 inches) over one half the amount (13.79 inches) specified in TABLE D? It is and hence the secondary symbol is **S**. Maracaibo thus has a **BS** climate.

SECOND EXAMPLE • As a second example of the application of the procedure of classification, the statistics for Iloilo in the Philippine Islands may be examined below.

We follow the same order as in the example of Maracaibo. First, is the average temperature of the warmest month below 50° F.? It is not; therefore the type is not **E**. Is the precipitation for the year less than the amount specified for the limit of the **B** climates? We must know three things to answer this question: (1) the average annual temperature; (2) the average annual precipitation; and (3) the distribution of precipitation through the year. The warmer six months at Iloilo is the period of April through September. In that season, 60.8 inches of rain fall. Since 88.7 inches fall during the whole year, the amount in the cooler season is 88.7 minus 60.8, or 17.9 inches. Seventy per cent of 88.7 is 62.09. Neither the amount which falls in the warmer season nor that which falls in the cooler season is equal to or more than 62.09. Therefore, the precipitation may be considered to be evenly distributed through the year. Referring to TABLE D, we find 81 in the first column. Opposite it in the third column is 27.14. This represents the amount of precipitation which, under these conditions of temperature, limits the **B** climates. The amount of

	J	F	M	A	M	J	J	A	S	O	N	D	YEAR
Iloilo													
TEMP.	78.0	78.5	80.0	80.7	82.3	81.3	80.5	80.7	80.0	80.0	79.7	78.8	81.0
PREC.	2.4	1.8	1.3	1.6	5.9	10.5	16.3	13.8	12.7	10.3	7.7	4.4	88.7

precipitation at Iloilo is more than 27.14; therefore, the climate at Iloilo is not **B**.

We proceed to the next question. "Is the average temperature of the coolest month 64.4° F. or above?" The coolest month at Iloilo has an average temperature of 78.0° F. This is above 64.4° F. and, therefore, Iloilo has an **A** climate.

There is a threefold division within the **A** climates. We must now discover into which of these three Iloilo fits. The first question is "Is the precipitation for the driest month 2.4 inches or more?" The driest month at Iloilo has 1.3 inches of rain. The answer to the question is in the negative and consequently the symbol **f** does not apply. The second question asks "Is the precipitation of the driest month more than

the amount specified in TABLE E?" In order to use that table, we must know the average annual precipitation and the precipitation of the driest month. At Iloilo, the average annual precipitation is 88.7 inches; the precipitation of the driest month is 1.3 inches. On TABLE E in the column headed "Total yearly precipitation," the figure 88.5 can be found. This is the figure closest to 88.7. Opposite it in the column headed "Precipitation of the driest month" is the figure .40. Returning to the question, we can see that the precipitation of the driest month at Iloilo (1.3 inches) is more than the amount specified in TABLE E (.40 inch). Therefore, the symbol **m** can be used. The climate at Iloilo is of the **Am** type.

PART IV. THE WORLD DISTRIBUTION OF CLIMATIC TYPES

SINCE climatic types represent quantitative measurements of temperature and precipitation, it is easy to erect a simplified plan, indicating diagrammatically the place of occurrence of the major types. One such plan is shown in FIG. A. Each of the corners of the rectangle represents extreme combinations of the two elements, temperature and precipitation. The upper left-hand corner indicates the extreme of cold and dry; the lower left-hand corner, hot and dry; the upper right-hand corner, cold and wet; and the lower right-hand corner, hot and wet.

The Generalized Continent Diagram

The very simple pattern shown on FIG. A takes into account only the factor of quantity

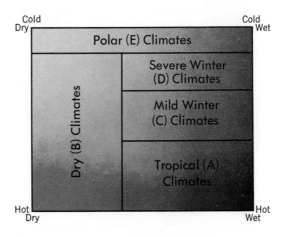

A

SCHEMATIC *diagram showing the relationship of temperature and precipitation to major classifications of climate.*

for both of the basic climatic elements. To get at the pattern for the world, there must be included some indication of the distribution of land and water, which is so powerful a control of distribution for both temperature and precipitation.

It will be remembered that there are two great "world islands," the Americas on the one hand and the Europe-Asia-Africa land mass on the other. These "world islands" are roughly triangular in broad outline. Their widest extent occurs at about 60° North latitude and they taper into the Southern Hemisphere where both of them pinch out in the middle latitudes. After a short break, land appears again in the circumpolar continent of Antarctica. In the Northern Hemisphere, the continents fray out poleward toward the Arctic Ocean and do not extend to the Pole.

This very generalized distribution of land in each hemisphere is represented diagrammatically in FIG. B. The outline circle represents the outer edge of a hemisphere. The top-shaped figure upon it represents the outline of land.

The continent thus delineated indicates simply land as opposed to water. No attempt is made to show generalized differences of elevation, nor is any attempt made to show detailed position of any actual coastline. The smaller triangular figure is a generalization of the Antarctic continent. The whole figure is called the *generalized continent diagram.*

Distribution of Major Climatic Categories

The zone of greatest heating and of highest precipitation for the world as a whole occurs along the equator, ·and the greatest cold, whether dry or wet, occurs in the higher latitudes near, but not at, the Poles. In the higher latitudes, coastal positions are wet and continental positions are comparatively dry. The remaining combination, hot and dry, is found within the tropics extending inland from the continental west coasts. These facts can be placed upon the generalized continent diagram as in FIG. C.

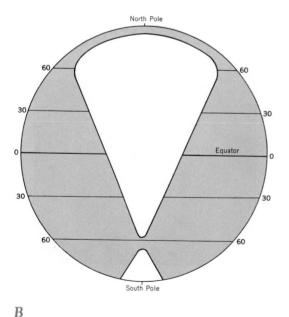

B

GENERALIZED *continent diagram—distribution of land and water.*

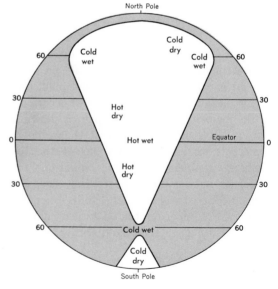

C

GENERALIZED *continent diagram—distribution of descriptive climatic terms.*

Now, instead of the pattern which appeared on the rectangular diagram (FIG. A), a new pattern can be drawn. A line must appear between the hot-wet and the hot-dry focal points. Lines must be drawn between the hot-dry and the two cold-wet locations. Finally, there must be indicated the limit, in the continental interior, where dryness becomes less significant than coldness. There are thus formed, on the generalized continent diagram, curving loops which extend from the west coasts between about 20° and 30° latitude both North and South into the continental interiors of the higher middle latitudes (FIG. D). The areas within the loops are distinguished by their dryness; everything outside, by wetness. The loops, then, outline the areas of DRY (**B**) climate. Outside them lie the TROPICAL MOIST (**A**); the MOIST, MILD WINTER (**C**); the MOIST, SEVERE WINTER (**D**); and the POLAR (**E**) climates.

Across the polar reaches in both hemispheres, perennial cold is so dominant that relative wetness and dryness are not significant. Lines may be drawn (FIG. E) in both hemispheres to indicate the equatorward limit of the POLAR (**E**)

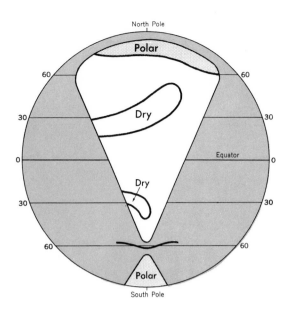

E

GENERALIZED *continent diagram*—POLAR (**E**) *and* DRY (**B**) *climates.*

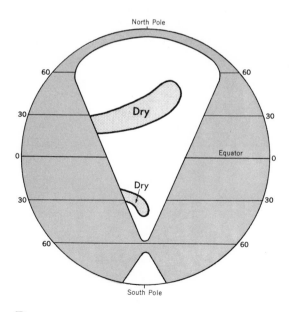

D

GENERALIZED *continent diagram*—DRY (**B**) *climates.*

climates. The portion of the generalized continent not yet subdivided includes now only TROPICAL MOIST (**A**); MOIST, MILD WINTER (**C**); and MOIST, SEVERE WINTER (**D**) types.

Temperatures characteristic of the TROPICAL MOIST (**A**) climates occur only within the low latitudes. On the generalized continent, the only portion of these latitudes remaining unspecified is that between and east of the two areas of DRY (**B**) climate. A line in each hemisphere from the east coast to the dry interior approximately at the edges of the low latitudes provides the remaining boundaries for the TROPICAL MOIST (**A**) climates (FIG. F).

There remain only the MOIST, MILD WINTER (**C**) and MOIST, SEVERE WINTER (**D**) climates to delimit. There is not sufficient continentality in the Southern Hemisphere to allow the development of the MOIST, SEVERE WINTER (**D**) type. Hence, it is only necessary to indicate the separation between the two in the Northern Hemisphere. To the east, the west, and the north of the DRY (**B**) zone, climate is char-

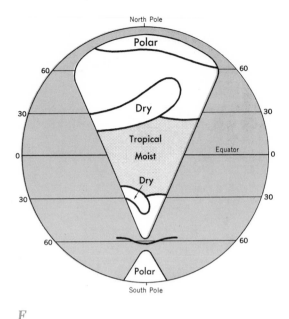

F

GENERALIZED *continent diagram*—TROPICAL MOIST (**A**), POLAR (**E**), *and* DRY (**B**) *climates.*

---

acterized as humid or wet. As one proceeds away from the equator, coldness increases. Therefore, the boundary between the MOIST, MILD WINTER (**C**) and the MOIST, SEVERE WINTER (**D**) climates must cross the diagram from east to west. Latitude for latitude, west-coast temperatures in the middle latitudes are higher for winter than are those of the east coast. Hence, the limit between the MOIST, MILD WINTER (**C**) and the MOIST, SEVERE WINTER (**D**) climates begins on the west coast at approximately 60° North latitude, curves equatorward across the continent, and leaves the east coast at about 45° North. In the section where it crosses the DRY (**B**) climate, its significance is lost for the climates are dry on either side of it. In that section, the line is omitted from the diagram. The *generalized* distribution of the five major categories of climate as they occur over the land thus appears in FIG. G.

It must be thoroughly understood that FIG. G is not a detailed map of climatic distribution over the world. It is simply a key to the *relative* position assumed by each major category on any one land mass. Variations from this pattern are induced first by irregularities of land surface and secondly by the detailed position of the coastline.

The effects of irregularities of surface can be seen in many places on the map showing the world distribution of all climatic types (PLATE IV). For example, consider the African portion of that map. The TROPICAL MOIST (**A**) climates do not extend to the east coast of that continent north of the equator. On the generalized continent diagram (FIG. G), the TROPICAL MOIST (**A**) climates extend the whole breadth of the tropics along the east coast. Eastern Africa is a plateau region with hills and mountain masses upon it. The surface character is not the whole reason for the absence of TROPICAL MOIST (**A**) climates along the east coast, but it is a strong contributory factor. Another instance occurs in South America. On the generalized diagram (FIG. G), the TROPICAL MOIST (**A**) climates extend along the equator

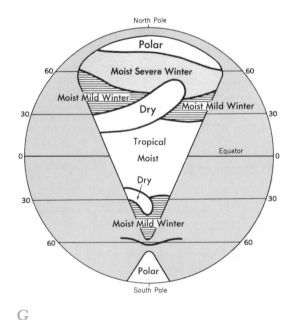

G

GENERALIZED *continent diagram*—*five major climatic types.*

unbroken from east coast to west coast. In South America, a break occurs near the west coast (PLATE IV). The break is located where the towering Andes stretch north-south across the equator. Their high elevations produce temperatures lower than those which characterize the TROPICAL MOIST (A) climates.

The effect of irregularities of coastline are well illustrated in the Caribbean region of the Americas. The climatic map (PLATE IV) shows that the DRY (B) climate comes to the east coast near the boundary between Mexico and the United States. On the generalized continent diagram (FIG. G), the DRY (B) climates are seen to be well inland from the east coast. The apparent contradiction results from the fact that the coastline on the generalized continent omits the large indentation of the Gulf of Mexico.

Again, part of the reason for the lack of TROPICAL MOIST (A) climate on the African east coast north of the equator is the actual position of the coastline, this time in relation to wind directions. Prevailing winds are parallel to this coast no matter what the season. Consequently, little moisture is carried onshore from the Indian Ocean. The precipitation necessary to the TROPICAL MOIST (A) climates is therefore lacking from that source. When this is coupled with the control induced by the surface, which was stated above, the greater part of the dryness of the African east coast is explained and the absence of TROPICAL MOIST (A) climate is reasonably well understood.

Distribution of Climatic Types

The use of the generalized continent diagram may be further enhanced by the addition to it of the facts of seasonal distribution of precipitation. On continental west coasts between approximately 25° and 40° latitude both North and South, there is a zone in which such precipitation as falls is concentrated in the winter half of the year. This zone extends inland to form rough half ovals, as in FIG. H. Within the

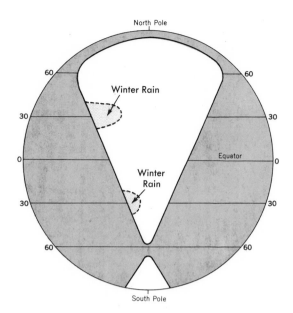

H

GENERALIZED *continent diagram—areas of winter precipitation.*

shaded areas, precipitation occurs mainly during the winter and the summer is droughty.

The opposite condition, summer rain and winter drought, is characteristic of truly continental locations. As has been explained previously, there is a tendency toward an indraft of air into continents in summer and an outdraft in winter. This means that more moisture is available for precipitation in summer than in winter. The indraft is pronounced only when there is a very considerable land mass, but the characteristic tendency toward summer precipitation concentration is everywhere prominent away from coastline locations. Generalization of the regions in which this condition prevails is indicated on FIG. I.

The only other possibility is that precipitation be relatively evenly spread through the year. When the zone of winter concentration (FIG. H) and the zone of summer concentration (FIG. I) are plotted, that which is left is the area of year-round precipitation. FIGURE J shows the characteristic location of each of the three possible rainfall regimes.

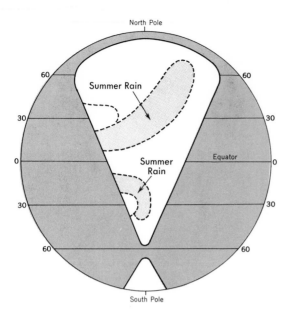

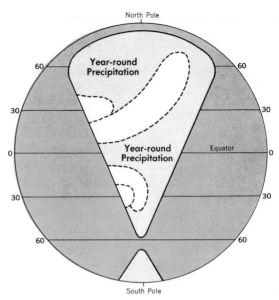

I

GENERALIZED *continent diagram—areas of summer precipitation.*

J

GENERALIZED *continent diagram—areas of year-round precipitation.*

We now have one diagram (FIG. G) showing the generalized pattern of the five major categories of climate: TROPICAL MOIST (A), DRY (B), MOIST, MILD WINTER (C), MOIST, SEVERE WINTER (D), and POLAR (E); and one diagram (FIG. J) showing the generalized pattern of precipitation types. By superposition (FIG. K), we secure the key to the expected location of the major climatic types on the generalized continent. As has been stated previously, departures from this design result primarily from the controls emphasized by irregularities of surface and by detail of coastline position.

Further subdivision of the MOIST, MILD WINTER (C) and MOIST, SEVERE WINTER (D) climates is made on the basis of the character of the summers. Without discussing this breakdown in detail, the generalized pattern is shown in FIG. L. In this diagram, part of the Northern Hemisphere portion of the generalized continent has been enlarged so as to show the relationship of the types more clearly.

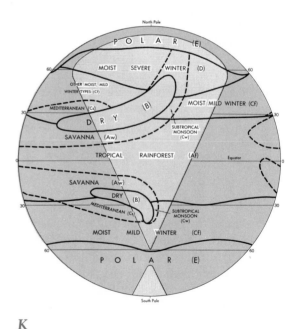

K

GENERALIZED *continent diagram—distribution of climatic types over both land and ocean.*

604 | *Appendix B*

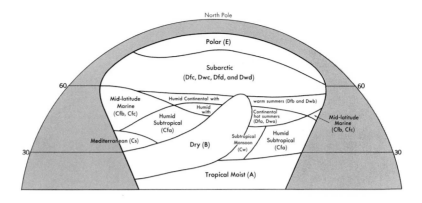

L

NORTHERN *Hemisphere portion of generalized continent diagram, showing in greater detail the distribution pattern of the subdivisions of* MOIST, MILD WINTER (**C**) *and* MOIST, SEVERE WINTER (**D**) *climates.*

Climate of the Oceans

Largely because human beings live permanently on the land masses, climate over the oceans is generally neglected. Nevertheless, the same major types are found there as on land. The pattern is shown on FIG. K.

Two specific features should be noted. First, the area of DRY (**B**) climate is greatly reduced over the ocean. This is to be expected, for the existence of DRY (**B**) climate is based primarily on two conditions: (1) the absence of large amounts of water vapor in the air and (2) the absence of some means of forcing the condensation of such vapor as is present. Over the oceans both of these deficiencies are generally restricted to sections close to the continental west coasts. Second, the area of MOIST, SEVERE WINTER (**D**) climate is likewise very small in proportion to that over the continent. By definition, the MOIST, SEVERE WINTER (**D**) climates have very large temperature ranges. In other words, they are continental. As we have

seen, the presence of large water bodies tends to reduce temperature range. The result of this tendency is to produce insufficient range over the oceans to satisfy the definition of the MOIST, SEVERE WINTER (**D**) type in all except two small areas off the coasts of the higher middle latitudes in the Northern Hemisphere.

Finally, it should be noted that there is a much more regular belted arrangement of climates over the oceans than over the land. This reflects the facts already pointed out in the discussion of temperature and precipitation.

Though climatic maps may show the distribution over the oceans, the boundaries between one type and another are much more broadly generalized than those over the land. Realization of the fact that the climatic types are not confined to the land is essential; so also is the generalized distribution of those types; knowledge of their precise distribution over the sea is neither possible nor particularly vital.

PART V. SELECTED CLIMATIC STATISTICS

North and Middle America and the Caribbean Area

	J	F	M	A	M	J	J	A	S	O	N	D	YEAR
1. San Juan, PUERTO RICO													
TEMP.	75	75	75	77	79	80	80	80	80	80	78	76	78
PREC.	4.1	3.0	3.0	4.1	5.2	5.4	5.8	5.9	6.0	5.7	7.0	5.4	60.6

	J	F	M	A	M	J	J	A	S	O	N	D	YEAR

2. Miami, FLORIDA

	J	F	M	A	M	J	J	A	S	O	N	D	YEAR
TEMP.	66	68	72	74	79	81	82	82	81	77	73	69	75
PREC.	3.3	2.5	2.8	3.1	5.9	7.9	7.2	7.3	9.9	9.2	2.4	2.2	63.7

3. Port-au-Prince, HAITI

	J	F	M	A	M	J	J	A	S	O	N	D	YEAR
TEMP.	78	78	79	80	81	83	84	84	82	81	80	78	81
PREC.	1.2	2.7	4.1	6.7	8.0	4.0	2.7	4.8	7.7	7.4	4.2	0.9	54.4

4. Acapulco, MEXICO

	J	F	M	A	M	J	J	A	S	O	N	D	YEAR
TEMP.	78	78	79	80	83	83	83	81	81	83	80	79	81
PREC.	0.6	0	0	0	1.7	16.5	6.0	6.3	14.7	5.9	1.9	0.7	54.3

5. Veracruz, MEXICO

	J	F	M	A	M	J	J	A	S	O	N	D	YEAR
TEMP.	70	71	74	78	81	81	81	81	80	78	75	71	77
PREC.	1.0	0.6	0.5	0.6	1.7	11.4	13.0	10.7	12.0	5.7	3.1	1.0	61.3

6. Medicine Hat, CANADA

	J	F	M	A	M	J	J	A	S	O	N	D	YEAR
TEMP.	13	16	28	45	55	63	69	67	56	45	30	19	42
PREC.	0.6	0.6	0.6	0.7	1.6	2.5	1.8	1.4	1.2	0.6	0.7	0.7	13.0

7. Goodland, KANSAS

	J	F	M	A	M	J	J	A	S	O	N	D	YEAR
TEMP.	29	33	40	50	59	70	77	74	66	54	41	30	52
PREC.	0.3	0.6	1.0	1.8	2.5	2.8	2.7	2.5	1.6	1.0	0.6	0.6	18.0

8. San Diego, CALIFORNIA

	J	F	M	A	M	J	J	A	S	O	N	D	YEAR
TEMP.	54	55	56	58	61	64	67	69	67	63	59	56	61
PREC.	1.8	2.0	1.5	0.6	0.3	0.1	0.1	0.1	0.1	0.3	0.9	1.8	9.6

9. Mexico City, MEXICO

	J	F	M	A	M	J	J	A	S	O	N	D	YEAR
TEMP.	54	57	61	63	65	64	62	62	61	59	57	55	60
PREC.	0.2	0.3	0.5	0.7	1.9	4.1	4.5	4.3	4.1	1.6	0.5	0.3	23.0

10. Phoenix, ARIZONA

	J	F	M	A	M	J	J	A	S	O	N	D	YEAR
TEMP.	50	54	60	67	75	84	90	88	82	70	59	52	69
PREC.	1.0	0.7	0.6	0.4	0.1	0.1	1.3	1.0	0.7	0.5	0.8	0.7	7.9

11. La Paz, MEXICO

	J	F	M	A	M	J	J	A	S	O	N	D	YEAR
TEMP.	63	65	68	71	74	78	82	84	82	79	72	66	74
PREC.	0.2	0.1	0	0	0	0	0.4	1.2	1.4	0.6	0.5	1.1	5.5

12. Cairo, ILLINOIS

	J	F	M	A	M	J	J	A	S	O	N	D	YEAR
TEMP.	44	47	57	67	76	85	88	87	81	70	56	46	67
PREC.	3.9	3.2	4.1	3.9	3.8	3.9	3.0	3.0	2.9	2.8	3.6	3.3	41.4

13. New York, NEW YORK

	J	F	M	A	M	J	J	A	S	O	N	D	YEAR
TEMP.	30	31	38	49	59	69	75	73	66	55	44	34	52
PREC.	3.3	3.3	3.5	3.3	3.5	3 4	4.1	4.4	3.4	3.4	3.6	3.3	42.5

14. Washington, D.C.

	J	F	M	A	M	J	J	A	S	O	N	D	YEAR
TEMP.	33	35	42	53	64	73	77	75	68	57	45	36	55
PREC.	3.1	3.1	3.5	3.3	3.7	3.7	4.3	4.1	3.3	3.1	2.6	3.0	40.8

15. San Antonio, TEXAS

	J	F	M	A	M	J	J	A	S	O	N	D	YEAR
TEMP.	53	55	63	69	75	81	83	83	79	70	61	54	69
PREC.	1.4	1.6	1.8	2.7	3.2	2.7	2.5	2.6	3.5	2.0	2.2	1.8	28.0

16. Montgomery, ALABAMA

	J	F	M	A	M	J	J	A	S	O	N	D	YEAR
TEMP.	48	51	58	65	73	80	82	81	76	66	56	49	66
PREC.	5.1	5.5	6.4	4.3	3.8	4.2	4.7	4.2	2.9	2.4	3.1	4.5	51.1

	J	F	M	A	M	J	J	A	S	O	N	D	YEAR

17. Sitka, ALASKA
	J	F	M	A	M	J	J	A	S	O	N	D	YEAR
TEMP.	30	32	35	40	46	51	55	55	51	44	37	33	42
PREC.	7.1	6.8	5.6	5.4	4.3	3.5	4.0	7.1	9.7	11.7	8.8	7.4	81.4

18. St. Paul, MINNESOTA
	J	F	M	A	M	J	J	A	S	O	N	D	YEAR
TEMP.	12	15	28	46	58	67	72	70	61	48	31	19	44
PREC.	0.9	0.8	1.4	2.4	3.4	4.1	3.5	3.5	3.4	2.0	1.4	1.0	27.8

19. Albany, NEW YORK
	J	F	M	A	M	J	J	A	S	O	N	D	YEAR
TEMP.	23	24	33	47	59	68	72	71	63	50	39	28	48
PREC.	2.6	2.5	2.7	2.7	3.5	4.0	4.1	3.8	3.4	3.4	3.0	2.7	38.4

20. Dubuque, IOWA
	J	F	M	A	M	J	J	A	S	O	N	D	YEAR
TEMP.	20	23	35	49	60	70	75	72	64	52	37	25	48
PREC.	1.5	1.4	2.2	2.6	3.9	4.5	3.7	3.4	4.0	2.5	1.9	1.5	33.1

21. Edmonton, CANADA
	J	F	M	A	M	J	J	A	S	O	N	D	YEAR
TEMP.	6	12	22	40	51	57	61	59	50	41	26	14	37
PREC.	0.8	0.7	0.8	0.9	1.7	3.1	3.2	2.4	1.3	0.7	0.7	0.8	17.1

22. Toronto, CANADA
	J	F	M	A	M	J	J	A	S	O	N	D	YEAR
TEMP.	22	23	30	42	53	63	69	67	60	48	37	27	45
PREC.	2.8	2.7	2.4	2.5	2.8	2.7	2.9	2.8	3.1	2.4	2.8	2.6	32.5

23. Halifax, CANADA
	J	F	M	A	M	J	J	A	S	O	N	D	YEAR
TEMP.	23	23	30	39	49	58	65	65	58	49	39	28	44
PREC.	5.5	4.9	4.9	4.6	4.1	3.7	3.8	4.5	3.6	5.2	5.5	5.3	55.6

24. Duluth, MINNESOTA
	J	F	M	A	M	J	J	A	S	O	N	D	YEAR
TEMP.	10	13	24	38	48	58	66	65	57	45	29	17	39
PREC.	1.0	1.0	1.5	2.1	3.4	4.4	3.9	3.5	3.7	2.7	1.5	1.2	29.9

25. Norman, CANADA
	J	F	M	A	M	J	J	A	S	O	N	D	YEAR
TEMP.	−19	−13	−2	19	41	54	59	54	41	24	−1	−15	20
PREC.	0.4	0.5	0.6	0.5	1.1	1.3	1.8	1.9	1.0	0.8	0.4	0.4	10.7

26. Churchill, CANADA
	J	F	M	A	M	J	J	A	S	O	N	D	YEAR
TEMP.	−21	−17	−2	17	30	44	54	52	41	27	6	−11	18
PREC.	0.6	1.1	1.1	1.0	0.9	2.0	1.8	2.4	2.6	1.3	1.2	0.8	16.8

27. Father Point, CANADA
	J	F	M	A	M	J	J	A	S	O	N	D	YEAR
TEMP.	9	10	22	34	44	53	58	56	49	41	30	17	36
PREC.	2.5	2.4	2.4	1.9	3.0	3.6	2.9	3.2	3.1	3.3	2.9	2.8	34.0

28. Upernivik, WEST GREENLAND
	J	F	M	A	M	J	J	A	S	O	N	D	YEAR
TEMP.	−7	−10	−7	6	25	35	41	41	34	25	14	1	17
PREC.	0.4	0.4	0.6	0.5	0.6	0.6	1.0	1.1	1.0	1.2	1.1	0.5	9.0

29. Angmagssalik, EAST GREENLAND
	J	F	M	A	M	J	J	A	S	O	N	D	YEAR
TEMP.	18	16	19	25	34	41	45	43	38	30	23	20	29
PREC.	3.3	2.0	2.4	2.4	2.4	2.1	1.9	2.4	3.7	5.7	3.3	2.8	34.4

South America

30. Medellín, COLOMBIA
	J	F	M	A	M	J	J	A	S	O	N	D	YEAR
TEMP.	71	72	71	71	71	71	71	71	71	69	69	70	71
PREC.	2.7	3.5	3.3	6.6	7.7	5.5	4.1	4.6	6.2	6.9	5.2	2.5	58.8

31. Santos, BRAZIL
	J	F	M	A	M	J	J	A	S	O	N	D	YEAR
TEMP.	76	78	76	73	69	66	66	66	67	69	73	76	71
PREC.	10.4	9.2	8.1	6.8	6.1	2.4	4.4	4.6	5.6	6.1	7.8	7.0	78.5

	J	F	M	A	M	J	J	A	S	O	N	D	YEAR

32. Manaus, BRAZIL

| TEMP. | 80 | 80 | 80 | 80 | 80 | 80 | 81 | 82 | 83 | 83 | 82 | 81 | 81 |
| PREC. | 9.2 | 9.0 | 9.6 | 8.5 | 7.0 | 3.6 | 2.2 | 1.4 | 2.0 | 4.1 | 5.5 | 7.7 | 69.8 |

33. Rio de Janeiro, BRAZIL

| TEMP. | 79 | 79 | 78 | 75 | 72 | 70 | 69 | 70 | 70 | 72 | 74 | 77 | 74 |
| PREC. | 4.9 | 4.8 | 5.2 | 4.3 | 3.1 | 2.3 | 1.7 | 1.7 | 2.6 | 3.2 | 4.1 | 5.4 | 43.3 |

34. Coquimbo, CHILE

| TEMP. | 64 | 64 | 62 | 59 | 57 | 54 | 54 | 54 | 55 | 57 | 59 | 62 | 58 |
| PREC. | 0 | 0 | 0 | 0 | 1.1 | 1.5 | 1.1 | 0.5 | 0.2 | 0 | 0 | 0 | 4.4 |

35. Lima, PERU

| TEMP. | 73 | 74 | 74 | 70 | 66 | 63 | 61 | 61 | 61 | 63 | 66 | 70 | 67 |
| PREC. | 0 | 0 | 0 | 0 | 0 | 0.1 | 0.2 | 0.4 | 0.4 | 0.4 | 0.2 | 0.1 | 1.8 |

36. Buenos Aires, ARGENTINA

| TEMP. | 74 | 73 | 69 | 61 | 55 | 50 | 49 | 51 | 55 | 60 | 66 | 71 | 61 |
| PREC. | 3.1 | 2.8 | 3.9 | 4.8 | 2.8 | 2.0 | 2.1 | 2.2 | 2.9 | 3.3 | 4.0 | 4.0 | 37.9 |

37. Puerto Montt, CHILE

| TEMP. | 60 | 58 | 56 | 52 | 50 | 46 | 46 | 46 | 47 | 51 | 54 | 57 | 52 |
| PREC. | 4.6 | 4.4 | 5.9 | 7.4 | 10.6 | 10.0 | 10.8 | 9.3 | 6.3 | 5.5 | 5.5 | 5.4 | 85.7 |

38. Mar del Plata, ARGENTINA

| TEMP. | 67 | 66 | 64 | 59 | 53 | 47 | 46 | 47 | 50 | 53 | 59 | 64 | 56 |
| PREC. | 2.1 | 3.1 | 3.1 | 3.1 | 1.9 | 2.4 | 2.1 | 1.8 | 2.6 | 2.4 | 2.6 | 2.7 | 29.9 |

39. Santiago, CHILE

| TEMP. | 69 | 67 | 62 | 57 | 51 | 46 | 46 | 49 | 52 | 57 | 62 | 67 | 57 |
| PREC. | 0 | 0.1 | 0.2 | 0.6 | 2.4 | 3.3 | 2.8 | 2.1 | 1.3 | 0.5 | 0.2 | 0.2 | 13.7 |

40. Tucumán, ARGENTINA

| TEMP. | 77 | 75 | 72 | 66 | 60 | 54 | 54 | 57 | 64 | 69 | 73 | 75 | 66 |
| PREC. | 6.3 | 7.5 | 5.5 | 3.1 | 1.2 | 0.6 | 0.3 | 0.5 | 0.6 | 2.3 | 4.2 | 5.9 | 38.0 |

Europe

41. Astrakhan, U.S.S.R.

| TEMP. | 19 | 21 | 32 | 49 | 64 | 73 | 78 | 75 | 64 | 50 | 38 | 26 | 49 |
| PREC. | 0.5 | 0.3 | 0.4 | 0.5 | 0.6 | 0.7 | 0.5 | 0.5 | 0.5 | 0.4 | 0.4 | 0.5 | 5.8 |

42. Turin, ITALY

| TEMP. | 33 | 37 | 46 | 54 | 61 | 69 | 74 | 73 | 65 | 54 | 43 | 35 | 54 |
| PREC. | 2.2 | 1.6 | 2.3 | 4.4 | 4.8 | 4.2 | 2.3 | 2.6 | 2.8 | 3.6 | 2.6 | 1.6 | 35.0 |

43. Trieste, ITALY

| TEMP. | 39 | 41 | 47 | 54 | 62 | 69 | 74 | 73 | 66 | 58 | 49 | 43 | 56 |
| PREC. | 2.2 | 2.3 | 2.8 | 2.9 | 3.7 | 4.1 | 3.7 | 3.7 | 4.0 | 4.7 | 3.6 | 3.4 | 41.1 |

44. Paris, FRANCE

| TEMP. | 37 | 39 | 43 | 51 | 56 | 62 | 66 | 64 | 59 | 51 | 43 | 37 | 51 |
| PREC. | 1.4 | 1.1 | 1.4 | 1.5 | 1.9 | 2.1 | 2.0 | 1.9 | 1.9 | 2.1 | 1.9 | 1.6 | 20.8 |

45. Dublin, IRELAND

| TEMP. | 40 | 41 | 42 | 45 | 49 | 55 | 58 | 57 | 54 | 48 | 44 | 41 | 48 |
| PREC. | 2.2 | 1.9 | 1.9 | 1.9 | 2.1 | 2.0 | 2.6 | 3.1 | 2.0 | 2.6 | 2.9 | 2.5 | 27.7 |

46. Reykjavik, ICELAND

| TEMP. | 30 | 30 | 31 | 36 | 43 | 49 | 52 | 51 | 46 | 39 | 34 | 30 | 39 |
| PREC. | 3.9 | 3.3 | 2.7 | 2.4 | 1.9 | 1.9 | 1.9 | 2.0 | 3.5 | 3.4 | 3.7 | 3.5 | 34.1 |

	J	F	M	A	M	J	J	A	S	O	N	D	YEAR

47. Frankfurt am Main, WEST GERMANY

	J	F	M	A	M	J	J	A	S	O	N	D	YEAR
TEMP.	32	36	41	49	57	63	66	64	58	49	41	35	49
PREC.	1.5	1.4	1.7	1.2	1.9	2.2	2.6	2.2	1.9	2.1	1.8	2.0	22.5

48. Edinburgh, SCOTLAND

	J	F	M	A	M	J	J	A	S	O	N	D	YEAR
TEMP.	38	39	40	45	49	55	58	57	54	47	42	39	47
PREC.	2.0	1.8	1.7	1.5	1.9	2.4	2.7	3.0	2.5	2.4	2.3	2.3	26.5

49. Athens, GREECE

	J	F	M	A	M	J	J	A	S	O	N	D	YEAR
TEMP.	48	50	53	58	66	74	80	80	73	66	57	52	63
PREC.	2.1	1.8	1.3	0.9	0.8	0.6	0.3	0.6	0.7	1.4	2.9	2.5	15.9

50. La Coruña, SPAIN

	J	F	M	A	M	J	J	A	S	O	N	D	YEAR
TEMP.	49	50	52	55	58	62	64	64	62	57	53	50	57
PREC.	2.7	3.5	3.2	2.9	2.0	1.4	0.9	1.1	1.7	3.1	3.5	3.5	29.5

51. Granada, SPAIN

	J	F	M	A	M	J	J	A	S	O	N	D	YEAR
TEMP.	44	48	52	58	63	70	77	77	70	60	51	44	59
PREC.	2.0	1.7	2.2	2.1	1.8	0.8	0.1	0.2	1.1	1.8	1.9	1.9	17.6

52. Lisbon, PORTUGAL

	J	F	M	A	M	J	J	A	S	O	N	D	YEAR
TEMP.	51	52	55	58	62	67	71	72	69	63	57	51	61
PREC.	3.4	3.3	3.4	3.1	1.8	0.6	0.2	0.2	1.3	2.4	3.6	4.3	27.6

53. Bucharest, ROMANIA

	J	F	M	A	M	J	J	A	S	O	N	D	YEAR
TEMP.	26	31	41	52	62	69	73	72	64	53	40	31	51
PREC.	1.2	1.1	1.5	1.7	2.3	4.3	2.2	2.2	2.0	1.6	1.6	1.2	22.9

54. Odessa, U.S.S.R.

	J	F	M	A	M	J	J	A	S	O	N	D	YEAR
TEMP.	25	28	35	48	59	68	73	71	62	52	41	31	49
PREC.	0.9	0.7	1.1	1.1	1.3	2.3	2.1	1.2	1.4	1.1	1.6	1.3	16.1

55. Oslo, NORWAY

	J	F	M	A	M	J	J	A	S	O	N	D	YEAR
TEMP.	25	26	31	41	51	60	63	60	52	42	33	27	43
PREC.	1.1	1.1	1.3	1.3	1.7	1.9	2.8	3.5	2.4	2.5	1.9	1.7	23.2

56. Moscow, U.S.S.R.

	J	F	M	A	M	J	J	A	S	O	N	D	YEAR
TEMP.	12	15	23	38	53	62	66	63	52	40	28	17	39
PREC.	1.7	0.9	1.2	1.5	1.9	2.0	2.8	2.9	2.2	1.4	1.6	1.5	21.6

57. Stockholm, SWEDEN

	J	F	M	A	M	J	J	A	S	O	N	D	YEAR
TEMP.	27	26	30	38	48	57	62	59	53	43	35	29	42
PREC.	1.4	1.3	1.3	1.5	1.5	1.7	2.4	2.9	1.9	1.8	1.9	1.9	21.5

58. Tromsö, NORWAY

	J	F	M	A	M	J	J	A	S	O	N	D	YEAR
TEMP.	26	24	27	32	39	47	52	51	44	36	30	27	36
PREC.	4.3	4.4	3.1	2.3	1.9	2.2	2.2	2.8	4.8	4.6	4.4	3.8	40.8

59. Archangel, U.S.S.R.

	J	F	M	A	M	J	J	A	S	O	N	D	YEAR
TEMP.	7	9	19	30	41	54	60	57	47	35	22	12	33
PREC.	0.8	0.7	0.8	0.7	1.0	1.5	2.2	2.1	2.0	1.5	1.1	0.8	15.2

60. Vardö, NORWAY

	J	F	M	A	M	J	J	A	S	O	N	D	YEAR
TEMP.	22	21	23	30	35	42	48	48	43	35	28	24	33
PREC.	2.6	2.8	2.1	1.7	1.4	1.6	1.7	2.0	2.4	2.5	2.5	2.6	25.9

Africa

61. Nouvelle-Anvers, REPUBLIC OF THE CONGO

	J	F	M	A	M	J	J	A	S	O	N	D	YEAR
TEMP.	79	80	79	78	78	78	77	78	78	77	77	77	78
PREC.	4.1	3.5	4.1	5.6	6.2	6.1	6.3	6.3	6.3	6.6	2.6	9.3	67.0

	J	F	M	A	M	J	J	A	S	O	N	D	YEAR

62. Freetown, SIERRA LEONE

	J	F	M	A	M	J	J	A	S	O	N	D	YEAR
TEMP.	81	82	82	82	82	80	78	77	79	80	81	81	80
PREC.	0.6	0.5	1.1	5.4	14.8	21.3	36.8	39.6	32.5	15.2	5.3	1.3	174.4

63. Banana, REPUBLIC OF THE CONGO

	J	F	M	A	M	J	J	A	S	O	N	D	YEAR
TEMP.	80	81	82	80	79	75	73	73	76	79	80	80	78
PREC.	2.1	2.3	3.7	6.1	1.9	0	0	0.1	0.1	1.6	5.9	4.7	28.5

64. Mombasa, KENYA

	J	F	M	A	M	J	J	A	S	O	N	D	YEAR
TEMP.	80	80	82	81	78	77	75	76	77	78	79	80	79
PREC.	0.8	0.9	2.3	7.8	13.7	3.6	3.5	2.2	1.9	3.4	5.0	2.2	47.3

65. Kimberley, SOUTH AFRICA

	J	F	M	A	M	J	J	A	S	O	N	D	YEAR
TEMP.	76	75	72	64	56	50	51	56	62	68	73	76	65
PREC.	2.8	3.0	2.8	2.0	0.7	0.5	0.1	0.3	0.2	0.8	2.1	2.9	18.2

66. Gorée, SENEGAL

	J	F	M	A	M	J	J	A	S	O	N	D	YEAR
TEMP.	69	66	68	69	72	78	81	82	82	82	78	72	75
PREC.	0	0	0	0	0	0.9	3.6	9.9	5.2	0.7	0.1	0	20.4

67. Cairo, EGYPT

	J	F	M	A	M	J	J	A	S	O	N	D	YEAR
TEMP.	54	57	63	70	77	82	84	83	78	75	66	59	71
PREC.	0.3	0.2	0.2	0.2	0	0	0	0	0	0.1	0.1	0.2	1.3

68. Swakopmund, SOUTH-WEST AFRICA

	J	F	M	A	M	J	J	A	S	O	N	D	YEAR
TEMP.	61	63	63	60	61	59	57	55	56	58	59	62	59
PREC.	0	0.1	0.2	0	0	0	0	0	0	0.1	0	0.2	0.6

69. Cape Town, SOUTH AFRICA

	J	F	M	A	M	J	J	A	S	O	N	D	YEAR
TEMP.	69	70	68	63	59	56	55	56	57	61	64	67	62
PREC.	0.7	0.6	0.9	1.8	3.9	4.4	3.5	3.3	2.2	1.6	1.1	0.8	24.8

70. Algiers, ALGERIA

	J	F	M	A	M	J	J	A	S	O	N	D	YEAR
TEMP.	53	55	58	61	66	71	77	78	75	69	62	56	65
PREC.	4.2	3.5	3.5	2.3	1.3	0.6	0.1	0.3	1.1	3.1	4.6	5.4	30.0

71. Pretoria, SOUTH AFRICA

	J	F	M	A	M	J	J	A	S	O	N	D	YEAR
TEMP.	72	71	68	63	57	53	52	57	63	68	69	71	64
PREC.	5.5	3.9	3.5	1.1	0.6	0.2	0.1	0.2	1.1	1.8	3.7	4.2	25.9

Asia and Adjacent Islands

72. Legaspi, PHILIPPINES

	J	F	M	A	M	J	J	A	S	O	N	D	YEAR
TEMP.	78	78	80	82	83	82	81	81	81	81	80	79	81
PREC.	15.2	13.0	7.7	5.4	5.3	8.8	10.1	7.2	10.2	13.0	17.3	18.7	131.9

73. Manokwari, NEW GUINEA

	J	F	M	A	M	J	J	A	S	O	N	D	YEAR
TEMP.	78	78	79	79	79	79	79	79	79	80	80	79	79
PREC.	10.8	10.7	13.0	11.1	7.8	8.3	6.0	5.3	5.1	4.2	6.6	10.6	99.5

74. Medan, INDONESIA

	J	F	M	A	M	J	J	A	S	O	N	D	YEAR
TEMP.	75	77	78	79	79	78	78	78	77	77	76	76	77
PREC.	5.4	3.9	4.1	5.2	7.0	5.2	5.2	6.9	8.7	9.8	10.1	8.9	80.4

75. Yap, CAROLINE ISLANDS

	J	F	M	A	M	J	J	A	S	O	N	D	YEAR
TEMP.	80	80	80	81	81	81	80	80	80	81	81	81	81
PREC.	7.0	6.8	4.9	5.2	9.6	10.8	16.6	16.2	13.4	11.8	10.1	8.9	121.3

76. Jakarta, INDONESIA

	J	F	M	A	M	J	J	A	S	O	N	D	YEAR
TEMP.	78	78	79	80	80	79	79	79	80	80	79	79	79
PREC.	11.9	13.4	7.9	5.6	4.1	3.7	2.6	1.6	2.8	4.5	5.7	7.6	71.4

	J	F	M	A	M	J	J	A	S	O	N	D	YEAR

77. Moulmein, BURMA

	J	F	M	A	M	J	J	A	S	O	N	D	YEAR
TEMP.	76	79	84	85	83	80	79	79	80	81	79	76	80
PREC.	0.2	0.2	0.5	2.8	20.0	37.8	45.2	42.8	28.1	8.5	2.2	0.3	188.6

78. Colombo, CEYLON

	J	F	M	A	M	J	J	A	S	O	N	D	YEAR
TEMP.	79	80	81	82	82	80	80	81	80	79	80	79	80
PREC.	3.2	1.9	4.7	11.4	12.1	8.4	4.5	3.8	5.0	14.4	12.5	6.4	88.3

79. Bombay, INDIA

	J	F	M	A	M	J	J	A	S	O	N	D	YEAR
TEMP.	75	75	78	82	85	82	80	79	79	81	79	76	79
PREC.	0.1	0	0	0.1	0.5	20.6	24.6	14.9	10.9	1.8	0.5	0.1	74.1

80. Tehran, IRAN

	J	F	M	A	M	J	J	A	S	O	N	D	YEAR
TEMP.	34	42	48	61	71	80	85	83	77	61	51	42	62
PREC.	1.2	0.9	2.4	0.9	0.4	0	0.4	0	0.1	0.1	1.2	1.3	8.9

81. Tashkent, U.S.S.R.

	J	F	M	A	M	J	J	A	S	O	N	D	YEAR
TEMP.	30	34	47	58	70	77	81	77	67	54	43	36	56
PREC.	1.8	1.4	2.6	2.6	1.1	0.5	0.1	0.1	0.2	1.1	1.4	1.7	14.6

82. New Delhi, INDIA

	J	F	M	A	M	J	J	A	S	O	N	D	YEAR
TEMP.	58	62	74	86	92	92	86	85	84	79	68	60	77
PREC.	1.0	0.6	0.7	0.3	0.7	3.2	8.4	7.4	4.4	0.4	0.1	0.4	27.6

83. Karachi, WEST PAKISTAN

	J	F	M	A	M	J	J	A	S	O	N	D	YEAR
TEMP.	65	68	75	81	85	87	84	82	82	80	74	67	78
PREC.	0.6	0.3	0.1	0.1	0	0.4	3.2	1.8	0.7	0	0.2	0.2	7.6

84. Tokyo, JAPAN

	J	F	M	A	M	J	J	A	S	O	N	D	YEAR
TEMP.	37	38	44	54	62	69	75	78	72	61	50	41	57
PREC.	2.0	2.6	4.3	5.3	5.9	6.3	5.6	4.6	7.5	7.2	4.3	2.3	57.9

85. Shanghai, CHINA

	J	F	M	A	M	J	J	A	S	O	N	D	YEAR
TEMP.	38	39	46	56	66	73	80	80	73	63	52	42	59
PREC.	2.2	2.3	3.4	3.8	3.7	6.5	5.5	5.9	4.7	3.2	1.7	1.2	44.1

86. Wuhan, CHINA

	J	F	M	A	M	J	J	A	S	O	N	D	YEAR
TEMP.	39	40	49	61	71	78	84	83	76	65	54	43	62
PREC.	2.1	1.1	2.8	4.8	5.0	7.0	8.6	4.6	2.2	3.9	1.1	0.6	43.8

87. Varanasi, INDIA

	J	F	M	A	M	J	J	A	S	O	N	D	YEAR
TEMP.	60	65	77	87	91	89	84	83	83	78	68	60	77
PREC.	0.7	0.5	0.3	0.1	0.6	5.5	12.5	11.2	6.5	2.2	0.2	0.2	40.5

88. Darjeeling, INDIA

	J	F	M	A	M	J	J	A	S	O	N	D	YEAR
TEMP.	40	42	50	56	58	60	62	61	59	55	48	42	53
PREC.	0.8	1.1	2.0	4.1	7.8	24.2	31.7	26.0	18.3	5.3	0.2	0.2	121.7

89. Peiping, CHINA

	J	F	M	A	M	J	J	A	S	O	N	D	YEAR
TEMP.	24	29	41	57	68	76	79	77	68	55	39	27	53
PREC.	0.1	0.2	0.2	0.6	1.4	3.0	9.4	6.3	2.6	0.6	0.3	0.1	24.8

90. Irkutsk, U.S.S.R.

	J	F	M	A	M	J	J	A	S	O	N	D	YEAR
TEMP.	−5	1	17	35	48	59	65	60	48	33	13	1	31
PREC.	0.6	0.5	0.4	0.6	1.2	2.3	2.9	2.4	1.6	0.7	0.6	0.8	14.6

Australia and New Zealand

91. Darwin, AUSTRALIA

	J	F	M	A	M	J	J	A	S	O	N	D	YEAR
TEMP.	84	84	84	84	82	79	77	79	83	85	86	85	83
PREC.	15.2	13.5	9.6	4.1	0.6	0.1	0.1	0.1	0.5	2.0	4.7	9.8	60.3

	J	F	M	A	M	J	J	A	S	O	N	D	YEAR
92. Hall's Creek, AUSTRALIA													
TEMP.	86	85	83	78	71	66	64	69	76	84	87	87	78
PREC.	5.7	4.8	3.0	0.8	0.4	0.2	0.2	0.1	0.2	0.6	1.5	3.3	20.8
93. Alice Springs, AUSTRALIA													
TEMP.	83	82	77	73	60	54	53	58	66	74	79	82	70
PREC.	1.7	1.7	1.2	0.7	0.6	0.6	0.4	0.4	0.4	0.7	1.0	1.5	10.9
94. Marble Bar, AUSTRALIA													
TEMP.	93	92	90	84	75	68	67	71	78	84	90	92	82
PREC.	2.6	3.2	1.9	0.9	0.7	1.1	0.6	0.2	0	0.2	0.4	1.3	13.1
95. Auckland, NEW ZEALAND													
TEMP.	66	66	64	61	57	54	52	52	55	57	60	63	59
PREC.	2.6	3.3	3.0	3.5	4.6	5.0	5.0	4.2	3.7	3.6	3.4	2.9	44.8
96. Melbourne, AUSTRALIA													
TEMP.	68	68	65	59	54	50	49	51	54	58	61	65	59
PREC.	1.8	1.8	2.1	2.2	2.1	2.0	1.8	1.8	2.4	2.6	2.2	2.2	25.0
97. Hobart, TASMANIA													
TEMP.	62	62	59	55	51	47	46	48	51	54	57	60	54
PREC.	1.8	1.6	1.7	1.9	1.8	2.2	2.1	1.8	2.1	2.2	2.4	1.9	23.5
98. Adelaide, AUSTRALIA													
TEMP.	74	74	70	64	58	54	52	54	57	61	67	71	63
PREC.	0.7	0.8	1.0	1.7	2.7	3.1	2.6	2.4	2.1	1.7	1.1	0.9	20.8
99. Mackay, AUSTRALIA													
TEMP.	80	79	77	74	68	64	62	64	68	73	77	79	72
PREC.	15.0	13.7	15.4	7.3	4.4	2.7	2.3	0.9	1.1	2.4	2.7	7.3	75.2

Indian Ocean

	J	F	M	A	M	J	J	A	S	O	N	D	YEAR
100. KERGUELEN ISLANDS													
TEMP.	44	45	39	39	35	37	33	34	33	34	39	41	38

C Areas and Populations: World Summary

	AREA (IN SQUARE MILES)	POPULATION (IN THOUSANDS)	ARITHMETIC DENSITY
WORLD TOTAL	57,284,599	2,901,992	51
Africa	11,691,698	246,711	21
Algeria	919,591	10,930	12
Angola	481,351	4,550	9
Ascension Island	34	.3	9
Basutoland	11,716	674	58
Bechuanaland	275,000	337	1
British Cameroons [1]	34,081	1,621	48
Cameroun	166,988	3,225	19
Cape Verde Islands	1,546	195	126
Central African Republic	238,224	1,185	5
Chad	495,753	2,600	5
Comoro Islands	838	185	221
Congo (Brazzaville)	132,046	795	6
Congo (Léopoldville)	905,379	13,821	15
Dahomey	44,696	2,000	45
Egypt	386,100	25,365	66
Ethiopia	457,266	21,800	48
French Somaliland	8,494	70	8
Gabon	103,089	420	4
Gambia	4,003	301	75
Ghana	91,843	4,911	53
Guinea	94,925	2,727	29
Ifni	579	53	92
Ivory Coast	124,503	3,103	25
Kenya	224,960	6,450	29
Liberia	43,000	1,250	29
Libya	679,359	1,172	2
Malagasy Republic	227,799	5,239	23
Mali	464,873	4,300	9
Mauritania	419,230	730	2

SOURCE: Compiled and calculated from *United Nations Demographic Yearbook, 1960*. Area figures converted from square kilometers; densities calculated on basis of converted areas. Population based on midyear 1959 estimates. There have been later censuses in some countries, but the United Nations estimates provide a uniform date as a basis for comparison.

[1] In a plebescite held in the autumn of 1961, the northern part of British Cameroons voted to unite with Nigeria, the southern part with Cameroun.

	AREA (IN SQUARE MILES)	POPULATION (IN THOUSANDS)	ARITHMETIC DENSITY
Mauritius	720	621	863
Morocco	171,305	10,550	62
Mozambique	302,328	6,310	21
Niger	458,994	2,555	6
Nigeria	339,169	33,663	99
Portuguese Guinea	13,948	565	41
Réunion	970	324	344
Rodrigues and adjacent islands	89	19	213
Rhodesia and Nyasaland, Federation of	483,829	8,130	17
Ruanda-Urundi	20,915	4,780	228
St. Helena	47	5	106
São Tomé and Principe	372	64	172
Senegal	76,124	2,550	33
Seychelles	156	43	276
Sierra Leone	27,925	2,400	86
Somalia	246,201	1,990	8
South Africa	472,359	14,673	31
South-West Africa	318,099	554	2
Spanish Guinea	10,831	216	20
Spanish Possessions in North Africa (Ceuta and Melilla)	82	145	1,768
Spanish Sahara	102,703	25	4
Sudan	967,499	11,459	12
Swaziland	6,704	250	37
Tanganyika	361,800	9,076	25
Togo	22,008	1,442	66
Tristan da Cunha and adjacent islands [2]	81	.3	.27
Tunisia	48,332	3,935	81
Uganda	93,981	6,517	69
Upper Volta	105,839	3,537	33
Zanzibar and Pemba	1,020	304	298
Antarctica	5,100,000	0	0
Asia [3]	10,405,229	1,612,462	154
Aden (colony)	75	150	2,000
Aden (protectorate)	112,000	660	6
Afghanistan	250,965	13,150	52
Bahrain	231	143	619
Bhutan	19,305	660	34
Bonin Islands	40	.206	5
Brunei	2,226	83	37
Burma	261,789	20,457	78
Cambodia	66,607	4,845	73
Ceylon	25,332	9,612	379

[2] A violent and continuing eruption of a volcano (thought to have been extinct) on Tristan da Cunha in the autumn of 1961 necessitated the evacuation of the total population of the island to England.

[3] Excluding U.S.S.R., including Turkey.

	AREA (IN SQUARE MILES)	POPULATION (IN THOUSANDS)	ARITHMETIC DENSITY
China (mainland)	3,691,506	669,000	181
China (Taiwan)	13,885	10,232	737
Cyprus	3,572	558	156
Gaza Strip	78	350	4,488
Hong Kong	391	2,857	7,307
India	1,259,990	402,600	320
Indonesia	575,893	90,300	157
Iran	636,293	20,149	32
Iraq	171,599	6,952	41
Israel	7,992	2,061	258
Japan	142,726	92,740	650
Jordan	37,301	1,636	44
Korea (North)	47,862	8,100	169
Korea (South)	37,424	23,848	637
Kuwait	6,000	219	37
Laos	91,429	1,760	19
Lebanon	4,015	1,550	386
Macao	6	215	35,833
Malaya, Federation of	50,700	6,698	132
Maldive Islands	115	89	774
Mongolian People's Republic	591,120	1,057	2
Muscat and Oman	82,000	550	7
Nepal	54,362	9,044	166
Netherlands New Guinea	160,618	700	4
North Borneo	29,387	419	14
Pakistan	364,373	86,823	238
Philippines	115,707	24,718	214
Portuguese India	1,619	649	401
Portuguese Timor	5,763	496	86
Qatar	8,500	40	5
Ryukyu Islands	848	855	1,008
Sarawak	48,342	688	14
Saudi Arabia	617,761	6,036	10
Sikkim	2,744	150	54
Singapore	224	1,580	7,054
Syria	71,227	4,539	64
Thailand	198,456	21,881	110
Trucial Oman	32,278	86	3
Turkey [4]	301,381	27,017	90
Viet-Nam, North	59,934	15,170	253
Viet-Nam, Republic of	65,948	13,790	209
Yemen	75,290	4,500	60
Australia and Oceania	**3,298,014**	**15,360**	**5**
American Samoa	76	20	263
Australia	2,974,579	10,061	3
British Solomon Islands	11,500	115	10
Canton and Enderbury Islands	20	.272	15
Christmas Island	60	3	50

[4] Includes European portion of Turkey.

	AREA (IN SQUARE MILES)	POPULATION (IN THOUSANDS)	ARITHMETIC DENSITY
Cocos Islands	5	1	200
Cook Islands	90	18	200
Fiji Islands	7,055	381	54
French Polynesia	1,544	80	52
Gilbert and Ellice Islands	349	45	129
Guam	206	69	335
Midway Islands	2	.416	208
Nauru	8	4	500
New Caledonia	7,335	70	10
New Guinea [5]	93,000	1,376	15
New Hebrides	5,700	58	10
New Zealand	103,736	2,331	22
Niue	100	5	50
Norfolk Island	14	1	71
Pacific Islands [6]	687	73	106
Papua	90,540	480	5
Pitcairn	2	.146	73
Tokelau Islands	4	2	500
Tonga	269	62	230
Wake Island	3	.349	116
Western Samoa	1,130	104	92
Europe [7]	**1,903,298**	**421,287**	**221**
Albania	11,100	1,556	140
Andorra	175	7	40
Austria	32,374	7,049	218
Belgium	11,779	9,104	773
Bulgaria	42,729	7,798	182
Channel Islands	75	103	528
Czechoslovakia	49,366	13,559	275
Denmark	16,619	4,547	274
Faeroe Islands	540	34	63
Finland	130,119	4,416	34
France	212,822	45,097	212
Germany, Democratic Republic	41,479	16,213	391
Germany, Federal Republic of	95,737	52,785	551
BERLIN, *East*	156	1,085	6,955
BERLIN, *West*	186	2,211	11,887
Gibraltar	2	26	13,000
Greece	51,182	8,258	161
Holy See	.16	1	6,250
Hungary	35,919	9,953	277
Iceland	39,768	172	4
Ireland	27,136	2,846	105
Isle of Man	227	54	238

[5] Northeastern part, plus the Bismarck Archipelago and several hundred smaller islands, all under Australian trusteeship.
[6] The Caroline, Mariana, and Marshall Islands, all under U.S. trusteeship.
[7] Excluding U.S.S.R. and Turkey.

	AREA (IN SQUARE MILES)	POPULATION (IN THOUSANDS)	ARITHMETIC DENSITY
Italy	116,303	49,052	422
Liechtenstein	61	16	262
Luxembourg	998	324	325
Malta and Gozo	122	325	2,664
Monaco	.77	23	29,870
Netherlands	12,529	11,346	906
Norway	125,064	3,556	28
Poland	120,359	29,257	243
Portugal [8]	35,598	9,052	254
Romania	91,699	18,256	199
San Marino	24	13	542
Spain [9]	194,396	29,894	154
Svalbard and Jan Mayen Islands [10]	24,111	(4)	
Sweden	173,622	7,454	43
Switzerland	15,941	5,240	329
United Kingdom	94,215	52,157	554
Yugoslavia	98,766	18,448	187
North and Middle America	**9,366,958**	**259,677**	**28**
Bahama Islands	4,400	103	23
Bermuda	20	44	2,200
British Honduras	8,866	90	10
Canada	3,851,806	17,442	5
Canal Zone	553	42	76
Cayman Islands	100	9	90
Costa Rica	19,575	1,126	58
Cuba	44,218	6,599	149
Dominican Republic	18,816	2,894	154
El Salvador	8,260	2,520	305
Guadeloupe	687	264	384
Greenland	840,000	30	—
Guatemala	42,042	3,652	87
Haiti	10,714	3,464	323
Honduras	43,277	1,887	44
Jamaica	4,411	1,671	379
Martinique	425	271	637
Mexico	760,373	33,304	44
Netherlands Antilles	371	195	526
Nicaragua	57,143	1,424	25
Panama	28,573	1,024	36
Puerto Rico	3,435	2,347	683
St. Pierre and Miquelon	93	5	54
Turks and Caicos Islands	166	7	42
United States of America [11]	3,615,207	177,700	49
Virgin Islands (U.K.)	67	8	119

[8] Including the Azores and Madeira Islands.
[9] Including the Balearic and Canary Islands.
[10] Inhabited in winter only. Population figure is only for Norwegians and is also included in population of Norway. (About 3,000 Russians live there in the winter; they are included in the population of the U.S.S.R., below.)
[11] Including Hawaii.

	AREA (IN SQUARE MILES)	POPULATION (IN THOUSANDS)	ARITHMETIC DENSITY
Virgin Islands (U.S.A.)	133	30	226
West Indies, Federation of	3,327	1,525	458
South America	**6,869,904**	**135,995**	**20**
Argentina	1,072,746	20,614	19
Bolivia	424,163	3,416	8
Brazil	3,287,198	64,216	20
British Guiana	83,000	549	7
Chile	286,397	7,465	26
Colombia	439,513	13,824	31
Ecuador	104,506	4,169	40
Falkland Islands	4,618	2	—
French Guiana	35,135	31	1
Paraguay	157,047	1,718	11
Peru	496,222	10,524	21
Surinam	55,144	255	5
Uruguay	72,172	2,700	37
Venezuela	352,143	6,512	18
U.S.S.R.	**8,649,498**	**210,500**	**24**

APPENDIX

D Some Suggested References

1. Some Objectives of Geographic Study

BOWMAN, ISAIAH. *Geography in Relation to the Social Sciences*. N.Y.: Scribner's, 1934.

BRUHNES, JEAN. *Human Geography*. N.Y.: Rand McNally, 1920.

EAST, WILLIAM GORDON. *The Geography Behind History*. N.Y.: Nelson, 1938.

LOWIE, ROBERT HARRY. *An Introduction to Cultural Anthropology*, rev. ed. N.Y.: Farrar & Rinehart, 1940.

MacCURDY, GEORGE GRANT. *Human Origins*. N.Y.: Appleton, 1924.

RITTER, CARL. *Comparative Geography*. Philadelphia: Lippincott, 1865.

VIDAL DE LA BLACHE, PAUL. *Principles of Human Geography*. N.Y.: Holt, 1926.

2. Gross Features of the Earth

BARNETT, L., AND THE EDITORIAL STAFF OF *Life*. *The World We Live In*. N.Y.: Time, Inc., 1955.

GAMOW, GEORGE. *The Birth and Death of the Sun*. Baltimore: Penguin, 1945.

HARRISON, LUCIA CAROLYN. *Sun, Earth, Time, and Man*. Chicago: Rand McNally, 1960.

HORROCKS, NORMAN KENDALL. *Physical Geography and Climatology*. London: Longmans, Green, 1953.

KUIPER, GERARD P., ed. *The Earth as a Planet*. Chicago: Univ. of Chicago Press, 1955.

MARR, JOHN EDWARD. *The Scientific Study of Scenery*, 9th ed. London: Methuen, 1943.

MILL, HUGH ROBERT. *The Realm of Nature*. N.Y.: Scribner's, 1892.

RUSSELL, HENRY NORRIS, RAYMOND SMITH DUGAN, and JOHN QUINCY STEWART. *Astronomy, Vol. I: The Solar System*, rev. ed. Boston: Ginn, 1945.

3. The Tools of Geography

AMIRAN, D. H. K., and A. P. SCHICK, compilers and eds. *Geographical Conversion Tables*. Zurich: Aschmann & Scheller, 1961.

BARTHOLOMEW, JOHN, ed. *The Times Atlas of the World, Mid-Century Edition*, 5 vols. London: Times Pub. Co., 1955–60.

BROWN, LLOYD A. *The Story of Maps*. Boston: Little, Brown, 1949.

CHAMBERLIN, WELLMAN. *The Round Earth on Flat Paper*. Washington, D.C.: National Geographic Society, 1947.

DEETZ, CHARLES H., and OSCAR S. ADAMS. *Elements of Map Projection*. Washington, D.C.: U.S. Coast and Geodetic Survey, 1945.

ESPENSHADE, E. B., JR., ed. *Goode's World Atlas*, 11th ed. Chicago: Rand McNally, 1960.

GREENHOOD, DAVID. *Down to Earth: Mapping for Everybody*. N.Y.: Holiday House, 1951.

JOHNSON, WILLIS E. *Mathematical Geography*. N.Y.: American Book, 1907.

LOBECK, A. K. *Block Diagrams and Other Graphic Methods Used in Geology and Geography*. N.Y.: Wiley, 1924.

RAISZ, ERWIN. *General Cartography*. N.Y.: McGraw-Hill, 1948.

RIDGEWAY, JOHN L. *Scientific Illustration*. Stanford, Calif.: Stanford Univ. Press, 1938.

ROBINSON, ARTHUR H. *Elements of Cartography*. N.Y.: Wiley, 1960.

STAMP, L. D., ed. *A Glossary of Geographical Terms*. N.Y.: Wiley, 1961.

STEER, JAMES A. *An Introduction to the Study of Map Projections*. London: Univ. of London Press, 1943.

WILLIAMS, J. E., ed. *Prentice-Hall World Atlas*. Englewood Cliffs, N.J.: Prentice-Hall, 1958.

NOTE: Descriptive pamphlets and booklets dealing with globes and their use are available from

many map-publishing companies, such as De-
noyer-Geppert, A. J. Nystrom, Rand McNally,
etc.

4. The Earth's Waters

ADDISON, H. *Land, Water and Food*. London:
Chapman & Hall, 1955.

BEHRE, CHARLES H., JR. "Our Most Important
Mineral—Water." *Focus*, Vol. VII, No. 5 (Jan.
1957).

BIRD, JOHN A. *Western Ground Waters and Food
Production*. Washington, D.C.: U.S. Dept. of
Agriculture, 1942.

CARSON, RACHEL L. *The Sea Around Us*. N.Y.:
Oxford Univ. Press, 1951.

The Colorado River. Washington, D.C.: U.S.
Dept. of the Interior, 1946.

The Columbia River. Washington, D.C.: U.S.
Dept. of the Interior, 1947.

DUGAN, JAMES. *Man Under the Sea*. N.Y.:
Harper, 1956.

ENGEL, L., AND THE EDITORS OF *Life*. *The Sea*.
N.Y.: Time, Inc., 1961.

FINCH, V. C., G. T. TREWARTHA, A. H. ROBIN-
SON, and E. H. HAMMOND. *Elements of Geography*. N.Y.: McGraw-Hill, 1957.

FRANK, BERNARD, and ANTHONY NETBOY. *Water,
Land, and People*. N.Y.: Knopf, 1950.

HATCHER, HARLAN. *The Great Lakes*. N.Y.: Oxford Univ. Press, 1944.

HILLS, T. L. *The St. Lawrence Seaway*. N.Y.:
Praeger, 1959.

Irrigation Agriculture in the West. Washington,
D.C.: U.S. Dept. of Agriculture, 1948.

KRUTILLA, J. V., and OTTO ECKSTEIN. *Multiple
Purpose River Development*. Washington,
D.C.: Resources for the Future, Inc., 1958.

KUENEN, P. H. *Realms of Water*. N.Y.: Wiley,
1955.

LANE, F. C. *The World's Great Lakes*. N.Y.:
Doubleday, 1948.

———. *Earth's Grandest Rivers*. N.Y.: Doubleday, 1949.

*The Nation Looks at Its Resources (Report of the
Mid-Century Conference on Resources for the
Future)*. Washington, D.C.: Resources for the
Future, Inc., 1954.

RICHIE, CALDER. *Men Against the Desert*. N.Y.:
Macmillan, 1952.

Rivers of America Series. N.Y.: Rinehart. (For
example, WALTER HAVIGHURST, *The Upper
Mississippi*, 1944.)

SCHURR, S. H., and B. C. NETSCHERT. *The Nation's Energy Position*. Washington, D.C.: Resources for the Future, Inc., 1959.

SHEPHARD, F. P. *The Earth Beneath the Sea*.
Baltimore: Johns Hopkins Press, 1959.

SVERDRUP, H. U., M. W. JOHNSON, and R. H.
FLEMING. *The Oceans: Their Physics, Chem-
istry, and General Biology*. Englewood Cliffs,
N.J.: Prentice-Hall, 1942.

THOREAU, HENRY D. *Walden: or Life in the
Woods*.

TWAIN, MARK. *Life on the Mississippi*.

Water: Yearbook of Agriculture, 1955. Washington, D.C.: U.S. Dept. of Agriculture, 1955.

Water Facts. Washington, D.C.: U.S. Dept. of
Agriculture, 1957.

WILLIAMS, ALBERT N. *The Water and the Power*.
N.Y.: Duell, Sloan & Pearce, 1951.

5. Introduction to Landforms

FINCH, V. C., G. T. TREWARTHA, A. H. ROBIN-
SON, and E. H. HAMMOND. *Elements of Geography*. N.Y.: McGraw-Hill, 1957.

LEE, WILLIS T. *The Face of the Earth as Seen
from the Air*. N.Y.: American Geographical
Society, 1922.

LIGHT, R. U. *Focus on Africa*. N.Y.: American
Geographical Society, 1941.

LOBECK, A. K. *Geomorphology*. N.Y.: McGraw-
Hill, 1939.

RICH, JOHN L. *The Face of South America: An
Aerial Traverse*. N.Y.: American Geographical
Society, 1942.

THORNBURY, WILLIAM D. *Principles of Geomorphology*. N.Y.: Wiley, 1954.

6. Landforms and the Agents of Erosion and Deposition

ANTEVS, ERNST. *The Last Glaciation*. N.Y.: American Geographical Society, 1928.

BOWMAN, ISAIAH. *Desert Trails of the Atacama*.
N.Y.: American Geographical Society, 1924.

COTTON, C. A. *Landscape*. Christchurch, New
Zealand: Whitcomb & Tombs, 1948.

DAVIS, W. M. *Geographical Essays*. Boston:
Ginn, 1909.

FLINT, RICHARD F. *Glacial and Pleistocene Geology*. N.Y.: Wiley, 1957.

HINDS, N. E. A. *Geomorphology*. Englewood Cliffs, N.J.: Prentice-Hall, 1943.

JOHNSON, DOUGLAS W. *Shore Processes and Shoreline Development*. N.Y.: Wiley, 1919.

LEOPOLD, A. S., AND THE EDITORS OF *Life*. *The Desert*, N.Y.: Time, Inc., 1961.

STRAHLER, A. N. *Physical Geography*. N.Y.: Wiley, 1960.

THOMAS, WILLIAM L., JR., ed. *Man's Role in Changing the Face of the Earth*. Chicago: Univ. of Chicago Press, 1956. (Esp. pp. 621–47 of section on "Slope and Soil Changes Through Human Use.")

VON ENGELN, O. D. *Geomorphology*. N.Y.: Macmillan, 1942.

7. *The Landforms of the Continents*

American Mountain Series. N.Y.: Vanguard. (For example, WALLACE W. ATWOOD, *The Rocky Mountains*, 1945.)

ATWOOD, WALLACE W. *The Physiographic Provinces of North America*. Boston: Ginn, 1940.

CRESSEY, G. B. *Asia's Lands and Peoples*. N.Y.: McGraw-Hill, 1951.

FENNEMAN, N. M. *Physiography of Western United States*. N.Y.: McGraw-Hill, 1931.

———. *Physiography of Eastern United States*. N.Y.: McGraw-Hill, 1938.

FITZGERALD, WALTER. *Africa*. N.Y.: Dutton, 1945.

GOTTMAN, JEAN. *A Geography of Europe*. N.Y.: Holt, Rinehart & Winston, 1962.

JAMES, PRESTON E. *Latin America*. N.Y.: Odyssey Press, 1959.

MILNE, L. J., MARGERY MILNE, AND THE EDITORS OF *Life*. *The Mountains*. N.Y.: Time, Inc., 1962.

PEATTIE, RODERICK. *Mountain Geography*. Cambridge: Harvard Univ. Press, 1936.

8. *Elements and Controls of Climate*

BERRY, F. A., E. BOLLAY, and NORMAN R. BEERS. *Handbook of Meteorology*. N.Y.: McGraw-Hill, 1945.

BLUMENSTOCK, D. *The Ocean of Air*. New Brunswick, N.J.: Rutgers Univ. Press, 1959.

DONN, WILLIAM L. *Meteorology–With Marine Applications*, 2nd ed. N.Y.: McGraw-Hill, 1951.

PETTERSSEN, SVERRE. *Introduction to Meteorology*. N.Y.: McGraw-Hill, 1941.

TREWARTHA, GLENN T. *An Introduction to Weather and Climate*, 3rd ed. N.Y.: McGraw-Hill, 1954.

9. *Climatic Elements Over the World*

BROOKS, C. E. P. *Climate: A Handbook for Businessmen, Students, and Travellers*. N.Y.: Scribner's, 1930.

HARE, F. K. *The Restless Atmosphere*. London: Hutchinson, 1961.

KENDREW, W. G. *Climatology*. Oxford: Clarendon Press, 1949.

KIMBLE, GEORGE, and RAYMOND BUSH. *The Weather*. Baltimore: Pelican, 1946.

KOEPPE, C. E., and G. C. DeLONG. *Weather and Climate*. N.Y.: McGraw-Hill, 1958.

LEHR, PAUL E., R. WILL BURNETT, and HERBERT S. ZIM. *Weather: A Guide to Phenomena and Forecasts*. N.Y.: Simon & Schuster, 1957.

STEWART, GEORGE R. *Storm*. N.Y.: Modern Library, 1947.

TANNEHILL, I. R. *Weather Around the World*. Princeton, N.J.: Princeton Univ. Press, 1943.

10 *and* 11. *Climatic Types*

HAURWITZ, BERNHARD, and JAMES M. AUSTIN. *Climatology*. N.Y.: McGraw-Hill, 1944.

KENDREW, W. G. *The Climates of the Continents*, 4th ed. Oxford: Clarendon Press, 1953.

TREWARTHA, GLENN T. *An Introduction to Weather and Climate*, 3rd ed. N.Y.: McGraw-Hill, 1954.

12. *Soils: Their Formation and Distribution*

BENNETT, H. H. *Elements of Soil Conservation*, 2nd ed. N.Y.: McGraw-Hill, 1955.

GLINKA, K. D. *The Great Soil Groups of the World and Their Development*, trans. from the German by C. F. Marbut. Ann Arbor, Mich.: Edwards Brothers, 1927.

KELLOGG, CHARLES E. *The Soils That Support Us*. N.Y.: Macmillan, 1941.

MICKEY, KARL B. *Man and the Soil*. Chicago: International Harvester Co., 1945.

Soils: The Yearbook of Agriculture 1957. Washington, D.C.: U.S. Dept. of Agriculture, 1957.

Soils and Men: The Yearbook of Agriculture 1938. Washington, D.C.: U.S. Dept. of Agriculture, 1938.

13. Natural Vegetation and Animal Life

CAIN, STANLEY A. *Foundations of Plant Geography*. N.Y.: Harper, 1944.

FARB, PETER, AND THE EDITORS OF *Life*. *The Forest*. N.Y.: Time, Inc., 1961.

FORESTER, C. S. *The Sky and the Forest*. Boston: Little, Brown, 1948.

Grass: The Yearbook of Agriculture 1948. Washington, D.C.: U.S. Dept. of Agriculture, 1948.

HESSE, R., W. C. ALLEE, and K. P. SCHMIDT. *Ecological Animal Geography*. N.Y.: Wiley, 1951.

LEOPOLD, A. S., AND THE EDITORS OF *Life*. *The Desert*. N.Y.: Time, Inc., 1961.

LILLIARD, RICHARD G. *The Great Forest*. N.Y.: Knopf, 1948.

POLUNIN, N. *Introduction to Plant Geography*. N.Y.: McGraw-Hill, 1960.

SCHIMPER, A. F. W. *Plant Geography upon a Physiological Basis*. Oxford: Oxford Univ. Press, 1903.

Trees: The Yearbook of Agriculture 1949. Washington, D.C.: U.S. Dept. of Agriculture, 1949.

14. Regions in Physical Geography

FINCH, V. C. "Geographical Science and Social Philosophy." *Annals of the Association of American Geographers*, Vol. 29, No. 1 (Mar. 1939), 1–28.

HARTSHORNE, RICHARD. "The Nature of Geography." *Annals of the Association of American Geographers*, Vol. 29, Nos. 3 and 4 (Sept. and Dec. 1939), 171–658.

JAMES, PRESTON E. *A Geography of Man*. Boston: Ginn, 1959.

WHITE, C. LANGDON, and G. T. RENNER. *College Geography*. N.Y.: Appleton-Century-Crofts, 1957.

15. World Population

CARR-SAUNDERS, A. M. *World Population*. Oxford: Clarendon Press, 1936.

DAVIS, KINGSLEY, ed. "World Population in Transition." *Annals of the American Academy of Political and Social Science*, Vol. 237 (Jan. 1945).

Demographic Yearbook, 1960. N.Y.: United Nations, 1961.

MOORE, WILBERT E. *Economic Demography of Eastern and Southern Europe*. League of Nations Publication (Economic and Financial), 1945, II.A.9. N.Y.: Columbia Univ. Press, 1946.

NOTESTEIN, FRANK W., and others. *The Future Population of Europe and the Soviet Union: Population Projections 1940–1970*. League of Nations Publication (Economic, Financial and Transit Dept.), 1944, II.A.2. N.Y.: Columbia Univ. Press, 1944.

STAMP, L. DUDLEY. *Land for Tomorrow*. Bloomington: Indiana Univ. Press, 1952.

THOMPSON, WARREN S. *Population Problems*, 4th ed. N.Y.: McGraw-Hill, 1953.

16. Settlement Types and Contrasts

AUROUSSEAU, M. "The Arrangement of Rural Populations," *Geographical Review*, Vol. 10, 1920, 223–40; "The Distribution of Population: A Constructive Problem," *Geographical Review*, Vol. 11, 1921, 563–92; and "Recent Contributions to Urban Geography: A Review," *Geographical Review*, Vol. 14, 1924, 444–55.

DICKINSON, ROBERT E. *City Region and Regionalism: A Geographical Contribution to Human Ecology*. London: Keegan Paul, Trench, Trubner, 1947.

HAWLEY, AMOS H. *Human Ecology: A Theory of Community Structure*. N.Y.: Ronald, 1950.

MUMFORD, LEWIS. *The Culture of Cities*. N.Y.: Harcourt, Brace & World, 1938.

———. *The City in History*. N.Y.: Harcourt, Brace & World, 1961.

PIDDINGTON, RALPH. *An Introduction to Social Anthropology*, Vol. I. Edinburgh: Oliver & Boyd, 1950.

TAYLOR, T. GRIFFITH. *Urban Geography*. N.Y.: Dutton, 1949.

17. Agriculture and Animal Husbandry

BENGTSON, NELS A., and WILLIAM VAN ROYEN. *Fundamentals of Economic Geography*. Englewood Cliffs, N.J.: Prentice-Hall, 1955.

DICKEN, S. M. *Economic Geography*. Boston: Heath, 1955.

GLOVER, J. G., and W. B. CORNELL. *The Development of American Industries*. Englewood Cliffs, N.J.: Prentice-Hall, 1959.

HIGBEE, EDWARD. *American Agriculture*. N.Y.: Wiley, 1958.

JENSEN, L. B. *Man's Foods*. Champaign, Ill.: Garrard Press, 1953.

JONES, C. F., and G. G. DARKENWALD. *Economic Geography*. N.Y.: Macmillan, 1954.

KLIMM, L. E., O. P. STARKEY, J. A. RUSSELL, and V. H. ENGLISH. *Introductory Economic Geography*. N.Y.: Harcourt, Brace & World, 1956.

Land: The Yearbook of Agriculture, 1958. Washington, D.C.: U.S. Dept. of Agriculture, 1958.

SAUER, C. O. *Agricultural Origins and Dispersals*. N.Y.: American Geographical Society, 1952.

SMITH, J. R., M. O. PHILLIPS, and T. R. SMITH. *Industrial and Commercial Geography*. N.Y.: Holt, 1955.

THOMAN, R. S. *The Geography of Economic Activity*. N.Y.: McGraw-Hill, 1962.

18. Utilization of Forests

ALLEN, S. W., and GRANT WILLIAM. *An Introduction to American Forestry*. N.Y.: McGraw-Hill, 1960.

FARB, PETER, AND THE EDITORS OF *Life. The Forest*. N.Y.: Time, Inc., 1961.

Forest Resources of the World. Washington, D.C.: Div. of Forestry and Forest Products, Food and Agricultural Organization of the United Nations, 1948.

Forest Trees and Forest Regions of the United States. Washington, D.C.: U.S. Dept. of Agriculture, 1936.

Forests and National Prosperity: A Reappraisal of the Forest Situation in the United States. Washington, D.C.: U.S. Dept. of Agriculture, 1948.

GLOVER, J. G., and W. B. CORNELL. *The Development of American Industries*. Englewood Cliffs, N.J.: Prentice-Hall, 1959.

HADEN-GUEST, S., J. K. WRIGHT, and E. M. TECLAFF, eds. *A World Geography of Forest Resources*. N.Y.: Ronald, 1956.

JONES, C. F., and G. G. DARKENWALD. *Economic Geography*. N.Y.: Macmillan, 1954.

KLIMM, L. E., O. P. STARKEY, J. A. RUSSELL, and V. H. ENGLISH. *Introductory Economic Geography*. N.Y.: Harcourt, Brace & World, 1956.

Lumber Production in the United States, 1799–1946. Washington, D.C.: U.S. Dept. of Agriculture, 1948.

Timber Resources for America's Future. Washington, D.C.: U.S. Dept. of Agriculture, 1958.

Trees: The Yearbook of Agriculture, 1949. Washington, D.C.: U.S. Dept. of Agriculture, 1949.

WHITAKER, J. R., and E. A. ACKERMAN. *American Resources*. N.Y.: Harcourt, Brace & World, 1951.

World Forest Resources. N.Y.: Food and Agricultural Organization of the United Nations, 1955.

19. Products of the Sea

BENGTSON, NELS A., and WILLIAM VAN ROYEN. *Fundamentals of Economic Geography*. Englewood Cliffs, N.J.: Prentice-Hall, 1955.

Bureau of Fisheries, U.S. Dept. of the Interior, Washington, D.C. Various publications.

ENGEL, L., AND THE EDITORS OF *Life. The Sea*. N.Y.: Time, Inc., 1962.

GLOVER, J. G., and W. B. CORNELL. *The Development of American Industries*. Englewood Cliffs, N.J.: Prentice-Hall, 1959.

HARDY, A. C. *The Open Sea* (Vol. I, *The World of Plankton*, 1956; Vol. II, *Fish and Fisheries*, 1959). Boston: Houghton Mifflin.

JONES, C. F., and G. G. DARKENWALD. *Economic Geography*. N.Y.: Macmillan, 1954.

MORGAN, R. *World Sea Fisheries*. London: Methuen, 1956.

SMITH, R. J., M. O. PHILLIPS, and T. R. SMITH. *Industrial and Commercial Geography*. N.Y.: Holt, 1955.

Statistical Abstract of the United States. Washington, D.C.: Bureau of the Census, U.S. Dept. of Commerce. Published annually.

THOMAS, W. L., JR., ed. *Man's Role in Changing the Face of the Earth*. Chicago: Univ. of Chicago Press, 1956. (Esp. pp. 487–503 of section on "Man's Effects on the Seas and Waters of the Land.")

Yearbook of Fishery Statistics. Rome, Italy: Food and Agricultural Organization of the United Nations. Published annually.

20. Coal and Petroleum: The Chief Sources of Industrial Energy

Britannica Book of the Year. Chicago: Encyclopaedia Britannica. Published annually.

Energy Resources of the World. Washington, D.C.: U.S. Dept. of State, 1949.

FANNING, LEONARD M. *The Rise of American Oil*. N.Y.: Harper, 1946.

GLOVER, J. G., and W. B. CORNELL. *The Development of American Industries*. Englewood Cliffs, N.J.: Prentice-Hall, 1959.

JONES, C. F., and G. G. DARKENWALD. *Economic Geography*. N.Y.: Macmillan, 1954.

KLIMM, L. E., O. P. STARKEY, J. A. RUSSELL, and V. H. ENGLISH. *Introductory Economic Geography*. N.Y.: Harcourt, Brace & World, 1956.

MANN, M. *Peacetime Uses of Atomic Energy*. N.Y.: Studio Publications, 1957.

Minerals Yearbook. Washington, D.C.: Bureau of Mines, U.S. Dept. of the Interior. Published annually.

PRATT, WALLACE E., and DOROTHY GOOD. *World Geography of Petroleum*. American Geographical Society, Special Publ. 31. Princeton, N.J.: Princeton Univ. Press, 1950.

SCHURR, S. H., and B. C. NETSCHERT. *Energy in the American Economy, 1850–1975*. Washington, D.C.: Resources for the Future, Inc., 1960.

21. Iron and the Ferroalloys

Britannica Book of the Year. Chicago: Encyclopaedia Britannica. Published annually.

DE KRUIF, PAUL. *Seven Iron Men*. N.Y.: Harcourt, Brace & World, 1929.

HAVIGHURST, WALTER. *The Long Ships Passing*. N.Y.: Macmillan, 1942.

JONES, C. F., and G. G. DARKENWALD. *Economic Geography*. N.Y.: Macmillan, 1954.

LOVERING, THOMAS S. *Minerals in World Affairs*. Englewood Cliffs, N.J.: Prentice-Hall, 1944.

Minerals Yearbook. Washington, D.C.: Bureau of Mines, U.S. Dept. of the Interior. Published annually.

THOMAN, R. S. *The Geography of Economic Activity*. N.Y.: McGraw-Hill, 1962.

22. Some Significant Nonferrous Minerals

BENGTSON, NELS A., and WILLIAM VAN ROYEN. *Fundamentals of Economic Geography*, Englewood Cliffs, N.J.: Prentice-Hall, 1955.

Britannica Book of the Year. Chicago: Encyclopaedia Britannica. Published annually.

DE MILLE, JOHN B. *Strategic Minerals: A Summary of the Uses, World Output, Stockpiles, Procurement*. N.Y.: McGraw-Hill, 1947.

JONES, C. F., and G. G. DARKENWALD. *Economic Geography*. N.Y.: Macmillan, 1954.

KLIMM, L. E., O. P. STARKEY, J. A. RUSSELL, and V. H. ENGLISH. *Introductory Economic Geography*. N.Y.: Harcourt, Brace & World, 1956.

THOMAN, R. S. *The Geography of Economic Activity*. N.Y.: McGraw-Hill, 1962.

23. Industrialization

BENGTSON, NELS A., and WILLIAM VAN ROYEN. *Fundamentals of Economic Geography*, Englewood Cliffs, N.J.: Prentice-Hall, 1955.

CRESSEY, GEORGE B. *Asia's Lands and Peoples*. N.Y.: McGraw-Hill, 1951.

DICKEN, SAMUEL N. *Economic Geography*. Boston: Heath, 1955.

GLOVER, J. G., and W. B. CORNELL. *The Development of American Industries*. Englewood Cliffs, N.J.: Prentice-Hall, 1959.

GOTTMANN, JEAN. *A Geography of Europe*, rev. ed. N.Y.: Holt, 1954.

JAMES, PRESTON E. *Latin America*. N.Y.: Odyssey Press, 1950.

JONES, C. F., and G. G. DARKENWALD. *Economic Geography*. N.Y.: Macmillan, 1954.

KLIMM, L. E., O. P. STARKEY, J. A. RUSSELL, and V. H. ENGLISH. *Introductory Economic Geography*. N.Y.: Harcourt, Brace & World, 1956.

SMITH, J. R., M. O. PHILLIPS, and T. R. SMITH. *Industrial and Commercial Geography*, 4th ed. N.Y.: Holt, 1955.

THOMAN, R. S. *The Geography of Economic Activity*. N.Y.: McGraw-Hill, 1962.

24. The World Pattern of Routes

BELLOC, HILAIRE. *The Road*. N.Y.: Harper, 1926.

EAST, WILLIAM GORDON. *An Historical Geography of Europe*. London: Methuen, 1948.

FREDERICK, JOHN H. *Commercial Air Transportation*. Homewood, Ill.: Richard D. Irwin, 1947.

HOLBROOK, STEWART H. *The Story of American Railroads*. N.Y.: Crown, 1947.

SMITH, J. R., M. O. PHILLIPS, and T. R. SMITH. *Industrial and Commercial Geography*, 4th ed. N.Y.: Holt, 1955.

THOMAN, R. S. *The Geography of Economic Activity*. N.Y.: McGraw-Hill, 1962.

VAN ZANDT, J. PARKER. *The Geography of World Air Transport*. Washington, D.C.: Brookings Institution, 1944.

Index of Geographical Terms

Index

Boulder Dam. *See* Hoover Dam
Brass, 518
Braided stream pattern, 81, *illus.* 82
Bratsk, U.S.S.R., hydroelectric plant, 85
Brazil: area, 618; cacao production, 423; cane sugar production, 420; coal fields, 484; cotton production, 425; forests, hardwood, 445, Paraná pine, 332, tropical scrub, *illus.* 321; hogs, 435; industrial regions, 551; iron mining, 493; iron-ore deposits, 493, 500; jute production, 426; maize production, 412; manganese production, 501; mountains, 165; plateaus, 180; population, 618, distribution of, 356; prairie, 325; regulation of agriculture, 403; sisal production, 427; soils, 300, 302; southeastern, climate, 245; "sugar-loaf" hills, 190. *See also* Amazon Basin; Amazon river; Rio de Janeiro, São Paulo
Brazil nuts, 319
Brazilian Highlands or Uplands, 180, 182; beef production, 432; hardwood forests, 445
Breadfruit, tropical production, 416
Breakfast foods, production of, in Northeastern Industrial Region, 533
Bremen, W. Germany, industry, 541
Bridalveil Falls, Yosemite National Park, Cal., 153, *illus.* 154
Brisbane, Australia: coal fields, 484; industry, 550; population nucleus, 356; railroad net, 573
Britain. *See* United Kingdom
British Cameroons, area and population, 613
British Columbia, Canada: Douglas fir forest, *illus.* 327; fisheries, 469; lumbering, *illus.* 452
British Guiana; area, 618; bauxite production, 514; population, 618
British Honduras, area and population, 617
British Isles. *See* United Kingdom
British Solomon Islands, area and population, 615
Broadleaf forest. *See* Forest, broadleaf
Broadleaf tree, 312
Bronze, 516
Brooks Range (mountains), Alaska, 163; glaciation, continental (Pleistocene), 150, valley, 153
Brown coal. *See* Lignite
Bruges, Belgium, harbor silting, 15
Brunei, area and population, 614
Brussels, Belgium, industry, 540
BSh and BSk climates (Köppen), 590, 592. *See also* Semiarid (BS) climate
Bucaramanga, Colombia, *illus.* 180, 182
Bucharest, Romania, climate statistics, 609
Budapest, Hungary, industry, 541
Buenos Aires, Argentina: climate statistics, 608; industry, 551; railroad center, 573
Buffalo, extermination of, 325
Buffalo, N.Y.: flour milling, 533; iron and steel production, 530; iron-ore port, 496–97
Buffalo fish, 469
Bulgaria: area, 616; hill regions, 186; population, 616
Burdwan, India, industry, 545
Burma: area, 614; hardwood forests, 445; mountains, 164; plains, 175; population, 614, distribution of, 353; rice production, surplus, 409

Bushmen, South African, hunting-fishing-collecting economy, 363
Bussaco, Portugal, Mediterranean forest, *illus.* 327
Butte, *diag.* 137, 137–38
Butte, Mont., copper ore, 516
Butter: commercial production, 434–35; in Northeastern Industrial Region, 533. *See also* Dairy farming
BWh and BWk climates (Köppen), 590, 592. *See also* Arid (BW) climate

C

c (climate symbol), 591, 593, 596
C climates (Köppen), 589–93. *See also* Moist, Mild Winter (C) climates
C-horizon, 288, *diag.* 288
Cacao, 407; as crop, spread of cultivation, 398; fungus disease of, 399; as selva product, 319; world production, 423–24, *map* 424
Caingan agriculture, 405
Cairo, Egypt, climate statistics, 610
Cairo, Ill., climate statistics, 606
Calama, Chile, precipitation, 230
Calcification, 292; effects of, *table* 294
Calcutta, India: industrial region, 545; low-latitude city, 388; railroad center, 573
Caldron volcano. *See* Volcano, dome
California, 536; beet sugar production, 421; citrus fruit production, 417–19, influence of landforms on, 396, *illus.* 397; clay production, 508; farming, commercial, 508; fisheries, 467–68; gold production, 513; grape production, 419; grapefruit production, 417–19; hills, coastal, *illus.* 187; iron and steel production, 530; iron ranges, 493; laws regulating agriculture, 404; lemon production, 419; magnesium production, 516; mercury production, 521; oranges, production of, 417–19, transport of, 402; petroleum refining, 488; southern, winter rain in, 266; temperature, 215; vegetable growing, commercial, 416. *See also* Los Angeles; San Francisco; Central Valley; etc.
California Current, effect on world temperature distribution, 215
Calving (icebergs), 143
Cambodia: area, 614; plains, 175; population, 614; rubber production, 428
Camels, herding region, 431
Cameroun, area and population, 613
Campina Grande, Brazil, tropical scrub forest, *illus.* 321
Canada: agricultural regions, *map* 408, climate as limit of, 395; airlines, importance of, 574; aluminum production, 514; area, 617; central, climate, 592; coal fields, 481; copper production, 517; dairy farming, 433–34; farming, capital requirements for, 400, labor requirements for, 401, subsistence, 406–07; fisheries, 459, 466, 469; forests, 446; gold production, 512; hydroelectricity, 529; iron mining, 493; lead and zinc production, 518–19; lumbering, 454; magnesium production, 515; nickel production, 503; northern, as habitat, 310; Northern Forest Lands, 337–38, *illus.* 334, 338; petroleum fields, 490; plateaus, 182; population, 617, density of, 359; rail-

roads, 570; rural settlement, 377; silver production, 513; southern, oats production, 418; sulfur production, 508; uranium production, 521; wheat production and export, 414–15
Canal Zone, area and population, 617
Canary Current, 74
Cancer, Tropic of. *See* Tropic of Cancer
Cane sugar, 407; tropical production, 420, *map* 421
Canebrake, 329
Canneries, fish, *illus.* 468
Canton, China, low-latitude city, 388
Canton and Enderbury Islands, area and population, 615
Cape Cod, Mass., *illus.* 29
Cape Juby, Africa, temperature range, 261
Cape Town, Republic of South Africa: climate statistics, 610; industry, 551; railroad net, 573
Cape Verde Islands, area and population, 613
Capillary water, 89, *diag.* 89; as agent of soil formation, 290
Capital: as factor limiting agriculture, 400–01; requirement for industrial regions, 526–27
Capricorn, Tropic of. *See* Tropic of Capricorn
Carbon dioxide, in atmosphere, 193
Carbonation (chemical weathering), 112
Carborundum, 514
Cardiff, Wales: industry, 539; population density, 359
Caribbean Sea and region, 27; banana production, 416–17, *map* 417; cacao production, 423; climate type, effect of coastline on, 603; hardwood forests, 445; mountains, 165; temperature, 214
Caribou: in taiga, 331; in Tundra (ET) climate, 281
Carlsbad, N.M., potash production, 510
Carlsbad Caverns, N.M., karst region, 131
Carnivore, 315
Carnotite, 521
Carp, 469
Carpathian Mountains, 165
Carrara, Italy, marble quarries, 508
Cartography, 40
Cascade Range (mountains), Pacific Coast, 162; forest, virgin, 446; glaciation, continental, 150; Pacific Coast Forest, 449
Caspian Sea and region: fisheries, 465; petroleum fields, 48; soils, 302
Catfish, 469
Cattle: beef, *see* Beef cattle; dairy, *see* Dairy cattle; European, 433; herding regions, 431; humped (zebus), 433; world distribution, *map* 433
Caucasus Mountains, 165; forests, 445; glaciation, continental (Pleistocene), 150, valley, 153; industry, 543; petroleum fields, 489
Cave, sea, 141
Cave drawings, in Vézère valley, 12
Cavern (karst), 131
Caviar, 460
Cayman Islands, area and population, 617
Cedar, 330, 338, 447; red, 449; Spanish, 455
Cedar Rapids, Iowa, temperature, 273

Economies, 9, 362–65; agricultural, 363; commercial, 361; exploitative, 364; hunting-fishing-collecting, 362; manufacturing, 363–64; pastoral, 363; related to settlement, 365; variety within, 364–65

Ecuador: area, 618; cacao production, 423, fungus damage, 399; hill regions, 186; population, 618, pattern of, related to distribution of intermont plateaus, map 181. See also Quito

Edaphic (soil) factors, 304

Edinburgh, Scotland, climate statistics, 609

Edmonton, Canada, climate statistics, 607

EF climate (Köppen), 590, 592. See also Icecap (EF) climate

Eflation. See Deflation

Egypt: area, 613; cotton production, 425; early agriculture, 391–92; population, 613. See also Nile river valley

El Paso, Tex., copper refinery, 517

El Salvador, area and population, 617

Elbe river, water route, 568

Elburz Mountains, Iran, 165

Eldorado Mine, Canada, pitchblende, illus. 506

Electrical machinery, manufacture of, in Northeastern Industrial Region, 531

Electricity, production of: in United States, 477; from water power, 82, illus. 83. See also Hydroelectricity

Elephant, in tropical forests, 320

Elevation. See Altitude

Elk, illus. 309

Ellesmere Island, continental (Pleistocene) glaciation, 150

Elm, 312, 448

Eluviation, 291

Ems river, water route, 568

Endogenous processes, 109–12

Energy: atmospheric, 197; petroleum as source of, in United States, 486; principal sources, in United States, 85, chart 477; radiated from sun, 22, related to seasons, 35–36; running water as source of, 82

England: chinaware production, 508; climate change, 579; forests, 454; hill regions, 186. See also United Kingdom

Epiphyte, 317

Equal-area map projections, 44, diag. 44

Equator, 31, diag. 32; distance from, effect on annual temperature range, 271; insolation at, 250

Equatorial Countercurrent, 71, map 72–73

Equatorial regions, 250; precipitation, 229

Equidistant map projections, 44

Equinox: autumnal, 35; vernal, 35

Eratosthenes, 42

Erg (desert), 135, illus. 136; relationship to dunes, 156

Erie, Lake, illus. 29, 77. See also Great Lakes

Erie, Pa.: iron and steel production, 530; iron-ore port, 497

Erosion, 113–15; agents of, 113; of cultivated soil, 304; due to forest destruction, 330; by glaciers, 143–44, drainage in area of, diag. 149, in Pleistocene period, map 151; hills created by, 183, 189–90; man-induced, 304–06, 330, illus. 444;

mountains created by, 183; plains created by, 175–76, diag. 175, illus. 176; by streams, 92–93, illus. 93, rill, 124, sheet, 124, illus. 305; on unprotected land, illus. 144; by waves and currents, 140–42, diag. 141; by wind (aeolian), 114–15, illus. 114, 154–55

Erosion cycle: in dry lands, 140, diag. 140; of interfluves, diag. 130; in karst, 133–34; of valleys, 125–26, diag. 126

Escanaba, Mich., iron-ore port, 496

Esker, illus. 116, 147, illus. 148

Eskimos: absence of agriculture, 399; cultural changes, 368–69; fishing village, 471; mobile population, 370; reindeer economy, 431

Essen, W. Germany, iron and steel production, 540

ET climate (Köppen), 590, 592. See also Tundra (ET) climate

Ethiopia (Abyssinia): area, 613; climate, 592; mountains, 166; population, 613; sedentary subsistence farming, 406

Eurasia: major fisheries, 461–65; Northern Forest Lands, 337; tundra, 332. See also Asia; Europe

Europe, 25–27; area, 616; beef cattle, 432; cities, 383, 389; coal deposits, 482–83, map 482; commercial farming, 408, 415; dairy produce, 408, 433–34; early maps, 42; famine, 393; flax production, 426; forests, man-made, 445, mid-latitude, 445, removal, 445, 453–54; hill regions, 186–87, agriculture in, 186; hogs, 435; iron ranges, 498–500, map 499; lumbering, 453–54; Mediterranean, soils, 300; mountains, 165; glaciation, continental (Pleistocene), 148–49, map 151; plains, 173–74; plateaus, 178–79; prairies, 326; population, 348, 616, density of, 358–59, distribution of, 351, 354–55; railroads, 570–72; road pattern, 566; rural settlement, 374; rye production, 415; sheep, 435; subtropical fruit production, 417; urban settlements, 383, 389; volcanoes, 120; NORTH: barley and oats production, 415; NORTHWEST: air route focus, 560, climate, 592, Industrial Age, 560, planned urban growth, 385, population growth, 350, waterways, 567–68; SOUTH: maize production, 412; WEST: coastal temperatures, 215–16, fisheries, 461–63, forest management, 454, industrial regions, 537–41, map 538, wheat production, 412–13

Europe–eastern South America ocean route, 558

Evaporation, rate of, as factor in climate classification, 590

Exfoliation, illus. 111

Exogenous processes, 112–15

Exotic stream, 79

Exploitation (economy), 9, 364

Exposure, effects on climate, 281

Extrusion (volcanic), 111

Eye (of storm), 237, illus. 238

Eyre, Lake, Australia, playa, 78

Everest, Mount, elevation, 24

Evergreen tree, 311–12

F

f (climate symbol), 591–93, 596

F (climate symbol), 591, 593, 596

Factories, production of raw materials for, 394–95

Factory section, 383

Faeroe Islands, area and population, 616

Falkland Islands: area, 618; fishing settlements, 471, illus. 472; population, 618; whaling, 465

Fall. See Autumn

Falls, ribbon, 153, illus. 154

Famine, 393–94

Fan, alluvial. See Alluvial fan

Fang agriculture, 405

Far East, rubber plantations, 428. See also Asia; China; Japan

Farm machinery. See Agricultural machinery

Farming, commercial, 408–09. See also Agriculture; Dairy farming; names of individual crops

Father Point, Canada, climate statistics, 607

Fault-block mountains. See Mountains

Fault scarp, 110, illus. 110, illus. 580

Faulting (fracturing), diag. 109, 110

Fenno-Scandian Shield, Norway, continental (Pleistocene) glaciation, 148–49

Ferris Glacier, Alaska, illus. 145

Ferroalloys, 501–04; world ore distribution, map 502, map 503

Fertility, of soil, 304, 397

Fertilizer: from fisheries products, 461; mineral, 509–10

Fields, salt-water ice, 74–75

Fig wasp, as pollinating agent, 399

Figs, subtropical production, 417

Fiji Islands, area and population, 616

Finland: area, 616; forest products, 454; hill regions, 187; population, 616; pulpwood manufacture, 454; vanadium production, 503

Fiords, illus. 108, 109; formation, 115, 144

Fir, 329–30, 447; balsam, 338, 447, 453; Douglas, 449

Fire, destruction of forest by, 449–50

Fish, game: preservation of, 443; in taiga, 331

Fish cake, 461

Fish meal, 461, 463–64

Fish oils, 460–61, 463–64

Fisheries, 459–69; Americas, 465–69; Australia, 465; Canada, 469; China (mainland), 464–65; Eurasia, 461–65; India, 465; Japan, 463; Mediterranean Sea, 463; Persian Gulf, 465; Red Sea, 465; U.S.S.R., 465; United States, 466–69; western Europe, 362–63

Fisheries products: nature of, 459; uses of, 460–61, for human and animal food, 460–61, for oils, 461, for fertilizer, 461

Fishermen, use of forest by, 443

Fishing: chief nations, 459; history, 458–59. See also Fisheries

Fishing banks, 459, map 460; of United States and Canada, map 466

Fishing boats, illus. 458, illus. 463, illus. 464, illus. 468

Fishing grounds, 459, map 460

Fishing settlements, illus. 458, 471; nonprimitive, 471; primitive, 471

Flanders Plain, population density, 359

Flax, world production, 426

Flies: in taiga, 331; tsetse, in savanna, 323

Flint, Mich., automobile manufacture, 531

Good Hope, Cape of, ocean route, 558
Goodland, Kan., climate statistics, 606
Gorée, Senegal, climate statistics, 610
Gores, on globes, 31, *illus.* 31
Gorki, U.S.S.R., industry, 543
Gothenburg, Kan., tornado, *illus.* 238
Governments, control of agriculture by, 402–04
Grain elevator, *illus.* 403
Granada, Spain, climate statistics, 609
Grand Bank, Newfoundland, 459, 466; fogs, 74
Grand Canyon region, Ariz., *illus.* 98, *illus.* 99, 104, 183; dissected plateau, 183; erosion, 123. *See also* Colorado Plateau; Colorado river
Grand Coulee Dam, hydroelectric power plant, 85
Grand Erg Oriental, Sahara desert, 135
Grand Teton National Park, Wyo., *illus.* 309
Grangesberg district, Sweden, iron and steel production, 500
Granite, 119; banded, *see* Gneiss; as building material, 508; quarry, *illus.* 509
Grapefruit: subtropical production, 417; world production, 418–19
Grapes: Concord, mid-latitude production, 419–20; raisin, 419; seedless, 397; subtropical production, 417; tropical production, 416; world production, 419
Graphitic coal, 478
Grasses, of savannas, 321–23
Grasslands, 313; middle latitude, 325–26; park, 322; tropical, *see* Savannas
Gravitational attraction, 22
Gravitational water, 89, *diag.* 89; as agent of soil formation, 290–91
Gravity, law of, 22
Gray-brown podsolic soils. *See* Soils
Great Basin, U.S., 181–82
Great Bear Lake, Canada, uranium deposits, 77
Great Britain. *See* United Kingdom
Great circle, 31, *illus.* 32
Great Dividing Range (hills), Australia, 189; mountains, 166
Great Falls, Mont., copper refinery, 517
Great Ice Age, glaciation, *map* 150, *map* 151. *See also* Glaciation
Great Lakes, 76–77, *map* 77; fisheries, 468–69; iron-ore transport, *map* 495, 496–98, *illus.* 497; nonsalinity, 68; steamers, *illus.* 78; water route, 566–67
Great Lakes region: Central Hardwood Forest, 448; climate, 592; forests, 445; furniture manufacture, 535; hemlock bark production, 456; lumbering, 451; Mixed Northern Forest, 447; soils, 301
Great Lakes–St. Lawrence Seaway, 15, 77, *map* 77; industrial region, 537; water route, 567
Great Plains, Argentina, 172
Great Plains, U.S., 103; beet sugar production, 421; chinook, 204; climate, 592; dryness, 230; wind action, *illus.* 114, 154
Great Plains province, U.S., coal deposits, 481
Great Smoky Mountains, 165
Great Swamp, U.S.S.R., as physical geographic region, 340
Great Valley, Cal. *See* Central Valley, Cal.

Greece: area, 616; bauxite production, 514; fisheries, 462; lemon production, 419; hill regions, 186; plains, 173–74; population, 616
Greeks, ancient: classification of climate, 241–42; use of globes, 30; use of maps, 41–42
Greenland: area, 617; climate, 592; glaciation, 150–51; ice plateaus, 182, explorers' camp, 142, *illus* 143; icebergs, 74–75, formation of, 143, *illus.* 144; mountains, 165; population, 617, density of, 359; temperature, 214
Greenland Sea, 27
Greenwich, England: climate, *chart* 267, 269; temperature, 265
Greenwich meridian, 31
Greenwich Time, 37
Grid: on globe, 32; on map projection, 42, *diag.* 43; in rectangular land survey, 375, *diag.* 376, *map* 376
Ground water, 88–91; problems relating to, 95–96, *diag.* 96
Guadeloupe, area and population, 617
Guam, area and population, 616
Guatemala, area and population, 617
Guayas Lowland, Ecuador, banana harvesting, *illus.* 400
Guiana Highlands: hardwood forests, 445; hill regions, 185; mountains, 165; plateau regions, 180
Guinea: area, 613; hardwood forests, 446; oil palm production, 416; population, 613; rural settlement, 374
Gulf Coast, U.S.: climate, 592; forests, 312; industry, 535–36; petroleum refining, 488; prairie, 325
Gulf Coast–Caribbean–Bahamas fisheries, 467
Gulf Coastal Plain, 103; forests, 445, 447; landforms, 108
Gulf province, U.S., coal deposits, 481
Gulf Stream, 74; effect on world temperature distribution, 215; significance to fishing grounds, 459
Gullying (erosion), *illus.* 305, *illus.* 306, *illus.* 444
Gum, red (tree), 448
Gums, as selva products, 319

H

h (climate symbol), 591–92, 596
H climates (Köppen), 590–92. *See also* Mountain (H) climates
Habitat: human, 3–17; cultural (human) elements, *table* 4, 7–10; effect of animal life, 310; effect of vegetation, 309–10; modification by climate, 243; physical (natural) elements, 3–5, *table* 4; variety and change in, 13–15
Hachure map, 52
Haddock, 462, 466
Hail: as destructive agent, 210; formation of, 210
Hainan, China, population concentration, 353
"Hair seal" fisheries, 470–71
Haiti: area, 617; mountains, 165; population, 617; sponge-fishing, 467
Haleakala, Mount, Hawaii, 169, *illus.* 170
Half Dome, Yosemite Valley, Cal., *illus.* 163
Halibut, 466, 469
Halifax, Canada, climate statistics, 607
Hall's Creek, Australia, climate statistics, 612

Halophyte, 89
Hamada, 135, *illus.* 136
Hamburg, W. Germany, industry, 541
Hamilton, Canada, industry, 537
Hamlet, 372
Hangchou, China, industry, 549
Hanging valley, 153, *illus.* 154
Hanyang, China, industry, 549
Hard lead. *See* Antimony
Hard wheat. *See* Wheat, hard
Hard Winter Wheat Belt, U.S., 414
Hardpan, 291
Harney Basin, Ore., playa, *illus.* 139
Harz Mountains, potash deposits, 510
Hawaii: cane sugar production, 420; climate, 251; volcanic structure, 169, *illus.* 170
Hay and Dairy Belt, U.S., 433–34, *illus.* 434
Haystack (karst landform), 131
Heat, transfer of: by conduction, 202, *diag.* 202, by convection, 202–03, *diag.* 204; by radiation, 201–02
Heat balance, atmospheric, 204
Heat wave, 226, *map* 227
Heating, adiabatic, of atmosphere, 204
Heath, 329
Hebgen fault scarp, Mont., *illus.* 110
Hematite, 493
Hemlock, 329–30, 447; western, as pulpwood source, 453
Hemlock bark, tannin source, 456
Hemp, world production, 426
Herbivore, 315
Herculaneum, Italy, destruction of, 169
Herding, nomadic. *See* Nomadic herding
Herring, 462, 466, 468–69
Hevea brasiliensis, 428
Hibbing, Minn., open-pit iron-ore mine, *illus.* 492
Hickory, 312, 329, 448
High Atlas Range (mountains), Africa, 165
High plain, 103
High sun period, 35
Hills, *diag.* 103, 108, 184–90, *map* 185; Africa, 188; Asia, 187; Australia and New Zealand, 188–89; erosional, 104, 183, 189–90; Europe, 186–87, *illus.* 188; North America, *illus.* 184, 184–85; map 186, *illus.* 187, *illus.* 189; South America, 185–86; structural, 189; "sugar-loaf," in Brazil, 190; types, 189–90
Hilo, Hawaii, seismic wave, 70–71
Himalaya Mountains, 164; yak herding, 431
Hindu Kush Mountains, 165
Hiroshima, Japan, industry, 550
Hobart, Tasmania, climate statistics, 612
Hogs: commercial production, 435; in U.S., *map* 435
Hokkaido, Japan: coal fields, 484; rural settlement, 374. *See also* Japan
Holy See, area and population, 616
Honduras, area and population, 617
Hong Kong: area, 615; climate, *chart* 265, 269; industry, 549; population, 615; temperature, 264–65
Honshu, Japan: coal fields, 484; industry, 549–50; mountains, 163; population distribution, influence of landforms on, 100, *map* 100; soils, 300; volcanoes, 170. *See also* Japan
Hook (shore landform), 141
Hoover (Boulder) Dam, *illus.* 85; hydroelectric power plant, 85
Hopi Indians, subsistence farming, 407

R

Rabbit, Australian agricultural pest, 398–99
Radial stream pattern, 80, *diag.* 82
Radial street pattern, 381
Radiation: solar, *see* Insolation; terrestrial, 201–02
Railroads, 568–73; Africa, 573; Asia, 573; Australia, 573; Canada, 570; Europe, 570–72; Mexico, 570; United States, 570, *map* 571; world density of, *map* 569
Rain, 210; summer, areas of, 603, *diag.* 604, effect on plant growth, 266; winter, areas of, 603, *diag.* 603, effect on plant growth, 267
Rainfall. *See* Precipitation
Ramie, 427
Ranchi, India, industry, 545
Rand district, Republic of South Africa, gold production, 512
Range (U.S. land survey system), 375, *diag.* 376, *map* 376
Raw materials: agricultural production of, 394–95; as requirement for industrial regions, 525; water as source of, 67–68
Rayon, 438; U.S. production, 535
Recreation: importance of forests for, 443; importance of water for, 68; as urban function, 378
Rectangular land survey system. *See* Land survey system
Rectangular street pattern, 381
Red bay (tree), 312
Red cedar, 449
Red Sea, fisheries, 465
Redwoods, in Pacific Coast Forest, 449
Refineries: copper, *illus.* 517; petroleum, in Aruba, 490, *illus.* 490, in Curaçao, 490, in U.S., 488
Refining, petroleum, in Northeastern Industrial Region, 535
Reg (landform), 135, *illus.* 136; creation, by deflation, 155
Regions: physical geographic, *see* Physical geographic regions; types of, 335–36
Regolith, 112, 287
Regulations, government, as factors limiting agriculture, 402–04
Reindeer, 281, 431
Reindeer economy, 431
Relative humidity, 205–07
Relief: influence on location of roads, 563; maps, *see* Maps, relief; methods of indicating on maps, 55–57; models, *see* Models, relief
Religion: as element of human habitat, 8; differences in, as influence on settlement pattern, 365, *map* 367
Representative fraction. *See* Scales (map), fractional
Residence zone, 384, *diag.* 384
Resin, 319, 455–56, *illus.* 456
Rest from growth (plants), 245; effect on tree types, 311–12; in monsoon forest, 319; related to seasonal activity, 264
Réunion, area and population, 614
Revolution, of earth, 25
Reykjavik, Iceland, climate statistics, 608
Rhine river: international navigation agreements, 95; population nucleus, 354, 359; water route, 567, *illus.* 568
Rhine–Ruhr area, population density, 359
Rhodesia and Nyasaland, Federation

of: area, 614; chromium production, 501; copper production, 517; population, 614. *See also* Northern Rhodesia; Southern Rhodesia
Rhodope Mountains, 165
Rhône river, water route, 568
Rhône valley, France, 173
Ribbon falls, 153, *illus.* 154
Rice: cultivation, 409, spread of, 399; "dry," 409; irrigation in growing, 67; "wet-land" ("paddy"), *illus.* 391; world production, 409, *map* 410
"Rice culture," of Orient, 399, 409; as example of subsistence agriculture, 407
Ridge-and-valley country, Tenn., *diag.* 56, *illus.* 189
Rio de Janeiro, Brazil: climate statistics, 608; industry, 551; low-latitude city, 388; railroad center, 573
Río de la Plata industrial region, South America, 551
Rio Grande, shifting course, 93–94
Rio Grande valley, Tex.: climate, 593; oxbow lake, *illus.* 127
Río Paraguay, quebracho-processing mills, 456
Rivers, 79–80; control of drainage basins, 92. *See also* Waterways; names of individual rivers
Roads, 562–66; function, 562–63; general world pattern, 565–66, *map* 567; quality, 563–64; pattern or design, 563–64, related to drainage pattern, 82
"Robbery," zone of, 288
Roche moutonnée, 143, *diag.* 145
Rochelle Park, N.J., traffic cross-over, *illus.* 578
Rock(s): classes of, 117–18; composition of, 116–17, *table* 117; consolidated (indurated), 118; igneous, 117; metamorphic, 117–18; sedimentary, 117, occurrence of petroleum in, 486–87, *diag.* 486, *map* 487; unconsolidated (nonindurated), 118
Rock pediment, 138
Rock shelters, as primitive dwellings, 12
Rocky Mountains, 162; change in landforms, 579; chinook, 204; doming, 168; effect of altitude on temperature, 218; foothills, 185; forests, 446, 448–49; glaciation, continental (Pleistocene), 150, valley, 153; soils, 302
Rocky Mountain province, U.S., coal deposits, 481
Rocky Mountain states, phosphate production, 510
Rodrigues and adjacent islands, area and population, 614
Rolling stock, U.S. manufacture, 532
Roman Empire: growth, 573; road maintenance, 564–65; road system, 562
Romania: area, 617; petroleum fields, 489–90; plains, 173; population, 617
Rome, Italy, urban characteristics, 388
Rosario, Argentina, industry, 551
Rosin, 455–56
Ross Ice Barrier, Antarctica, *illus.* 263
Rostov-on-Don, U.S.S.R., industry, 543
Rotation, of earth, 24–25
Rourkela, India, iron and steel production, 545
Routes: air, 558–61, *map* 559; intercontinental, 556–61; intracontinen-

tal, 561–74; ocean, *see* Ocean routes; world pattern, 554–75, as feature of Western culture, 574–75. *See also* Railroads; Roads; Transportation; Waterways
Routes Nationales, France, *map* 564
Ruanda-Urundi: area, 614; population, 614, distribution, 356
Rubber: liana, 428; natural, 428; plantation, Malaya, 319, 408, *illus.* 429; plantation grown, 428; spread of cultivation, 398; synthetic, 428; wild, 428; world production, 427–28, *map* 428
Rubber goods, U.S. manufacture, 535
Ruhr Valley, W. Germany: coal deposits, 483, relation to Lorraine iron ore, 498; as industrial region, 540; as population nucleus, 354
Rural density (population), 357
Rural population. *See* Population, rural
Rural settlement. *See* Settlement, rural
Rural-urban fringe, 384
Russia: European, soils, 300–02; forests, 445; mountains, 164–65; prairie, 326; steppes, soils, 297; western, plateaus, 179. *See also* Union of Soviet Socialist Republics
Russian Plain, 173, *illus.* 173; coal deposits, 483; hemp production, 426; loess deposits, 157; tobacco production, 429; wheat production, 414
Rutland, Vt., temperature, 273
Ruwenzori, Mount, Africa, zoning of vegetation, 332
Rye, world production, 415
Ryukyu Islands, area and population, 615

S

s (climate symbol), 591, 593, 596
S (climate symbol), 591–92, 596
Saar Basin, W. Germany, coal fields, 483
Sacramento, Cal.: climate, *chart* 265, 270; displacement of agriculture by gold mining, 404; precipitation, 266; table grape production, 419; temperature, 264–65
Sacramento river, Cal., relationship to Central Valley, 341
Sahara desert, 324; camel herding, 431; climate, 592, as limit on agriculture, 395; hill regions, 188; mountains, 166; as physical geographic region, 336; plateaus, 177; precipitation, 230; temperature, 214; wind action, 154
St. Clair, Lake (Great Lakes system), 76–77
St. Clair river (Great Lakes system), 76
St. Helena, area and population, 614
St. John, Lake. *See* Lake St. John Lowland
St. John Island, V.I., *illus.* 251
St. Lawrence, Gulf of, fisheries, 469
St. Lawrence river: valley, *map* 77; lowland (corridor), 172, 184–85, *map* 186; origin in Great Lakes, 77; railroad net, 516. *See also* Great Lakes–St. Lawrence Seaway
St. Léon sur Vézère, France, 10, 12
St. Louis, Mo., printing center, 535
St. Marys river (Great Lakes system), 76
St. Paul, Minn.: climate statistics, 607; flour milling, 533; meat packing, 533; temperature, 273

Z

Back end paper shows part of

KODIAK, ALASKA

Alaska Topographic Series

U.S. GEOLOGICAL SURVEY
Department of the Interior
WASHINGTON 25, D.C.

FRACTIONAL SCALE: 1:250,000
(representative fraction)

LINEAR SCALE:

0 ⊨⊨⊨⊨⊨ 5 miles

CONTOUR INTERVAL: 200 feet

BOUNDING PARALLELS

of whole quadrangle:
57° N *and* 58° N

of this portion:
57° 56′ 3″ N *and* 57° 24′ 25″ N

BOUNDING MERIDIANS

of whole quadrangle:
152° W *and* 154° W

of this portion:
152° 5′ 23″ W *and* 153° 40′ W